John M Fabio

GAS DYNAMICS

ALI BULENT CAMBEL

Professor and Chairman of Mechanical Engineering
Gas Dynamics Laboratory, Northwestern University
Evanston, Illinois

BURGESS H. JENNINGS

Director, Research Laboratory
American Society of Heating and Air-conditioning Engineers
Cleveland, Ohio

McGRAW-HILL BOOK COMPANY, INC.

New York   Toronto   London

1958

GAS DYNAMICS

This book is dedicated to
Northwestern University

PREFACE

Within the last two decades the importance of gas dynamics as a field of study has received continuously increasing recognition. The relations of gas dynamics to aerodynamics, to underlying combustion phenomena, to the flight of missiles and rockets, and to propulsion have all contributed to this increased interest.

This book has been written to provide the advanced undergraduate and the beginning graduate student with a foundation of the theory and concepts underlying compressible-fluid flow and combustion. The subject matter is particularly pertinent to the internal-flow problems of jet engines, to rocket motors, to missiles, to gas turbines, and to other compressible-flow machinery. Its usefulness is apparent not only for mechanical engineers but for aeronautical, chemical, and propulsion engineers as well. The book is written to serve both as a textbook and as a reference book. References are cited so that those interested in further study of a particular topic may find additional source material.

A number of illustrative examples are interspersed throughout the text, and problems for solution have been included at the end of each chapter. The scope of the book is such that it could be covered completely in a two-semester sequence meeting three times a week. For shorter courses, it is felt that many teachers will not wish to use all the chapters in the book, and by judicious choice a coverage can be selected to suit the specific purposes of a class or group.

In general, a knowledge of thermodynamics, fluid mechanics, combustion, and advanced calculus will suffice as prerequisites for an understanding of the topics covered.

The authors have attempted to indicate fully all references. It is possible, however, that certain research and ideas may have been inadvertently included without direct reference. The authors hope that they will be forgiven for such oversights, and they will be most happy to rectify any which are called to their attention. The authors have relied heavily on the several fine gas-dynamics monographs which have appeared in recent years.

The present book is an outcome of courses presented at the State University of Iowa and at Northwestern University. Thanks are extended to the many students who have helped in the development of the manuscript through the solution of illustrative problems and related research projects. Among the students and colleagues who should be particularly mentioned in this connection are Ellsworth A. Brown, Roy P. Choudhury, T. C. Peng, and Robert Sadler of Northwestern University, Professor Milan Jovanovic of the South Dakota School of Mines, and Allan B. Schaffer and Richard W. Ziemer of the Ramo-Wooldridge Corporation. Miss M. Puster typed the manuscript, and Mr. Anton Mathisen prepared photographs. Particular thanks are due to Professor S. J. Kline of Stanford University for his meticulous scrutiny of the manuscript and for his advice and helpful suggestions as to the manner of presentation.

Suggestions as to possible inconsistencies, errors, and other faults of the book will be most welcome from any reader.

Ali Bulent Cambel
Burgess H. Jennings

SPECIAL ACKNOWLEDGMENTS

In the preparation of any manuscript there are usually a number of persons who contribute to the finished product in one way or another. To the many who have helped with this work I wish to extend my thanks and appreciation. Especially, I should like to extend my gratitude to several individuals whose aid and influence have been paramount.

Among my former teachers, Dean Huber O. Croft, formerly of the University of Iowa, showed me the fascination of transcending rigid departmental lines and treating diverse fields such as thermodynamics, fluid mechanics, heat transfer, and combustion as one unified discipline. Professor Duncan W. Rannie of the California Institute of Technology and Dr. Edward R. Van Driest, formerly of Massachusetts Institute of Technology, inculcated in me an appreciation for the analytical description of engineering problems.

Edward F. Obert, of Northwestern University, supplied technical material and showed me the details of manuscript preparation. Thomas Farrell, Jr., of the University of Michigan, Hunter Rouse of the State University of Iowa, Hermann Stoever of Iowa State College, and E. R. Van Driest of North American Aviation, Inc., read parts of this manuscript and made invaluable suggestions.

Last but not least I am grateful to my wife, Marion de Paar Cambel, without whose devoted encouragement and constant help this text would not have been possible. She and our children shared considerable patience while this material was being prepared.

ALI BULENT CAMBEL

CONTENTS

CHAPTER 1

BASIC CONCEPTS OF GAS DYNAMICS
AND GAS PROPERTIES

1-1. Definition. The science of gas dynamics is primarily concerned with the motion of gases and consequent effects. Gas dynamics differs from classical fluid dynamics in that, although both deal with fluid motion, fluid dynamics usually does not consider thermal or chemical effects, and gas dynamics may.

The term *gas dynamics* is open to criticism as being too general, and other names have been suggested. For example, *supersonic flow, compressible flow, aerothermochemistry,* and *aerothermodynamics* have been considered. Of these, *supersonic flow* is too restricted because it deals with one particular domain, namely, velocities which are greater than sonic speed. *Compressible flow* may be misleading because gas density does not necessarily vary in a flow process. The term *aerothermochemistry* implies at once that chemical phenomena must enter the picture. This is true, for example, in the combustion chamber of a jet engine, but not true for the diffuser of the engine. The last term, *aerothermodynamics*, appears to be a more appropriate name for the field covered by gas dynamics, but as yet it has relatively few proponents.

In this text, phenomena which involve gases undergoing fluid-dynamic, thermodynamic, and aerodynamic as well as thermochemical processes will be considered.

1-2. Compressibility. Gases, vapors, and liquids are all fluids. It is commonly assumed that gases and vapors are compressible and that liquids are incompressible. The preceding assumption is not absolutely correct, because one cannot reach a conclusion about the compressibility of a system without studying the processes involved in the system. For example, it is possible to make a gas or a vapor undergo a flow process in which its density will not change. Such a process could be achieved when a gas is made to flow at a low velocity while its temperature is maintained constant. Air flow in air-conditioning ducts is a typical example of this. In contrast, it is possible to carry a liquid such as water through a process in which its density changes, merely by subjecting the water to extreme pressures. Thus a system is defined as *compressible* or *incompressible* in terms of the processes by which it is governed.

In many cases of flow, a gas, while traveling at a velocity of several hundred feet per second, may at the same time exchange energy with its surroundings. Or a gas may expand adiabatically in a nozzle and in so doing experience a drop in temperature. A gas may also serve as the carrier of a chemical reaction. In all these cases, the density of the gas cannot be considered as remaining constant. It is mainly with such applications that gas dynamics is concerned. Because the widely used field of incompressible fluid flow is actually a special case of compressible fluid flow, gas dynamics is extremely broad in scope.

1-3. Physical Domain of Gas Dynamics. It is accepted that matter consists of molecules and that these are in continual motion. In solids and in liquids these molecules are fairly close to one another, but in gases they are relatively far apart. For example, if we assume the molecules to behave as elastic spheres, the mean free path in air at 32°F and 1 atm pressure is found to be 2.4×10^{-6} in. Experiments and intuitive reasoning both indicate that the mean free path increases with temperature. Moreover, the mean free path is substantially greater than the diameter of the molecules themselves. It is also of interest to note that in a volume of 1 m^3 on the average there are some 5×10^9 collisions per second.

From kinetic theory it is known that the temperature of a system is a criterion of the molecular action within the system. The higher the temperature of the gas enclosed within a volume under consideration, the greater will be the molecular agitation. Moreover, depending on the phase of a system, its molecules may be close to one another or may be far apart. In fact, the average distance between the molecules will depend on the density of the system and will be influenced by the pressure and the temperature at which the system finds itself. This may be seen pictorially in Fig. 1-1.

Gas dynamics is not particularly concerned with the behavior of the constituent molecules. In fact, it deals only with the motion of the gas as a mass, or continuum. In most engineering applications, one may safely assume that air behaves as a continuum. However, at very high altitudes the concepts of classical gas dynamics may be inadequate because, owing to the reduced pressure, the mean distance between molecules increases so much that the behavior of individual molecules must be studied. For example, at an altitude of 50 miles the mean free path of air molecules is 1 in., but at 75 miles the mean free path increases to 1 ft. The more rarefied the gas, the longer will be the mean free path. The dynamics of rarefied gases may be studied by judiciously applying the principles of gas dynamics, kinetic theory, and statistical mechanics. These form the basis

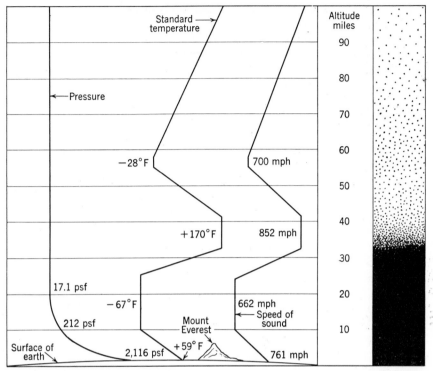

FIG. 1-1. Variation of atmospheric temperature, pressure, and acoustic velocity with altitude.

of a still newer science, sometimes called *rarefied gas dynamics* or *superaerodynamics*.

In determining the applicable mechanics of the gas flow, it is customary to use the dimensionless ratio l/L as a criterion. In this ratio, l is the mean free path of the molecules of the gas, and L is the characteristic length of the body in the fluid stream. Gas dynamics may be applied whenever the Knudsen number, namely, the ratio l/L, is negligible. When l/L is not negligible, the gas will not act as a continuum and should therefore be looked upon as consisting of individual discrete particles. Flow for which the Knudsen number is not negligible is generally termed *free-molecule flow* or *slip flow* depending on the magnitude of the test ratio. It is customary to use the classification outlined in Table 1-1.

TABLE 1-1. REGIONS OF FLOW

Ratio l/L	Name
$l/L \leqq 0.01$..........	Gas dynamics
$l/L = 1$.............	Slip flow
$l/L \geqq 10$............	Free-molecule flow

1-4. Applications. Both the mechanical engineer and the aeronautical engineer are interested in gas dynamics, but there is a difference in their particular fields of interest. Subjectively, it may be said that the aerodynamicist is concerned with how an object in motion is influenced as it flies through still air. In contrast, the thermodynamicist is more interested in the cases in which the object is stationary and the fluid is in motion. Actually there is no sharp line of demarcation. Furthermore, it is of little importance whether the gaseous environment of an object is in motion or not, because the velocity used in most gas-dynamical studies is the relative velocity between fluid and object. Thus it is unimportant which is still and which is in motion. Consider as a specific example a jet-propelled aircraft. Here the aerodynamicist would be interested mainly in the necessary contours of the structure, and the thermodynamicist might be concerned more with the fluid-flow processes within it. This text will mainly concern itself with the principles of classical gas dynamics which the mechanical engineer needs in his work.

1-5. Acceleration of Gravity. In gas dynamics, the acceleration of gravity assumes more importance than is the case in conventional thermodynamics. This is true because gas-dynamical systems often undergo processes in which the effect of gravity does not remain constant, but varies. The influence of gravity at a particular locale, the so-called *coefficient of gravity acceleration* g, varies with elevation and latitude, according to the following equation:

$$g = g_0(1 - 0.0026 \cos 2\phi - 6z \times 10^{-9}) \quad ft/sec^2 \quad (1\text{-}1)$$

where g_0 = standard acceleration of gravity taken as 32.1739 ft/sec^2
ϕ = latitude, deg
z = altitude above standard sea level, ft

In most engineering problems, the approximate value of g_0 may be used. Thus $g_0 \cong 32.2$ ft/sec^2.

1-6. Units and Dimensions. Several systems of units are encountered in engineering. First should be mentioned the centimeter-gram-second (cgs) system, which is commonly used in physics. In this system, the unit of mass is the *gram*. The unit of force, called the *dyne*, can give a mass of 1 g an acceleration of 980.7 cm/sec^2. In this system, the fundamental units are mass, length, and time.

A second system is the foot-pound-second (fps) system. In this system, the unit of force is the *pound force*, denoted by lb$_f$. By definition the mass which is accelerated by 1 lb$_f$ at the rate of 1 ft/sec^2 is called the *slug*. The fundamental units in this system are those of force, length, and time.

A third system may be set up by calling the unit of mass the *pound mass*, denoted by lb$_m$, and the unit of force, the pound force, is denoted by lb$_f$.

By definition, unit force (1 lb_f) can accelerate a 1-lb mass (1 lb_m) at the rate of 32.1739 ft/sec². In this system, both mass and force are fundamental units and therefore the system is known as the *force-mass-length-time* system. Because the pound force used in both systems is one and the same, it follows that 32.1739 lb_m equals 1 slug. The slug is a collective unit, analogous to a ton, for example. Thus, rather than saying 2,000 lb, we can say 1 ton, or rather than saying 32.1739 lb, we can say 1 slug.

The last two systems are consistent, and both are used in engineering. In Table 1-2, units for the various systems are summarized.

TABLE 1-2. COMPARISON OF FORCE-MASS-LENGTH-TIME SYSTEMS

Item	System		
	MLt	*FLt*	*FMLt*
Mass..........	Gram	Slug	Pound mass
Force..........	Dyne	Pound force	Pound force
Power..........	Erg/sec	Ft-lb_f/sec	Ft-lb_f/sec
Energy.........	Erg	Ft-lb_f	Ft-lb_f
g_c............	$\dfrac{1 \text{ g-cm}}{\text{dyne-sec}^2}$	$\dfrac{1 \text{ slug-ft}}{lb_f\text{-sec}^2}$	$32.1739 \dfrac{lb_m\text{-ft}}{lb_f\text{-sec}^2}$

Relations in which mass and force occur must take into consideration correct dimensionality. Thus, Newton's law is written

$$F = \frac{1}{g_c} ma \qquad (1\text{-}2)$$

in which g_c is a dimensional constant entirely different from the coefficient of gravity. If, as is customary in engineering practice, the force is given in pounds force and the mass is given in pounds mass, the dimensions of g_c are lb_m-ft/(lb_f)(sec²). Furthermore, by the definition of a pound mass it follows that in the *FMLt* system

$$g_c = 32.1739 \ lb_m\text{-ft}/(lb_f)(\text{sec}^2) \qquad (1\text{-}3)$$

As an approximation, one may use $g_c \cong 32.2 \ lb_m$-ft/(lb_f)(sec²). If, on the other hand, the mass is given in slugs and the force is given in pounds force as before, then by the definition of the slug

$$g_c = 1 \ \text{slug-ft}/(lb_f)(\text{sec}^2) \qquad (1\text{-}4)$$

6   GAS DYNAMICS

A comparison of Eqs. (1-3) and (1-4) confirms what has already been stated, that

$$1 \text{ slug} \cong 32.2 \text{ lb}_m$$

The slug and pound are both units of mass having different magnitudes.

Weighing a quantity of matter by using a balance (not a spring scale) is a process of comparing the mass of the matter with that of a standard mass. The number obtained is commonly called the *weight* of the body, although it is actually the mass of the body. The terms *weight* and *mass* are widely used as synonyms for referring to the mass of a body, and the same practice will be followed in this text. Mass, under the action of gravity, exerts a force which is also called *weight*. However, the weight force varies because of variations in the acceleration of gravity from place to place on the earth. For example, a pound of mass requires a supporting force of 1.003 lb$_f$ at the North Pole, but of only 0.997 lb$_f$ at the equator. No matter where the standard masses (scale weights) are moved on the earth, they are subject to the same gravitational pull as is the body being weighed. Consequently, although a statement of the weight of a body is almost precisely a statement of its mass, it is only approximately a statement of its gravitational force. The gravitational force F_g acting on a given weight or mass m can be found at any spot, where the acceleration of gravity is g, from

gravity force →
$$F_g = m \frac{g}{g_c} \qquad (1\text{-}5)$$

and for this equation the conventional units can be seen to balance:

$$\text{lb}_f \equiv (\text{lb}_m \text{ or } \text{lb}_{wt}) \frac{|g| \text{ ft/sec}^2}{32.2 \text{ lb}_m\text{-ft}/(\text{lb}_f)(\text{sec}^2)} \equiv \text{lb}_f$$

The vertical lines in $|g|$ indicate that the numerical value of g is to be employed.

Example 1. A kit of supplies weighed in Chicago for air shipment was recorded at 200 lb. The kit was flown to mid-Greenland where it was again weighed and recorded at 200 lb. Disregarding variations in atmospheric buoyancy and elevation, find the mass of the kit and the gravitational pull exerted on the kit at the two locations. The value of g at Chicago is 32.16 ft/sec^2 and at mid-Greenland is 32.24 ft/sec^2.

Solution. The mass of the kit and its weight are invariant and both are 200 lb$_m$. The gravitational pull or the reaction push by Eq. (1-5) is

$$F_g = 200 \left(\frac{32.16}{32.2}\right) = 199.94 \text{ lb}_f \qquad \text{at Chicago}$$

$$F_g = 200 \left(\frac{32.24}{32.2}\right) = 200.43 \text{ lb}_f \qquad \text{in Greenland}$$

Returning again to the term *weight*, it is not incorrect to use this term as a measure of gravitational force exerted on a body. Thus, if we are told that a cubic foot of water at 68°F weighs 62.3 lb, we understand that there is 62.3 lb_m of water per cubic foot. Moreover, this cubic foot is subject to a gravitational pull or force of

$$F_g = 62.3 \frac{g}{g_c} = \frac{62.3 \text{ lb}_m}{32.2 \text{ lb}_m\text{-ft}/(\text{lb}_f)(\text{sec}^2)} g \frac{\text{ft}}{\text{sec}^2}$$

$$= 62.3 \frac{g}{32.2} \text{ lb}_f \cong 62.3 \text{ lb}_f$$

since g at most locations is approximately 32.2. Thus weight in its force concept closely equals weight in its mass concept in numerical value. Using the weight-force concept, we define a term *specific weight* which in the fps system is weight per cubic foot or pounds force per cubic foot, namely,

$$\gamma \equiv \frac{\text{lb}_m}{\text{ft}^3} \times \frac{g}{g_c} \equiv \frac{\text{lb}_f}{\text{ft}^3} \qquad (1\text{-}6)$$

With specific weight γ known in pounds force per cubic foot, the density ρ in slugs per cubic foot can be found thus:

$$\rho = \frac{\gamma}{g} \qquad slugs/ft^3 \qquad (1\text{-}7)$$

Also, as g is closely 32.2 at many places on the earth, the density in slugs per cubic foot is numerically

$$\rho \equiv \frac{\gamma}{32.2} \qquad (1\text{-}8)$$

1-7. The Perfect-gas Equation. The slug has been used as the basic mass unit in aerodynamic practice for many years. However, for those familiar with classical thermodynamics, the use of the slug in preference to the pound mass at first appears awkward. Consequently, some explanation in this connection is in order. The equation of the perfect gas in conventional thermodynamics is usually written

$$pv = R'T \qquad (1\text{-}9)$$

or

$$\frac{p}{\rho'} = R'T \qquad (1\text{-}10)$$

where p = absolute pressure, psf = 144 × psi
 v = specific volume, ft^3/lb_m
 T = temperature, °F absolute, or °R
 R' = gas constant, $1{,}545/M$ ft-lb/(lb_m)(°R)
 M = molecular weight of gas   mol wt
 ρ' = density, lb_m/ft^3
For air, with its molecular weight of 28.97, the value of $R' = 53.34$.   AIR ONLY

Consider Eqs. (1-9) and (1-10) when transformed to the basis of the slug as the unit of mass. Here

$$\frac{p}{\rho} = RT \tag{1-11}$$

where ρ is the density in slugs per cubic foot.

Because the slug as the unit of mass is 32.2 times larger than the pound mass, the value of R necessarily becomes

slugs

$$R = \frac{1,545 \times 32.2}{M} = \frac{49,709}{M} \tag{1-12}$$

For the specific case of air as the gas under consideration, the equation appears as

$$\frac{p}{\rho} = 1,716T$$

$$\rho = \frac{p}{1,716T} \tag{1-13}$$

Another case worthy of consideration is concerned with specific heats. In customary thermodynamic units, specific heat has dimensions of Btu per pound mass–degree Fahrenheit. If the slug is the basis of mass, the corresponding specific-heat value must necessarily be 32.2 times greater than for the pound mass. Thus it is merely necessary to multiply the customary unit by 32.2 in order to change to this basis. In the slug system, specific heat has units of Btu per slug–degree Fahrenheit or Btu per slug–degree Rankine.

Units and dimensional accuracy must necessarily be established before any type of equation or computation is made. However, in the basic developments leading to final working forms of equations, it is often convenient to use a symbolism independent of specific dimensions, and this practice will be followed throughout this book. That is, it will be assumed that in eventual utilization every equation must be made dimensionally consistent, but even though we may think, for example, of thermal energy in terms of Btu and of work in terms of foot-pounds, in developing the equations the factor J, or 778.26 ft-lb per Btu, would not be employed.

Example 2. Eighty pounds of air per minute is flowing at low velocity in a duct under a pressure of 60 psia and at a temperature of 800°R. The air cools to 740°R after traversing 100 ft of pipe, and at the same time it drops in pressure to 58 psia. The mean specific heat of air in this temperature range is 7.818 Btu/(slug)(°R). Find the density at the two points in the duct and the heat lost per minute in the 100 ft of run.

Solution. Use Eq. (1-11) to find density:

$$\frac{p}{\rho} = RT$$

The value of R can be computed or found in a tabular listing. By computation, using 28.97 as the molecular weight of air and 1,545 ft-lb$_f$/(mole)(°R) as the universal gas constant,

$$R = \frac{1,545}{28.97} \times 32.2 = 1,716 \text{ ft-lb}_f/(\text{slug})(°R)$$

Substituting for ρ at the entry and exit points,

$$\frac{(144)(60)}{\rho_1} = (1,716)(800) \qquad \rho_1 = 0.0629 \text{ slug/ft}^3$$

$$\frac{(144)(58)}{\rho_2} = (1,716)(740) \qquad \rho_2 = 0.0658 \text{ slug/ft}^3$$

As 32.2 lb$_m$ = 1 slug, 80 lb of air per minute is

$$G = \frac{80}{32.174} = 2.49 \text{ slugs/min}$$

$$Q = mc_{pm} \Delta T = (2.49)(7.818)(800 - 740) = 1167 \text{ Btu/min}$$

An understanding of units and dimensions as discussed here is essential as preparation for solving many of the problems of gas dynamics. The mature reader rapidly attains a facility with units, and only in elementary textbooks is it necessary to interpret for the reader whether lb$_m$ or lb$_f$ is implied when lb is used. Consequently except where emphasis on units appears essential the simple form lb, for either pound mass or pound force, will be used and a similar practice will be followed with other units.

1-8. Fluid Properties. Any study of gas dynamics is intimately related to the properties of the system under consideration. In analytical work it may be desirable to express properties which are difficult to measure in terms of the properties which can be determined conveniently. Or the work may entail a rearrangement of properties into useful dimensionless parameters. If the study is experimental, the investigator must know the techniques which are most suitable for the measurement of any particular property, and he must also know the pertinent factors by means of which a property may be varied. Most of the properties used in gas dynamics are common to basic thermodynamics. Nevertheless, there are significant peculiarities which arise, and an attempt will be made here to review as well as discuss further some of the more important properties.

1-9. Temperature. Temperature is an intensive property. Temperature of a gas is commonly determined by establishing thermal equilibrium between the gas and the sensing element of the temperature-measuring device. When a volume of gas is in a stationary state its temperature is measured

conveniently with a suitable thermometric device. This is also possible
when the gas travels at moderate velocities, say less than 100 fps. However, the true temperature of a high-velocity gas stream cannot be determined merely by inserting a thermometer into it, as a temperature higher
than the true temperature of the gas will be indicated. This phenomenon,
which will be treated in greater detail in later sections, arises from the fact
that the kinetic energy of the portion of the gas stream impacting the
thermometer is adiabatically brought to rest. Thus, kinetic energy of the
stream is converted into thermal energy with a resultant increase in apparent temperature. The temperature read on a stationary thermometer in a
moving stream, influenced by dynamic effects, is called the *stagnation
temperature* or *total temperature*. Even the stagnation temperature is difficult to measure with extreme accuracy. The true temperature of the gas
independent of its motion is called the *static* or *free-stream temperature*.
The gas-dynamical equations which relate the static temperature to the
stagnation temperature will be derived later. It should be emphasized
that in the equations of classical thermodynamics as, for example, the
perfect-gas equation of state [Eq. (1-11)], it is the static temperature which
must be used and not the stagnation temperature.

Because most relations in gas dynamics involve ratios, absolute temperature must be used. The familiar conversion equation

$$°R = °F + 459.7 \qquad (1\text{-}14)$$

may frequently be written with sufficient accuracy as

$$°R \cong °F + 460 \qquad (1\text{-}15)$$

Much labor can be eliminated simply by using the absolute-temperature
scale exclusively rather than Fahrenheit or centigrade temperature and
converting. This has been done in the air tables.

1-10. Variations of the Atmospheric Temperature. Data collected by
rockets and sounding balloons indicate that the temperature of the atmosphere does not remain constant but varies with altitude. Figure 1-1 shows
this variation in graphical form. The same type of data, presented in
detailed tabular form, has been prepared by the National Advisory Committee for Aeronautics in two of its publications.[1,2] An abbreviated summary of these data from reference 1 is reproduced here as Table A-1.†
The data contained in both Fig. 1-1 and Table A-1 will be discussed later
in appropriate sections of this text.

It is sometimes desirable to know, in equational form, the variations of
temperature and pressure with altitude. A number of instruments such
as altimeters employ equational data in the layout of their mechanisms.

† The letter A indicates that the table appears in the Appendix.

The equations are developed from the fact that the change in temperature with altitude is constant over certain ranges. This can be corroborated from Fig. 1-1. If the height above the ground level is denoted by z, then the lapse rate λ is defined by the following equation:

$$\frac{dT}{dz} = \pm \lambda \tag{1-16}$$

In Eq. (1-16) the positive sign is used when the temperature increases with increasing height, and the negative sign is applicable when the temperature decreases with increasing height. Both types of change occur over the range shown in Fig. 1-1.

1-11. Variation of Atmospheric Pressure. The atmospheric pressure decreases with increasing height, and this may be expressed by the hydrostatic equation

$$\frac{dp}{dz} = -\rho g \tag{1-17}$$

go over & note assumptions made to get (1-24)

in which p is in pounds per square foot, z is in feet, ρ is in slugs per cubic foot, and g is in feet per second per second. It can be assumed that air at moderate pressures obeys the perfect-gas equation of state [Eq. (1-11)], and substituting ρ from this one obtains

$$\frac{dp}{p} = -\frac{dz}{RT} g \tag{1-18}$$

which may be combined with Eq. (1-16) to give

$$\frac{dp}{p} = \mp \frac{1}{\lambda R} \frac{dT}{T} g \tag{1-19}$$

This may easily be recognized as a separable differential equation, and denoting each reference datum by the subscript 0 and placing integral signs,

$$\int_{p_0}^{p} \frac{dp}{p} = \mp \frac{g}{\lambda R} \int_{T_0}^{T} \frac{dT}{T}$$

R const, g const with altitude

which upon integration and rearranging can be written as follows:

$$\left(\frac{p}{p_0}\right)^{\mp \lambda R/g} = \frac{T}{T_0} \tag{1-20}$$

For the polytropic process of a perfect gas, the relation between pressure and temperature can be expressed by

$$\left(\frac{p}{p_0}\right)^{(n-1)/n} = \frac{T}{T_0} \tag{1-21}$$

By comparison of the exponents of Eqs. (1-20) and (1-21)

To find λ

$$\lambda = \mp \frac{(n-1)g}{nR} \tag{1-22}$$

Computations from Table 1-3 show that in the lower ranges of altitude the lapse rate λ has a value of the order of magnitude 0.0036°F/ft. A relation between temperature and altitude is obtained simply by integrating Eq. (1-16), and there results

$$T - T_0 = \pm\lambda(z - z_0) \tag{1-23}$$

Further, by combining Eq. (1-20) with Eq. (1-23), it can be shown that

°/ft $\frac{lbf - ft}{lbm \cdot °F}$ $\frac{1}{lbf}$

lbm ft/sec² lbf

$$z - z_0 = \pm \frac{T_0}{\lambda}\left[\left(\frac{p}{p_0}\right)^{(\lambda R/g)} \frac{g_c}{} - 1\right] \tag{1-24}$$

The operation of barometric altimeters is based on Eq. (1-24).

1-12. Pressure. The pressure of a gas is the normal force which it exerts upon a surface. The surface may actually exist or may be hypothetical as far as the definition is concerned. The pressure at a point within a gas is the force exerted by the gas on unit area.

Because in gas dynamics there commonly is relative motion between a gas and a reference body, both static and dynamic pressures may be obtained. These are represented pictorially in Fig. 1-2. It should be noted

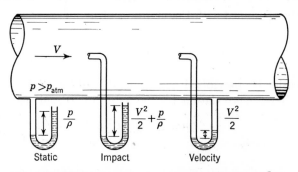

FIG. 1-2. Types of pressure measurement in stream flow.

that the indicated direction of pressure unbalance in the manometers depends on the existing pressures, and it may occur in either sense with respect to the reference datum of the open-ended manometers.

Just as with temperature, it is the static pressure which is used in most thermodynamic equations. However, there are numerous gas-dynamics equations which relate static and dynamic pressures, and both types of pressures can usually be measured directly by proper instrumentation.

In gas dynamics, pressure is generally expressed in pounds per square foot absolute (psfa or psf).

1-13. Density. The density of a gas is its mass per unit volume and is the reciprocal of its specific volume. If in a flow system the density of the fluid remains constant not only with regard to time but also with regard to coordinates, then the fluid is said to be incompressible. If, on the other hand, the density varies, then the fluid is said to be a compressible one. It was pointed out before that no fluid is truly incompressible, but that the process is the influencing factor in the variation of the density. The density of a gas may vary in different ways. The system may undergo drastic temperature changes or it may undergo appreciable pressure changes, or both the temperature and the pressure may vary.

If the temperature of a gas is changed while its pressure remains the same, its density will be a function of the temperature only and this is expressed as

$$\rho = f(T)_p$$

The volume of a perfect gas at constant pressure increases with increasing temperature. Applying this to the density as it changes from datum temperature T_0 to final temperature T, the following equation applies:

$$\rho = \rho_0[1 - \alpha_m(T - T_0)]_p \tag{1-25}$$

In this, ρ_0 is the standard density corresponding to the temperature T_0 and α_m is the mean coefficient of thermal expansion. In general, the instantaneous coefficient of expansion, α, is defined as follows:

$$\alpha = -\frac{1}{\rho_0}\left(\frac{\partial \rho}{\partial T}\right)_p \tag{1-26}$$

If the velocity is high (say about 400 fps or more for air) the pressure change associated with the generation of this velocity which the gas must undergo would be large enough to influence the density, and thus the flow would be compressible. In such cases, not only temperature but also pressure influences the gas density. Accordingly, Eq. (1-25) is no longer sufficient, and the equation of state for the gas must be used.

As is obvious from the foregoing discussion, the density of air is different at different altitudes. Table A-1 lists values of density up to 260,000 ft.

The definitions of density and density as a physical concept have meaning only if the fluid volume under consideration contains a large number of gas molecules, or if a state of continuum exists. Thus the stipulations concerning density must be revised if highly rarefied gases are under consideration. At extremely high altitudes, as may be encountered in interplanetary flight, the mean free path of the molecules will be very large, and therefore the density at any one point will have no meaning.

1-14. Standard Conditions. Every field has its particular standard conditions usually chosen as a matter of convenience. In gas dynamics, *standard air* at sea level is chosen to be at a temperature of 59°F and a pressure of one standard atmosphere. At these conditions air will have a standard density. Standard conditions for air are summarized in Table 1-3 from the data of *NACA Report* 1235.[2]

TABLE 1-3. STANDARD CONDITIONS FOR DRY AIR

Elevation at sea level = 0 ft
Acceleration due to gravity = g_0 = 32.17405 ft/sec² $\cong$ 32.2 ft/sec²
Temperature = 59°F or 518.688°R $\cong$ 519°R $\cong$ 520°R
Pressure = 29.92126 in. Hg at 32°F or 2,116.2 lb$_f$/ft²
Density = 0.0023769 slug/ft³ or 0.076475 lb$_m$/ft³
Specific weight = 0.076475 lb$_f$/ft³
Apparent molecular weight = 28.966 $\cong$ 29
Gas constant R = 53.342 $\cong$ 53.3 ft-lb$_f$/(lb$_m$)(°R) $\cong$ 1,716 ft-lb$_f$/(slug)(°R)
　$\cong$ 1,716 ft²/(sec²)(°R)
Heat capacity at constant pressure c_p = 6,012.4 ft-lb$_f$/(slug)(°R)
Dynamic viscosity μ = 0.00001205 lb$_m$/(ft)(sec) = 0.000000374 slug/(ft)(sec)
Kinematic viscosity = 0.0001574 ft²/sec
Specific-heat ratio c_p/c_v = k = 1.40

1-15. Viscosity. Viscosity of a fluid is a measure of the internal friction or resistance to shear possessed by the fluid and is an inherent property of the fluid. The shear stress that a fluid can withstand under conditions of relative motion depends upon the velocity gradient in shearing. Figure 1-3 shows two possible velocity-gradient patterns in a fluid with the veloc-

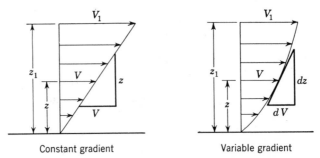

Constant gradient　　　　　　　　Variable gradient

FIG. 1-3. Diagrammatic representation of velocity gradient and fluid shear.

ity varying from a value of zero at one boundary to a magnitude of V at a second reference point. Mathematically the velocity gradient is dV/dz whether the gradient is constant or variable. The shearing stress τ at any point in a fluid is proportional to the velocity gradient. Thus,

$$\tau \propto \frac{dV}{dz} \quad \text{and} \quad \tau = \mu\frac{dV}{dz} \tag{1-27}$$

When a plate or surface of area A is moved in a fluid, a force F is required to overcome the shearing stress; thus

$$\frac{F}{A} = \tau = \mu \frac{dV}{dz}$$

$$F = \mu A \frac{dV}{dz} \tag{1-28}$$

The proportionality factor μ represents the viscosity of the fluid and is a measure of the ratio shearing stress to rate of shearing strain (velocity gradient):

$$\mu = \frac{F/A}{dV/dz}$$

Where the gradient is constant, as is essentially true,

$$\mu = \frac{F/A}{V/z}$$

The proportionality factor μ is called the *absolute coefficient of viscosity*, or *dynamic viscosity*, of a fluid and its customary units are

$$\mu \equiv \frac{lb_f \times sec}{ft^2}$$

In the metric system, the unit of viscosity is named the *poise*, and with force F expressed in dynes, the dimensions of μ are

$$\mu \equiv \frac{dyne \times sec}{cm^2}$$

Using appropriate dimensional transformation constants, it is possible to set up the following tabulation of viscosity equivalents:

$$1 \text{ poise} = 100 \text{ centipoises} = \frac{1 \text{ dyne} \times sec}{cm^2} = \frac{g \text{ mass}}{cm \times sec}$$

$$= 0.0672 \frac{poundal \times sec}{ft^2} = 0.0672 \frac{lb \text{ mass}}{ft \times sec}$$

$$= 0.00209 \frac{lb_f \times sec}{ft^2} = 0.00209 \frac{slug}{ft \times sec} \tag{1-29}$$

The viscosity of gases is greatly influenced by temperature. At extremely high pressures the pressure also should be taken into consideration. In general, the viscosity of liquids decreases with increasing temperature, and the viscosity of gases increases with increasing temperature. In Fig. 1-4 the variation of viscosity with temperature at low pressures is plotted from the data tabulated by Keenan and Kaye.[3] Although the

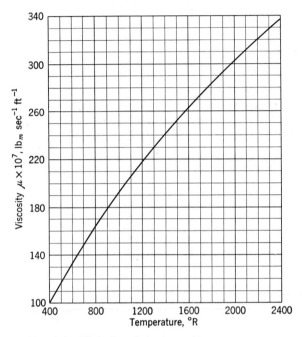

FIG. 1-4. Viscosity of air at varying temperatures.

viscosity of air is very often treated as a linear function of temperature, it can be seen from Fig. 1-4 that this is not absolutely correct. The Sutherland formula for air is nonlinear and appears as

$$\mu = 2.22 \times 10^{-8} \frac{T^{3/2}}{T + 180} \qquad \mu = 3.059 \times 10^{-8} \frac{T^{3/2}}{T + 114} \tag{1-30}$$

where μ is in slugs per foot per second and T is in degrees Rankine.

The dynamic viscosity as expressed in Eq. (1-27) is defined for laminar or streamline flow. If, however, the flow is turbulent, then the shear stress becomes

$$\tau = (\mu + \epsilon) \frac{dV}{dz} \tag{1-31}$$

in which ϵ is the so-called *eddy viscosity*. Although the dynamic viscosity is a property, the eddy viscosity is not, because it depends on flow conditions.

Shearing stresses exist in all real fluids and hence these fluids are said to be viscous. Frequently it is convenient, however, to imagine a fluid which has a coefficient of viscosity equal to zero. Such a fluid is called an *inviscid fluid* and shearing stresses presumably do not exist, although shearing strain does occur. Accordingly, in contrast to a viscous fluid, an inviscid fluid glides by surfaces without sticking to them.

1-16. Kinematic Viscosity. In many problems the ratios of viscosity and density occur together. Thus it is convenient to define the ratio μ/ρ as a *parameter* and this is commonly denoted by the Greek letter nu, ν. If the viscosity and the density of the gas are given in consistent units, ν will be given in square feet per second or square centimeters per second. Because it denotes kinematic properties (properties which deal with distance and time) ν itself is called the *kinematic viscosity*.

1-17. Specific Heat. The term *specific heat* was used previously in this chapter, and customary units and dimensions were indicated. The specific heat of real gases changes with temperature, usually increasing as temperature increases, and for most gases also increases with pressure. However, at pressures below 100 psi, the effect of pressure on the specific heat of gases is relatively small, so small that the effect of pressure can usually be disregarded. Thus, wide use is made of zero-pressure data determined spectroscopically, from which specific-heat values are computed by methods developed from statistical mechanics. Thus the term *low-pressure specific heat* should imply that the data are reasonably accurate to some 100 to 200 psi, although rigorously the values apply only to an idealized zero-pressure gas. Various equations have been proposed [4,5] which represent the variation in specific heat of gases in terms of absolute temperatures. Three such equations [5] are reproduced here for carbon dioxide, water vapor, and air for a range of 540 to 5000°R.

For low-pressure carbon dioxide, CO_2,

$$c_p = 0.368 - \frac{14.84}{T} + \frac{32,000}{T^2} \tag{1-32}$$

For low-pressure water vapor, H_2O,

$$c_p = 1.103 - \frac{33.15}{\sqrt{T}} + \frac{416.6}{T} \tag{1-33}$$

For dry air

$$c_p = 0.340 - \frac{1.246}{\sqrt{T}} - \frac{82.40}{T} + \frac{3.12 \times 10^4}{T^2} \tag{1-34}$$

where c_p = specific heat at constant pressure, $Btu/(lb_m)(°R)$, and T = temperature, °R.

Inasmuch as the variation in specific heat over a range of temperature usually is relatively small, the question often arises as to whether the specific heat can be assumed to be constant throughout the range of temperature in question. For the perfect gas, whose characteristics are expressed by the equation of state of Eq. (1-11), the specific heat is constant and by definition is so treated in some derivations for real gases. Even though the end result may be slightly in error, the convenience of perfect-gas approaches in the development justifies the use of this approximation to real

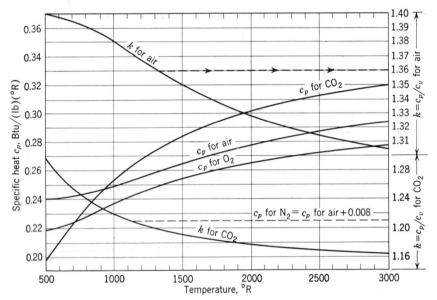

FIG. 1-5. Constant-pressure specific-heat values for low-pressure air, carbon dioxide, and oxygen.

gases. Specific-heat values on a $Btu/(lb_m)(°R)$ basis are presented graphically in Figs. 1-5 and 1-6, and instantaneous specific-heat values are given for air and their variations indicated at the bottom of each enthalpy column of Table A-3.

The mean or average specific heat over a temperature range can be computed by means of the following equation:

$$c_{pm} = \frac{1}{T_2 - T_1} \int_{T_1}^{T_2} c_p(T)\, dT \qquad (1-35)$$

The value of specific heat at any given temperature is known as the *instantaneous specific heat*.

1-18. Air Tables. Atmospheric air is a mechanical mixture of gases, of which oxygen, amounting to 23.19 per cent by weight, represents the chemically active constituent, and nitrogen, 75.47 per cent by weight, and argon, 1.3 per cent by weight, represent the most important remaining constituents of air. Carbon dioxide, hydrogen, and other rare gases make up the remainder of the weight composition of dry air.

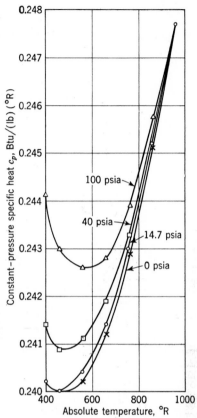

Because of its importance in combustion, in flow processes, and as an environmental medium for aerodynamic bodies, the properties of air have been carefully delineated. Extensive tables giving the properties of air and other gases have been prepared by Keenan and Kaye.[3] In this text, Table A-3 gives thermodynamic properties of air covering a temperature range of 400 to 3000°R. This table, prepared by Jennings and Rogers, is reproduced from reference 6 by permission of the authors and publisher. In tables of this type, the enthalpy datum is arbitrarily selected as a matter of convenience. For example, the Keenan and Kaye tables use 0°R as the datum, whereas the Jennings and Rogers tables use 460°R (0.3°F). Temperature is used as the reference variable, and against the respective values of temperature are listed enthalpy h in Btu per pound, internal energy u in Btu per pound, entropy s_p in Btu per pound mass–degree Rankine based on con-

FIG. 1-6. Effect of pressure on the specific heat of air at varying temperatures. (F. O. Ellenwood, N. Kulik, and N. Gray, Cornell Univ. Eng. Expt. Sta. Bull. 30, 1942.)

stant pressure, and relative-pressure ratio p_r. Enthalpy is computed from the datum of 460°R by use of the equation

LIMITATIONS

$$h = \int_{460}^{T} c_p \, dT \tag{1-36}$$

Internal energy is found from enthalpy by use of

$$u = h - pv \tag{1-37}$$

Entropy is computed by use of the equation   *LIMIMITATIONS*

$$s_p = \int_{460}^{T} \frac{c_p \, dT}{T}$$ (1-38)

It will be assumed that the reader is familiar with the use of the basic thermodynamic functions, such as enthalpy, internal energy, and entropy, so these will not be discussed here except in so far as restatements of them are required for an understanding of the tables.

The entropy function is important in connection with reversible adiabatic changes because during such processes the entropy remains constant. The entropy function is also important as an index of change during other processes, both reversible and irreversible in nature. The relative-pressure function p_r provides an easy method of computing reversible-adiabatic (isentropic) changes. To explain its source and use, the basic expression for entropy change in a perfect gas, which follows directly from the first and second laws of thermodynamics, can be written in the following form:

BE ABLE TO DERIVE.

$$s_2 - s_1 = \int_{T_1}^{T_2} c_p \frac{dT}{T} - R \ln \frac{p_2}{p_1} = (s_p)_{T_1}^{T_2} - (s_T)_{p_1}^{p_2}$$ (1-39)

In this equation it will be noted that the first integral term represents a change in entropy taking place under conditions where the pressure is assumed to remain constant. It is this value, carrying the symbol s_p, which is listed in Table A-3 for each respective temperature. The following term, symbolically represented by s_T, indicates the change in entropy which would occur under conditions for which the temperature can be assumed to remain constant while the pressure changes from a value of p_1 to p_2. These two arbitrary process changes were taken for convenience as two possible processes under which a change in entropy from state 1 to state 2 could take place, namely, one at constant pressure and the other at constant temperature.

In the reversible-adiabatic (isentropic) process the entropy does not change, and for this case in Eq. (1-39), $s_2 - s_1 = 0$; thus,

$$\frac{R'}{J} \ln \frac{p_2}{p_1} = (s_p)_{T_1}^{T_2} = (s_p)_{460}^{T_2} - (s_p)_{460}^{T_1}$$

For any temperature T above the 460°R datum of the tables, we could thus write

$$\frac{R'}{J} \ln \frac{p_2}{p_1} = (s_p)_{460}^{T} = s_p$$ (1-40)

where s_p is the value listed. Corresponding to each temperature in the table, it is possible to substitute specific values for air in the left-hand side of the preceding equation and solve for the pressure ratio p_2/p_1 as follows:

$$\log \frac{p_2}{p_1} = \frac{J}{(R')(2.3026)} s_p = \frac{778.2}{(53.34)(2.3026)} s_p = 6.3359 s_p$$

$$\frac{p_2}{p_1} = \text{antilog } 6.3359 s_p$$

$$\frac{ft \ 16_{f}}{1b_m \cdot {}^{\circ}R}$$

For example, at 480°R

$$\frac{p_2}{p_1} = \text{antilog } (6.3359 \times 0.01021) = 1.160$$

and this value is seen tabulated in the column marked p_r. The use of the symbol p_r was employed by Keenan and Kaye,[3] and II was used by the NACA in its air tabulations. In this derivation, the p_r values found above are associated with the pressure ratios that exist only in isentropic expressions or expansions. The p_r values, commonly called *relative pressures*, are no longer in logarithmic form, so that arithmetic work is simplified. Thus, for a given pressure ratio occurring in a process, namely p_2/p_1, the corresponding isentropic pressure ratio would necessarily be p_{r2}/p_{r1}. Further,

$$r = \frac{p_2}{p_1} = \frac{p_{r2}}{p_{r1}} \quad \text{for any isentropic process} \tag{1-41}$$

In the case of a compression, $p_2 > p_1$, and $p_2 = rp_1$, and similarly, $p_{r2} = rp_{r1}$.

For example, consider an isentropic compression from 480°R to a pressure ratio of $r = 6$. This would be expressed as

$$\frac{p_2}{p_1} = 6 = \frac{p_{r2}}{p_{r1}}$$

and $$p_{r2} = 6p_{r1} = 6(1.16) = 6.96$$

where 1.16 is the value corresponding to 480°R in Table A-3, and the answer read opposite 6.962 in Table A-3 shows a final temperature, after isentropic compression, of 799°R.

For an expansion, the final value of p_{r2} decreases in relation to the pressure ratio and would appear as

$$r = \frac{p_1}{p_2} = \frac{p_{1r}}{p_{2r}}$$

$$p_{2r} = \frac{p_{1r}}{r} \tag{1-42}$$

Although the steady-flow energy equation is discussed in Chap. 2, it seems desirable also to present it here.

$$Q = h_2 - h_1 + \frac{V_2{}^2 - V_1{}^2}{2g_cJ} + \frac{W_s}{J} + \frac{z_2 - z_1}{J}\frac{g}{g_c} \tag{1-43}$$

Expressed in words, for any steady-flow process, Eq. (1-43) states: The heat added $(+Q)$ appears as the summation of the change in enthalpy $(h_2 - h_1)$, change in kinetic energy $[(V_2{}^2 - V_1{}^2)/2g_cJ]$, and change in potential energy $[(z_2 - z_1)g/Jg_c]$ plus the work done by the work devices of the flow system (W_s/J). When the equation is applied to the case of a gaseous medium undergoing adiabatic compression or expansion $Q \equiv 0$. Also potential-energy changes are usually trivial, so that

$$\frac{W_s}{J} = h_1 - h_2 + \frac{V_1{}^2 - V_2{}^2}{2g_cJ} \tag{1-44}$$

where W_s/J = work delivered during an expansion, Btu per pound, or with minus sign the work that is absorbed during a compression

h_1, h_2 = enthalpy in Btu per pound before and after expansion (compression)

V_2, V_1 = velocities, fps

Equation (1-44) can be transformed to a power equation by inserting the mass flow rate G'. The equation then represents a power interchange of P Btu/sec, with the other units having the same values as indicated above. In equational form this appears as

$$P = G'\left(h_1 - h_2 + \frac{V_1{}^2 - V_2{}^2}{2g_cJ}\right)$$

$$= G'\left[h_1 + \frac{V_1{}^2}{2g_cJ} - \left(h_2 + \frac{V_2{}^2}{2g_cJ}\right)\right] \tag{1-45}$$

$$P = G'(h_{01} - h_{02}) \tag{1-46}$$

It will be noticed that the enthalpy and kinetic energy can be combined into a single term called, most frequently, by the name *stagnation enthalpy*. In equational form it appears as

$$h_0 = h + \frac{V^2}{2g_cJ} \tag{1-47}$$

In Eqs. (1-44) to (1-46), if W_s and P are positive, an expansion process with delivery of work or power has occurred. In a compression process, W_s and P are negative in sense (when the previous convention of sign is followed). This merely indicates that the fluid is absorbing work or power.

Example 3. In a compressor, air enters at 60.3°F and 14.75 psia with a velocity of 25 fps. It leaves the compressor at a temperature of 242.3°F, pressure of 34.5 psia, and velocity of 125 fps. (a) If the compressor can be considered to operate adiabatically, find the shaft work required for compression per pound of air moving through the compressor. (b) If 10 slugs/min of air flows through this compressor, how much horsepower is required for its drive?

Solution. (a) From Table A-3, at a temperature of 520°R = 459.7 + 60.3 read $h_1 = 14.393$. Consequently, the stagnation enthalpy of the entering air is

$$h_{01} = h_1 + \frac{V_1^2}{2g_c J} = 14.393 + \frac{25^2}{(64.34)(778)} = 14.406 \text{ Btu/lb}$$

Similarly, if the exit conditions are at 702°R = 459.7 + 242.3

$$h_{02} = 58.204 + \frac{125^2}{(64.34)(778)} = 58.516 \text{ Btu/lb}$$

and by Eq. (1-44), the work is $14.406 - 58.516 = -44.110$ or the work input is $+44.110$ Btu/lb.

(b) The power input, by Eq. (1-46), becomes

$$P = 32.17(2)(44.110) = 2836 \text{ Btu/sec}$$

Expressed in horsepower, this is

$$\text{hp} = \frac{2,836}{550/778} = \frac{2,836}{0.707} = 4,020$$

Example 4. A gas turbine is supplied with gaseous products, largely air, at a temperature of 1700°R, at a negligibly low velocity, and at a pressure of 75 psia. If the gaseous products (air) expand isentropically to 15 psi in the turbine and leave at trivially low velocity, compute the isentropic work of expansion.

Solution. Using Table A-3 at 1700°R, $h_1 = 312.990$, $p_{r1} = 115.434$. The ratio of expansion $r_e = 75/15 = 5$. By Eq. (1-42), $p_{r2} = p_{r1}/r_e = 115.434/5 = 23.087$. Corresponding to this value of p_{r2}, read in Table A-3 the value of h_{2s} as 159.660. Substituting in Eq. (1-44), we get

$$W_s = 312.99 - 159.660 + \frac{0 - 0}{2g_c J} = +153.330 \text{ Btu/lb}$$

If it is known that this turbine has an internal efficiency, $\eta_{it} = 87.2$ per cent, based on work delivered to the turbine wheels compared to the isentropically available energy, find the actual work delivered to its shaft and the true enthalpy at exit.

$$W_s = (h_{2s} - h_1)(\eta_{it}) = (153.33)(0.872) = 133.704 \text{ Btu/lb}$$

Example 5. In a heat exchanger for a closed-system gas turbine, air entering at 800°R and 400 psia and at a velocity of 100 fps increases in temperature to 1200°R, during which time a pressure drop of 10 psi takes place. If the flow into the exchanger is 30 lb/sec, and the exit velocity is essentially the same as the inlet velocity, compute the heat addition in Btu per hour.

Solution

$$h_2 = 181.570 \text{ at } 1200°R \text{ from Table A-3}$$

$$h_1 = 81.980 \text{ at } 800°R \text{ from Table A-3}$$

Use Eq. (1-43) realizing that there is no work interchange and the potential-energy term is not involved; thus

$$Q = h_2 - h_1 + \frac{V_2{}^2 - V_1{}^2}{2g_cJ}$$

$$Q = 181.570 - 81.980 + \frac{100^2 - 100^2}{50,070} = 99.590 \text{ Btu/lb}$$

$$\text{Btu/hr} = (10)(3,600)(99.590) = 3,585,000$$

Note that the change in stagnation enthalpy measures the heat transferred independent of any pressure change.

PROBLEMS

1-1. A missile is flying at an altitude of 264,000 ft. What is the physical domain? The over-all length of this missile is 46 ft and its maximum diameter is 5.4 ft.

1-2. For a plane plate in longitudinal flow, the boundary-layer thickness δ is defined by the equation $\delta = 4.64x/\sqrt{Re}$. What kind of flow exists in this boundary layer? Discuss your answer.

1-3. The adiabatic lapse rate is defined as

$$\lambda = \frac{n-1}{nR} g$$

For air, consider $n = k = 1.4$ and compute the adiabatic lapse rate. It will be noted that the adiabatic value is appreciably higher than the measured lapse rate for altitudes up to 10 miles.

1-4. Compute the barometric pressure at an altitude of 15,000 ft. Consider T_0 at 519°R and p_0 at 14.7 psia.

1-5. A standard 1-lb mass is being used in the tropics at a location where the latitude is 10°N, and the elevation 7,500 ft above sea level. Find the acceleration of gravity in this location and the actual force exerted by the mass on the platform of a scale. Note that the weight of the mass is 1 lb.

1-6. For the air flowing in Example 5 of this chapter, compute the inlet inside cross-sectional flow area of the heat-transfer tubes for the air being heated.

1-7. Air is heated isobarically from 520 to 1849°R. Find (a) the change in enthalpy, and (b) the change in entropy.

1-8. One pound of dry air at 14.7 psia, 520°R undergoes an isentropic process. The final temperature is 2000°R. Find the final pressure and the change in volume and the final density in slugs per cubic foot.

1-9. Use the air tables to compute the work required to compress air reversibly in an adiabatic compressor from 15 psia at 0.3°F (460°R) to a final leaving pressure of 90 psia.

1-10. Air expands in a gas turbine from 1600°R and 75 psia to 15 psia. If the expansion is reversible and adiabatic, compute the work delivered per pound of air by use of the air tables and the entropy function.

1-11. For temperatures of 500 and 1000°R check the values of relative pressure p_r found in Table A-3.

1-12. A gas which can be considered to have the properties of air enters a cooler at 300 fps at a temperature of 800°R and a pressure of 400 psia. It is cooled to 600°R while transferring heat to water-cooled tubes and leaves with a velocity of 100 fps at slightly less than 400 psia pressure. (a) Compute the stagnation enthalpy of the entering and leaving gas. (*b*) Find the heat absorbed by the water per pound of gas passing through the cooler.

1-13. Air is heated in a cross-tube gas-fired unit from 90.3 to 490.3°F by combustion gases. The entering air has a velocity of 150 fps and the leaving air a velocity of 50 fps. Find (*a*) the stagnation enthalpy of the entering and leaving air, and (*b*) the heat absorbed per pound of air. (*c*) By what per cent would the answer to part *b* be in error if kinetic-energy effects were disregarded?

REFERENCES

1. Aiken, William S., Jr.: Standard Nomenclature for Airspeeds with Tables and Charts for Use in Calculating Air Speed, *NACA TR* 837, 1946.
2. Standard Atmosphere—Tables and Data for Altitudes to 65,800 Feet, *NACA Rept.* 1235, 1955.
3. Keenan, J. H., and J. Kaye: "Gas Tables," John Wiley & Sons, Inc., New York, 1946.
4. Ellenwood, F. O., N. Kulik, and N. R. Gray: The Specific Heats of Gases over Wide Ranges of Pressures and Temperatures, *Cornell Univ. Eng. Expt. Sta. Bull.* 30, 1942.
5. Sweigert, R. L., and N. F. Beardsley: Empirical Specific Heat Equations Based on Spectroscopic Data, *Georgia School Technol. State Eng. Expt. Sta. Bull.* 2, 1938.
6. Jennings, B. H., and W. L. Rogers: "Gas Turbine Analysis and Practice," McGraw-Hill Book Company, Inc., New York, 1953.

CHAPTER 2

FUNDAMENTAL EQUATIONS OF STEADY FLOW

2-1. Introduction. In the applications of gas dynamics, the equations involved may become very complicated. It is at times possible, however, to facilitate matters by making certain simplifying assumptions. One such assumption is that the flow is one-dimensional. By this is meant that the flow properties change in one direction only, in particular in the direction of flow. It should not be inferred, however, that one-dimensional flow must be restricted exclusively to constant-area sections. It is readily possible to apply one-dimensional analyses to the variable-area sections that exist in nozzles and diffusers as, in general, the flow properties may be assumed to remain the same in any one plane perpendicular to the flow direction.

In gas-dynamical analyses it is necessary to satisfy four equations. These are the equations of the conservation of mass, of energy, and of momentum, along with the equation of state of the fluid used. If one considers three-dimensional flow, it is necessary that component equations in three directions must be considered. This obviously makes the manipulation of the equations cumbersome at best. In fact, the analysis of certain cases becomes impossible if multidimensional flow is considered. Aside from analytical difficulties, multidimensional flow also presents measurement difficulties.

The assumption that flow is one-dimensional is admittedly only an approximation. In the true sense, one-dimensional flow would be correct only when applied to trivial cases or to flow through a stream tube of infinitesimal size. Thus, for flow past airfoils or turbine blades, one-dimensional analysis is not adequate. However, in many cases in which the flow properties change more rapidly in the direction of flow than in the direction normal to the flow, the simplifying assumption is acceptable. It may also be permissible to resort to one-dimensional flow analysis if the flow properties change appreciably in planes perpendicular to the direction of flow, provided this change is the same in all planes along the flow axis but perpendicular to it. In summary, one-dimensional analysis is usually valid when the changes in the direction of flow are large compared with the changes in the other two directions.

Since the laws of mass and energy conservation are always obeyed, care must be taken to ensure that the equations written do not violate them. Because the mass rate of flow or the flux must be known before an energy balance can be completed, the law of conservation of mass deserves some attention.

The law of conservation of mass states: Matter can neither be created nor destroyed. The equation of continuity is the statement of the law of conservation of mass for a control volume. In deriving the equation of continuity for steady one-dimensional flow, consider a stream tube as shown in Fig. 2-1, having an infinitesimal cross-sectional area dA. The cross-sectional area of the stream

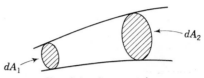

FIG. 2-1.   Stream tube.

tube may vary along its length, but it is imperative for one-dimensional flow that at any point within the stream tube the properties do not change.

In accordance with the law of conservation of matter the mass rate of flow through the stream tube must remain constant, and therefore

$$\frac{dm_1}{dt} = \frac{dm_2}{dt} = \text{constant} \tag{2-1}$$

where the subscripts 1 and 2 denote the stations depicted in Fig. 2-1.

The mass rate of flow † G' can be computed under steady-flow conditions from the equation of continuity as

$$G' = \rho V A = \text{constant} \tag{2-2}$$

where V, the velocity over the flow area, is assumed to be a representative average value. It should be remembered that in steady flow the volume rate of flow is constant only for an incompressible fluid.

Sometimes it is convenient to consider that variations in density, velocity, and area can occur. To treat this case differentiate Eq. (2-2) and then divide the differential by the original equation, or employ logarithmic differentiation. These operations lead to the following equation:

$$\frac{d\rho}{\rho} + \frac{dV}{V} + \frac{dA}{A} = 0 \tag{2-3}$$

G', being a constant, disappears in differential form. This equation may be written in several other ways. For example, differentiating the equation of state for perfect gases ($p/\rho = RT$), and then dividing the

† In this text, the mass rate of flow, in mass units per unit time, is denoted by G', and the mass rate of flow per unit area, otherwise called the *mass velocity*, is denoted by G.

differential by the original equation, one obtains

$$\frac{dp}{p} = \frac{d\rho}{\rho} + \frac{dT}{T} \qquad (2\text{-}4)$$

Equation (2-4) may then be combined with Eq. (2-3) to give

$$\frac{dp}{p} + \frac{dV}{V} + \frac{dA}{A} - \frac{dT}{T} = 0 \qquad (2\text{-}5)$$

2-2. Control Volume. In thermodynamic analyses it is customary to use the concept of an arbitrarily defined so-called *system*. A similar though different concept is used in gas dynamics, namely, the so-called *control volume*. This is an arbitrary volume, fixed in space, which is bounded by a closed surface, called the *control surface*. The control volume may be infinitesimally small or it may be of finite size, the latter being of more frequent use. Although the control volume is fixed in space relative to a stationary observer, fluid may enter or leave it across the control surface. Thus, the material within the volume may change, although the control volume itself is unaltered. The system, which defines an arbitrary collection of matter of fixed identity, may change because of the influx and/or efflux, but the control volume remains invariant for purposes of analysis.

Consideration of the two basic characteristics of the control volume, (1) that it is fixed in space, and (2) that matter may enter or leave it, leads to important consequences. The first leads to the Eulerian equations of motion, which it should be noted are in contrast to the Lagrange equations. The latter equations stipulate a moving frame of reference, a condition which is demonstrated by mathematical analyses in Secs. 10-4 and 10-5.

The permissibility of matter crossing the control surface results in equations which differ from those which result when applied to a system of fixed mass. This can be demonstrated by considering Newton's law of motion after writing this in the form

$$F = \frac{d}{dt} mV$$

When this is differentiated, it is found that

$$F = m\frac{dV}{dt} + V\frac{dm}{dt}$$

For a control volume, both terms on the right-hand side exist, and for a system of fixed mass the differentiated form becomes

$$F = m\frac{dV}{dt}$$

The last two equations apply both to steady and to unsteady flow.

2-3. The Momentum Equation. In jet propulsion, the relationship between pressure and momentum changes is of great importance. Here, usually a hot gas at high pressure expands to a lower pressure with a resulting increase in kinetic energy, and a portion or all of this velocity increase is used to propel the vehicle by jet action.

Consider the flow channel, depicted in Fig. 2-2, showing area changes in the direction of flow. For this flow channel the free-body diagram shown in Fig. 2-3 can be of assistance in writing the dynamic-flow equation.

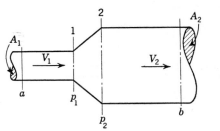

FIG. 2-2. Flow channel.   FIG. 2-3. Free-body diagram.

The walls of the channel exert a force F_W on the fluid. This force has two components, one in the direction of flow, denoted by F_T, and the other normal to the direction of flow, denoted by F_N. Consider forces only in the direction of flow, and assign a positive sign to a flow direction from left to right:

$$F_1 - F_2 + F_T = G'(V_2 - V_1) \qquad (2\text{-}6)$$

This may be rewritten after substitution of Eq. (2-2) in the following form:

$$p_1 A_1 - p_2 A_2 + F_T = \rho_2 A_2 V_2{}^2 - \rho_1 A_1 V_1{}^2 \qquad (2\text{-}7)$$

The time rate of momentum change is the difference of momenta entering and leaving the control volume. The change in momentum must be in equilibrium with the external forces on or within it.

Equation (2-7) is called the *momentum equation* and must be obeyed in gas-dynamical studies. It applies regardless of whether the flow is reversible, but in this form it is restricted to steady flow. When, as is frequently true, area changes and wall forces need not be taken into consideration, Eq. (2-7) becomes

$$p_1 + \rho_1 V_1{}^2 = p_2 + \rho_2 V_2{}^2 \qquad (2\text{-}8)$$

Later in this chapter, and also in Chap. 10, momentum equations will be discussed in further detail.

2-4. The Thrust Function. When a fluid in a duct experiences a change in momentum, thrust is developed. The term *duct* as here used may represent a turbojet engine, a ramjet burner, or merely a length of pipe. For the first two cases the fluid may be assumed to be in steady flow and to be receiving energy perhaps from a combustor. The forces which act on the fluid are as follows:

1. Pressure forces on each end
2. Normal forces exerted by the duct on the fluid
3. Friction forces between fluid and duct walls
4. Other drag forces due to objects (such as an impeller) in the fluid stream

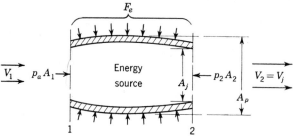

FIG. 2-4.   Duct flow.

These forces may be visualized in Fig. 2-4. Consider forces in x direction only and combine the resultant of items 3 and 4 into a single force vector F_i; then

$$F_x = p_1A_1 - p_2A_2 + F_i \qquad (2\text{-}9)$$

and by Newton's law the net force in direction x on the duct device is balanced by the dynamic action of the fluid flowing:

$$F_x = G'(V_2 - V_1)$$

F_i represents the action of the duct and energy source on the fluid, and therefore the fluid must exert an equal amount of force (but in opposite direction) on the duct and the energy source. This force, F_i, has been called the *internal thrust*. Thus

$$F_i = F_x + p_2A_2 - p_1A_1$$
$$F_i = G'(V_2 - V_1) + (p_2A_2 - p_1A_1) \qquad (2\text{-}10)$$

If application of this equation is made to a jet aircraft, p_1 is the atmospheric pressure, V_1 is the air flight velocity of the craft, and V_2 is the velocity of the exhaust jet relative to the craft.

In a jet engine, the mass rates of flow consist of the mass rate of air flow and of fuel flow. Using the subscripts 1 and f respectively, and recalling that $V_2 = V_j$, the changes in momenta are

$$\text{Momentum change of air stream} = G'_a(V_j - V_1)$$
$$\text{Momentum change of fuel stream} = G'_f(V_j - 0) = G'_f V_j$$

(The momentum change of the fuel stream is $G'_f V_f$ because presumably the fuel would start from rest relative to the jet engine.) Hence, the internal thrust becomes

$$F_i = G'_a(V_j - V_1) + G'_f V_j + p_2 A_2 - p_a A_1 \qquad (2\text{-}11)$$

in which $p_a = p_1$.

So far only the internal forces were considered. However, the engineer in his design work will have to take into consideration the external forces which may act on the body of the total jet device, namely, the aerodynamic forces. Without discussing these in detail, let all of the external forces acting normally on the device be denoted by F_e. The net thrust F_n is made up of the summation of the external and the internal forces. Thus, by definition

$$F_n = F_e + F_i$$

From Fig. 2-4, with the normal pressure p_a while the projected area is A_p one may write an expression for the external thrust as follows:

$$F_e = p_a(A_p - A_2) - p_a(A_p - A_1)$$

This equation becomes at once

$$F_e = p_a(A_1 - A_2) \qquad (2\text{-}12)$$

By Eqs. (2-11) and (2-12) one is now ready to write an equation for the net thrust as follows:

$$F_n = G'_a(V_j - V_1) + G'_f V_j + A_2(p_2 - p_a) \qquad (2\text{-}13)$$

In many practical applications, G'_f is very small in comparison with G'_a

$$G'_a \gg G'_f \qquad \text{and} \qquad p_2 \cong p_a$$

Hence, as an approximation, the net thrust from Eq. (2-13) can be expressed as

$$F_n = G'_a(V_j - V_1) + G'_f V_j \qquad (2\text{-}14)$$

and further
$$F_n \cong G'_a(V_j - V_1)/g_c \qquad (2\text{-}15)$$

From the above one sees at once that the thrust may be increased by increasing either the mass rate of flow or the difference $V_j - V_1$, or by both procedures. In propeller aircraft, a relatively large air mass is moved by the propeller, but the difference $V_j - V_1$ is small. In jet-propelled aircraft, the mass flow-rate velocity is relatively less but the jet velocity is high. Considering turbojet-type aircraft, several items may be defined as follows:

The thrust power is

$$P = [G_a'(V_j - V_1) + G_f'V_j]V_1 \tag{2-16}$$

or as

$$P \cong G_a'(V_j - V_1)V_1 \tag{2-17}$$

The thrust horsepower is

$$\text{hp} = [G_a'(V_j - V_1) + G_f'V_j]V_1\, \tfrac{1}{550} \tag{2-18}$$

or as

$$\text{hp} \cong \frac{G_a'}{550}(V_j - V_1)V_1 \tag{2-19}$$

It was seen already that the velocity of the entering air V_1 is greatly different from the velocity of the jet, thus representing an appreciable change in kinetic energy. This change in kinetic energy is

$$\Delta\text{KE} = \frac{G_a'}{2}(V_j{}^2 - V_1{}^2) + \frac{G_f'}{2}(V_j{}^2 - 0^2) \tag{2-20}$$

or approximately

$$\Delta\text{KE} \cong \frac{G_a'}{2}(V_j{}^2 - V_1{}^2) \tag{2-21}$$

The ratio of the thrust power and the time rate of kinetic-energy change defines the propulsive efficiency η_p. Using approximate values, it is possible to show in simple terms an important relation between the variables involved.

$$\eta_p = \frac{G_a'(V_j - V_1)V_1}{G_a'/2(V_j{}^2 - V_1{}^2)}$$

$$\eta_p = \frac{2V_1}{V_j + V_1} = \frac{2}{V_j/V_1 + 1} = \frac{2\sigma}{1 + \sigma} \tag{2-22}$$

where $\sigma = V_1/V_j$.

It follows at once that the propulsive efficiency depends on the ratio $V_j/V_1 = 1/\sigma$ and to obtain high propulsion efficiency the jet-efflux velocity V_j must not greatly exceed the air velocity V_1 of the jet (or propeller) engine.

A rocket carries within its structure both the charge of fuel and the oxidant for the fuel. Rockets with solid propellants have the fuel and oxidant combined in a somewhat homogeneous mass; in other types the fuel and oxidant are brought together for burning under the action of suitably controlled pumping mechanisms. In the rocket, the mass of the fuel itself contributes significantly to the production of thrust, and for that reason a different approach can be followed to advantage in developing an expression for propulsive efficiency.

For the rocket, the power equation representing the useful power produced by the rocket and corresponding to Eq. (2-17) appears as

$$P \cong G'(V_j - 0)V_1 \qquad \text{rocket}$$

The total available-power input to the rocket consists of the useful power and that portion of the input power which goes to waste in the form of kinetic energy carried away by the jet. This waste energy is commonly known as the *exit-loss power* and in equational form appears as

$$P_{\text{loss}} = \frac{G'}{2}(V_j - V_1)^2 \qquad \text{loss} \quad \text{rocket}$$

The propulsive efficiency can obviously be expressed as the ratio of useful output power to total input power; thus,

$$\eta_p = \frac{\text{useful power}}{\text{input power}} = \frac{\text{useful power}}{\text{useful power} + \text{exit-loss power}}$$

$$\eta_p = \frac{G'V_jV_1}{G'V_jV_1 + (G'/2)(V_j - V_1)^2} = \frac{2V_jV_1}{V_j^2 + V_1^2}$$

If σ representing V_1/V_j is introduced, the propulsive efficiency of the rocket becomes

$$\eta_p = \frac{2\sigma}{1 + \sigma^2} \qquad \text{rocket} \qquad (2\text{-}23)$$

where V_1 = flight speed of rocket
V_j = velocity of efflux from rocket nozzle
G' = mass of products expelled from rocket

Notice that the propulsive efficiency of a rocket differs in form from the propulsive efficiency of an air-breathing jet engine.

In the case of the rocket, the efflux velocity V_j is greatly in excess of the flight speed V_1 of the rocket, and consequently rocket-propulsive efficiency is low. This is true of course with rockets which start from rest, and with these the greatest service of the rocket is associated with the acceleration phase, since following acceleration the rocket usually coasts through its trajectory.

Equation (2-10) can be written in the following form:

$$F_i = A_2p_2 + G'V_2 - (A_1p_1 + G'V_1) \qquad (2\text{-}24)$$

When written in this manner, it is obvious that the internal thrust produced is measured by the difference between the two composite terms indicated. The composite term, $Ap + G'V$, is called by the name *thrust function*. The thrust function can vary from section to section in a duct or other device through which a fluid is flowing. Tabulated values of the thrust function greatly facilitate thrust computations.

Example 1. Consider a jet engine propelling an airplane at a constant speed of 300 mph (440 fps) and producing a thrust of 1,790 lb. The flow capacity of this engine varies from 60 lb of air per second to 960 lb/sec flow. For the extreme conditions, compute for each case the requisite jet velocity, the propulsion efficiency, the thrust horsepower, and the jet horsepower.

Solution. At 60 lb/sec

$$G_a' = \frac{60}{32.2} = 1.87 \text{ slugs/sec}$$

At 960 lb/sec

$$G_a' = \frac{960}{32.2} = 29.8 \text{ slugs/sec}$$

For the thrust of 1,790 lb, using Eq. (2-15) and the smaller air flow,

$$1,790 = 1.87(V_j - 440)$$

$$V_j = 1,400 \text{ fps}$$

Using appropriate velocities in Eq. (2-22) for the smaller air flow the propulsion efficiency appears as 47.8 per cent, by Eq. (2-19) the thrust horsepower is 1,430, and the jet horsepower is 2,990.

For the greater mass flow of 29.8 slugs/sec, it is found by similar computation that the jet velocity $V_j = 500$ fps, the propulsion efficiency $\eta_p = 93.5$, the thrust horsepower = 1,430, and the jet horsepower = 1,528.

This problem shows in striking form the improved performance which results when the jet or efflux velocity is brought closer to the flight velocity V_1.

Figure 2-5 summarizes the characteristics of various types of aircraft in which gas dynamics plays an important part.

Example 2. It is desired to find the internal thrust of an athodyd (i.e., an aerothermodynamic jet) which would have the following characteristics:

Diameter of circular inlet = 1 ft
Diameter of circular outlet = 1.25 ft
Inlet air = standard sea-level atmosphere
Outlet temperature = 2120°F, 2580°R
Ideal propulsion efficiency = 73 per cent
Flight velocity = 500 mph, $V_1 = (500)(1.467) = 733$ fps

Assume that $G_a' \gg G_f'$ and that the perfect-gas equation of state is applicable.

Solution. The thrust will be equal to the difference of the thrust functions. Thus,

$$\text{Thrust} = F_2 - F_1$$

$$= p_2 A_2 + G'V_j - (p_1 A_1 + G'V_a)$$

In order to solve this equation, one must know, in addition to the specified characteristics, p_2 and $G_a'V_j$.

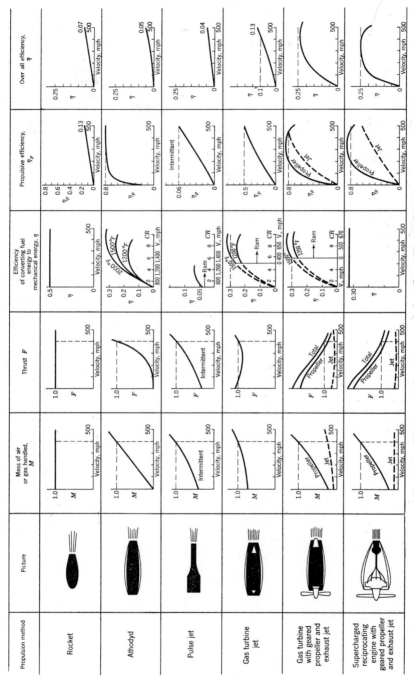

Fig. 2-5. Characteristics of types of aircraft. (*Westinghouse.*)

35

First, find $G'_a = AV\rho$, using the conditions at the inlet.

$$A_1 = \frac{\pi D^2}{4} = \frac{\pi}{4} \text{ ft}^2$$

$$\rho_1 = 0.00238 \text{ slug/ft}^3 \text{ (from Table 1-3)}$$

Therefore,

$$G'_a = \frac{\pi}{4} \times 733 \times 0.002378$$

$$= 1.37 \text{ slugs/sec}$$

The jet velocity V_j is now found from the definition of the ideal propulsion efficiency:

$$0.73 = \frac{2}{1 + V_j/733}$$

$$V_j = 1,263 \text{ fps}$$

The static pressure at the exit may be found from the equation of state for perfect gases:

$$p_2 = \rho_2 R T_2$$

However, before this may be done, it is necessary to know the density at the exit. This is found from the equation of continuity. Thus

$$\rho_1 A_1 V_a = \rho_2 A_2 V_j = G'$$

$$\rho_2 = \frac{G'}{A_2 V_j} = \frac{1.37}{\pi \times 1.25^2/4 \times 1,263}$$

$$= 0.000887 \text{ slug/ft}^3$$

$$p_2 = \frac{0.000887 \times 53.3 \times 32.2 \times 2,580}{144}$$

$$p_2 = 27.8 \text{ psia}$$

$$\text{Thrust} = \frac{27.8 \times 144 \times \pi \times 1.25^2}{4} + 1.37 \times 1,263$$

$$- \left(\frac{14.7 \times 144 \times \pi \times 1^2}{4} + 1.37 \times 733 \right)$$

$$= 4,925 + 1,732 - (1,660 + 1,004)$$

$$= 3,991 \text{ lb}$$

2-5. The Dynamic Equation and Euler's Equation. The momentum equation will now be derived using an approach somewhat different from that followed in Sec. 2-4. This derivation will include, in addition to the external forces, internal forces like the wall friction force F_f and a term for drag or body-friction force F_d. Note that F_f and F_d represent forces in the x direction interacting between the stream and the walls (obstructions). Consider a diverging flow section as shown in Fig. 2-6; the net force acting on the fluid element in direction x can be written as

$$F_x = pA - (p + dp)(A + dA) + \left(p + \frac{dp}{2}\right) dA + dF_f + dF_d \quad (2\text{-}25)$$

The wall-reaction term $[(p + dp/2) \, dA]$ in this equation is obtained as follows: Let the annulus circumferential area of the length dx be dA_w in the direction of flow. The pressure acting perpendicularly to this area at its mid-point is $p + dp/2$, and the force on the wall is thus $(p + dp/2) \, dA_w$.

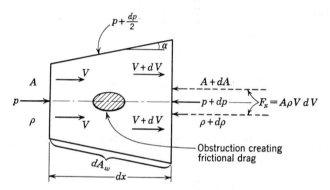

FIG. 2-6. Diverging flow section.

This force can be resolved into two components, one horizontal and the other vertical. In Eq. (2-25) forces in the direction of flow are those under consideration, and therefore the appropriate force component is $(p + dp/2) \, dA_w \sin \alpha$ or $(p + dp/2) \, dA$. Accordingly, Eq. (2-25) becomes

$$F = -A \, dp + dF_f + dF_d$$

Let us now consider the momentum change on the fluid element contained in the infinitesimal flow section at any instant. The force F_x is

$$F_x = \text{volume} \times \text{density} \times \text{acceleration}$$

and

$$F_x = \left(A + \frac{dA}{2}\right) dx \, \rho \, \frac{dV}{dt} \quad (2\text{-}26)$$

For one-dimensional flow, the velocity is a function of time t and position x; thus

$$V = f(x,t)$$

The velocity V may undergo a change in two ways, with respect to time and with respect to variation of position. The former is the local differential quotient, and the latter is the spatial differential quotient. The total change is because of the superimposition of the two changes and is expressed by the substantial differential quotient. This is

$$\frac{dV}{dt} = \frac{\partial V}{\partial t} + \frac{\partial V}{\partial x}\frac{dx}{dt}$$

For steady flow, time has no influence on the flow properties at any one state point and hence the local differential quotient is zero. Because velocity is thus a function of location only, one may use total differentials and write

$$\frac{dV}{dt} = \frac{dV}{dx}\frac{dx}{dt}$$

$$= V\frac{dV}{dx}$$

Neglecting differentials of higher order in Eq. (2-26), the equation reduces to

$$F = A\rho V\,dV \qquad\qquad (2\text{-}27)$$

Substituting Eq. (2-27) in Eq. (2-25) and again neglecting higher-order differentials, the following equation is obtained:

$$dp + \rho V\,dV - \frac{dF_f}{A} - \frac{dF_d}{A} = 0 \qquad\qquad (2\text{-}28)$$

Equation (2-28) is called the *dynamic equation* and is, in principle, a momentum equation. Other effects such as gravity, elevation change, magnetism, etc., may be taken into consideration by adding appropriate terms in the equation.

When no friction losses exist in a system, the dynamic equation reduces to

$$\frac{dp}{\rho} + V\,dV = 0 \qquad\qquad (2\text{-}29)$$

This is called *Euler's equation* for one-dimensional steady flow in the absence of losses. It is applicable only to nonviscous fluids.

2-6. Bernoulli's Equation. *Incompressible Case.* The well-known Bernoulli equation may be obtained directly by integrating Euler's equation, considering the density to be constant, giving

$$\frac{p}{\rho} + \frac{V^2}{2} = \text{constant} \qquad\qquad (2\text{-}30)$$

or integrating between limits:

$$\frac{p_1}{\rho} + \frac{V_1{}^2}{2} = \frac{p_2}{\rho} + \frac{V_2{}^2}{2} \qquad\qquad (2\text{-}31)$$

Compressible Case. When the flow is concerned with compressible fluid, a relation between pressure and density must be known or assumed. For the case of perfect gases undergoing isentropic processes, the equation p/ρ^k = constant is applicable. Differentiate this in terms of pressure, and

$$dp = Ck\rho^{k-1}\,d\rho \qquad (2\text{-}32)$$

Substituting in Euler's equation, integrating, and simplifying, the compressible-flow Bernoulli equation appears as

$$\frac{k}{k-1}\frac{p}{\rho} + \frac{V^2}{2} = \text{constant} \qquad (2\text{-}33)$$

or when integration between limits is performed, the expression becomes

$$\frac{V_1^2}{2} + \frac{k}{k-1}\frac{p_1}{\rho_1} = \frac{V^2}{2} + \frac{k}{k-1}\frac{p_2}{\rho_2} \qquad (2\text{-}34)$$

2-7. Steady-flow Energy Equation. Thermodynamics is the basic science which deals with energy conversions, and an underlying basic hypothesis of thermodynamics is that energy can be neither created nor destroyed, but can be transformed from one form into another. This firmly founded hypothesis is often stated as the *first law of thermodynamics* and is, of course, obeyed in all gas-dynamical considerations.

If thermal energy and mechanical energy cross the boundaries of a gas-dynamical system, changes in other energy variables of the system in general take place. Thus, if a steady-flow device absorbs an amount of thermal energy as heat Q and delivers mechanical or shaft work in amount W_s, the difference must be made up by energy changes of other forms, namely,

$$Q - W_s = u_1 - u_2 + \frac{p_1}{\rho_1} - \frac{p_2}{\rho_2} + \frac{V_1^2 - V_2^2}{2} + z_1 - z_2 \qquad (2\text{-}35)$$

This equation is called the *steady-flow energy equation*. It is written for unit mass passing through a *control volume* under steady-flow conditions. It is often presented in differentiated form as follows:

$$dQ - dW_s = d\left(u + \frac{p}{\rho}\right) + V\,dV + dz \qquad (2\text{-}36)$$

$$dQ - dW_s = dh + V\,dV + dz \qquad (2\text{-}37)$$

$$dQ - dW_s = du + \frac{1}{\rho}\,dp - \frac{p}{\rho^2}\,d\rho + V\,dV + dz \qquad (2\text{-}38)$$

In Eq. (2-37) the thermodynamic function enthalpy h is introduced for the composite term $u + p/\rho$. If mechanical losses occur in a steady-flow

$$A\frac{\partial}{\partial t}\left[\rho + \left(u + \frac{v^2}{2}\right)\right] = -\frac{\partial}{\partial x}\left[\rho A v\left(h + \frac{v^2}{2}\right)\right]$$

process, the mechanical energy dissipated reappears in thermal form as increased enthalpy. Thus, the actual effect of mechanical losses in a gas-dynamical system will be to increase at the final section both the enthalpy and the temperature. This is shown in Fig. 2-7, where a reversible-adiabatic (isentropic) system undergoing expansion is illustrated as passing from a to b with the change in enthalpy $h_a - h_b$. However, with mechanical losses in an adiabatic system, the enthalpy change is less for a given pressure decrease, as indicated by $h_a - h_c$, and an entropy increase also takes place. There is a decrease in available energy whenever irreversibilities accompany the flow.

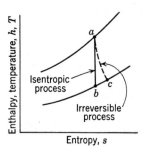

FIG. 2-7. Expansion flow processes.

As previously indicated, in both the statement and the derivation of equations, consistent units are assumed to apply, and thus conversion factors like J and constants like g_c are not always inserted into the equations. However, for reference and problem work it appears desirable to assign consistent units to the equations.

2-8. General Remarks. To develop the various relations in this chapter, certain assumptions must be valid. First, it is assumed that the flow is one-dimensional. Second, steady-flow conditions are prescribed. In some instances perfect-gas behavior and specific processes, such as the isentropic, are assumed. An attempt will be made now to discuss these premises. The requirements for one-dimensional flow were considered earlier in this chapter. However, it might be added that one-dimensional approaches are often used in initial analyses of more complex problems. In starting an entirely new problem, the one-dimensional approach serves as a basis of orientation before initiating more rigorous study. Sometimes by specifying a one-dimensional study certain phenomena can be ruled out a priori. For example, in developing Euler's equation no mention is made at this stage that it is also true for a certain type of multidimensional flow which is called *irrotational*. This approach is legitimate, however, because such considerations require more than one direction, and at this point one-dimensional flow alone is under discussion.

Referring to the steady-flow properties of the stream, it is assumed by definition that there are no changes in the properties at any cross section with respect to time. However, it is possible to assume a flow to be steady even if at any point within any device the properties vary periodically, provided the mass rate of flow G' and the rates at which heat and work cross the boundaries remain the same, and if the properties at the entrance and at the exit sections do not change with time.

Truly steady flow should be limited to the case in which the fluid particles move along streamlines. Thus, small eddy movements which exist in flow streams should preclude the assumption of steady flow. However, as suggested by Zucrow,[1] it is permissible in most cases to use the concept of steady flow in the presence of small eddies if one assumes that imaginary lines tangent to the average flow direction may be drawn in the stream, thereby assuming that the fluid motion is along these lines.

The applicability of thermodynamics to nonequilibrium processes has become an active topic of discussion, and even though a detailed study of this is beyond the scope of this text [2,3] a few words are in order at this point. In the true sense, thermodynamics is the science dealing with equilibrium states. In fact, the name *thermostatics* has been suggested in recent years. Thus one may question the applicability of thermodynamics to gas-dynamical problems in which the fluid particles undergo changes of state at a finite rate. This is certainly contradictory to the concept of equilibrium. Fortunately, as pointed out by Shapiro,[4] the departure from thermodynamic equilibrium is very small in most cases. Of course, this is not always the case, and great care must be exercised in shock phenomena where there are drastic departures from equilibrium conditions.

Although superficially the momentum equation and the energy equation appear to be similar, they are very different in physical nature. Thus, friction forces are not included in energy equations, but they are in momentum equations. The reason for this is that when wall friction exists, momentum is removed by friction at the walls but energy is not. Accordingly, in energy equations it is necessary to speak of the increase in internal energy and enthalpy of the system which accrues from the conversion of internal mechanical-work effects in overcoming losses. On the other hand, the energy equation can treat heat transfer across the walls, but the momentum equation cannot. This is true because in heat transfer energy is exchanged but momentum is not.

PROBLEMS

2-1. A jet engine develops 1,000 lb thrust at a flight velocity of 500 mph in level flight. Find (*a*) the thrust horsepower, and (*b*) the velocity at which the thrust in pounds and the thrust horsepower are equal numerically. (*c*) Using 100 lb thrust as a basis at varying speeds plot a graphical relation for horsepower.

2-2. For a turbojet engine will the power developed by the turbine proper be less than, greater than, or the same as the power necessary to drive the compressor and the accessories? Explain.

2-3. For a turbopropeller engine will the power developed by the turbine proper be less than, greater than, or the same as the power necessary to drive the compressor? Explain.

2-4. The efflux velocity from a jet unit is 1,762 fps for an air flow of 79 lb/sec through the unit. The airplane is flying at 400 mph. Compute the approximate thrust developed, the thrust horsepower, and the propulsion efficiency.

2-5. A jet-propelled airplane travels at 550 mph and employs two jet engines, each of which develops 4,000 lb of thrust. When flying at an altitude equivalent to a barometric pressure of 7 psia, it was found that the pressure in the tail-cone outlet at the point at which the exit velocity was measured amounted to 7.31 psia. The tail-cone area at the point of measurement was 1.65 ft^2, and 174 lb of air per second moved through each compressor. Disregarding the weight of fuel, compute the value of exit velocity from the jet at the measuring point. If 4,400 lb of fuel is used per hour by each engine, compute the efflux velocity required to produce the same thrust.

2-6. A jet engine in flight at 580 mph inducted 120 lb of air per second and used 4,650 lb of a gasoline fuel per hour. The tail-jet efflux velocity was 1,800 fps. Disregard pressure-area corrections, and compute the gross thrust and the thrust horsepower.

2-7. An afterburner with the preceding jet unit makes it possible to increase the jet-efflux velocity to 2,100 fps, and when in use fuel is consumed at the rate of 8,700 lb/hr. The flight speed also increases to 620 mph. Compute the thrust and thrust horsepower for afterburning conditions.

2-8. A propeller-jet airplane has a net shaft-horsepower output to the propeller gearing of 2,700. The jet exit velocity is 990 fps from the tail cone, and the airplane speed is 500 mph. Air flow through the jet system is 62 lb/sec. The propeller-propulsion efficiency is 78 per cent, and the transmission efficiency through the gearing is 95 per cent. (a) Compute the total equivalent horsepower produced by propeller and jet. (b) Compute the total thrust in pounds. (c) This unit shows a performance of somewhat better than 0.8 lb of gasoline per hour per pound of thrust when using gasoline with heating values of 18,900 (20,390 higher) Btu/lb and specific gravity of 0.73. Compute the probable fuel used per hour and the thermal efficiency based on both lower and higher heating values.

2-9. Find the mass rate of flow for two orifices placed in series in a 3-in.-ID pipe. The upstream pressure is 50 psia and the exit pressure is atmospheric. The diameter of the first orifice is 1½ in., and that of the second is 2 in. The temperature of the air entering the first is 59°F. Assume that there is no friction in the pipe and that the process is adiabatic. The orifice coefficient for each orifice is 0.68. HINT: Use a trial-and-error solution employing the equation of continuity.

2-10. The fuel nozzle of a two-stroke-cycle diesel engine is 0.02 in. in diameter. At 200 rpm the nozzle must deliver 66×10^{-5} lb of fuel oil per pump stroke made in 50° angular travel of the crank. The combustion pressure is 800 psia. (a) Find the nozzle pressure. (b) Compute the time rate of fuel flow. (c) Find the discharge velocity.

2-11. A V-2 rocket motor has the following characteristics:

	Combustion chamber, spherical	Throat	Exit
Diameter, ft............	3.11	1.32	2.41
Pressure, psia..........	294	157	14.7
Temperature, °R........	5,430	4,840	3,000
Velocity, fps...........	0	2,000	7,000
Fuel consumption, lb/sec	275		
Velocity, mph..........	3,400		

Find (a) thrust, (b) propulsion efficiency.

REFERENCES

1. Zucrow, M. J.: "Principles of Jet Propulsion and Gas Turbines," John Wiley & Sons, Inc., New York, 1948.
2. DeGroot, S. R.: "Thermodynamics of Irreversible Processes," Interscience Publishers, Inc., New York, 1952.
3. Prigogine, I.: "Introduction to the Thermodynamics of Irreversible Processes," Charles C Thomas Publisher, Springfield, Ill., 1955.
4. Shapiro, A. H.: "The Dynamics and Thermodynamics of Compressible Fluid Flow," vol. I, The Ronald Press Company, New York, 1953.

CHAPTER 3

ISENTROPIC FLOW

3-1. Introduction. The compression or the expansion of a gas can take place in numerous ways, the most important of which will be considered here. Classifications can follow many patterns depending on which characteristics are of greatest importance, but it should be remembered that no classification is perfect. In fluid dynamics it is often useful to designate flow according to a dimensionless parameter, the *Reynolds number*. This is a useful criterion in gas dynamics as well. However, the Reynolds number, defined as the ratio of the inertia forces to the viscous forces, is a mechanical concept and does not consider the thermal effects so important in any study of gas dynamics. Accordingly, it is necessary to employ other approaches when both fluid-dynamic and thermodynamic factors are present.

One significant approach is to classify the flow of gases on the basis of the change of entropy accompanying the process. A flow process is isentropic if it proceeds reversibly and *adiabatically* (exchanging no heat with its surroundings). A different type of flow is one which proceeds without frictional losses, but during the flow the gas exchanges heat with its surroundings. Such a reversible flow is called *diabatic*. During diabatic flow, the entropy may increase or decrease (in accordance with the second law of thermodynamics) depending on the direction of the heat exchange between the gas and its surroundings. A flow process is said to be irreversible if events take place which reduce the total available energy of the system and the surroundings. Such flows are accompanied by losses of the type associated with friction or shock waves. If irreversible processes take place adiabatically, then the second law specifies that the entropy must increase.

In this chapter, isentropic flow will be discussed in detail. Several parameters derived on the basis of adiabatic reversibility will be considered and their significance indicated.

3-2. Acoustic Velocity. The acoustic velocity, or the velocity of sound in a fluid medium, is by definition the speed with which a small disturbance is transmitted through the fluid.

Consider a piston which may slide without friction in a tube, as shown in Fig. 3-1, and assume that the piston and the gas in the tube are at rest originally. Let the pressure of the gas be p, uniform throughout the tube. If a small impulse is given to the piston, the gas immediately adjacent to the piston will experience a slight rise in pressure or, in other words, it will be compressed. The change in density takes place because the gas is compressible and there is therefore a lapse of time between the motion of the piston and the time this is observed at the far end of the tube. Thus it will take the pulse a certain time to reach the far end of the tube or, in other words, there is a finite velocity of propagation which, by definition, is the acoustic velocity. Let the change in pressure be denoted by dp, and let the change in density of the gas, due to the compression of the latter, be $d\rho$. The bulk modulus E is defined as

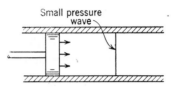

Fig. 3-1. Small pressure wave.

$$E = \rho \frac{dp}{d\rho} \qquad (3\text{-}1)$$

Dimensionally, $\sqrt{E/\rho}$ from Eq. (3-1) is a velocity, and it can be shown that this is also the acoustic velocity

$$a = \sqrt{\frac{E}{\rho}} \qquad (3\text{-}2)$$

By comparison with Eq. (3-1) it is also true that

$$a = \sqrt{\frac{dp}{d\rho}} \qquad (3\text{-}3)$$

An examination of Eq. (3-3) shows that the velocity with which a small pressure wave is propagated, and thus the velocity of sound, are related to the compressibility of the medium. It can be seen from Eq. (3-3) that the greater the compressibility of the gas, the lower will be the speed of sound. The velocity of a pressure wave cannot always be defined by Eq. (3-3) as this is valid only when the pressure and the velocity increments across the wave are so small that they can be approximated by their differentials. If the variations in pressure, velocity, and temperature are vanishingly small, it can be concluded that the process takes place reversibly. Also, the process takes place very rapidly and no drastic temperature gradients are involved, so that the process is essentially adiabatic and a sound wave can be treated as an isentropic phenomenon. Hence the derivative in Eq. (3-3) must be taken along an isentropic process. It is therefore more correct to use partial differential notation, namely,

$$a = \sqrt{\left(\frac{\partial p}{\partial \rho}\right)_s}$$ (3-4)

where the subscript s limits the applicability of the analysis to isentropic conditions. As long as the disturbance is very small, its geometry is immaterial.

On this assumption that the process is adiabatic and reversible, an expression for the acoustic velocity can be derived. The isentropic relationship for the perfect gas is

$$\frac{p}{\rho^k} = \text{constant}$$ (3-5)

which, after logarithmic differentiation, yields

$$\frac{dp}{d\rho} = k\frac{p}{\rho}$$

When this is combined with the gas equation $p/\rho = RT$, it becomes

$$\frac{dp}{d\rho} = k\frac{p}{\rho} = kRT$$

Thus, in a perfect gas the acoustic or sonic velocity is defined as

$$a = \sqrt{kRTg}$$ (3-6)

or

$$a = \sqrt{k\frac{p}{\rho}g}$$ (3-6a)

The acoustic velocity was defined as the speed with which a small disturbance propagates under isentropic conditions. The following question may be asked: Can a pressure wave move faster than the speed of sound in the medium? This question can be answered by a simple derivation outlined by Binder [1] which makes use of the equations of the conservation of mass, of energy, and of momentum. As before, consider a volume of a gas within a piston-cylinder arrangement to be subject to the force exerted by the piston, as shown in Fig. 3-2. Assume that the system is adiabatic, the piston frictionless, and that one-dimensional-flow analysis is applicable. Let the piston and gas be at rest at the start with V_1 zero and the pressure throughout the gas p_1. When the piston is pushed into the tube with some velocity V_2, the static pressure in the immediate vicinity of the piston will no longer be p_1, but will rise to some value p_2. The pressure in the whole system does not become p_2 immediately because each portion of gas remains at pressure p_1 until the pressure wave has traveled downstream with some velocity a'. As soon as the disturbance arrives at each point the fluid there will be set into motion, thereby acquiring a velocity V_2 and a pressure p_2. The pressure wave is then a discontinuity across which the velocity, the pressure, and the density are different. Across this discontinuity one may apply the equations of continuity, momentum,

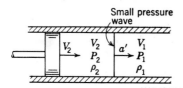

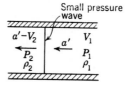

Fig. 3-2. Small pressure wave.   Fig. 3-3. Observer traveling with wave.

and energy. To the conditions on each side of the discontinuity an acoustic velocity will correspond. The equations can be applied most conveniently by assuming that the observer travels with the disturbance, as represented in Fig. 3-3. By the continuity equation we can write

$$a'\rho_1 = (a' - V_2)\rho_2$$

The momentum equation, as expressed in Eq. (2-8), gives

$$p_1 + \rho_1 a'^2 = p_2 + \rho_2(a' - V_2)^2$$

According to the energy equation,

$$\frac{k}{k-1}\left(\frac{p_2}{\rho_2} - \frac{p_1}{\rho_1}\right) = \frac{a'^2 - (a' - V_2)^2}{2}$$

The acoustic velocity corresponding to the initial state is given by

$$a_1 = \sqrt{k\frac{p_1}{\rho_1}}$$

Combining these four relations, eliminating ρ_1, ρ_2, and V_2, and solving for the ratio a'/a_1, there results

$$\frac{a'}{a_1} = \sqrt{\frac{1}{2k}\left[k - 1 + (k+1)\frac{p_2}{p_1}\right]}$$

It may be seen from this equation that the previously undefined velocity a', namely, that of the pressure wave, is equal to the acoustic velocity a_1 only when $p_1 = p_2$ or, in other words, when the pressure change across the wave is infinitesimal. This statement becomes very obvious by plotting a'/a_1 vs. p_2/p_1 for air in the above equation as in Fig. 3-4. Thus, when the pressure ratio p_2/p_1 is appreciably greater than unity, the velocity of the pressure wave will be supersonic, and the process will no longer be isentropic. In conclusion, it may be said that the acoustic velocity is the lowest velocity with which a compression wave may travel.

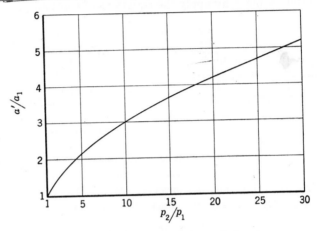

FIG. 3-4.   Disturbance velocity ratio for air.

In a paper published in 1687,[2] Newton computed the acoustic velocity with the assumption that the temperature remains constant in the condensations and rarefactions accompanying the transmission of sound. Differentiating the perfect-gas equation of state, $p/\rho = RT$, while holding the temperature constant, he obtained $dp/d\rho = RT$ and, upon substitution in Eq. (3-3),

$$a = \sqrt{RT}$$

This equation is the definition of Newton's acoustic velocity. However, for reasons already explained, experimental measurements yielded, for the acoustic velocity, values exceeding Newton's results. Laplace suggested that because the compressions taking place in sound waves are extremely rapid, there is no possibility for the heat of compression to be taken away, and therefore the process must be considered as taking place adiabatically. In adiabatic conditions, the change in pressure, corresponding to a given condensation or rarefaction, is greater, and hence the acoustic velocity is greater than the results obtained by the isothermal hypothesis.

The Newton equation and Eq. (3-6) differ by the ratio $\sqrt{k}$, and this is called, in honor of Laplace, *Laplace's correction*. It should be remembered that in isothermal flow, or even when the flow is nonadiabatic, a sound wave propagates isentropically.

The velocity of sound, as defined by Eqs. (3-6) and (3-6a), is in reasonable agreement with experimental data. Nevertheless, the equation is developed on the premise that the gas under consideration obeys perfect-gas laws. Because this is not always the case, it may be necessary to introduce a correction factor into Eq. (3-6) or to use specifically obtained experimental data. The NACA standard velocity at 59°F is 1,117 fps. In comparison, the speed of sound in steel is 16,480 fps, and in water it is 4,794 fps at normal temperature and pressure.

In observing Eq. (3-6), it is obvious that the only variable involved is temperature. In order to simplify calculations for a given medium, it is thus necessary only to evaluate the constants involved, and with air as an example Eq. (3-6) becomes

$$a = 49.1\sqrt{T} \tag{3-7}$$

where a = sonic velocity, fps, and T = temperature, °R.

Regardless of the velocity of a gas-dynamical system, the molecules making up the gas are constantly in random motion. Because different molecules in the body of a gas have different velocities at varying times, any gas on a molecular basis is considered to satisfy the concepts of statistical probability. Kinetic theory and Maxwell-Boltzmann distributions are used extensively in such studies. In this connection, the mean-square velocity is defined by

$$\overline{V}^2 = \frac{\Sigma V_i^2}{n}$$

in which n is the number of molecules in a control volume, and V_i is the velocity of specific molecules. It may be shown further by kinetic theory that the root-mean-square velocity $\overline{V}$ is

$$\overline{V} = 388 \sqrt{\frac{T}{M}} \quad \text{fps} \tag{3-8}$$

where M = molecular weight and T = temperature, °R.

It follows that for any perfect gas, the root-mean-square velocity and the acoustic velocity are related by the ratio

$$\frac{\overline{V}}{a} = \sqrt{\frac{3}{k}} \tag{3-9}$$

provided that they are both considered to be at the same temperature.

Example 1. Compute the root-mean-square velocity and the acoustic velocity for nitrogen at 68°F.

Solution. By Eq. (3-8)

$$V = 388 \sqrt{\frac{528}{28}}$$

$$V = 1{,}690 \text{ fps}$$

By Eq. (3-6)

$$a = \sqrt{1.4 \times 32.2 \times \frac{1{,}545}{28} \times 528}$$

$$= 1{,}150 \text{ fps}$$

This example shows that the root-mean-square velocity is greater than the velocity with which a disturbance travels in a system. This seems logical, because the position of the fluid particles determines the position of the disturbance wave.

Table A-1 lists the acoustic velocity at various altitudes, as well as the ratio of the acoustic velocity at any height to that at sea level for atmospheric air.

Example 2. What is the acoustic velocity in air at 30,000 ft altitude?
Solution. From Table A-1 one can read immediately the acoustic velocity as 678.5 mph. This same value results if the temperature at 30,000 ft is used in Eq. (3-7). Thus,

$$a = 49.1 \sqrt{411.4}$$

$$a = 996 \text{ fps}$$

$$a = 996 \times \frac{3{,}600}{5{,}280} = 678.5 \text{ mph}$$

3-3. Mach Number, Mach Line, and Mach Angle. In Chap. 1, the influence of velocity and temperature on certain gaseous properties was discussed. In defining compressibility phenomena also, both temperature and velocity must be taken into consideration. A convenient criterion for this purpose is the so-called *Mach number*, which is defined as the ratio of the local flow velocity to the acoustic velocity of the medium at the same location. Accordingly,

$$\text{M} = \frac{V}{a} = \frac{V}{\sqrt{kRT}} \tag{3-10}$$

Flow may be classified according to the value of the existing Mach number, as in Table 3-1. But because in many applications the velocity changes from one region to another, we refer also to the transonic regime which includes speeds just below and just above the speed of sound. It should be noted that Table 3-1 is based on velocity and not on frequency. In acoustical work, the term *ultrasonic* is used in referring to the frequencies above the audible range. This usage has no place in gas dynamics. One further note of caution is in order here, namely, in Eq. (3-10) the temperature T refers to the free-stream temperature at the same point as that at which the velocity exists. Only in this way can the local Mach number be found. ~~However, it is permissible to compute the Mach number referred~~ to standard air $(T = 519°R)$ provided mention is made of this fact.

TABLE 3-1. CLASSIFICATION OF FLOW

Mach number	Classification
M < 1	Subsonic flow
M = 1	Sonic (acoustic) flow
M > 1	Supersonic flow
M > 5	Hypersonic flow

It is often desirable to define variations of the Mach number in terms of changes in velocity and temperature. To do this consider the square of the Mach number. It will be noticed that this is dimensionless and a ratio of kinetic energies:

$$\text{M}^2 = \frac{V^2}{kRT} \qquad (3\text{-}11)$$

Differentiating Eq. (3-11) logarithmically, there results

$$\frac{d\text{M}}{\text{M}} = \frac{dV}{V} - \frac{1}{2}\frac{dT}{T} \qquad (3\text{-}12)$$

Equation (3-12) is particularly useful in isothermal-flow analyses.

Whenever an acceleration is imparted to a fluid, a pressure (sound) wave is set up. The amplitude of this wave depends on the magnitude of the component of the acceleration which is at right angles to the surface of the body. Furthermore, the velocity change due to the pulse will be in the direction of the pulse.

Consider a piston-cylinder arrangement. A finite small acceleration imparted to the piston will set up a small pressure pulse which will travel downstream at acoustic velocity with respect to the undisturbed fluid. As the wavefront progresses, the stationary portion of the fluid will attain the subsonic velocity of the piston. The pressure within the fluid will be altered as a result of the pulse, but this change takes place after the pressure pulse has traveled downstream.

Consider a point source traveling with a velocity $V < a$ as shown in Fig. 3-5. At reference time zero the point disturbance is assumed to be at A. At unit time later, $1t$, the point source will have moved to B, a distance Vt. At two time units later, $2t$, the source will have moved to point C, a distance $2Vt$. Meanwhile, the spherical-pressure wavefront which started out from A will have grown after time $2t$ to have a radius $2at$, and the wavefront from B which could not start until the source reached B will have grown to a radius at. At time $2t$ the source will have just reached point C.

This step-by-step analysis of a point source moving at subsonic velocity indicates that each succeeding wavefront will always be contained within the initial or preceding wavefront sphere.

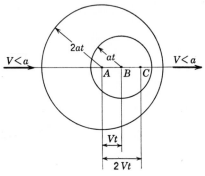

If the point source moves at a speed V such that $V > a$, the wavefront circles will no longer contain the source. The condition is shown in Fig. 3-6. The envelope to this family of circles is a straight line, known as the *Mach line*. It is easy to recognize that $\sin \alpha = a/V$ and hence $\alpha = \arcsin 1/M$. The angle between the Mach line and the direction of flow is known as the *Mach angle*.

FIG. 3-5. Wavefronts produced by a point source moving at subsonic velocity.

The Mach line constitutes a demarcation. It is easy to see that in Fig. 3-3 the fluid outside the Mach line will not receive any signal from the source because the disturbances travel with a speed equal to that of sound. Von Kármán[3] has appropriately called this phenomenon "the rule of forbidden signals." Further, von Kármán called the region ahead of the

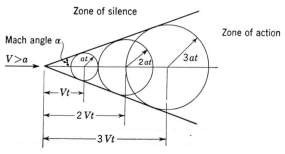

FIG. 3-6. Rule of forbidden signals from a point source moving at supersonic velocity.

Mach lines "the zone of silence" and the region inside the Mach lines "the zone of action."

3-4. The Flow System. Essentially, all problems of gas dynamics may be considered to take place in a flow system which may be considered as represented in Fig. 3-7. This consists of an infinite reservoir and a flow section. The conditions in the reservoir are denoted by the subscript 0. The flow section may be of any shape. It may be a convergent section, a straight section, or a convergent-divergent section. If it is convergent or convergent-divergent, the narrowest section is termed the *throat*. In the flow section there is a point where the Mach number is equal to unity and this is called the *critical point*. In a convergent-divergent flow section, and with reversible adiabatic flow, the throat is always the critical section.

To define a flow, the properties of the system must be known. It should be remembered that the flow properties of a system which define the state of the system are the static properties and not the dynamic properties. In other words, the properties which define a state are those which are determined by measuring devices which have a velocity of zero relative to the flow stream.

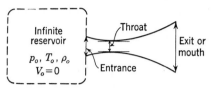

FIG. 3-7.   Flow system.

The enthalpy ($h = u + p/\rho$) of a perfect gas above an appropriate datum can be written as

$$h - h_0 = c_p(T - T_0) = \frac{kR}{k-1}(T - T_0)$$

This expression can be differentiated into the following equivalent forms:

$$dh = c_p\,dT = \frac{kR}{k-1}\,dT = -\frac{p\,d\rho}{\rho^2} + \frac{1}{\rho}\,dp + du \qquad (3\text{-}13)$$

Therefore, for isentropic flow in the absence of shaft work and when no changes in elevation occur, the energy equation (2-37) with Eq. (3-13) appears as

$$dQ - dW_s = dh + V\,dV + dz$$

$$\frac{kR}{k-1}\,dT + V\,dV = 0 \qquad (3\text{-}14)$$

Equation (3-14) is basic to most derivations involving isentropic flow. From it many equations may be obtained as, for example, the variation of the velocity with temperature. Dividing Eq. (3-14) by kRT there results

$$\frac{1}{k-1}\frac{dT}{T} + \frac{V\,dV}{kRT} = 0$$

and after multiplying and dividing the second term by V, it can be shown that

$$\frac{1}{k-1}\frac{dT}{T} + \mathrm{M}^2\frac{dV}{V} = 0$$

Rearranging,

$$\frac{dT}{T} = (1-k)\mathrm{M}^2\frac{dV}{V} \qquad (3\text{-}15)$$

3-5. Flow Parameters. The integration of Eq. (3-14) between conditions in the reservoir and any point in the flow section gives

$$\frac{kR}{k-1} \int_{T_0}^{T} dT + \int_{V_0=0}^{V} V \, dV = 0$$

$$\frac{kR}{k-1} T + \frac{V^2}{2} = \frac{kR}{k-1} T_0 \tag{3-16}$$

Introducing the definition of the acoustic velocity, Eq. (3-16) becomes

$$\frac{a^2}{k-1} + \frac{V^2}{2} = \frac{a_0^2}{k-1} \tag{3-17}$$

This equation implies that in a reversible adiabatic-expansion process, the acoustic velocity based on the reservoir conditions is greater than the local acoustic velocity at any point of the flow section. On the basis of temperature this means that the reservoir temperature is higher than the local temperature at each subsequent point. This can easily be understood if it is remembered that a gas is cooled when it is expanded reversibly and adiabatically.

Now let the temperature at some point in the expansion section be reduced hypothetically to absolute zero. It follows from the perfect-gas equation of state that at this point the term $kRT/(k-1)$ in Eq. (3-16) approaches zero. Hence, the local velocity V would reach a maximum but finite value which is set by the existing reservoir conditions. Denote the local velocity corresponding to the absolute vacuum by V_{max}; then

$$V_{max}^2 = \frac{2}{k-1} a_0^2 \tag{3-18}$$

$$V_{max} = a_0 \sqrt{\frac{2}{k-1}} \tag{3-19}$$

Evaluating Eq. (3-19) for air, it is found that

$$V_{max} = 2.24 a_0 \qquad \text{fps} \tag{3-20}$$

It follows that the maximum velocity for any particular gas is determined by the temperature existing in the reservoir. Thus for air

$$V_{max} = 109.7 \sqrt{T_0} \qquad \text{fps} \tag{3-21}$$

In practical applications, V_{max} is not reached; nevertheless Eq. (3-21) shows why the air entering supersonic wind tunnels must be heated if extremely high velocities such as those encountered in hypersonic wind tunnels are desired in the test section. The velocity V_{max}, although un-attainable, is of importance because it places a limit on the magnitude which the local velocity may assume. In practice this limiting velocity, V_{max}, could be reached only if it were possible to convert all of the thermal energy of the system into mechanical energy. This would mean that a thermometric device traveling with the stream at velocity of V_{max} would indicate absolute-zero temperature, and at this point the Mach number would be infinite.

Let us now consider subsonic flow and imagine a gradual increase of the local velocity V until the acoustic velocity is approached at a particular location. The expansion and increase in velocity results in a lowering of temperature and this also lowers the local acoustic velocity. Thus, while the local velocity increases, the local acoustic velocity decreases. With further expansion, the stream velocity could become equal to the acoustic velocity $V \equiv a$. At this condition, the acoustic speed is said to have reached its critical condition and this point is denoted by a^*. It follows from Eq. (3-17) that

$$a^{*2} = \frac{2}{k+1} a_0{}^2 \tag{3-22}$$

For air, the critical acoustic velocity and the acoustic velocity in the reservoir are related by

$$a^* = 0.913 a_0 \tag{3-23}$$

Example 3. Find the highest possible velocity which could result from the expansion of air at standard temperature of 59°F.

Solution. The highest velocity will be obtained when all of the thermal energy is converted into kinetic energy and this would happen at zero temperature absolute, 0°R. The limiting velocity V_{max} is related to the reservoir acoustic speed by Eqs. (3-20) and (3-7):

$$V_{max} = 2.24 a_0$$

$$a_0 = 49.1 \sqrt{519} = 1{,}120 \text{ fps}$$

Therefore, $V_{max} = 2.24 \times 1{,}120 = 2{,}508$ fps.

It follows that for any particular reservoir the maximum possible velocity is limited. However, it should not be inferred from this that the speed of aircraft is limited by these same considerations. Theoretically, there is no limit on the maximum speed which airplanes may reach.

The critical acoustic velocity serves a very useful purpose in defining a velocity ratio based on it, namely,

$$M^* = \frac{V}{V^*} = \frac{V}{a^*} \tag{3-24}$$

in which V is the velocity at any point and $V^* = a^*$. Although this is in the form of a Mach number, it pertains to no particular local conditions, but constitutes a reference ratio. There are two advantages to defining M*. First, it is a parameter which for any particular section is a function of the velocity only. Second, at extremely high speeds the acoustic velocity decreases (because of the decrease in temperature due to the rapid expansion) while the velocity itself increases. Hence the Mach number tends toward infinity, complicating its use in equations. Defining the Mach number M based on $a*$ obviates this difficulty.

3-6. Stagnation Temperature. Again considering the flow system of gas dynamics, introduce a thermometer in the flow section. In analyzing the system it is not hard to see that the energy of the system at reservoir conditions is purely thermal. As the expansion takes place the thermal energy is converted into kinetic energy. Upon reaching the thermometer, the gas particles in its immediate vicinity are brought to rest. Thus their kinetic energy is converted into thermal energy. From Eq. (3-14) the following integral equation results:

$$\frac{kR}{k-1}\int_{T_0}^{T} dT + \int_{V_0=0}^{V} V\,dV = 0 \tag{3-25}$$

$$\frac{kR}{k-1}T + \frac{V^2}{2} = \frac{kR}{k-1}T_0 \tag{3-16}$$

and

$$c_pT + \frac{V^2}{2} = c_pT_0 = h_0 \tag{3-26}$$

Here T_0 represents the existing stagnation temperature when V reaches zero as the gas is brought to rest.

It follows from Eq. (3-26) that theoretically the enthalpy of the gas brought to rest at the thermometer equals the enthalpy in the reservoir and therefore this is called the *stagnation enthalpy*. Furthermore the temperature read by a stationary thermometer, called the *stagnation temperature*, is also equal theoretically to the temperature read in the reservoir. Irrespective of the location of the thermometer, the stagnation conditions are set by the reservoir conditions.

From this discussion it appears that the free-stream temperature cannot readily be determined. To develop an equation which will permit estimating the free-stream temperature, consider the energy equation (3-16) which defines the events, namely,

$$\frac{kR}{k-1}T + \frac{V^2}{2} = \frac{kR}{k-1}T_0 \tag{3-27}$$

Solving for the stagnation temperature, we find

$$T_0 = T + \frac{V^2}{2C_p} \qquad (3\text{-}28)$$

If the temperature is given in degrees Fahrenheit, we can approximate for air by the equation

$$T_0 \cong T + \frac{V^2}{12,000} \qquad (3\text{-}29)$$

where the velocity is given in feet per second. Dividing Eq. (3-27) by kRT and introducing the Mach number M, there results

$$\frac{T_0}{T} = 1 + \frac{k-1}{2} M^2 \qquad (3\text{-}30)$$

The free-stream temperature of the gas may then be determined by Eq. (3-30) if the stagnation temperature, the ratio of the specific heats,

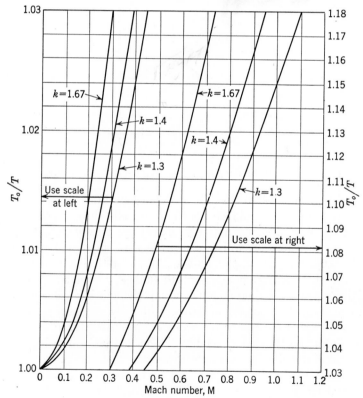

FIG. 3-8.   Stagnation-temperature rise ratio at low Mach numbers.

and the Mach number are known. In Fig. 3-8 are plotted values of the temperature ratio T_0/T for various monoatomic ($k = 1.67$), diatomic ($k = 1.4$), and triatomic ($k = 1.3$) gases. This figure shows the influence of the atomic configuration on the expansion process. For air, using a constant value of $k = 1.4$, the ratio T_0/T vs. the Mach number is plotted in Fig. 3-9 for subsonic as well as hypersonic flow.

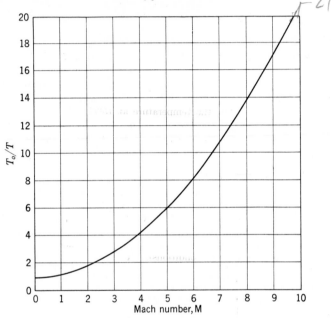

FIG. 3-9.   Stagnation-temperature rise ratio at high Mach numbers.

It should be emphasized that T_0, as defined by Eqs. (3-26) to (3-30), is the temperature that would be read theoretically on a thermometer inserted in the flow stream. Actually, unless specifically designed for the purpose, no thermometer will measure the true stagnation temperature, but will indicate a value approaching it. Theoretically, it is impossible to measure the free-stream temperature (unless the relative velocity between the gas and the thermometer sensing element is zero) but it is possible to measure the stagnation temperature. In engineering work it is necessary to know the factor by which a given stagnation thermometer deviates from the theoretical reading. This matter will be discussed in more detail in the chapter dealing with measurement techniques.

For a particular reservoir condition, T_0 remains the same irrespective of the local temperature, as temperature in any flow system varies with the local Mach number only. The conditions at any two points in the flow system may be interrelated through Eq. (3-30). Thus at a flow station indicated by subscript 1, Eq. (3-30) becomes

$$\frac{T_0}{T_1} = 1 + \frac{k-1}{2} M_1{}^2 \tag{3-31}$$

and at some station 2

$$\frac{T_0}{T_2} = 1 + \frac{k-1}{2} M_2{}^2 \tag{3-32}$$

Dividing the first equation by the second, there results

$$\frac{T_2}{T_1} = \frac{1 + [(k-1)/2]M_1{}^2}{1 + [(k-1)/2]M_2{}^2} \tag{3-33}$$

Example 4. Consider a missile traveling at 150,000 ft altitude with a Mach number of 7.0. Find the stagnation (theoretical) temperature at the nose of the missile.

Solution. From Table A-1, the temperature at 150,000 ft is 573.2°R. Therefore, the temperature at the nose is

$$T_0 = 573.2 \left(1 + \frac{1.4-1}{1.4} 7^2 \right)$$

$$T_0 = 8600°R$$

It should be noted that this is the temperature felt at the nose of the missile, as well as the temperature which a reservoir would have to have in order to produce a stream of air at a Mach number of 7 at the point where the temperature is 573.2°R. As far as the thermodynamic properties are concerned, it is immaterial whether the missile moves and the air is stationary (flight conditions), or whether the air moves and the missile is stationary (wind-tunnel conditions).

3-7. Stagnation Pressure. A relation between the stagnation pressure and the static pressure may be had by using certain of the perfect-gas relationships. For perfect-gas isentropic flow, the relationship between pressure and temperature, as the stagnation pressure p_0 is created from a static flow pressure p, appears as

$$\left(\frac{p_0}{p} \right)^{(k-1)/k} = \frac{T_0}{T} \tag{3-34}$$

and hence

$$\frac{p_0}{p} = \left(1 + \frac{k-1}{2} M^2 \right)^{k/(k-1)} \tag{3-35}$$

The variation of the ratio p_0/p with Mach number is plotted for different values of k in Fig. 3-10.

The dynamic pressure q is now defined as

$$q = \tfrac{1}{2}\rho V^2 \tag{3-36}$$

Combine Eq. (3-36) with Eq. (3-11), and it is seen that the dynamic pressure can be written in the form

$$q = \tfrac{1}{2}kpM^2 \tag{3-37}$$

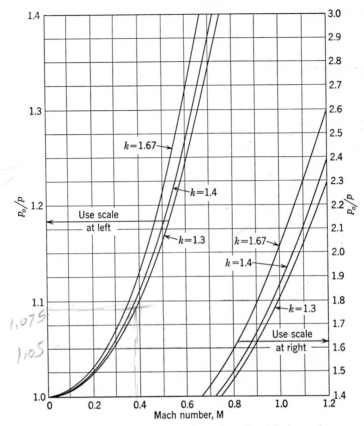

FIG. 3-10. Stagnation-pressure rise ratio at low Mach numbers.

Introducing the dynamic pressure into Eq. (3-35), we obtain

$$\frac{p_0 - p}{q} = \frac{2}{k\mathrm{M}^2}\left[\left(1 + \frac{k-1}{2}\mathrm{M}^2\right)^{k/(k-1)} - 1\right] \qquad (3\text{-}38)$$

It is frequently desirable to express Eq. (3-38) in the form of a series. This can be done by the use of the binomial theorem, which is frequently written as

$$(1 + x)^n = 1 + nx + \frac{n(n-1)x^2}{2!} + \frac{n(n-1)(n-2)x^3}{3!} + \cdots$$

provided $x^2 < 1$. Accordingly, when $[(k-1)/2]\mathrm{M}^2 < 1$, it can be found that

$$\left(1 + \frac{k-1}{2}\mathrm{M}^2\right)^{k/(k-1)} = 1 + \frac{k}{2}\mathrm{M}^2 + \frac{k}{8}\mathrm{M}^4 + \frac{2}{48}(2-k)\mathrm{M}^6 + \cdots$$

Substituting this in Eq. (3-38) and later introducing Eq. (3-37), there results

$$\frac{p_0 - p}{q} = \frac{2}{kM^2}\left[\frac{k}{2}M^2 + \frac{k}{8}M^4 + \frac{2(2-k)}{48}M^6 + \cdots\right] \qquad (3\text{-}39)$$

and

$$p_0 = p + \tfrac{1}{2}\rho V^2\left(1 + \frac{M^2}{4} + \frac{2-k}{24}M^4 + \cdots\right) \qquad (3\text{-}40)$$

In contrast, for incompressible flow, Bernoulli's equation (2-30) gives

$$p_0 = p + \tfrac{1}{2}\rho V^2 \qquad (3\text{-}41)$$

Equations (3-40) and (3-41) are plotted in Fig. 3-11.

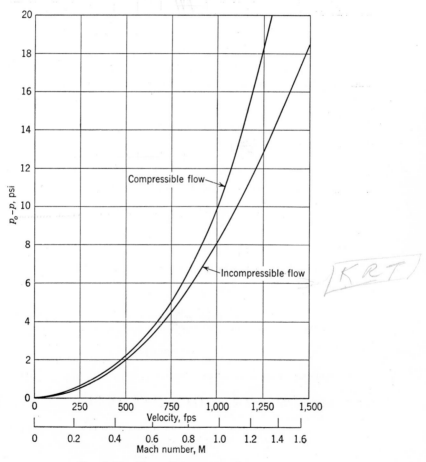

FIG. 3-11. Stagnation-pressure rise.

One of the important cases for which the phenomena of Fig. 3-11 are applicable is the aircraft speed indicator. It can readily be seen that if the speed indicator is calibrated without taking the effect of compressibility into consideration serious inaccuracy results.

Example 5. An uncorrected air-speed indicator reads 380 mph at the NACA 15,000-ft altitude. Find the true air speed.

Solution. Whether or not the indicator needs correction can be seen from Fig. 3-11. The individual must decide what percentage error is permissible.

For convenience, convert the speed in miles per hour into feet per second. Thus

$$380 \times 1.467 = 558 \text{ fps}$$

From Fig. 3-11 at 558 fps, the difference between $p_0 - p$ for compressible and that for incompressible flow is 0.25 psi. From Table A-1, the pressure at 15,000 ft altitude is 1,194.3 lb/ft^2 (psf), and the density is 0.001497 slug/ft^3. From the incompressible Bernoulli equation

$$p_0 - p = \frac{\rho V^2}{2} = \frac{(0.001497)(558)}{2}$$

$$= 233.5 \text{ psf}$$

Therefore, the stagnation pressure of the uncorrected indicator is

$$p_0 = p + (p_0 - p)$$

$$p_0 = 1,194.3 + 233.5 = 1,427.8 \text{ psf}$$

The stagnation pressure for the corrected indicator is

$$p_0 = 1,427.8 + 0.25 = 1,428.05 \text{ psf}$$

The Mach number may be found now from Eq. (3-35) or by the use of Fig. 3-10. Thus

$$\frac{p_0}{p} = \frac{1,428.1}{1,194.3} = \left(1 + \frac{0.4}{2} M^2\right)^{1.4/0.4}$$

from which $M = 0.51$

Also, $V = a\text{M}$, and at 15,000 ft from Table A-1, $a = 721.2$ mph. Therefore, the true air velocity V is

$$V = 721.2 \times 0.51$$

$$V = 368 \text{ mph}$$

PROBLEMS

3-1. Find the lowest speed of sound which may be encountered in the standard atmosphere.

3-2. Compute the speed of sound at an altitude of 20,000 ft, and compare this value with the one given in Table A-1.

3-3. The speed of sound in air in miles per hour may be computed by the equation $a = C\sqrt{T}$. If T is given in degrees Rankine, find the value and the units of the constant C.

3-4. Show that for air $a = 49.1\sqrt{T}$ fps.

3-5. A model is placed in a wind tunnel operating at a test-section Mach number of 1.2. (a) Find the velocity of the air stream based on standard air. (b) Find the Mach angle.

3-6. Make a sketch depicting the events when a point source of disturbance moves at the same subsonic speed as does the fluid.

3-7. Make a sketch depicting the events when a point source of disturbance moves at the same supersonic speed as does the fluid.

3-8. What is the dynamic pressure at 15,000 ft NACA altitude when the velocity is 380 mph?

3-9. For a hypersonic wind tunnel having a test-section Mach number of 10, find (a) the pressure ratio p_0/p, and (b) the temperature ratio T_0/T. (c) Discuss the possibility of the air being liquefied because of its drastic expansion.

3-10. Standard air at zero velocity expands to M = 0.9. Find (a) the final density, and (b) the density change.

3-11. Standard air at 30 mph is accelerated isentropically in a nozzle to 500 mph. Find (a) the change in temperature, (b) the change in pressure, (c) the change in density, (d) the change in stagnation temperature, and (e) the change in stagnation pressure.

3-12. It is desired to design a supersonic wind tunnel which will have in the test section standard air and a Mach number of 5. Find the conditions of the air in the reservoir.

3-13. An aircraft at 15,000 ft altitude has a true speed of 360 mph. Find (a) the critical velocity, and (b) the maximum possible velocity. Assume that friction is negligible.

3-14. During research test runs in the Northwestern University Gas Dynamics Laboratory, a pitot-static tube indicated a static pressure of 9.5 psig. At the same conditions, the manometer difference between stagnation and static pressures was 4.38 in. Hg. The corrected barometric pressure was 29.62 in. Hg and the stagnation temperature 95.3°F. Find the air velocity.

3-15. Air flows in a pipe having an internal diameter of 0.732 in., with a Mach number of 0.5. The air entering the pipe is at 80 psig and 100°F. The capacity of the compressor supplying the air is 1,500 cfm of free air. Find the stagnation temperature in the air stream.

3-16. Air from a standard reservoir enters a DeLaval nozzle. It is observed that at a section where the Mach wave is 28°, the static pressure is 5 psia. Find (a) the Mach number, (b) the temperature at the point where the pressure is 5 psia, and (c) the velocity at the point where the pressure is 5 psia.

3-17. Show that for isentropic flow

$$V_{\max} = \sqrt{\frac{2a^2}{k-1} + V^2}$$

3-18. Show that for isentropic flow

$$a^* = \sqrt{\frac{2a^2 + V^2(k-1)}{k+1}}$$

3-19. For air undergoing an isentropic process derive the equation

$$a^* = C\sqrt{T_0}$$

and determine the numerical value of the constant C when a^* is given in feet per second and T_0 in degrees Rankine.

3-20. Show that

$$M^* = \frac{(M^2/2)(k+1)}{M^2[(k-1)/2] + 1}$$

REFERENCES

1. Binder, R. C.: Wave Velocities above the Velocity of Sound, *J. Eng. Educ.*, vol. 58, no. 10, p. 631, 1951.
2. Rayleigh, Lord: "Theory of Sound," vol. II, p. 19, Dover Publications, New York, 1945.
3. von Kármán, Theodore: Supersonic Aerodynamics: Principles and Applications, *J. Aeronaut. Sci.*, vol. 14, no. 7, p. 373, July, 1947.

CHAPTER 4

DIABATIC FLOW

4-1. Introduction. Although many engineering processes can be assumed to be adiabatic, this is far from true in others. Heat exchangers and combustion chambers are two devices in which heat interchanges occur. Whether the heat is added across the system boundaries as in a heat exchanger, or whether it is added internally by virtue of a chemical reaction as in a combustion chamber, does not alter the analysis in principle, and the generic term *diabatic process* is applicable to both of these related types of phenomena. The equations describing nonadiabatic or diabatic processes are complicated and consequently certain limiting assumptions are usually required in order to make solutions of the equations possible. The assumptions are that:

1. The flow takes place in a constant-area section.
2. There is no friction.
3. The gas is perfect and hence has constant specific heats.
4. The composition of the gas does not change.
5. There are no devices in the system which deliver or receive mechanical work.
6. The flow is steady.

It may be argued that these assumptions are somewhat tenuous, which is true. Nevertheless, they are acceptable and yield results which, within a margin of error, agree with experimental values or those obtained by more elaborate analysis.

4-2. Stagnation-temperature Change. It was noted that heat may be added to a gaseous system either by external or by internal means. The flow system in each case is slightly different. Thus, if the heat is added as in a heat exchanger the situation can be represented as shown in Fig. 4-1. It is also possible for a thermal manifestation of heat addition to occur in a thin discontinuity as depicted in Fig. 4-2. For this it is assumed that the duct is insulated so that theoretically there is no heat exchange between the fluid within the control boundaries and the surroundings, and furthermore, that there is no heat transfer between parts of the fluid in the control volume due to convection, conduction, and radiation. That the heat addition takes place by virtue of a thin discontinuity may seem

65

to be an overly exaggerated simplification, but it actually can be strongly supported. A typical example would be a flame front traveling in a combustion tube, and experiments show that such a flame front is actually very thin.

In all cases obeying the assumptions listed in Sec. 4-1, the steady-flow energy equation (2-37) for diabatic flow (neglecting changes in potential energy and when no shaft work is done) is

unidirectional flow

$$dQ = \frac{kR}{k-1} dT + V\,dV \tag{4-1}$$

The general development of the equation in this form was made for the adiabatic case in Eq. (3-14), and is applicable here provided dQ is not

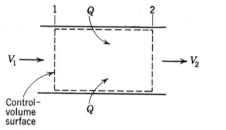

FIG. 4-1. Heat-exchanger model.

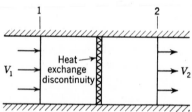

FIG. 4-2. Heat addition.

equated to zero. Equation (4-1) can be integrated between the conditions indicated at 1 and 2 in Figs. 4-1 and 4-2. When this is done, the resulting expression appears as

$$Q_{1 \to 2} = c_p(T_2 - T_1) + \frac{V_2^2 - V_1^2}{2} = h_2 - h_1 + \frac{V_2^2 - V_1^2}{2} \tag{4-2}$$

If stagnation enthalpy is introduced, using Eq. (1-47),

$$Q_{1 \to 2} = h_{02} - h_{01}$$

This in turn can be expressed in terms of stagnation temperatures following Eq. (3-26), giving

$$Q_{1 \to 2} = c_p(T_{02} - T_{01}) \tag{4-3}$$

Because for diabatic flow $Q_{1 \to 2} \neq 0$ and because $c_p > 0$ always, it follows that

$$T_{02} \neq T_{01}$$

This inequality states that in diabatic flow the stagnation temperature is not solely determined by the reservoir conditions, as is the case with adiabatic flow.

It now remains to investigate the effect of heat exchange on the change of stagnation temperature. This problem can be answered easily because $c_p > 0$ and hence the difference in stagnation temperatures on each side of the heat-exchange discontinuity, namely, $T_{02} - T_{01}$, must have the same sign as the conventional sign for heat exchange. It follows at once that heating raises the stagnation temperature and cooling lowers it.

4-3. Rayleigh Line. The locus of points of properties during a constant-area, frictionless flow with heat exchange is called the *Rayleigh line*. Along the Rayleigh line the continuity equation and the momentum equation must apply. Thus, for steady flow in a constant-area duct the equation of continuity [Eq. (2-2)] appears as

$$G' = \rho V A \qquad (2-2)$$

the mass velocity is

$$G = \rho V$$

and the momentum relation by Eq. (2-8) is

$$p + \rho V^2 = \text{constant}$$

$$T_{0_1} = T_1 \left[1 + \frac{k-1}{2} \left(\frac{G}{P_1} \right)^2 \frac{RT_1}{kg_c} \right]$$

$$\theta = \rho V$$

Combining these two equations we obtain

$$p + \frac{G^2}{\rho} = \text{constant} \qquad (4\text{-}4)$$

which is one of the Rayleigh-line equations.

Any equation which expresses a relation among the properties of a system undergoing a diabatic process in conformity with Eq. (4-4) is a Rayleigh equation. Although an extensive number of these may be derived, only some of the more important ones will be discussed here.

4-4. Pressure Ratio. An equation expressing the pressure ratio for a Rayleigh process is derived as follows:

The momentum equation is

$$p + \rho V^2 = \text{constant}$$

and for a constant-area section

$$p_2 + \rho_2 V_2{}^2 = p_1 + \rho_1 V_1{}^2$$

and

$$p_2 - p_1 + \rho_2 V_2{}^2 - \rho_1 V_1{}^2 = 0$$

By definition, and from Eqs. (3-11) and (1-11),

$$M^2 = \frac{V^2}{kRT} \qquad \text{and} \qquad \frac{p}{\rho} = RT$$

The last two equations can be combined to give

$$V^2 \rho = kpM^2$$

When this is substituted in the momentum equation, there results

$$p_2 - p_1 + kp_2M_2{}^2 - kp_1M_1{}^2 = 0$$

and
$$1 + kM_2{}^2 - \frac{p_1}{p_2}(1 + kM_1{}^2) = 0 \qquad (4\text{-}5)$$

This equation when solved for the ratio p_2/p_1 becomes

Momentum

$$\boxed{\frac{p_2}{p_1} = \frac{1 + kM_1{}^2}{1 + kM_2{}^2}} \qquad (4\text{-}6)$$

It was shown in Sec. 4-2 that in diabatic flow the stations before and after the heat addition have different corresponding reservoir conditions because the stagnation temperature changes. Therefore, a new type of reference condition must be used, and it is convenient to define this at the conditions where the Mach number is unity. In Eq. (4-6) the conditions at either point may be used as reference. Arbitrarily selecting this condition at 1 and denoting the reference by the asterisk, we obtain

$$\frac{p}{p^*} = \frac{1 + k}{1 + kM^2} \qquad (4\text{-}7)$$

It was shown previously [Eq. (3-35)] that the stagnation pressure, static pressure, and Mach number are related by the following equation:

$$\frac{p_0}{p} = \left(1 + \frac{k-1}{2}M^2\right)^{k/(k-1)}$$

Writing this equation between two stations, 1 and 2, dividing one by the other, and finally substituting from the Rayleigh-line equation (4-6), we find that

$$\frac{p_{02}}{p_{01}} = \frac{1 + kM_1{}^2}{1 + kM_2{}^2}\left\{\frac{1 + [(k-1)/2]M_2{}^2}{1 + [(k-1)/2]M_1{}^2}\right\}^{k/(k-1)} \qquad (4\text{-}8)$$

By letting $M_1 = 1$ as before, and denoting this station by the asterisk, we obtain a relation for the stagnation pressure ratio p_0/p_0^*. The development of this equation is left to the student as an exercise (see Prob. 4-1).

4-5. Temperature Ratio. Equations relating the temperature change to the Mach number will now be developed.

At the upstream side of the heat addition, by the definition of the stagnation temperature as expressed in Eq. (3-30), we find that

$$\frac{T_{01}}{T_1} = 1 + \frac{k-1}{2}M_1{}^2$$

For the downstream side, the appropriate stagnation-temperature equation is

$$\frac{T_{02}}{T_2} = 1 + \frac{k-1}{2}M_2{}^2$$

Division then gives

$$\frac{T_{02}}{T_{01}} = \frac{T_2}{T_1}\frac{1 + [(k-1)/2]M_2{}^2}{1 + [(k-1)/2]M_1{}^2} \tag{4-9}$$

This equation, expressing the ratio of the stagnation temperatures, may be put into a form which is still more convenient.

On each side of the discontinuity the equation of state will apply, and for the perfect gas it follows that

$$\frac{p_1}{\rho_1} = RT_1 \quad \text{and} \quad \frac{p_2}{\rho_2} = RT_2$$

and division yields

$$\frac{T_2}{T_1} = \frac{p_2 \rho_1}{p_1 \rho_2} \tag{4-10}$$

For a constant-area flow by the equation of continuity,

$$\frac{\rho_1}{\rho_2} = \frac{V_2}{V_1} \tag{4-11}$$

Combining Eq. (4-6) with Eqs. (4-10) and (4-11), there results

$$\frac{T_2}{T_1} = \frac{V_2}{V_1}\frac{1 + kM_1{}^2}{1 + kM_2{}^2} \tag{4-12}$$

By the definition of the Mach number, we can write

$$M_1 = \frac{V_1}{\sqrt{kRT_1}} \quad \text{and} \quad M_2 = \frac{V_2}{\sqrt{kRT_2}}$$

Division then shows

$$\frac{V_2}{V_1} = \frac{M_2\sqrt{T_2}}{M_1\sqrt{T_1}}$$

Squaring and substituting in Eq. (4-12), the free-stream-temperature ratio becomes

$$\frac{T_2}{T_1} = \left(\frac{M_2}{M_1}\frac{1 + kM_1{}^2}{1 + kM_2{}^2}\right)^2 \tag{4-13}$$

Using Eq. (4-13) to substitute for T_2/T_1 in Eq. (4-9), it is found that

$$\frac{T_{02}}{T_{01}} = \frac{M_2{}^2(1 + kM_1{}^2)^2\{1 + [(k-1)/2]M_2{}^2\}}{M_1{}^2(1 + kM_2{}^2)^2\{1 + [(k-1)/2]M_1{}^2\}} \tag{4-14}$$

This equation is convenient because it is in terms of quantities which can be measured with relative ease. However, it is possible to modify it slightly and make it even more convenient for analytical work. To do this, we again let $M_1 = 1$ and denote all properties at this point by the superscript asterisk. Thus for $M_1 = M^* = 1$,

$$T_1 = T^* \qquad p_1 = p^* \qquad T_{01} = T_0^*$$

This condition yields two commonly used expressions, namely,

$$\frac{T}{T^*} = \frac{M^2(1+k)^2}{(1+kM^2)^2} \tag{4-15}$$

and

$$\frac{T_0}{T_0^*} = \frac{2M^2(k+1)\{1 + [(k-1)/2]M^2\}}{(1+kM^2)^2} \tag{4-16}$$

Tabulated values of T_0/T_0^*, T/T^*, p/p^*, p_0/p_0^*, ρ^*/ρ, and V/V^* as a function of Mach number will be found in the appropriate tables in the literature [7] and in abbreviated form in this text (Table A-4). It should be noted that for each value of k a different table must be constructed; however, in this text tables for $k = 1.4$ are included.

Example 1. Dry air at standard temperature and pressure and having a Mach number of 1.8 is heated in a 2-in.-ID pipe in a frictionless manner so that it is decelerated to a Mach number of unity. Find (a) the change in temperature, and (b) the amount of heat added.

Solution. (a) The change in temperature will be the difference between the final and the initial temperatures. The initial temperature is 519°R because standard air was specified. The final temperature may be found from Eq. (4-13) and in this particular problem also by the use of Eq. (4-15). However, here the use of the Rayleigh-line tables will be demonstrated in the solution. Thus from Table A-4 one finds $(T/T^*)_1$ = 0.60894. Because the final Mach number is unity, it follows that $T_2 = T^*$. Therefore,

$$T_2 = \frac{519}{0.60894} = 853°R$$

Hence the change in temperature is

$$853 - 519 = 334°R$$

(b) In determining the heat added, use either Eq. (4-2) or (4-3). If the solution is based on the former, it is necessary to find the local velocities from the corresponding Mach numbers. If the latter is used, it is necessary to find stagnation temperatures at each station. Using the former method, one proceeds as follows:

$$V_1 = a_1 M_1$$

$$a_1 = 49.1\sqrt{519} = 1{,}117 \text{ fps}$$

$$V_1 = 1{,}117 \times 1.8 = 2{,}011 \text{ fps}$$

From Table A-4 for a Mach number of 1.8

$$\frac{V}{V^*} = 1.4046$$

and
$$V_2 = V^*$$

Therefore,

$$V_2 = \frac{2,011}{1.4046} = 1,430 \text{ fps}$$

$$Q = 0.24(853 - 519) - \frac{(2,011)^2 - (1,430)^2}{2 \times 32.2 \times 778}$$

$$= 80.1 - 39.92$$

$$= 40.18 \text{ Btu/lb}$$

The variation of pressure, temperature, and density with Mach number for Rayleigh flow manifests certain peculiarities which are not self-evident without study. Accordingly, the various property ratios as obtained from the Rayleigh-line table have been plotted in Fig. 4-3. This table was developed by applying the various equations already discussed. It should be noted at once that the curves in this figure do not denote paths or processes in the usual sense. Instead, each curve in Fig. 4-3 represents the locus of the particular property ratio as defined by the Mach number. The specific-heat ratio for these graphs is 1.4.

In Fig. 4-3, the curve of T_0/T_0^* is probably the most basic because the direction of the stagnation-temperature change indicates the direction of heat transfer. The curve representing the values of the ratio T/T^* reaches its maximum at $M = 0.85 = 1/\sqrt{k}$. The curve for T_0/T_0^* is seen to reach a maximum for a Mach number of unity ($M = 1$). Furthermore, all of the curves pass through this point, but except for p_0/p_0^* and T_0/T_0^* they do not have a maximum or a minimum at $M = 1$. Now consider the addition of heat to a diatomic gas flowing in a pipe in the absence of friction. Because heat is added to the gas, its stagnation temperature must increase, and hence T_0/T_0^* will increase. Now if the flow is subsonic originally, Fig. 4-3 indicates that for a higher T_0/T_0^* there corresponds a greater Mach number, or, in other words, the flow is accelerated by the heat addition. Had the flow been supersonic to begin with, then the heat addition would have resulted in a deceleration because, as may be seen in Fig. 4-3, in the supersonic domain, T_0/T_0^* increases as M decreases.

The fact that the curve for T_0/T_0^* reaches a maximum at a Mach number of unity indicates categorically that it is impossible to pass from one domain into the other by the same heat-transfer process. Thus, if heat is added to a subsonic flow, the flow can be accelerated until its Mach number becomes unity. Further addition of heat will not cause any acceleration, but will result in choking of the flow. As a consequence of this, the flow must readjust itself; this it will do by lowering its initial Mach number. In order to prevent choking, it is necessary then that a fixed magni-

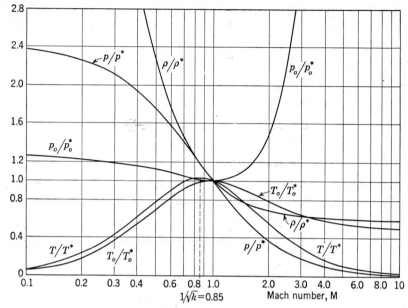

FIG. 4-3.   Diabatic-flow parameters.

tude of heat transferred cannot be exceeded.   The maximum amount of
heat which can be added to a gas without causing choking, and the reasons
for choking, will be studied in the subsequent parts of this chapter.   The
variation of the flow properties for heating and cooling in each domain are
shown in Table 4-1.

TABLE 4-1.   VARIATION OF FLOW PROPERTIES

| Property | Heating | | Cooling | |
	M > 1	M < 1	M > 1	M < 1
T_0	Increases	Increases	Decreases	Decreases
p	Increases	Decreases	Decreases	Increases
p_0	Decreases	Decreases	Increases	Increases
V	Decreases	Increases	Increases	Decreases
T	Increases always	Increases when $M < 1/\sqrt{k}$ Decreases when $M > 1/\sqrt{k}$	Decreases always	Decreases when $M < 1/\sqrt{k}$ Increases when $M > 1/\sqrt{k}$

Example 2. An athodyd starts in standard air while cold with a Mach number of 0.5, as it might do if dropped from the belly of a mother plane. The combustion chamber is of the constant-area can type. It is desired to obtain an exit total temperature (at exit of combustion zone) of 2595°R. Assuming that friction is negligible, determine whether or not there will be choking.

Solution. Choking will occur if $T_{02} > T_0^*$ because the extent of heating is limited by T_0^*. It is necessary, therefore, to find T_0^*, and this can be done as soon as T_{01} is known. (The statement of the problem specifies $T_{02} = 2595°R$.) The stagnation temperature at 1 can be found from the isentropic-flow table, or by Eq. (3-30):

$$\frac{T_0}{T} = 1 + \frac{k-1}{2} M^2$$

Thus,

$$T_{01} = 519 \left[1 + \frac{1.4 - 1}{2} (0.5)^2 \right]$$

$$T_{01} = 545°R$$

The ratio

$$\frac{T_{02}}{T_{01}} = \frac{2,595}{545} = 4.76$$

From Rayleigh-line data in Table A-4, it can be seen that at $M_1 = 0.5$ the ratio $(T_0/T_0^*)_1 = 0.69136$, and hence $T_0^* = 545/0.69136 = 790°R$. Because $T_{02} > T_0^*$, it is evident that choking will occur.

It is of interest to find the entrance Mach number after the flow readjusts itself while the exit Mach number is unity. In order to find the entrance Mach number after the flow readjusts itself, it is necessary to find T/T^* after the readjustment. To do this, first find T_2. Thus, again using Eq. (3-30),

$$T_2 = \frac{T_{02}}{1 + [(k-1)/2]M_2^2}$$

$$T_2 = \frac{2,595}{1 + [(1.4-1)/2]1^2}$$

$$T_2 = 2160°R$$

Also

$$\frac{(T/T^*)_2}{(T/T^*)_1} = \frac{T_2}{T_1}$$

The answer to the problem is the Mach number corresponding to $(T/T^*)_1$. From Rayleigh-line data in Table A-4 at $M_2 = 1$, $(T/T^*)_2 = 1$. Furthermore, $T_2/T_1 = 2,160/519 = 4.16$, and hence $(T/T^*)_1 = 1/4.16 = 0.24$. The Mach number corresponding to this temperature is found from Table A-4 and is approximately 0.22.

4-6. Entropy Considerations. It has already been pointed out that when heat is added to a gas traveling at either subsonic or supersonic speeds, the consequence is for the gas to reach a Mach number of unity. For originally subsonic velocities this brings about an acceleration, and for originally supersonic velocities a deceleration. It was further shown that if heat continues to enter the system once unit Mach number is reached, choking occurs and the flow rate diminishes. These phenomena will now be explained on the basis of the second law of thermodynamics.

Let the second law be applied to a Rayleigh process on the basis of the process being essentially reversible, with friction and unrestrained expansion absent. Let us write the familiar expression from elementary thermodynamics for the incremental change of entropy of the perfect gas, namely,

$$ds = \frac{kR}{k-1} \frac{dT}{T} - R \frac{dp}{p}$$

This can be integrated between stations 1 and 2 to give an expression for the entropy change in the following form:

$$s_2 - s_1 = \frac{kR}{k-1} \left[\ln \frac{T_2}{T_1} \left(\frac{p_1}{p_2} \right)^{(k-1)/k} \right] \tag{4-17}$$

Let us assign to Eq. (4-17) the arbitrary reference conditions $p_1 = 0$, $T_1 = 0$, for $s_1 = 0$ to obtain an expression for s in the simplest form:

$$s = \frac{kR}{k-1} \ln \frac{T}{p^{(k-1)/k}} \tag{4-18}$$

However, a more useful formulation can be found by substituting Eqs. (4-6) and (4-13) in Eq. (4-17), from which

$$s_2 - s_1 = \frac{kR}{k-1} \ln \left[\frac{M_2{}^2}{M_1{}^2} \left(\frac{1 + kM_1{}^2}{1 + kM_2{}^2} \right)^{(k+1)/k} \right] \tag{4-19}$$

Again use the reference datum of Mach number as unity and denote the entropy for this condition by the asterisk. Accordingly, Eq. (4-19) becomes

$$s - s^* = \frac{kR}{k-1} \ln M^2 \left(\frac{k+1}{1 + kM^2} \right)^{(k+1)/k} \tag{4-20}$$

Using the entropy equations just discussed, the loci of the Mach number for Rayleigh flow can be plotted using T-s coordinates.

Example 3. Construct a T-s diagram for air under Rayleigh-flow conditions, considering the air flowing from a standard reservoir. Draw lines for the constant pressures 100 and 10,000 psfa. Apply for a flow $G = \rho V = 0.2$ slug/(ft²)(sec). Refer to Fig. 4-4 for a layout of the system.

Solution. In solving the problem, first find the initial Mach number. This is necessary because the conditions in an imaginary reservoir have been given. To do this, consider a hypothetical nozzle to lead from the stipulated reservoir to the entrance of the Rayleigh flow (Fig. 4-4).

By definition of the Mach number, one may write

$$V_1 = M_1 \sqrt{kRT_1} \tag{a}$$

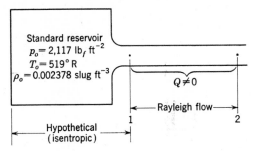

FIG. 4-4. Rayleigh flow system for representative flow conditions.

By definition of the stagnation temperature,

$$T_1 = \frac{T_0}{1 + [(k - 1)/2]M_1^2} \qquad (b)$$

Combining, we obtain

$$V_1 = M_1 \sqrt{\frac{kRT_0}{1 + [(k - 1)/2]M_1^2}} \qquad (c)$$

Between the reservoir and the beginning of the Rayleigh flow (in other words, in the imaginary nozzle)

$$\rho_1 = \rho_0 \left(\frac{T_1}{T_0}\right)^{1/(k-1)} \qquad (d)$$

Combining Eqs. (b) and (d), we obtain

$$\rho_1 = \rho_0 \left(1 + \frac{k - 1}{2}M_1^2\right)^{1/(k-1)} \qquad (e)$$

Substituting in the continuity equation,

$$\rho_0 \left(\frac{1}{1 + [(k - 1)/2]M_1^2}\right)^{1/(k-1)} M_1 \sqrt{\frac{kRT_0}{1 + [(k - 1)/2]M_1^2}} = G$$

Let us now substitute the values of ρ_0, k, R, T_0, and G in this equation in order to solve for M_1 by trial and error. The resulting computational equation is

$$M_1 \left(\frac{1}{5 + M_1^2}\right)^3 = 0.000603$$

Solution by trial and error gives two values for M_1, namely,

$$M_1 = 0.0753 \qquad \text{and} \qquad M_1 = 3.63$$

Theoretically, the Rayleigh flow can start with either one. It is now necessary to find the corresponding temperatures and pressures. Thus, employing Eq. (3-30), and with $T_0 = 519°R$ before heat addition (see Fig. 4-4), it is found that

$$T_1 = \frac{519}{1 + M_1^2/5}$$

and similarly by Eq. (3-34),

$$p_1 = 2,117 \left(\frac{T_1}{T_0}\right)^{k/(k-1)}$$

One finds that for $M_1 = 0.0753$

$$p_1 = 2{,}115 \text{ psf} \qquad T_1 = 518°R$$

and for $M_1 = 3.63$

$$p_1 = 23.2 \text{ psf} \qquad T_1 = 142.8°R$$

The Rayleigh line satisfying $M_1 = 3.63$ can now be drawn. To do this, it is necessary to set up a table for M_2, T_2, and s_2, proceeding as follows: By Eq. (4-13),

$$T_2 = T_1 \left(\frac{M_2}{M_1} \frac{1 + kM_1^2}{1 + kM_2^2} \right)^2$$

Also, by Eq. (4-19),

$$s_2 - s_1 = \frac{kR}{k - 1} \ln \frac{M_2^2}{M_1^2} \left(\frac{1 + kM_1^2}{1 + kM_2^2} \right)^{(k+1)/k}$$

Substituting the data for the initial station in these two equations, it is possible to solve for T_2 and s_2 at various assumed values of M_2. The data compiled following this procedure appear in Fig. 4-5 and in part in Table 4-2.

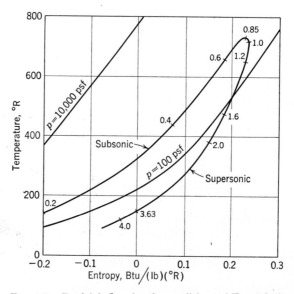

FIG. 4-5. Rayleigh flow for the conditions of Example 3.

The curve plotted in Fig. 4-5 is the Rayleigh-line curve. It can be seen that the maximum entropy occurs when the Mach number is unity. Because by the second law, the entropy change in a nonadiabatic process must bear the same sign as the conventional sign appropriate to the heat transfer, it follows that heating will tend to make the Mach number approach unity, and cooling will tend to make the Mach number recede from unity. Because the trend is the same both in subsonic and in supersonic flow, it is impossible to pass from one domain into the other by continuing the transfer of heat in the same direction. Otherwise, the entropy change would have to assume a sign opposite to the direction of heat transfer, a clear violation of the second law.

TABLE 4-2. TABULAR SOLUTION FOR EXAMPLE 3

M_2	T_2, °R	s_2, Btu/(lb)(°R)
0.1	39.9	−0.513
0.2	147	−0.196
0.4	435	0.077
0.6	653	0.186
0.85	730	0.234
1.00	712	0.239
1.2	649	0.233
1.6	472	0.186
2	376	0.155
3	149	0.053
4	120	−0.033

4-7. Maximum Heat Transfer. It was stated already that the amount of heat which may be added to a gas-dynamical system is limited. To develop this premise recall Eq. (4-3), which expresses the heat which is added to a system as

$$Q_{1 \to 2} = c_p(T_{02} - T_{01})$$

Dividing by $c_p T_1 T_{01}$ and rearranging, we obtain Damköhler's second ratio,

$$\frac{Q}{c_p T_1} = \frac{T_{01}}{T_1}\left(\frac{T_{02}}{T_{01}} - 1\right) \tag{4-21}$$

and this equation gives the ratio of heat added to a system when T_1, T_{01}, and T_{02} are known.

In order to find the maximum amount of heat which may be added at any Mach number, it is necessary to express Eq. (4-21) in terms of the Mach number. This is accomplished by substituting for T_{01}/T_1 its equivalent $1 + [(k - 1)/2]M_1{}^2$. Also, letting $M_2 = 1$ for maximum Q, Eq. (4-16) can be simplified to yield

$$\frac{Q}{c_p T_1} = \frac{(M^2 - 1)^2}{2M^2(k + 1)} \tag{4-22}$$

When this is plotted, Fig. 4-6 is obtained. This shows that in order to accelerate a very slow flow, exceedingly large amounts of heat must be added. Thus, if the Mach number is zero, $Q/c_p T_1 \to \infty$.

In the previous chapter, three flow parameters a_0, a^*, and V_{max} were defined for isentropic flow. These parameters exist for diabatic flow, but because one must account for the heat transfer they are expressed by

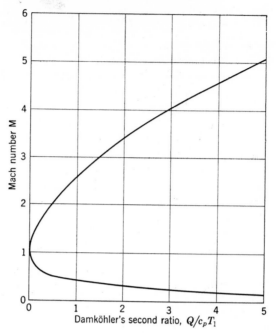

FIG. 4-6.   Damköhler's second ratio.

slightly different equations.   Thus the reservoir acoustic velocity after the pattern of Eq. (3-17) is

$$\frac{a_0^2}{k-1} = \frac{a^2}{k-1} + \frac{V^2}{2} - Q \qquad (4\text{-}23)$$

By the same token, the critical velocity a^* becomes

$$\frac{a^{*2}(1+k)}{2(k-1)} = \frac{a_0^2}{k-1} + Q \qquad (4\text{-}24)$$

The limiting or maximum velocity is

$$\frac{V_{\max}^2}{2} = \frac{a_0^2}{k-1} + Q \qquad (4\text{-}25)$$

From Eq. (4-25) it is again evident that the limiting velocity can be raised by heat addition.   This points to certain potentialities of diabatic flow which will be discussed further.

4-8. Detonation and Deflagration.   Some very interesting observations concerning diabatic flow may be made in relation to a combustible mixture † which passes through a transition region. On each side of such a transition, the properties such as temperature, pressure, and velocity are different. To simplify the analysis we shall assume that the observer moves with the transition, or the front. Under such a condition steady-flow considerations are applicable and the properties on each side of the transition are independent of time and vary with location only. For further simplicity we shall make the following assumptions:

1. The flow takes place in a tube or ducting of constant cross-sectional area. However, the analysis may be modified by incorporating area changes in the appropriate differential equations.[1]

2. By the choice of locating our observer on the transition, which for our particular study is a flame front or explosion wave, the flow is steady. However, our analysis will hold for unsteady waves as well, if they are very thin.

3. For the fluid itself, the gases on each side of the wave can be considered uniform and inviscid.

4. Thermodynamically, the gases on each side of the transformation obey the perfect-gas equation of state, and their properties such as specific heats do not change. Moreover, no change in molecular weight and composition is considered to occur.

5. Mathematically, the discontinuity or wave is infinitesimally thin.

6. As far as heat transfer is concerned, the gases are assumed to be nonconductive.

7. The chemical-reaction rate is large, but otherwise we are not concerned with the intimate chemistry of the phenomena or with the affiliated molecular processes. For a more rigorous study the chemistry must be considered as has been done by Friedman.[2] We assume that the addition of energy occurs instantaneously and only across the wave which is considered to be stable.

In summary, this approach is phenomenological, and the model is depicted in Fig. 4-7. Applying the conservation laws (mass, energy, and momentum) and eliminating the velocities on each side of the discontinuity by using the perfect-gas equation of state, it can be shown that

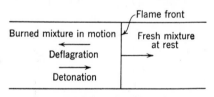

FIG. 4-7. Model for detonation and deflagration.

$$u_b - u_u - Q = \tfrac{1}{2}(p_u + p_b)\left(\frac{1}{\rho_u} - \frac{1}{\rho_b}\right) \qquad (4\text{-}26)$$

This is called the *Hugoniot equation*. This equation applies to an adia-

† By a *combustible mixture* we imply a gaseous mixture of fuel and oxidizer which liberates heat as it undergoes a chemical reaction.

batic shock front if $Q = 0$, whereas it applies to a combustion front if $Q > 0$.

We can plot Eq. (4-26) as in Fig. 4-8 and differentiate among various cases such as arise with deflagration, slow burning, and detonation. Of these the last has been the subject of many challenging studies by Jouget,[3] von Neumann,[4] Oppenheim,[5] Courant and Friedrichs,[6] and others.

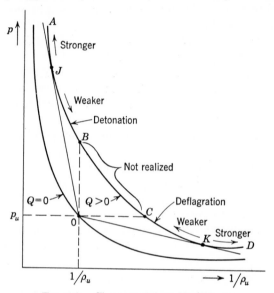

FIG. 4-8. Chapman-Jouget conditions.

Besides offering stimulating studies, detonation is of course of considerable interest in the design of combustion chambers of various types and applications. In most simple terms, a detonation wave occurs when two discontinuities, namely, an adiabatic shock wave and a diabatic flame front, are superimposed. We can differentiate between detonation and deflagration as follows:

	M_u	M_b	p_b/p_u	V_b/V_u	ρ_b/ρ_u	T_b/T_u
Detonation..........	>1	$\gtreqless 1$	>1	<1	>1	>1
Deflagration........	<1	>1	<1	>1	<1	>1

The subscripts u and b refer to the unburned mixture and the burned gases, respectively.

A detonation wave propagates at supersonic velocity, whereas a deflagration wave travels at subsonic velocity.

In Fig. 4-8, the Hugoniot curve ($Q > 0$) $AJBCKD$ is the locus of possible final states. It has two branches, namely, the detonation branch AJB and the deflagration branch CKD. The curve is constructed for the initial state 0 at p_u and $1/\rho_u$. In using the so-called *Chapman-Jouget hypothesis* tangents are drawn to the Hugoniot curve through 0 and have points of tangency at J and K where $M = 1$. A Rayleigh line which is tangent to the Hugoniot curve is called a *Chapman-Jouget process*, and the points of tangency, J and K, are called the *Chapman-Jouget states*. Each Chapman-Jouget state divides its domain into two subdomains, a weak one and a strong one. A strong deflagration cannot be reached because it would correspond to an expansion shock (see Chap. 7) which is ruled out by virtue of the second law of thermodynamics. A weak detonation is also ruled out on the basis of transport phenomena considerations. The Hugoniot curve for $Q = 0$ is commonly called the *Rankine-Hugoniot curve*, because it is the locus of end points of adiabatic shock transformations. The slope of the Rankine-Hugoniot curve at the initial point may be found to be $-k$, the negative of the specific-heat ratios. Again, along the Hugoniot curve, the arc BC is not realized physically because it indicates an imaginary V_b or a steady expansion shock which was already ruled out.

By the Chapman-Jouget analysis, a unique detonation velocity occurs at J in Fig. 4-8. Excellent agreement between theory and experiment exists for a variety of mixtures. As far as the deflagration point is concerned, indications are that it must lie between C and K along the deflagration branch of the Hugoniot curve.

In the first parts of this chapter we discussed Rayleigh flow, whereas in this section we stressed discontinuities. However, the Rayleigh-flow analysis is still valid as is evident from the Chapman-Jouget considerations. Thus this section complements the discussion but does not change it otherwise.

PROBLEMS

4-1. Show that an equation expressing the stagnation-pressure ratio p_0/p_0^* in terms of the specific-heat ratio and the Mach number is as follows:

$$\frac{k+1}{1+k\mathrm{M}^2}\left(\frac{2\{1 + [(k-1)/2]\mathrm{M}^2\}}{k+1}\right)^{k/(k-1)}$$

4-2. Show that an equation expressing the velocity ratio V/V^* in terms of the specific-heat ratio and the Mach number is as follows: $(k+1)\mathrm{M}^2/1 + k\mathrm{M}^2$.

4-3. Compute the numerical value of V/V^* for a perfect diatomic gas traveling with a Mach number of 1.2. Compare this value with that obtained from Table A-4.

4-4. Derive an expression relating the density ratio ρ_0/ρ_0^* to the specific-heat ratio and the Mach number.

4-5. Given a diabatic-flow system of dry air having at some station a Mach number equal to 3 and a stagnation temperature of 500°R while the static pressure is 0.5 atm. For some station where $M = 1.5$,

(a) Find the stagnation temperature.

(b) Find the stagnation pressure.

(c) Find the static pressure.

(d) Find the amount of heat transfer which caused the reduction in M. Is this positive or is it negative?

(e) Find the exponent of the polytropic equation $p/\rho^n = $ constant.

4-6. Show that for Rayleigh-line conditions

$$\frac{V_2}{V_1} = \frac{(1 + k\mathrm{M}_1{}^2)\mathrm{M}_2{}^2}{(1 + k\mathrm{M}_2{}^2)\mathrm{M}_1{}^2}$$

4-7. Dry air at standard temperature and pressure is to be accelerated from rest to a Mach number of 0.8 in a constant-area duct. (a) How much heat must be added to it? (b) What is the change in temperature?

4-8. How much heat must be rejected when air at standard temperature and pressure and having a Mach number of unity is accelerated until all of its thermal energy is expended?

4-9. Above what velocity will a thermometer inserted into a flow system register an error of more than 1°F because of stagnation-temperature rise?

4-10. Construct a T-s diagram for air undergoing Rayleigh flow when the mass velocity is $\rho V = 0.3$ slug/(ft²)(sec). Assume that a standard reservoir is used.

REFERENCES

1. Chambre, Paul, and Chia-Chiao Lin: On the Steady Flow of a Gas through a Tube with Heat Exchange or Chemical Reaction, *J. Aeronaut. Sci.*, vol. 13, no. 10, p. 537, October, 1946.

2. Friedman, Raymond: Kinetics of the Combustion Wave, *J. Am. Rocket Soc.*, vol. 23, no. 6, p. 349, November–December, 1953.

3. Jouget, E.: "Mechanique des explosifs," O. Doin et Fils, Paris, 1917.

4. von Neumann, J.: The Theory of Detonation Waves, Progress Report, Office of Scientific Research and Development, No. 549/PBL 31090(2-616), April, 1942.

5. Oppenheim, A. K.: A Contribution to the Theory of the Development and Stability of Detonation in Gases, *J. Appl. Mechanics*, March, 1952, p. 63.

6. Courant, R., and K. O. Friedrichs: "Supersonic Flow and Shock Waves," Interscience Publishers, Inc., New York, 1948.

7. Shapiro, A. H., W. R. Hawthorne, and G. M. Edelman: The Mechanics and Thermodynamics of Steady One-dimensional Gas Flow with Tables for Numerical Solutions, Meteor Report No. 14, Bureau of Ordnance Contract NOrd 9661, Dec. 1, 1947.

CHAPTER 5

FLOW WITH FRICTION

5-1. Introduction. In the previous chapter, nonadiabatic, frictionless flow in a duct of constant cross-sectional area was considered. This type of flow may simulate actual operation in technological devices, but more often than not friction must be taken into consideration. Hence it is necessary to be able to account properly for the losses incurred by friction. In this chapter, frictional phenomena will be considered in a simplified manner.

In the preceding chapter, certain assumptions were made which led to a type of flow which was called *Rayleigh flow*. In this chapter, too, certain assumptions will be made which, when followed, lead to a pattern known as *Fanno flow*. The requirements for Fanno flow are that (1) the flow must be steady; (2) the flow may be considered as being one-dimensional; (3) the cross-sectional area of the duct confining the gas is constant throughout (however, the section does not need to be circular as long as some characteristic diameter can be defined for it); (4) the flow is adiabatic; (5) there are no devices in the system which deliver or receive mechanical work; and (6) the gas is perfect and hence has constant specific heats.

5-2. Friction Loss. Although the first law of thermodynamics in the form of the steady-flow energy equation is applicable to flow with friction, it cannot predict the magnitude of loss (energy interchange) incurred by friction. The second law of thermodynamics is more useful because the loss in available energy from frictional effects causes an increase in entropy which can be used to indicate the amount of loss. According to the second law of thermodynamics, the entropy of a system increases in any adiabatic but irreversible process.

Whether a flow is reversible or not, a drop in pressure will usually take place in the direction of flow. For a reversible flow, this pressure drop is expressed by the Euler equation [Eq. (2-29)], namely,

$$dp = -\rho V \, dV$$

If friction accompanies the flow there will be a further drop in pressure although nothing else (like pipe length, for example) has been changed in

83

the system. Denoting this by dp_f, the total pressure drop becomes

$$dp_T = -(\rho V \, dV + dp_f) \qquad (5\text{-}1)$$

Euler's equation and the pressure drop due to acceleration have already been discussed. Accordingly, in the next section the pressure loss from friction will be considered as a separate item.

5-3. The Fanning Equation. The reduction in pressure from friction is given with reasonable accuracy by the D'Arcy-Weisbach equation or the Fanning equation. In principle, these equations are the same, but there are some minor differences between them.

The D'Arcy-Weisbach equation is

$$dp_f = -f' \frac{\rho V^2}{2D} \, dx \qquad (5\text{-}2)$$

where dp_f = pressure drop due to friction, psf
  f' = dimensionless friction factor for D'Arcy-Weisbach equation
  ρ = density, slugs/ft^3
  V = velocity, fps
  D = diameter of the passage, ft
  dx = length of the passage, ft

The negative sign is inserted because the pressure drop results in the direction of positive flow (increase in dx).

The Fanning equation is

$$dp_f = -f \frac{\rho V^2}{2r_h} \, dx \qquad (5\text{-}3)$$

in which f is the dimensionless friction factor for the Fanning equation; dp_f, ρ, V, and dx are as in Eq. (5-2); and r_h is the hydraulic radius of the passage, usually in feet.

The term *hydraulic radius* has particular significance when a duct or passage is not round in cross section or when the fluid does not fill the duct. The hydraulic radius r_h is defined as the ratio of the cross-sectional area to the wetted perimeter. Hence, for a circular duct or pipe

$$r_h = \frac{\pi r^2}{2\pi r} = \frac{r}{2} = \frac{D}{4}$$

Using this relation between diameter and hydraulic radius, the Fanning equation may be written for a circular duct as

$$dp_f = -f \frac{\rho V^2}{2r_h} \, dx = -4f \frac{\rho V^2}{2D} \, dx \qquad (5\text{-}4)$$

Comparing Eqs. (5-2) and (5-4), it becomes evident that the friction factor

$$\frac{P_2{}^2 - P_1{}^2}{2} \cdot \frac{1}{\rho \cdot 2RT} + \frac{RTG^2}{gc} \ln \frac{P_1}{P_2} + \frac{4f\,RTG^2}{2Dgc} L = 0$$

in the D'Arcy-Weisbach equation is four times that in the Fanning equation.

5-4. Friction Factor. Regardless of whether the Fanning or the D'Arcy-Weisbach equation is used, the friction coefficient is defined as the ratio of the shearing stress to the dynamic-flow pressure. To illustrate, consider a constant-area, insulated duct and a control volume of length dx as shown in Fig. 5-1. Let τ be the shearing stress between the wall and flow. Then, by definition, the coefficient of friction is

$$f = \frac{\tau}{\rho V^2 / 2} \qquad (5\text{-}5)$$

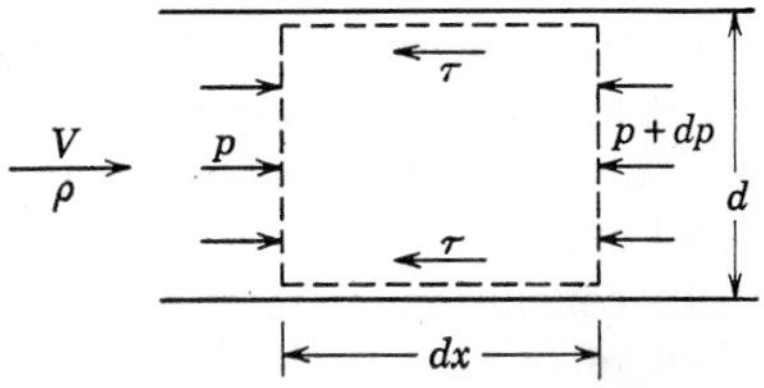

Unless otherwise noted, the Fanning equation and its friction factor, denoted simply by f, will be used in this text from now on.

FIG. 5-1.   Flow with friction.

Although much thought has been given to the actual value which the friction factor may have under different conditions, as yet no definite final answer is available. For incompressible flow, the available results have been summarized by Moody.[1] These results show that the friction factor is a function of the Reynolds number and of a dimensionless parameter ϵ/D, called the *roughness ratio*, in which ϵ is a linear measure of the absolute roughness of the inside pipe surface, and D is the internal diameter of the pipe. For compressible flow, Keenan and Neumann[2] and Kaye et al.[3] have conducted extensive studies in an attempt to determine the friction factor. They report that for supersonic flow of air in a tube, the friction coefficient is influenced as usual by the Reynolds number and a dimensionless parameter L/D, in which L is the length of the test section and D is the inside diameter of the tube. Because compressibility effects must be considered for supersonic flow, dimensional analysis indicates that at high velocities the friction coefficient will depend also on the Mach number. Keenan and Neumann studied frictional phenomena in smooth pipes for Mach numbers from 0.27 to 3.87 and for Reynolds numbers from 1×10^5 to 8.7×10^5. They found that at supersonic speeds the results were influenced greatly by the presence of shock waves. They concluded further that, when the ratio L/D was greater than 50, the friction factor was approximately equal to the friction factor for incompressible flow for the same value of the Reynolds number. They found also that supersonic flow can rarely be maintained if the L/D ratio is greater than 50. In other words, the effect of the Mach number is to limit the range of values of the ratio L/D. Kaye and his associates found that there is agreement between values of the friction coefficient for tubes and flat plates. However, they did note that for the same Reynolds number friction coefficients encountered in supersonic flow are considerably lower than those determined for fully developed turbulent incompressible flow. This may be because of entrance profile effects, as f is not always constant even in incompressible fluid-entrance sections.

It is thus evident that the coefficient of friction is not fully understood in all of its aspects. This is true not only because numerous experimental variables arise in its determination, but also because existing theories are based on certain assumptions which do not seem to be completely representative of actual situations. Moreover, in any one flow system the coefficient of friction can vary from place to place within the flow, and therefore it is necessary to consider an apparent or average coefficient rather than a local one.

In conclusion, it may be said that for most supersonic flow the coefficient of friction varies between 0.002 and 0.003. In contrast, for incompressible flow the range of the friction factor is approximately 0.003 to 0.0065. It has been suggested that as a rough approximation the friction factor in the supersonic regime is half that recommended for incompressible flow.

The student is cautioned to practice care in using any particular value of f. The importance of this will be demonstrated in illustrative Example 3 in Sec. 5-6 of this chapter.

5-5. The Friction Parameter. In the absence of gravity forces, the total pressure drop over a distance dx is found from Eq. (5-1), which may be combined with Eq. (5-4) to give

$$dp = -4f\frac{\rho V^2}{2D}dx - \rho V\,dV \tag{5-6}$$

Dividing Eq. (5-6) by p gives

$$\frac{dp}{p} = -4f\frac{V^2}{2D}\frac{\rho}{p}dx - \frac{\rho}{p}V\,dV$$

Also, in Sec. 4-4 it was shown that

$$V^2\frac{\rho}{p} = k\mathrm{M}^2 \quad \text{and further} \quad \frac{\rho}{p}V\,dV = k\mathrm{M}^2\frac{dV}{V}$$

Accordingly,

$$\frac{dp}{p} = -4f\frac{k\mathrm{M}^2}{2D}dx - k\mathrm{M}^2\frac{dV}{V}$$

$$4f\frac{dx}{2D}k\mathrm{M}^2 = -\frac{dp}{p} - k\mathrm{M}^2\frac{dV}{V} \tag{5-7}$$

For a constant-area duct, the perfect-gas equation (1-11), combined with the continuity equation (2-2), yields, because $dA = 0$,

$$\frac{dp}{p} = \frac{dT}{T} - \frac{dV}{V} \tag{2-5}$$

It was also shown in Eqs. (3-12) and (3-15) that

$$\frac{dT}{T} = 2\frac{dV}{V} - 2\frac{dM}{M} \quad \text{and} \quad \frac{dT}{T} = -(k-1)M^2\frac{dV}{V}$$

Combining the last two equations, we find that

$$\frac{dV}{V} = \frac{dM/M}{[(k-1)/2]M^2 + 1} \tag{5-8}$$

Combining Eqs. (5-7), (2-5), and (5-8), there results

$$4f\frac{dx}{D} = \frac{2(1 - M^2)\, dM}{kM^3\{[(k-1)/2]M^2 + 1\}} \tag{5-9}$$

This equation relates the drop in pressure in relation to the Mach number in a constant-area duct when the flow is accompanied by friction. The integration of Eq. (5-9) is cumbersome at best. Furthermore, in discussing the investigations of Keenan and Neumann it was mentioned that there are limitations on the interpretation of the ratio L/D. It will be shown (Sec. 5-6) also that in the presence of friction it is impossible to cross from the supersonic regime into the subsonic and vice versa. Accordingly, it becomes convenient to integrate Eq. (5-9) using a Mach number of unity as the reference. Thus,

$$\int_{x=0}^{x=L_{max}} 4f\frac{dx}{D} = 4f\frac{L_{max}}{D} = \int_{M}^{1} \frac{2(1 - M^2)}{M^3\{[(k-1)/2]M^2 + 1\}k}\, dM \tag{5-10}$$

The term $4fL_{max}/D$ is called the *friction parameter* and Table A-5 lists values of it for $k = 1.4$.

Example 1. Air is decelerated from $M = 3$ to sonic speed in a 2-in.-ID pipe having a friction factor of 0.002. Find the length of the pipe.

Solution. The length of the pipe can be found from Eq. (5-10), or more conveniently by the use of Table A-5. Employing the latter, it is found that, for $M = 3$,

$$4f\frac{L_{max}}{D} = 0.52216$$

and obviously, for $M = 1$,

$$4f\frac{L_{max}}{D} = 0$$

Thus
$$\frac{4f}{D} L_2 - \frac{4f}{D} L_1 = 0.52216$$

$$L_2 - L_1 = \frac{2 \times 0.52216}{12 \times 4 \times 0.002}$$

$$L_2 - L_1 = 10.88 \text{ ft pipe length}$$

As mentioned already, Table A-5 is based on a reference Mach number of unity, or, in other words, on the critical Mach number. Thus the

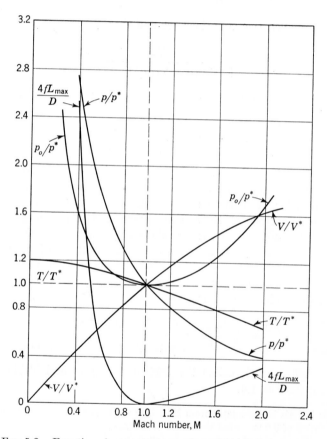

FIG. 5-2. Functions for constant-area flow with friction ($k = 1.4$).

changes in pressure (static and dynamic), temperature, velocity, density, and thrust function are expressed as ratios of their critical values. Some of these are plotted in Fig. 5-2 and the variations of the thermodynamic properties during a Fanno process are summarized in Table 5-1.

TABLE 5-1. FANNO-FLOW PHENOMENA

Property	Initial flow is subsonic	Initial flow is supersonic
M	Increases	Decreases
V	Increases	Decreases
p	Decreases	Increases
T	Decreases	Increases
ρ	Decreases	Increases

5-6. The Fanno Line. Frictional, steady flow which takes place in constant-area ducts in the absence of heat transport is generally termed *Fanno flow*. Furthermore, equations which are applicable to such flow are called *Fanno equations*. It is evident that numerous Fanno equations could be derived, each of which finds its origin in the energy, continuity, and momentum equations.

The stagnation enthalpy is defined as

$$h_0 = h + \frac{V^2}{2}$$

For steady flow, the mass flow rate $\rho A V$ is a constant and for a pipe the *mass velocity* $\rho V = G$ is also a constant. Thus,

$$h_0 = h + \frac{G^2}{2\rho^2} \qquad (5\text{-}11)$$

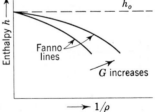

FIG. 5-3. Fanno-line trends.

From Eq. (5-11) it may be seen that when the density increases the enthalpy must increase also. This is depicted qualitatively in Fig. 5-3. For Fanno flow, curves of enthalpy are called *Fanno lines*.

For Fanno flow, which is adiabatic, the steady-flow energy equation appears as

$$du + d\left(\frac{p}{\rho}\right) + V\,dV = 0$$

Entropy can be introduced by making use of the equation

$$T\,ds = du + p\,dv = du - p\,\frac{d\rho}{\rho^2}$$

which is the fundamental equation developed by combining the first and the second laws of thermodynamics. Combining the two preceding equations, there results

$$T\,ds = \frac{dp}{\rho} + V\,dV$$

$$\rho T\,ds = dp + \rho V\,dV \tag{5-12}$$

When this equation is applied to an adiabatic but irreversible process, the magnitude of ds is a measure of the entropy increase introduced by friction.

Substituting dp from Eq. (5-6) into Eq. (5-12) and solving for ds, we find that

$$ds = \frac{4fV^2}{2TD}\,dx \tag{5-13}$$

Recalling from the definition of Mach number that $V^2 = \mathrm{M}^2(kRT)$ and substituting this in Eq. (5-13), it is found that

$$ds = \frac{4fkR}{2D}\,\mathrm{M}^2\,dx \tag{5-14}$$

Finally, using Eq. (5-9) and solving for $ds/d\mathrm{M}$ it is seen that

$$\frac{ds}{d\mathrm{M}} = \frac{R(1 - \mathrm{M}^2)}{\mathrm{M}\{[(k - 1)/2]\mathrm{M}^2 + 1\}} \tag{5-15}$$

It can be seen from Eq. (5-15) that the entropy will be a maximum, thus corresponding to equilibrium conditions, when $ds/d\mathrm{M} = 0$ or when $\mathrm{M} = 1$. In other words, if the flow is supersonic and there exists friction, the effect

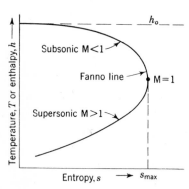

FIG. 5-4. Fanno line.

of the friction will be for the flow Mach number to approach a value of unity. Whether or not it will become unity depends on the extent of the friction, which, for any particular pipe, will be determined by its length. Friction decelerates a supersonic flow and this deceleration may continue, if there is enough friction, until the Mach number becomes unity. If the length for the flow or the friction exceeds a magnitude commensurate to a Mach number of unity, there will occur first shock phenomena and then finally choking. If the flow is subsonic originally, the effect of friction will be to accelerate the flow. Again, the limiting condition will be a Mach number of unity, which will be reached when the entropy becomes a maximum. If friction continues to exist after the equilibrium state is reached, the flow will be choked and will have to readjust itself. These phenomena are depicted qualitatively in Fig. 5-4.

Example 2. Construct a T-s diagram for air undergoing Fanno flow, having a mass velocity $G = \rho V = 0.2$ slug/(sec)(ft^2). Assume a standard reservoir.

Solution. The solution of this problem is very similar to that employed in plotting the Rayleigh line outlined in Example 3 of Chap. 4. As in that problem, the conditions just before the application of the friction must be found, and are the same, as the same reservoir conditions apply. Thus from that example we employ

$$p_1 = 23.2 \text{ psf} \qquad T_1 = 142.9°\text{R} \qquad M_1 = 3.63$$

Following this, the problem can be solved in several ways. To illustrate the use of the Fanno tables, these will be used and from Table A-5 we read

$$\frac{T_1}{T^*} = 0.3317 \qquad T^* = 431°\text{R}$$

$$\frac{p_1}{p^*} = 0.15942 \qquad p^* = 145.5$$

For convenience, a working tabulation for this problem is set up as shown in Table 5-2.

TABLE 5-2. TABULAR SOLUTION FOR EXAMPLE 2

M_2	T_2	p_2	s_2
5	86.1	13.00	−0.0819
2.5	229.5	42.5	0.0720
2.0	287	59.4	0.104
1.8	313	69.0	0.114
1.6	342	81.0	0.123
1.4	371	96.5	0.131
1.2	401	117.0	0.136
1.0	431	145.5	0.139
0.8	459	187.5	0.137
0.6	482	256.5	0.127
0.3	508	526	0.091
0.1	516	1,590	0.0186

The values of the entropy listed are computed from the basic thermodynamic equations [or from Eq. (5-18), which is discussed later] because the tables do not list them. Figure 5-5 is a plot to scale of the Fanno line for the flow conditions specified. If the Fanno line and the Rayleigh line for the same mass velocity and reservoir conditions are plotted on the same set of axes, they will intersect one another at two points as is shown in Fig. 5-6.

One point of intersection, a, lies in the supersonic regime, and the other, b, lies in the subsonic regime. A path connecting these two points repre-

sents a normal shock wave. As will be seen in the next chapter, a normal
shock occurs only when the flow is supersonic and the subsequent flow after
normal shock is always subsonic. Thus it can be reasoned that point a

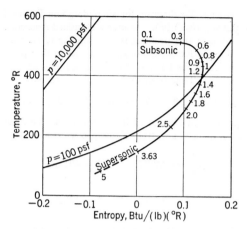

FIG. 5-5.   Fanno flow line for the conditions of Example 2.

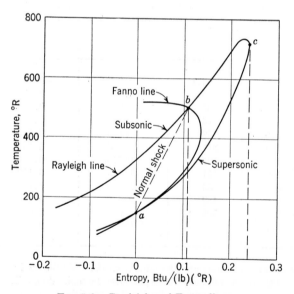

FIG. 5-6.   Rayleigh and Fanno lines.

must always lie to the left of point b because a shock causes a dissipation of
available energy and thus an increase in entropy. That point b is always
right of point a can also be proved without introducing shock phenomena.
In diabatic flow, there is no unique reservoir for the whole system because

of the heat exchange. However, for adiabatic flow one reservoir temperature defines the flow regardless of the existing friction. Thus, along the Fanno line $T_{0a} = T_{0b}$. For the Rayleigh line, the stagnation temperatures at a and b must be equal, because at this point the two curves intersect one another. As a matter of fact, every Rayleigh line will have only two points at which the stagnation temperatures are the same. At one of these the velocity will be relatively high and the free-stream temperature low. This point will occur in the supersonic part of the Rayleigh line. At a corresponding point in the subsonic regime of the Rayleigh line, the free-stream temperature will be relatively high, and the velocity low. Because at these points along the Rayleigh line

$$T_{0a} = T_{0b}$$

it follows that

$$T_{0b} - T_{0a} = Q_{b \to a} = 0$$

However,

$$Q_{b \to a} = Q_{b \to c} - Q_{c \to a}$$

and

$$Q_{b \to c} = \int_b^c T \, ds$$

$$Q_{c \to a} = \int_c^b T \, ds$$

because

$$Q_{b \to a} = 0$$

$$Q_{b \to c} = Q_{c \to a}$$

or

$$\int_b^c T \, ds = \int_c^a T \, ds$$

Therefore, in Fig. 5-6 the area under the Rayleigh-line segment from a to c must equal the area under the Rayleigh-line segment from c to b. However, this can happen only if point b is to the right of point a.

Example 3. Adiabatic flow with friction takes place in a 3-in.-ID pipe which is 12 ft long. The air enters the pipe with a Mach number of 3 and the Reynolds number is never greater than 7×10^5. State and prove whether choking or generation of shock waves will occur.

Solution. Generation of shock waves and/or choking will occur if the so-called *theoretical length* of the pipe is less than the actual given length of 12 ft. From Table A-5 for a Mach number of 3,

$$\frac{4fL_{max}}{D} = 0.52216$$

The pipe diameter $D = \frac{3}{12}$ ft, but the friction factor is not specified. Assume $f = 0.003$; then

$$\text{Theoretical length} = \frac{3}{4 \times 12 \times 0.003} \times 0.52216 = 10.89 \text{ ft}$$

Because this is less than the actual length, shocks or choking will occur. Now assume $f = 0.002$. In this case,

$$\text{Theoretical length} = \frac{3}{4 \times 12 \times 0.002} \times 0.52216 = 18.2 \text{ ft}$$

It follows that if $f = 0.002$, a longer length of pipe is permissible, and no disturbance will occur until the pipe length exceeds 18.2 ft. It can be shown by trial that in this particular case no disturbance will occur as long as $f < 0.0027$.

5-7. Fanno Equations. Several additional forms of the Fanno equation will now be derived to supplement those already given.

By Eq. (4-1), under conditions of adiabatic flow ($dQ = 0$),

$$kR\, dT + (k - 1)V\, dV = 0$$

Integrating between the reservoir conditions and any local point, we obtain

$$\frac{kR}{k-1}(T - T_0) + \frac{V^2}{2} = 0$$

Solve for V, giving

$$V = \sqrt{\frac{2kR}{k-1}(T_0 - T)}$$

By the definition of the stagnation temperature [Eq. (3-30)],

$$T = \frac{T_0}{1 + [(k-1)/2]\text{M}^2}$$

Upon substitution in the previous equation, it is found that

$$V = \sqrt{\frac{kRT_0\text{M}^2}{1 + [(k-1)/2]\text{M}^2}}$$

Introducing the mass velocity $\rho V = G$ into the equation of state for a perfect gas, and solving for the ratio T/V, we find that

$$\frac{T}{V} = \frac{p}{GR} = \frac{\dfrac{T_0}{1 + [(k-1)/2]\text{M}^2}}{\sqrt{\dfrac{kRT_0\text{M}^2}{1 + [(k-1)/2]\text{M}^2}}}$$

For any particular system experiencing Fanno flow, T_0, k, R, and G are constants. Accordingly, we may write

$$p\text{M}\sqrt{1 + [(k-1)/2]\text{M}^2} = \text{constant} \qquad (5\text{-}16)$$

or

$$\frac{p_1\text{M}_1\sqrt{1 + [(k-1)/2]\text{M}_1{}^2}}{p_2\text{M}_2\sqrt{1 + [(k-1)/2]\text{M}_2{}^2}} = 1 \qquad (5\text{-}17)$$

This equation can serve in developing an equation for the change in entropy. Equation (4-17) gives a relation between pressure, temperature, and entropy which can be reduced to the form

$$\frac{s_2 - s_1}{R} = \ln \left(\frac{T_2}{T_1}\right)^{k/(k-1)} \frac{p_1}{p_2} \qquad (4\text{-}17)$$

Using Eqs. (3-33) and (5-17) with Eq. (4-17) we find a relation for the entropy change, namely,

$$s_2 - s_1 = R \ln \left\{\frac{1 + [(k-1)/2]M_2{}^2}{1 + [(k-1)/2]M_1{}^2}\right\}^{k/(k-1)} \left\{\frac{M_2\sqrt{1 + [(k-1)/2]M_2{}^2}}{M_1\sqrt{1 + [(k-1)/2]M_1{}^2}}\right\}$$

$$(5\text{-}18)$$

PROBLEMS

5-1. Derive the equation

$$dp + \rho V \, dV + 2f\rho V^2 \frac{dx}{D} + \rho g \, dz = 0$$

Explain whether the Fanning equation or the D'Arcy-Weisbach equation is used in this relation. The term $\rho g \, dz$ is employed because of gravity.

5-2. Steady, one-dimensional air flow with friction is reduced in speed from $M = 2.6$ to $M = 1.5$ in a 2-in.-ID pipe. Compute the length of the pipe and discuss.

5-3. Show that for a constant-area duct one may write

$$\tau = -\frac{D}{4}\frac{dp}{dx}$$

5-4. Describe the circumstances when it is desired to effect a continuous change from subsonic to supersonic flow or from supersonic to subsonic flow.

5-5. Dry air is traveling at a supersonic speed at $M = 2.2$ in a 2-in.-ID pipe. The friction factor is 0.003. What is the maximum possible length this pipe may have?

5-6. Air having a Mach number of 5.0 is decelerated in a 3-in.-ID pipe to $M = 3.0$. Compute the length of pipe which will cause this deceleration if (a) $f = 0.002$, (b) $f = 0.003$, (c) $f = 0.005$.

REFERENCES

1. Moody, L. M. F.: Friction Factors for Pipe Flow, *Trans. ASME*, November, 1944.
2. Keenan, J. H., and E. P. Neumann, Jr.: Measurement of Friction in a Pipe for Subsonic and Supersonic Flow of Air, *J. Appl. Mechanics*, vol. 68, pp. A91–A100, 1946.
3. Kaye, J., T. Y. Toong, and R. H. Shoulberg, Jr.: Measurement of Recovery Factors and Friction Coefficients for Supersonic Flow of Air in a Tube, *J. Appl. Mechanics*, June, 1952.

CHAPTER 6

WAVE PHENOMENA

6-1. Introduction. When there is relative motion between a body and a fluid, the disturbance (if infinitely small) caused by the body is propagated through the fluid with the speed of sound. The speed of sound in such cases is the speed with which rarefactions or compressions of infinitely small amplitude propagate. When the compressions in the flow are of finite amplitude there usually occurs a discontinuous rise of pressure, and a shock wave exists. In addition to discontinuities in the pressure, there occur discontinuous increases in temperature, density, entropy, and other fluid properties. If initially the air is still and the shock wave is moving, then, after the passing of the shock, the air will move in the direction of the shock. Gas compressions which have a finite amplitude travel faster than the speed of sound, as is the case in big explosions. Although variations in flow density are generally observed by optical methods such as the Toepler-schlieren technique (which is discussed in a later chapter), jet-aircraft pilots are reported to have seen, by eye alone, shock waves springing out from the wings of their aircraft. Observers of atomic explosions are also known to have seen shock waves.

Across a shock wave the fundamental flow equations, namely, the equation of continuity, the energy equation, and momentum equation, apply. Because across a shock wave flow work is degraded to thermal energy, there is an increase in entropy. Therefore, it follows that in studying shock phenomena care must be exercised in applying thermodynamic formulas, because any relation which is based on isentropic flow assumptions is not applicable. However, it can be assumed that the flow takes place adiabatically although of course not reversibly.

Shock waves are a type of wave phenomenon, but it should be clearly recognized that all wave phenomena are not shock occurrences. To clarify this point it appears desirable to classify the various wave phenomena which are encountered. If wave phenomena are arbitrarily and qualitatively classified according to strength, we would meet both *weak waves* and *shock waves*. A Mach wave, for example, is a very weak wave. There are weak compression waves as well as weak expansion waves. The former would occur at a wall having a concave corner as shown in Fig. 6-1. In contrast, a weak expansion wave would occur at a convex wall corner as shown in Fig. 6-2. With very weak waves, it may be assumed that there

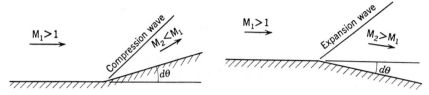

FIG. 6-1. Compression wave at concave corner.

FIG. 6-2. Expansion wave at convex corner.

are no drastic discontinuities because the deflection angle $d\theta$ is infinitesimally small and isentropic-flow analysis should be applicable across such a wave. Across a compression wave, the flow is decelerated and the gas density is increased, and across an expansion wave the flow is accelerated. A

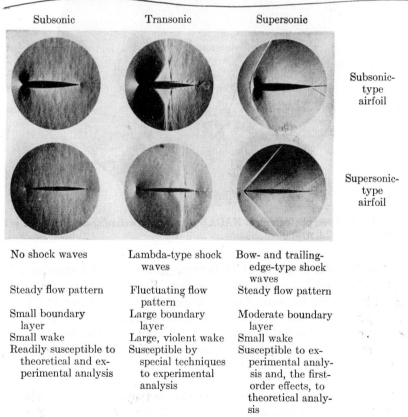

Subsonic	Transonic	Supersonic	
			Subsonic-type airfoil
			Supersonic-type airfoil
No shock waves	Lambda-type shock waves	Bow- and trailing-edge-type shock waves	
Steady flow pattern	Fluctuating flow pattern	Steady flow pattern	
Small boundary layer	Large boundary layer	Moderate boundary layer	
Small wake	Large, violent wake	Small wake	
Readily susceptible to theoretical and experimental analysis	Susceptible by special techniques to experimental analysis	Susceptible to experimental analysis and, the first-order effects, to theoretical analysis	

FIG. 6-3. Aerodynamic phenomena at various speeds. (*NACA photo.*)

shock wave, on the other hand, can only be of the compression type, and there is no rarefaction shock because this would require that the entropy decrease in an adiabatic process. In this chapter we refer to waves exhibiting entropy increases as *shock waves*, whereas waves across which the entropy is substantially constant will be referred to simply as *waves*.

Another manner of classifying waves is according to their relative velocity. Thus one may speak of *stationary shock waves* in contrast to *nonstationary shock waves*. A shock wave may be rendered stationary by

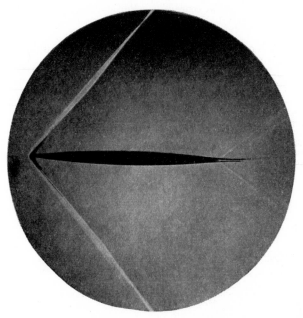

Fig. 6-4.   Schlieren photograph of NACA 6 per cent thick circular-arc airfoil. $\alpha = 0°$. M = 1.5.   (*NACA photo.*)

making the mass of gas in which it propagates travel at a speed equal to that of the shock but opposite in direction. Such occurrences may be observed in nozzles, for example. Stationary shocks are shown in Fig. 6-3. Stationary shock waves may be either *attached* to an object as in Fig. 6-4, or they may be *detached* as seen in Fig. 6-5, depending on the shape of the object and the Mach number. Nonstationary shock waves can readily be developed in shock tubes.

Finally, shock waves may be situated at right angles to the flow, in which case they are called *normal shocks*, or they may be located at an angle, in which case they are called *oblique shocks*. Normal shocks may be treated by a one-dimensional-flow analysis, but oblique wave phenomena (whether shock waves or weak waves) require two-dimensional-flow analysis. The discussion of wave phenomena requiring multidimensional-flow analysis will necessarily be limited in scope in this text.

One characteristic common to wave phenomena is that the stagnation temperature on each side of the wave is the same. This follows from the application of the energy equation to perfect gases. Thus, if we denote

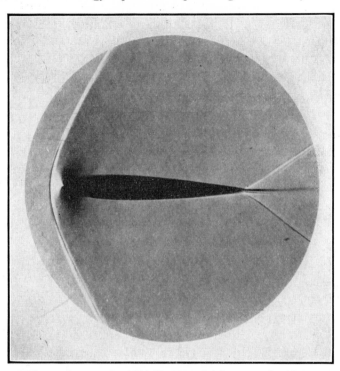

FIG. 6-5. Schlieren photograph of NACA 0012 airfoil. $\alpha = 0°$. $M = 1.5$. (*NACA photo.*)

the upstream conditions for a wave by the subscript 1, and the conditions downstream by 2, an energy equation using the notation employed in Sec. 3-6 would appear as

$$c_p T_1 + \frac{V_1^2}{2} = c_p T_2 + \frac{V_2^2}{2}$$

But

$$c_p T + \frac{V^2}{2} = T_0$$

Therefore,

$$T_{01} = T_{02}$$

There appears to be an erroneous tendency to think that wave phenomena are always undesirable. This viewpoint should be discouraged.

For example, shock fronts may be made to operate to good advantage in stabilizing certain flows, or may furnish the basis of operation of certain laboratory instruments.

6-2. Model Describing Formation of Shock Wave. The formation of a shock wave may be described conveniently by imagining the acceleration of a piston confined in a cylinder. The processes may be understood more conveniently by a model in which we consider a series of impulses given to

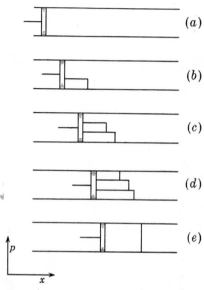

(a)

(b)

(c)

(d)

(e)

the piston rather than a continually increasing velocity. In principle, the phenomena are not changed, but the observations are facilitated.

Consider a long slender tube open at one end and having a piston at the other end as shown in Fig. 6-6a. Assume that originally both the gas confined in the tube and the piston are at rest and in equilibrium. Now let us impart to the piston a small velocity, thus compressing the gas. This will cause a weak compression wave which will travel into the tube with the speed of sound. As this disturbance passes through the gas, consecutive portions of it are accelerated. The portions of the gas closest to the piston are set into motion sooner than those farther away. Thus a portion

FIG. 6-6.   Wavefronts in piston-cylinder model.

of the gas is at a slightly higher pressure than existed previously, and so is the density. This is represented in Fig. 6-6b. Now let us impart to the piston an additional pulse and thereby produce another compression wave. Again the gas is compressed adiabatically and its pressure, density, and temperature are raised locally as shown in Fig. 6-6c. By successive repetitions of this process a series of wave terraces are formed. Each upper terrace has a higher velocity than the lower ones because the fluid in the upper terraces is at respectively higher temperatures and thus each has respectively a higher acoustic velocity. In each case the message produced will travel at acoustic speed relative to the fluid between two successive pulses. The various steps will thus be similar to a telescoping automobile-rod-type aerial. As the process is continued the steps become steeper (Fig. 6-6d) and eventually merge, completely forming a normal shock as in Fig. 6-6e.

Once the shock wave has been formed, it will travel ahead of the column of gas being pushed by the piston and its velocity will be greater than that of the piston. If the piston were stopped abruptly a rarefaction wave would develop and would follow the shock wave.

In further analyzing shock phenomena, assume that an observer moves with the wave as in Fig. 6-7. The gas previously unaffected will appear to this observer as entering the shock with a velocity V_1 and leaving it adiabatically compressed at a smaller velocity V_2. For nonviscous, adiabatic flow, we may write the basic laws, assuming that the coordinate system moves with the wavefront. By conservation of mass for a uniform-area section we have

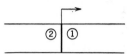

FIG. 6-7. Observer moving with normal wave.

$$\rho_1 V_1 = \rho_2 V_2$$

Conservation of momentum is expressed by Eq. (2-8) as

$$\rho_1 V_1{}^2 + p_1 = \rho_2 V_2{}^2 + p_2$$

Finally, as the energy equation [Eq. (2-35)] with irrelevant terms omitted must also hold,

$$u_1 + \frac{V_1{}^2}{2} + \frac{p_1}{\rho_1} = u_2 + \frac{V_2{}^2}{2} + \frac{p_2}{\rho_2}$$

Solve for V_2 in the continuity equation and substitute in the energy equation, giving

$$u_1 - u_2 = \frac{V_1{}^2}{2}\left(\frac{\rho_1{}^2}{\rho_2{}^2} - 1\right) + \frac{p_2}{\rho_2} - \frac{p_1}{\rho_1} \tag{6-1}$$

Similarly, after substituting in the momentum equation for V_2 from the continuity equation and solving for $V_1{}^2$, we obtain

$$V_1{}^2 = \frac{p_2 - p_1}{\rho_1(1 - \rho_1/\rho_2)} \tag{6-2}$$

Substituting Eq. (6-2) into Eq. (6-1) and simplifying, we get for the difference in internal energy

$$u_2 - u_1 = \frac{(p_1 + p_2)(\rho_2 - \rho_1)}{2\rho_1\rho_2} \tag{6-3}$$

This is the well-known *Hugoniot equation*, which can be used for determining the temperature rise across a normal shock if the functional relationship between internal energy and temperature is known.

Instead of a piston inside a tube, one may imagine a body which is given a series of impulses. As before, each impulse will generate a sound wave emanating from the body. The initial amplitude will differ at the various points of the body because it depends on the component of the acceleration perpendicular to the surface element. The pulse changes the flow charac-

teristics of every point it passes. This pressure and velocity persist until a
new pulse arrives and changes the flow properties. The pulses will radiate
in all directions from the body provided the velocity is subsonic relative to
the body everywhere. The flow pattern would extend to an infinite distance from the body.

Assume now that the body itself is brought to supersonic speed. In this
case the flow pattern, which formerly may have extended great distances
in front of the body, will be overtaken by the body itself. Thus let a body
be accelerated from just less than the sonic value to just greater than the
sonic value. The pressure pulses will merge into a single wave the speed
of which is slightly greater than the acoustic a. This wave may be seen in
Fig. 6-8. The wave will be halted at some distance from the body. It will

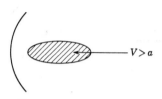

FIG. 6-8. Detached shock.

be normal to the velocity vector of the fluid at
the axis of the body. Away from the axis the
magnitude of the wave will diminish, so that
at infinity the limiting position of the wave
will form the Mach angle. If the velocity of
the body is gradually increased it will be found
to approach the pressure wave. Under certain
conditions the body may actually make con-
tact with the pressure wave in which case there exists a condition of
attached shock. This happens with slender bodies. If the nose of the body
is very blunt, then the shock at even high Mach numbers may be detached.
These cases were depicted respectively in Figs. 6-4 and 6-5. In the case of
a detached shock there is a region of subsonic flow between the wave and
the nose of the body.

6-3. Weak Waves. Wave phenomena take place so rapidly that they
may be considered to be adiabatic processes. Although some wave phenomena may also be reversible, and thus subject to isentropic criteria, not
all wave phenomena may be treated by isentropic considerations. Regardless of whether reversibility exists or not, the continuity equation, the
energy equation, and the momentum equation are applicable.

A Mach line is an example of a type of wave phenomenon which occurs
isentropically. It was shown in Sec. 6-1 that a Mach wave is formed when
a slight disturbance exists. It may also occur when a wedge having a very
small angle is introduced into a supersonic flow. Thus consider, for example, the arrangement depicted in Fig. 6-9 in which the wedge angle $d\theta$ is
infinitesimally † small. Such a flow obviously cannot be treated completely by one-dimensional analysis. We therefore assign two components
to the flow velocity, namely, the velocity component V_n which is normal
to the wave, and the component V_t which is tangent to it. We further

---

† In practice a wedge angle of less than about 3° may be considered to result in a
weak wave.

assume that the wall extends infinitely in the direction normal to the plane of the paper.

Although the Mach number after the wave will be less than on the upstream side, it may be supersonic. The entropy of the fluid in passing through the wave does not change.

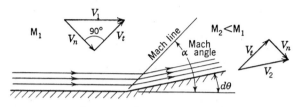

FIG. 6-9. Compression wave.

It is of interest to determine the magnitude of the velocity normal to the Mach wave. By the equation of continuity, we may write across the wave

$$\rho V_n = \text{constant} \tag{6-4}$$

We consider the velocity component normal to the wave because the tangential component will obviously not contribute to mass transfer across the wave. Thus

$$d(\rho V_n) = 0 \tag{6-5}$$

and

$$\rho \, dV_n + V_n \, d\rho = 0 \tag{6-6}$$

Writing Euler's equation [Eq. (2-29)] across the wave, it is seen that

$$\frac{dp}{\rho} + V_n \, dV_n = 0 \tag{6-7}$$

Combining Eqs. (6-6) and (6-7) and solving for V_n, there results

$$V_n = \sqrt{\frac{dp}{d\rho}} \tag{6-8}$$

As this conforms to the definition of acoustic velocity, V_n is equal to the speed of sound upstream of the wave. This is possible only for a reversible case because use of Euler's equation requires reversible conditions. We had also assumed that wave phenomena are adiabatic. Hence we have an isentropic occurrence which is presupposed in defining the acoustic velocity. Downstream from the wave the normal component of the velocity will be less than the acoustic if the position of the wedge is as shown in Fig. 6-9. Such a wave is an oblique wave and occurs in converging passages.

Expansion Wave. When supersonic flow occurs over a convex corner an expansion wave is created, as shown in Fig. 6-10. Such a wave may be encountered in a diverging passage. Probably the main difference between a compression wave and an expansion wave is that the normal velocity component on the downstream side of the expansion wave is greater than acoustic, although the upstream normal velocity component is acoustic in magnitude.

As before, the divergence in the wall surface will be felt by the fluid and, because of this disturbance, a Mach wave springs out at 0. Because of the expansion, the pressure downstream from the Mach line will be less than the pressure on the upstream side. Thus there is a pressure gradient

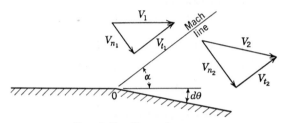

FIG. 6-10.   Expansion wave.

across the wave which acts at right angles to it. This pressure gradient will further accelerate the air so that the Mach number is increased. Obviously the direction of flow will tend to be parallel to the wall surface.

For an expansion wave, but equally true for compression and Mach waves, the following observations are pertinent:

1. All the turning of the flow will occur at the Mach line.

2. The angle which the Mach line makes with the original flow direction depends on the original Mach number only, and is thus

$$\alpha = \arcsin \frac{1}{M}$$

3. The turning is identical all along the Mach wave and hence the change in flow properties is the same at all points on the Mach wave. This follows from the assumption that the flow is two-dimensional. The wall is presumed to extend infinitely in the direction normal to the plane of the paper.

4. Because there is no pressure differential along the wave, the tangential velocity component V_t on each side of the wave will be the same.

5. The normal velocity component V_n will change across the wave.

6. The change in the flow parameters is infinitesimal.

7. A supersonic flow may negotiate relatively large-angle sharp expansions without experiencing losses.

6-4. Compression Waves—Oblique Shock.

Consider a stationary wedge in a flow system as shown in Fig. 6-11 so that the fluid must undergo a concave change of direction and assume that the wedge angle is relatively large. Because of the wedge, a shock will appear at the wedge, and this will make an angle θ_w with the original flow direction. This angle is called the *wave angle*, and will be larger than the Mach angle. Because a shock wave is exceedingly thin, and because drastic changes occur across it, it becomes inaccurate to speak of the macroscopic properties inside a shock.

Consider that upstream from the shock wave, the velocity V_1, the density ρ_1, and the pressure p_1 are known, and further, that the wave angle θ_w can be determined by optical observations. Starting from these data it is desired to find the velocity V_2, pressure p_2, and density ρ_2 after the shock wave. As before, each velocity has a tangential component V_t and a normal component V_n. The fundamental equations of fluid flow, namely, the continuity equation, the momentum equation, and the energy equation, must apply to the flow. From

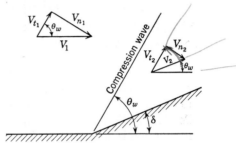

FIG. 6-11.   Compression wave.

the first of these, the flow rate entering the wave and leaving it must be the same. Because flow through the wave cannot be due to the tangential velocity component, the continuity equation can be written as

$$\rho_1 V_{n_1} = \rho_2 V_{n_2} \qquad (6\text{-}9)$$

The energy equation is applied across the shock wave by relating the conditions on each side to the critical acoustical velocity. Thus if we write the energy equation [Eq. (3-14)] between a point upstream of the shock wave and the critical condition corresponding to a Mach number of unity, we have in integral form

$$\frac{kR}{k-1}\int_{T_1}^{T^*} dT + \int_{V_1}^{a*} V\, dV = 0$$

which becomes

$$\frac{kR}{k-1}(T^* - T_1) + \tfrac{1}{2}(a^{*2} - V_1{}^2) = 0$$

Recalling that

$$kRT^* = a^{*2} \qquad \frac{p_1}{\rho_1} = RT_1 \qquad \text{and} \qquad V_1{}^2 = V_{n_1}^2 + V_{t_1}^2$$

we get, upon rearranging,

$$\frac{V_{n_1}^2 + V_{t_1}^2}{2} + \frac{k}{k-1}\frac{p_1}{\rho_1} = \frac{k+1}{2(k-1)}a^{*2} \qquad (6\text{-}10a)$$

Similarly, downstream of the shock wave we have

$$\frac{V_{n_2}^2 + V_{t_2}^2}{2} + \frac{k}{k-1}\frac{p_2}{\rho_2} = \frac{k+1}{2(k-1)}a^{*2} \tag{6-10b}$$

The pressures and the velocities across the shock wave are related by the momentum equation, and hence

$$p_1 + \rho_1 V_{n_1}^2 = p_2 + \rho_2 V_{n_2}^2 \tag{6-11}$$

Because the momentum must be conserved parallel to the shock wave, we write

$$\rho_1 V_{n_1} V_{t_1} = \rho_2 V_{n_2} V_{t_2} \tag{6-12}$$

By Eq. (6-9), the principle of continuity (mass conservation), the mass velocities are equal on each side of the wave, and hence it follows that

$$V_{t_1} = V_{t_2} \tag{6-13}$$

One may visualize this easily, because if the tangential velocity components were different there would occur shearing phenomena through the shock.

Combining Eqs. (6-9), (6-10), (6-11), and (6-13), the following important equation is obtained:

$$V_{n_1} V_{n_2} = a^{*2} - \frac{k-1}{k+1} V_t^2 \tag{6-14}$$

The algebraic derivation of Eq. (6-14) will not be presented here, but is proposed as Prob. 6-1 at the end of this chapter. Equation (6-14) relates the normal velocities on each side of the shock wave. This and other equations relating the properties on each side of the shock wave are sometimes called *Rankine-Hugoniot equations* and sometimes called *Prandtl equations*.

If $V_{t_1} = V_{t_2}$ is eliminated from Eqs. (6-10a) and (6-10b) it is found that

$$\frac{V_{n_1}^2}{2} + \frac{k}{k-1}\frac{p_1}{\rho_1} = \frac{V_{n_2}^2}{2} + \frac{k}{k-1}\frac{p_2}{\rho_2} \tag{6-15}$$

If the momentum equation [Eq. (6-11)] is combined with Eq. (6-15), the density ratio across the shock appears as

$$\frac{\rho_2}{\rho_1} = \frac{[(k+1)/(k-1)]p_2/p_1 + 1}{(k+1)/(k-1) + p_2/p_1} \tag{6-16}$$

Other equations which may be obtained in similar manner are the following:

$$\frac{p_2}{p_1} = \frac{[(k+1)/(k-1)]\rho_2/\rho_1 - 1}{(k+1)/(k-1) - \rho_2/\rho_1} \tag{6-17}$$

$$\frac{T_2}{T_1} = \frac{(p_2/p_1)[(k-1)p_2/p_1 + k + 1]}{(k+1)p_2/p_1 + k + 1} \tag{6-18}$$

From Fig. 6-11 it can be seen that the shock wave results in a change of flow direction and the wave angle θ_w is expressed as

$$\tan \theta_w = \frac{V_{n_1}}{V_{t_1}} \tag{6-19}$$

It may similarly be observed that the deflection angle δ, which is the angle between the downstream velocity and the upstream flow direction, can be expressed as

$$\tan (\theta_w - \delta) = \frac{V_{n_2}}{V_{t_2}} \tag{6-20}$$

Recalling from Eq. (6-13) that $V_{t_1} = V_{t_2} = V_t$ and dividing Eq. (6-19) by Eq. (6-20) it is seen that

$$\frac{\tan \theta_w}{\tan (\theta_w - \delta)} = \frac{V_{n_1}}{V_{n_2}} = \frac{\rho_2}{\rho_1} = \frac{(\kappa+1)\,M_1{}^2 \sin^2 \theta_w}{2 + (\kappa-1)\,M_1{}^2 \sin^2 \theta_w}$$

Numerous equations relating upstream and downstream density, pressure, and temperature to the Mach numbers on either side of the shock wave may be derived by combining Eq. (6-9) and subsequent equations. The significant conclusions which may be drawn from the shock equations are shown in Fig. 6-12 for various deflection angles and for a diatomic gas having a constant specific-heat ratio $k = 1.4$. From this figure it is apparent that for a given Mach number and a particular deflection angle two waves, both attached, are possible. One of these will turn the flow more than the other. Experience indicates that the wave which commonly occurs is the weaker wave, namely, the one which turns the flow to a lesser extent. It may be observed further from Fig. 6-12 that for any given Mach number there is a maximum deflection angle beyond which the wave will become detached from the wedge and the shock equations derived in this section will be no longer applicable.

Example 1. A wedge is introduced into a flow having a Mach number $M = 1.7$. (a) What are the possible wave angles if the flow is to be deflected by 13°? (b) What is the maximum angle which the flow can turn without becoming detached from the wedge?

Solution. (a) Enter Fig. 6-12 at the initial Mach number 1.7 and at the deflection angle of 13°. The two wave angles corresponding to these conditions are seen to be 54° and 77°.

(b) Again in Fig. 6-12, note that the curve which has a maximum at $M = 1.7$ contains the loci of 17° deflection angle points. Thus if the flow Mach number is 1.7 and the wedge angle is 17°, the wave will be attached to the wedge. Wedge-type objects introduced into this flow will cause attached shock waves as long as their wedge angles do not exceed 17°. In other words, for this particular case the 17° curve contains the loci of shock detachment. Objects which have greater angles will result in detached waves. It follows further that for a blunt body the wave will be a detached one if the Mach angle is not very high.

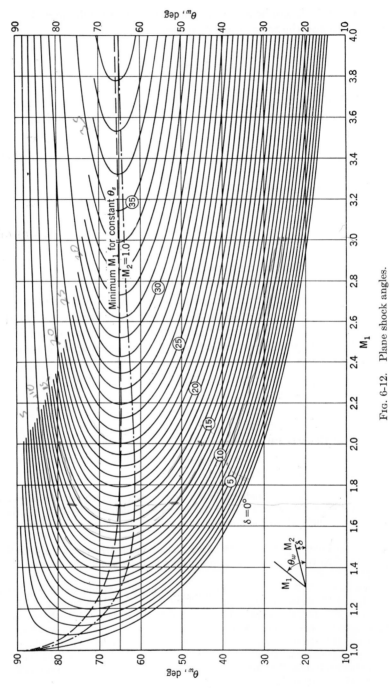

Fig. 6-12. Plane shock angles.

If instead of a wedge, a cone with its axis parallel to the stream and its apex facing upstream is inserted into the stream, the shock wave will have the form of a circular cone. Furthermore, just as in the case of wedges, two solutions appear for attached shock waves. Indications are that shock waves do not extend to infinity without change, but grow weaker because the loss incurred by the shock wave increases as the wave extends distances outward. Thus at a distance from the cone or wedge the change in density across a shock becomes vanishingly small, which means that the shock wave tends to become a Mach wave. The Mach number downstream from the shock will always be less than that on the upstream side, but it is not necessary that it become less than unity. The Mach number before and after a shock for various deflection angles is shown graphically in Fig. 6-12. Because a compression shock will take place in a very short distance, it may be assumed that wall friction is negligible.

6-5. Normal Shock Waves. The occurrence of normal shock was discussed in this chapter, and was treated earlier in connection with the intersection points which define a point upstream and downstream across a normal shock on the Rayleigh and Fanno curves (see Fig. 5-6). Basically, a shock is said to be normal if the flow direction upstream as well as downstream from it have the same direction. Oblique and normal shock are similar in nature in that both result in abrupt changes of the thermodynamic properties across

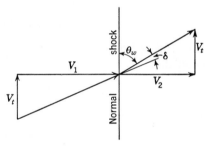

Fig. 6-13. Geometry of shock phenomena.

them. Geometrically, an oblique shock can be described by an observer who sees a normal shock while at the same time moving parallel to it with a velocity V_t. This is illustrated in Fig. 6-13. If the observer is stationary, the shock will appear to be normal to the flow. If the observer is in motion the shock will seem to occur at an angle θ_w with the flow. As the velocity of the observer increases, the shock will seem to become increasingly oblique to the flow.

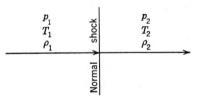

Fig. 6-14. Normal shock.

Assume that we are considering only normal shock as shown in Fig. 6-14. We have $V_1 = V_{n_1}$ and $V_2 = V_{n_2}$. Writing the continuity and momentum equations respectively, we have

$$\rho_1 V_1 = \rho_2 V_2$$

and

$$p_2 - p_1 + \rho_2 V_2{}^2 - \rho_1 V_1{}^2 = 0$$

Dividing the momentum equation by the continuity equation and rearranging we get

$$V_1 - V_2 = \frac{p_2}{\rho_2 V_2} - \frac{p_1}{\rho_1 V_1}$$

Also, by definition of the acoustic speed a, from Eq. (3-6a),

$$a^2 = k\frac{p}{\rho}$$

Substituting for the acoustic speed and rearranging,

$$k(V_1 - V_2) = \frac{a_2{}^2}{V_2} - \frac{a_1{}^2}{V_1} \tag{6-22}$$

Now write the following equation for the upstream and downstream sides of the shock, respectively, by an extension of Eq. (3-17):

$$2a_1{}^2 = 2a_0{}^2 - (k-1)V_1{}^2 \tag{6-23a}$$

$$2a_2{}^2 = 2a_0{}^2 - (k-1)V_1{}^2 \tag{6-23b}$$

Substituting Eqs. (6-23a) and (6-23b) in Eq. (6-22) and rearranging, it is found that

$$V_1 V_2 = \frac{2}{k+1}a_0{}^2 \qquad \text{reservior}$$

and by Eq. (3-22) this becomes

$$V_1 V_2 = a^{*2} \qquad \text{critical} \tag{6-24}$$

Equation (6-24) gives the velocity change across a normal shock and is usually known as the *Rankine-Hugoniot equation for normal shock*. For a normal-shock wave to occur, V_1 must be supersonic, and a^* is the critical acoustic velocity. It is easy to see from Eq. (6-24) that the velocity behind a normal-shock wave must be subsonic. In Fig. 6-15 is plotted the variation of the downstream Mach number when a normal-shock wave occurs in supersonic flow.

Frequently it is desirable to show explicitly the changes in density, pressure, or temperature across a normal shock. These variations of the Rankine-Hugoniot relation will now be obtained. To derive a relation for the pressure change across a normal shock, start with the momentum equation

$$p_1 + \rho_1 V_1{}^2 = p_2 + \rho_2 V_2{}^2$$

and from the continuity equation for a constant-area duct,

$$\rho_2 = \rho_1 \frac{V_1}{V_2}$$

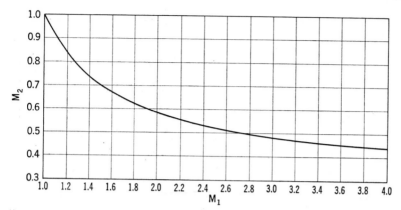

Fɪɢ. 6-15. Mach numbers across a normal shock.

Substituting in the momentum equation and dividing by p_1 for the pressure ratio across the shock, it can be shown that

$$\frac{p_2}{p_1} = 1 + \frac{\rho_1}{p_1} V_1(V_1 - V_2) \qquad (6\text{-}25)$$

Equation (6-24) may be modified still further to include the upstream Mach number. By Eq. (3-17) combined with Eq. (3-22) it can be shown that

$$\left(\frac{2}{k+1} + \frac{k-1}{k+1} M^2\right) a^2 = a^{*2} \qquad (6\text{-}26)$$

Using this with Eq. (6-24), it appears that

$$V_1 V_2 = \left(\frac{2}{k+1} + \frac{k-1}{k+1} M^2\right) a^2 \qquad (6\text{-}27)$$

in which the Mach number and the acoustic velocity must correspond to the same state point.

Substituting in Eq. (6-25), note that

$$\frac{p_2}{p_1} = 1 + \frac{\rho_1}{p_1}\left[V_1^2 - \left(\frac{2}{k+1} + \frac{k-1}{k+1} M^2\right) a^2\right] \qquad (6\text{-}28)$$

For state point 1, a_1^2 may be multiplied out, and recalling that $k = p/\rho a^2$,

$$\frac{p_2}{p_1} = 1 + \frac{2k(M_1^2 - 1)}{k + 1} \qquad (6\text{-}29)$$

TABLE 8

GAS TABLES
K = 1.4

$$M_2^2 = \frac{M_1^2 + 2/(K-1)}{\frac{2K}{K-1} M_1^2 - 1}$$

An expression defining the density variation across a normal shock is developed as follows:

$$\frac{a_1{}^2}{k-1} + \frac{V_1{}^2}{2} = \frac{k+1}{2(k-1)} V_1 V_2$$

$$\frac{2}{k+1}\frac{a_1{}^2}{V_1{}^2} + \frac{k-1}{k+1} = \frac{\rho_1}{\rho_2}$$

$K = 1.4$

TABLE 48

GAS TABLES

$$\frac{\rho_2}{\rho_1} = \frac{1}{2/[(k+1)M_1{}^2] + (k-1)/(k+1)} \qquad (6\text{-}30)$$

An expression for the temperature change across a normal shock may be obtained by the use of Eqs. (6-29) and (6-30) in connection with the equation of state for a perfect gas. By the perfect-gas equation applied across the shock,

$$\frac{T_2}{T_1} = \frac{p_2}{p_1}\frac{\rho_1}{\rho_2}$$

combination with Eqs. (6-29) and (6-30) results in

TABLE 48

GAS TABLES

$K = 1.4$

$$\frac{T_2}{T_1} = \left[1 + \frac{2k(M_1{}^2 - 1)}{k+1}\right]\left[\frac{2}{(k+1)M_1{}^2} + \frac{k-1}{k+1}\right] \qquad (6\text{-}31)$$

The change in the Mach number across a normal-shock wave can also be easily obtained. For station 1 before the shock wave

$$\frac{2}{k+1}\frac{a_1{}^2}{V_1{}^2} + \frac{k-1}{k+1} = \frac{a^{*2}}{V_1{}^2}$$

or similarly for station 2 after the shock

$$\frac{2}{k+1}\frac{a_2{}^2}{V_2{}^2} + \frac{k-1}{k+1} = \frac{a^{*2}}{V_2{}^2}$$

Then using Eq. (6-24),

$$\frac{2}{(k+1)M_1{}^2} + \frac{k-1}{k+1} = \frac{V_2}{V_1}$$

and

$$\frac{2}{(k+1)M_2{}^2} + \frac{k-1}{k+1} = \frac{V_1}{V_2}$$

Hence

$$\left[\frac{2}{(k+1)M_1{}^2} + \frac{k-1}{k+1}\right]\left[\frac{2}{(k+1)M_2{}^2} + \frac{k-1}{k+1}\right] = 1 \qquad (6\text{-}32)$$

In Chap. 3, it was shown that when the pressure ratio across a wave is substantially greater than unity, the velocity with which the disturbance is propagated is also substantially greater than the acoustic velocity. In other words, the changes across the shock are no longer isentropic. We will now demonstrate this idea in a somewhat different manner. In Fig. 6-16, plot the pressure rise across a normal-shock wave against the density rise. This can be done easily by using the Prandtl (Rankine-Hugoniot) equations. On the same coordinate axes plot the pressure rise using the isentropic-flow equations. It becomes evident at once that as the pressure-rise ratio increases, the deviations between the Rankine-Hugoniot flow and the isentropic flow become more extreme.

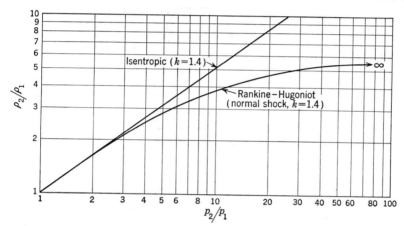

FIG. 6-16. Comparison of isentropic and Rankine-Hugoniot flows.

6-6. Entropy Consideration. The concept of entropy is most useful in wave studies and will be discussed briefly at this point.

For a perfect gas the incremental change of entropy appears as

$$ds = c_v \frac{dT}{T} + \frac{p}{T} d \left(\frac{1}{\rho} \right)$$

For the perfect gas also, by Eqs. (1-36) and (1-37) enthalpy in its differential form appears as

$$dh = c_p \, dT = c_v \, dT + d \left(\frac{p}{\rho} \right)$$

and entropy change can also be expressed as

$$ds = c_p \frac{dT}{T} - R \frac{dp}{p} \qquad\qquad (6\text{-}33)$$

This can be integrated for constant specific heats between the reservoir and any point along the flow section to give

$$s - s_0 = c_p \ln \frac{T}{T_0} - R \ln \frac{p}{p_0} \qquad (6\text{-}34)$$

Equation (6-34) can also be written as

$$s - s_0 = \ln \frac{(T/T_0)^{c_p}}{(p/p_0)^R} \qquad (6\text{-}35)$$

Making use of the perfect-gas relation

$$c_p = \frac{kR}{k - 1}$$

Eq. (6-35) becomes

NOTE   method

$$s - s_0 = \ln \frac{(T/T_0)^{kR/(k-1)}}{(p/p_0)^R} \qquad (6\text{-}36)$$

or

$$\frac{s - s_0}{R} = \ln \frac{(T/T_0)^{k/(k-1)}}{p/p_0} \qquad (6\text{-}37)$$

Again, for a perfect gas,

$$\frac{\rho_0 T_0}{p_0} = \frac{\rho T}{p} = \frac{1}{R}$$

and hence Eq. (6-37) becomes

$$\frac{s - s_0}{R} = \ln \left[\frac{p}{p_0} \left(\frac{\rho_0}{\rho} \right)^k \right]^{1/(k-1)} \qquad (6\text{-}38)$$

Solving for the pressure ratio, we get

$$\frac{p}{p_0} = \left(\frac{\rho}{\rho_0} \right)^k e^{[(k-1)/R](s-s_0)} \qquad (6\text{-}39)$$

The entropy concept will now be applied to shock phenomena considering the gases to behave as perfect gases. Writing Eq. (6-34) for the static conditions on each side of the shock one finds that

$$\Delta s = c_p \ln \frac{T_2}{T_1} - R \ln \frac{p_2}{p_1} \qquad (6\text{-}40)$$

Integrating Eq. (6-33) between the stagnation conditions on each side of the shock, and recalling that the stagnation temperature across the shock

$$\frac{P_{0_2}}{P_{0_1}} = e^{-\frac{\Delta s}{R/J}}$$

remains constant, the change of entropy appears as

$$\Delta s = -R \ln \frac{p_{02}}{p_{01}} \qquad (6\text{-}41)$$

Combining this with Eq. (6-40), it is seen that

$$\ln \frac{p_{02}}{p_{01}} = \ln \frac{p_2}{p_1} - \frac{k}{k-1} \ln \frac{T_2}{T_1} \qquad (6\text{-}42)$$

If we substitute into Eq. (6-40) from Eqs. (6-29) and (6-31) we get an expression for the change of entropy in terms of the specific-heat ratio k and the upstream Mach number M_1. Further analyzing we notice that an entropy increase results when $M_1 > 1$ but that the entropy would decrease when $M_1 < 1$. Because shock phenomena are considered to be adiabatic in nature, we conclude that a shock can exist only for supersonic flow, because otherwise the second law of thermodynamics would be violated.

Using the perfect-gas equation [Eq. (1-11)] to eliminate temperature, Eq. (6-42) becomes

$$\frac{p_{02}}{p_{01}} = \left[\frac{(\rho_2/\rho_1)^k}{p_2/p_1} \right]^{1/(k-1)} \qquad (6\text{-}43)$$

Substituting from Eqs. (6-29) and (6-30) in Eq. (6-43), we find that

$$\frac{p_{02}}{p_{01}} =$$

TABLE 48 (GAS TABLES)

$k = 1.4$

$$\left(\frac{1}{\{2/[(k+1)M_1^2] + (k-1)/(k+1)\}^k [1 + 2k(M_1^2 - 1)/(k+1)]} \right)^{1/(k-1)} \qquad (6\text{-}44)$$

Combining Eqs. (6-42) and (6-44), after some manipulation an expression for the change of entropy across the shock can be found as

$$\Delta s = c_p \left\{ \ln \left[\frac{2}{(k+1)M_1^2} + \frac{k-1}{k+1} \right] + \frac{1}{k} \ln \left(\frac{2kM_1^2}{k+1} - \frac{k-1}{k+1} \right) \right\} \qquad (6\text{-}45)$$

This equation is convenient because it expresses the entropy change in terms of the Mach number before the shock. This equation has been plotted in Fig. 6-17 for air using $k = 1.4$ and $c_p = 0.24$ Btu/(lb$_m$)(°R). According to the curve, for Mach numbers less than unity, there is a decrease in entropy, a clear violation of the second law of thermodynamics when an adiabatic process is considered. It follows from this that an expansion or rarefaction shock is impossible in a perfect gas. It should be noted in Eq. (6-44) and Fig. 6-17 that for Mach numbers less than 0.302 the expression becomes undefined because logarithms of negative numbers occur.

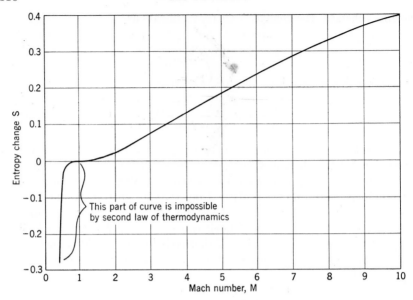

FIG. 6-17. Entropy variation with Mach number.

In Table 6-1 are tabulated the characteristics of various wave phenomena occurring in homogeneous fluids. The stagnation temperature
across a weak wave as well as a shock wave is *exactly* the same, and this was

TABLE 6-1. WAVE-PHENOMENA CHARACTERISTICS †

Items	Compres- sion shock	Compres- sion wave	Expansion wave	Normal shock	Mach wave
Upstream Mach num- ber M_1	$M_1 > 1$ $M_1 > M_2$	$M_1 > 1$ $M_1 > M_2$	$M_1 > 1$ $M_1 < M_2$	$M_1 > 1$ $M_1 > M_2$	$M_1 > 1$ $M_1 \cong M_2$
Downstream Mach number M_2	$M_2 > 1$	$M_2 > 1$	$M_2 > 1$	$M_2 < 1$	$M_2 \gtrless 1$
Velocity	Decreases	Decreases [3]	Increases [3]	Decreases	Same [2]
Pressure	Increases	Increases [3]	Decreases [3]	Increases	Same [2]
Stagnation pressure . .	Decreases	Decreases [3]	Increases [3]	Decreases	Same [2]
Temperature	Increases	Increases [3]	Decreases [3]	Increases	Same [2]
Stagnation tempera- ture	Remains the same	Same [1]	Same [1]	Same [1]	Same [1]
Density	Increases	Increases [3]	Decreases [3]	Increases	Same [2]
Entropy	Increases	Increases [3]	Decreases [3]	Increases	Same [2]

† See text for explanation of superscript numerals.

shown to be true in Sec. 6-1. This statement is true for the items denoted by (1) in Table 6-1. In the column for the Mach wave, all the items spec-

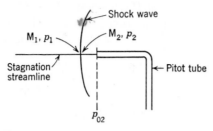

FIG. 6-18. Supersonic total-head tube.

ified "same" and denoted by (2) are not *exactly* the same, but *nearly* the same. All items denoted (3) in the columns for the compression and expansion waves increase or decrease very little and could have been termed the same, as expansion and compression waves are approximations and only little different from a Mach wave.

6-7. Rayleigh-Pitot Equation. If a pitot tube is introduced into a supersonic flow stream, there will be formed a shock wave ahead of the tube. Because a shock wave gives rise to an increase in entropy, Eqs. (3-35) and (3-40), which were derived for isentropic flow, cannot be used in conjunction with a supersonic total-head tube. Thus a different relation becomes necessary, and this is called the *Rayleigh-Pitot equation.*

Consider a shock wave ahead of a pitot tube as shown in Fig. 6-18. In front of the tube the shock wave is normal and hence the air entering through the stagnation streamline will pass through a normal shock and will thus decelerate, becoming subsonic. The flow before the shock

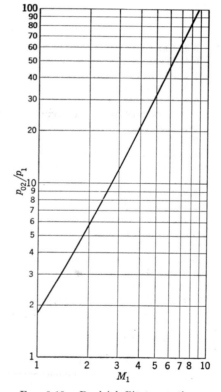

FIG. 6-19. Rayleigh-Pitot equation.

wave may be assumed to be isentropic. It then experiences an increase in entropy across the wave and is decelerated. After the shock wave, the flow is decelerated isentropically to the stagnation point p_{02}. Because the upstream and downstream conditions of a normal shock wave are defined by the two intersection points of Rayleigh and Fanno lines (see Fig. 5-6) we may combine the Rayleigh equation (4-6) with the Fanno equation (5-17) and further using Eqs. (3-35) and (6-29) we obtain the Rayleigh-Pitot equation

$K = 1.4$

TABLE 18
GAS TABLES.

$$\frac{p_{02}}{p_1} = \left\{ \frac{[M_1^2(k+1)/2]^k}{2kM_1^2/(k+1) - (k-1)/(k+1)} \right\}^{1/(k-1)} \tag{6-46}$$

A plot of Eq. (6-46) is shown in Fig. 6-19.

PROBLEMS

6-1. Derive the Rankine-Hugoniot equation as expressed in Eq. (6-14).

6-2. Show that for a Mach wave

$$\frac{dV}{d\theta} = \frac{V}{\sqrt{M^2 - 1}}$$

6-3. Can shock waves occur in subsonic flight? Explain.

6-4. What are the factors influencing the distance between the nose of a blunt body and a detached shock wave in supersonic flow?

6-5. How can a standing wave be produced?

6-6. Is the shock wave emanating from a model in a supersonic wind tunnel stationary or traveling?

6-7. How can a traveling shock wave be produced in the laboratory?

6-8. A wedge is introduced in a flow having a Mach number of 2.0. The flow is deflected by 15°. (a) What wave angles will the shock exhibit? (b) Which one will be probable? (c) What is the maximum angle which this flow can turn without becoming detached?

6-9. Given a flow having a Mach number of $M_1 = 2.0$. What is the significance of the angle $\delta = 0°$?

6-10. A cone having a total apex angle of 20° is introduced horizontally into a flow having a Mach number of $M_1 = 3.1$. An attached wave is formed which makes an angle of 20° with the horizontal. Is this a shock wave or a weak wave?

6-11. Wedges and cones are frequently used in supersonic wind tunnels to determine the tunnel speed. What is the maximum Mach number, if any, which can be used with a wedge having a 20° total included angle as a Mach indicator? Would the same value apply to a cone having an apex angle of 20°? Explain.

CHAPTER 7

VARIABLE-AREA FLOW

7-1. Introduction. In previous chapters parameters relating to varia-ble-area flow were not required, or it was assumed that the cross-sectional area for flow was constant. However, many engineering devices require variable-area flow sections and these may be convergent, divergent, or convergent-divergent. The flow patterns through such sections may be such as to produce either accelerations or decelerations of the flowing fluid. If the flow is accelerated, the section is called a _nozzle_, or if it is decelerated, it is called a _diffuser_. Whether a certain flow section will act as a nozzle or as a diffuser depends not only on its contour but also on the entering char-acteristics of the fluid.

Three important cases of variable-area flow will be considered in this chapter, namely, (1) variable-area adiabatic flow, (2) variable-area iso-thermal flow, and (3) generalized one-dimensional flow. Probably the only important limitations will be the restriction to one-dimensional flow and perfect-gas behavior. It should be emphasized that a gas may pass through a variable-area section without conflicting with requirements of one-dimen-sional analysis.

7-2. Velocity Variation with Isentropic Flow. The velocity at any sec-tion of a variable-area, perfect-gas flow system can be obtained directly from the isentropic energy equation (3-14), here rewritten as

$$\frac{kR}{k-1} dT + V \, dV = 0$$

$$c_p = \frac{kR}{k-1}$$

$$(3\text{-}14)$$

When it is not permissible to assume the approach velocity V_1 as zero, this must appear in the limits of integration:

$$\frac{kR}{k-1} \int_{T_1}^{T_2} dT + \int_{V_1}^{V_2} V \, dV = 0 \tag{7-1}$$

and hence

$$\frac{kR}{k-1}(T_2 - T_1) + \frac{V_2{}^2 - V_1{}^2}{2} = 0 \tag{7-2}$$

When the perfect-gas equation of state [Eq. (1-11)] is incorporated in Eq. (7-2), we find that

$$\frac{k}{k-1}\left(\frac{p_2}{\rho_2}-\frac{p_1}{\rho_1}\right)+\frac{V_2{}^2-V_1{}^2}{2}=0 \qquad (7\text{-}3)$$

In most engineering problems it is desired to compute the exit velocity V_2, since very frequently we are concerned with a nozzle converting thermal energy into kinetic energy. It will be noted that Eq. (7-3) is inconvenient because it includes terms which are not easy to measure, and thus it is desirable to rewrite it. This can be done by introducing the continuity equation (2-2),

$$A_1 V_1 \rho_1 = A_2 V_2 \rho_2$$

which, when solved for V_1, gives

$$V_1 = \frac{A_2}{A_1}\frac{\rho_2}{\rho_1} V_2$$

Substituting for V_1 in Eq. (7-3),

$$\frac{k}{k-1}\frac{p_1}{\rho_1}\left(\frac{p_2}{p_1}\frac{\rho_1}{\rho_2}-1\right)+\frac{V_2{}^2}{2}\left[1-\left(\frac{A_2}{A_1}\right)^2\left(\frac{\rho_2}{\rho_1}\right)^2\right]=0 \qquad (7\text{-}4)$$

The relation between pressure and density in the isentropic flow of a perfect gas is given by

$$\frac{p_1}{\rho_1{}^k}=\frac{p_2}{\rho_2{}^k} \qquad (3\text{-}5)$$

After substituting into Eq. (7-4) and upon solving for the isentropic V_2 value (V_{2s}), there results

$$V_{2s} = \frac{1}{\sqrt{1-(A_2/A_1)^2(p_2/p_1)^{2/k}}}\sqrt{\frac{2k}{k-1}\frac{p_1}{\rho_1}\left[1-\left(\frac{p_2}{p_1}\right)^{(k-1)/k}\right]} \qquad (7\text{-}5)$$

In Eq. (7-5) the pressures and the areas can easily be measured, and ρ_1 can be computed from the perfect-gas equation of state.

In Eq. (7-5) the separated radical in the denominator is usually considered as an area-correction factor. However, in many applications the entrance section may be assumed to be of infinite extent and in such a case the initial station is considered to be an infinite reservoir denoted by the subscript 0. When the approach velocity can be disregarded, the velocity at any section is expressed by

$$V_s = \sqrt{\frac{2k}{k-1}\frac{p_0}{\rho_0}\left[1 - \left(\frac{p}{p_0}\right)^{(k-1)/k}\right]} \qquad (7\text{-}6)$$

or

$$V_s = \sqrt{\frac{2kR}{k-1}T_0\left[1 - \left(\frac{p}{p_0}\right)^{(k-1)/k}\right]} \qquad (7\text{-}7)$$

In Eqs. (7-6) and (7-7) p is the only variable, and it, in turn, governs the magnitude of the velocity.

The flux or mass rate of flow may be computed from Eq. (7-6) or (7-7) upon combination with the equation of continuity. Thus

$$G' = AV\rho = A\rho\sqrt{\frac{2kR}{k-1}T_0\left[1 - \left(\frac{p}{p_0}\right)^{(k-1)/k}\right]}$$

$$G = \frac{G'}{A} = \rho\sqrt{\frac{2kR}{k-1}T_0\left[1 - \left(\frac{p}{p_0}\right)^{(k-1)/k}\right]} \qquad (7\text{-}8)$$

Now use the isentropic gas relationship [Eq. (3-5)] to give the value of ρ in terms of the initial density, and substitute in Eq. (7-8):

$$G = \frac{G'}{A} = \rho_0\sqrt{\frac{2kR}{k-1}T_0\left[\left(\frac{p}{p_0}\right)^{2/k} - \left(\frac{p}{p_0}\right)^{(k+1)/k}\right]} \qquad (7\text{-}9)$$

Because the flux G' is constant and the area A is a variable, the ratio G'/A must have a maximum. The condition for which the ratio $G'/A = G$ is a maximum is obtained by differentiating it with respect to p/p_0, setting the differential equal to zero, and solving for p/p_0. This gives the so-called *critical-pressure ratio*

$$\frac{p_c}{p_0} = \left(\frac{2}{k+1}\right)^{k/(k-1)} \qquad (7\text{-}10)$$

Equation (7-10) shows that the specific-heat ratio is the influencing factor of the critical pressure for any entrance pressure. For air at low temperatures where $k = 1.4$, the critical pressure p_c/p_0 equals 0.528.

Because for a convergent-divergent nozzle the mass velocity G is necessarily a maximum at the throat, it follows that the critical pressure p_c exists at the throat. Introducing Eq. (7-10) into Eq. (7-7) and solving for the velocity at the throat, it is seen that

$$V_t = \sqrt{\frac{2k}{k+1}RT_0} \qquad (7\text{-}11)$$

throat velocity

By Eq. (3-6) it is obvious that $\sqrt{kRT_0}$ represents a_0, the acoustic velocity, at inlet (reservoir) conditions. Thus

$$V_t = \sqrt{\frac{2}{k+1} a_0{}^2} \tag{7-12}$$

Comparison of Eq. (7-12) with Eq. (3-22) shows at once that this is the local acoustic velocity reached in a flow passage, and thus

Crit.cal

$$V_t = a^* = \sqrt{\frac{2}{k+1} a_0{}^2} = a_0 \sqrt{\frac{2}{k+1}} \tag{7-12a}$$

It follows, therefore, that for isentropic flow the velocity at the throat is equal to that of sound in the flowing medium, and the Mach number at the throat is consequently unity. Moreover,

$$V_t = a^* = \sqrt{kRT_t} \tag{7-13}$$

Equation (7-13) can also be derived by making use of the fundamental relationship between pressure and temperature during the isentropic expansion of a gas, namely,

$$\frac{T_t}{T_0} = \left(\frac{p_c}{p_0}\right)^{(k-1)/k}$$

Substituting Eq. (7-10) into the preceding equation,

$$\frac{T_t}{T_0} = \left[\left(\frac{2}{k+1}\right)^{k/(k-1)}\right]^{(k-1)/k}$$

$$\frac{T_t}{T_0} = \frac{2}{k+1}$$

Thus $T_0 = T_t(k+1)/2$, and when this is substituted in Eq. (7-11), there results, as before,

$$V_t = \sqrt{kRT_t} \tag{7-13}$$

Isentropic expansion in a nozzle assumes that the maximum conversion of thermal energy to kinetic form takes place reversibly. However, in real nozzles this is not the case as there is necessarily some friction at the walls and also a certain amount of turbulence in the flowing stream. Thus the velocity at any point in the nozzle V_2 is less than would apply in the isentropic nozzle at that point under the same control conditions V_{2s}. The nozzle velocity coefficient k_{nv} is stated as

$$k_{nv} = \frac{V_2}{V_{2s}} \tag{7-14}$$

Nozzle efficiency η_n measures the fraction of the available energy of expansion that is converted to kinetic form:

$$V_2 = \sqrt{\eta_n} \sqrt{V_1^2 + 2(h_1 - h_2')_s} \tag{7-15}$$

and

$$V_{2s} = \sqrt{V_1^2 + 2(h_1 - h_2')_s} \tag{7-16}$$

Comparing Eqs. (7-14), (7-15), and (7-16), it can be seen that

$$k_{nv} = \sqrt{\eta_n} \tag{7-17}$$

When the preceding general nozzle equations refer to the perfect gas, the enthalpy function can be readily transformed with the help of Eqs. (3-13), (3-5), and (1-11). Equation (7-15) then takes the form of Eq. (7-5), becoming

$$V_2 = \frac{\sqrt{\eta_n}}{\sqrt{1 - (A_2/A_1)^2 (p_2/p_1)^{2/k}}} \sqrt{\frac{2k}{k-1} \frac{p_1}{\rho_1} \left[1 - \left(\frac{p_2}{p_1}\right)^{(k-1)/k} \right]} \tag{7-18}$$

$$G' = A_2 V_2 \rho_2 = A_2 V_2 \left(\frac{p_1}{p_2}\right)^{1/k} \rho_1 \tag{7-19}$$

Example 1. Air at negligible velocity enters the nozzles of a gas turbine at 1340.3°F (1800°R) and 45 psia. Expansion is carried to 15 psia in the nozzles and 10 lb of air per second is flowing. The nozzle efficiency is 0.94. Find the efflux velocity and the mouth and throat areas.

Solution. First use the air tables in the solution. From Table A-3 read, at 1800°R, $h_1 = 340.15$ and $p_{r1} = 144.761$. For expansion to the mouth, $r_e = {}^{45}\!/_{15} = 3$, and by Eq. (1-42),

$$p_{r2} = \frac{144.761}{3} = 48.254$$

Corresponding to this value read the enthalpy after isentropic expansion as $h_2' = 221.94$ Btu/lb.

By Eq. (7-15),

$$V_2 = \sqrt{0.94} \sqrt{0 + (2)(32.2)(778)(340.15 - 221.94)_s}$$

$$V_m = 2,360\text{-fps exit velocity at mouth}$$

The temperature at exit from the nozzle can be found because the stagnation enthalpy is constant in an adiabatic nozzle:

$$h_0 = h_1 + \frac{V_1^2}{2} = h_2 + \frac{V_2^2}{2}$$

$$340.15 + 0 = h_2 + \frac{(2,360)^2}{50,070}$$

$$h_2 = 229.05 \text{ Btu/lb}$$

From Table A-3, the corresponding temperature is 1384.1°R. Knowing the temperature and pressure at the mouth, the density of the air can be found by use of Eq. (1-10) or Eq. (1-13).

For air, $R = 1,716$ ft-lb/(slug)(°R).

$$\frac{p}{\rho} = RT \qquad \rho_2 = \frac{(144)(15)}{(1,716)(1,384.1)}$$

$$\rho_2 = 0.000908 \text{ slug/ft}^3$$

Use Eq. (7-19), where $G' = 10/32.2 = 0.311$ slug/sec.

$$G' = A_2 V_2 \rho_2 = A_2(2,360)(0.000908) = 0.311$$

$$A_2 = 0.145 \text{ ft}^2 = 20.9 \text{ in.}^2 \text{ total mouth area}$$

The conditions at the throat will be worked out for illustrative purposes completely by perfect-gas relationships. First employ Eq. (7-10) to find the ideal throat pressure. The value of k for high-temperature air is not 1.4 as usually considered but, from Fig. 1-5 for the range of this problem, is about 1.342; thus

$$p_c = p_t = p_0 \left(\frac{2}{1.342 + 1}\right)^{1.342/(1.342-1)} = (45)(0.538) = 24.2 \text{ psia}$$

This is really the throat pressure which would exist in a frictionless nozzle, but as nozzles are high in efficiency this idealized pressure is sufficiently accurate to use in design work. It should be realized that with friction a slightly lower pressure will be needed to produce the acoustic velocity. At inlet to the nozzle find ρ_1 from Eq. (1-13).

$$\rho_1 = \frac{(144)(45)}{(1,716)(1,800)} = 0.002095 \text{ slug/ft}^3$$

Because of the negligible approach velocity, the denominator correction of Eq. (7-18) need not be used. Substituting

$$V_t = \sqrt{0.94} \sqrt{\frac{(2)(1.342)}{1.342 - 1} \frac{(144)(45)}{0.002095} \left[1 - \left(\frac{24.2}{45}\right)^{(1.342-1)/1.342}\right]}$$

$$V_t = 1,825 \text{ fps}$$

The temperature at the throat can be found from an enthalpy balance without using the air tables if desired.

error

$$h_1 + 0 = h_t + \frac{V_t^2}{2}$$

$$\frac{V_t^2}{2} = h_1 - h_t = c_p(T_1 - T_t)$$

Select a mean c_p from Fig. 1-5 from 1800° to about 1550°R.

$$\frac{1,825^2}{50,070} = 0.268(1,800 - T_t)$$

$$T_t = 1552°R \text{ throat temperature}$$

By Eq. (1-13),

$$\frac{(144)(24.2)}{\rho_t} = (1,716)(1,552)$$

$$\rho_t = 0.001308 \text{ slug/ft}^3$$

By Eq. (7-19),

$$G' = 0.311 = A_t(1,825)(0.001308)$$

$$A_t = 0.130 \text{ ft}^2 = 18.7 \text{ in.}^2$$

This is closely the throat area, but to find the exact minimum (throat) area and its conditions a series of similar computations at slightly less than 24.2 psia pressure would have to be carried out.

7-3. Criteria for Acceleration and Deceleration.

In this section it appears desirable to consider under what circumstances flow can be accelerated or decelerated.

Consider the continuity equation in its differentiated form as represented by Eq. (2-3):

$$\frac{d\rho}{\rho} + \frac{dV}{V} + \frac{dA}{A} = 0 \tag{2-3}$$

For incompressible flow $d\rho = 0$, and

$$\frac{dV}{V} = -\frac{dA}{A} \tag{7-20}$$

Accordingly, whenever the area decreases the velocity must increase, and whenever the area increases the velocity must decrease.

For the general case of compressible flow without losses (isentropic) substitute, from Euler's equation (2-29), $-V\,dV/dp$ for $1/\rho$ in Eq. (2-3):

$$-\frac{V\,dV}{dp}\,d\rho + \frac{dA}{A} + \frac{dV}{V} = 0 \tag{7-21}$$

$$-\frac{V^2\,d\rho}{dp}\frac{dV}{V} + \frac{dA}{A} + \frac{dV}{V} = 0 \tag{7-22}$$

From Eq. (3-3),

$$a^2 = \frac{dp}{d\rho}$$

and as $V^2/a^2 = M^2$,

$$V^2\frac{d\rho}{dp} = M^2$$

Thus
$$-M^2\frac{dV}{V}+\frac{dA}{A}+\frac{dV}{V}=0$$

and
$$\frac{dA}{A}=\frac{dV}{V}(M^2-1) \tag{7-23}$$

This equation relates changes in area and velocity to the Mach number. From it the following conditions can be stated:
1. For a convergent section with $M^2 > 1$, the velocity decreases.
2. For a divergent section with $M^2 > 1$, the velocity increases.
3. For a convergent section with $M^2 < 1$, the velocity increases.
4. For a divergent section with $M^2 < 1$, the velocity decreases.
5. For A = constant, either the velocity is constant or $M^2 = 1$.

For steady flow, the velocity remains the same at each point; accordingly at the throat section, where A = constant,

$$M^2 = 1 \qquad \text{or} \qquad M = 1$$

This discussion demonstrates that a supersonic jet can be obtained by proper disposition of the variables. Furthermore, the flow regime (subsonic or supersonic) is influenced not only by the passage contour but also by the Mach number at the entrance. Thus divergent passages do not necessarily accelerate the flow, and conversely, convergent passages need not decelerate.

7-4. Effect of Pressure Ratio on Nozzle Operation. Convergent Nozzle. Consider a convergent nozzle which has a large entrance area and a large exit area as depicted in Fig. 7-1. Let the nozzle operate between two reser-

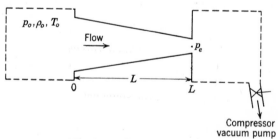

FIG. 7-1. Convergent nozzle.

voirs, and let the exit reservoir be connected to a compressor-vacuum-pump arrangement through a valve so that the exit pressure can be varied at will, provided $p_e \leqq p_0$. When $p_0 = p_e$, the pressure is the same all along the nozzle and there can be no flow. In Fig. 7-2, line a represents this condition. The flow rate vs. the pressure ratio is plotted in Fig. 7-3. Case a just mentioned is a point at the origin.

When the exit reservoir pressure is slightly lowered, flow occurs and the resulting pressure distribution along the nozzle is represented by curve b in Fig. 7-2 and also by point b in Fig. 7-3. When the pressure in the exit reservoir is reduced by further increments, increased flow results with each reduction until the exit pressure eventually reaches the critical pressure. At this condition, the Mach number at the exit has reached unity value.

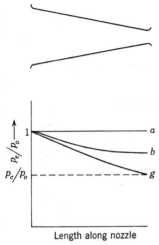

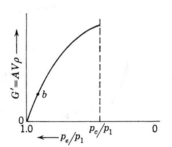

FIG. 7-2.   Pressure distribution
in convergent nozzle.

FIG. 7-3.   Flow rate.

The pressure in the exit reservoir can be reduced still further, but this produces no change within the nozzle itself, although various changing phenomena can occur outside the nozzle. This can be explained as follows: The disturbance created by a reduction in pressure between $1 > p_e/p_0 > p_c/p_0$ produces a pressure wave which travels upstream and through the nozzle at sonic speed. This disturbance induces an increased flow. However, when the pressure ratio becomes equal to the critical-pressure ratio, the exit velocity has reached the sonic velocity, and thus the pressure pulse can no longer travel into the nozzle. Thus the flow inside the nozzle and in the entrance reservoir remains unaffected by the subcritical pressure in the exit reservoir.

7-5. Effect of Pressure Ratio on Nozzle Operation. Convergent-Divergent Nozzle. When the flow completely fills the nozzle, exit pressures below the critical cannot exist in a convergent nozzle. However, in convergent-divergent nozzles the pressure along the nozzle may be less than the critical at any point past the throat.

Consider a convergent-divergent nozzle inserted between two reservoirs as in Fig. 7-4. As before, there will be no flow if $p_e/p_0 = 1$ (case a in Fig.

7-5). If p_e is now reduced so that it is very slightly less than the entrance pressure, the convergent-divergent nozzle will act like a conventional venturi tube as represented by curve b in Fig. 7-5. For this case, the flow is always subsonic and resembles incompressible flow. When pressure is reduced further, the critical pressure can be reached at the throat as curve

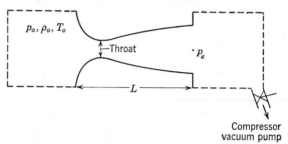

FIG. 7-4.   Convergent-divergent nozzle.

g shows. In this case, the velocity is sonic at the throat, but is never supersonic within the nozzle, even though the pressure at the throat corresponds to the critical. The minimum pressure which can exist in the nozzle is depicted by point d. For this case also, the pressure at the throat will be the critical and the velocity in the converging section is subsonic. In the diverging section it is supersonic, and at the throat it is sonic. For the range of exit pressures from (d) up to (g), the rate-of-flow curve is the same

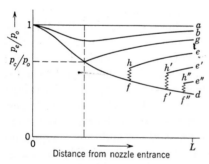

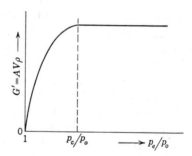

FIG. 7-5. Pressure distribution in convergent-divergent nozzle.

FIG. 7-6. Flow rate.

and is plotted in Fig. 7-6. The flow rate reaches a maximum value and remains at this value over this wide range of exit pressures.

The convergent-divergent nozzle in the absence of friction can give truly isentropic performance for the range of exhaust pressures from (a) to (g) in Fig. 7-5, and for only one other pressure, namely, that at (d). The pressures p_g and p_d are the significant mouth-design pressures for a given nozzle. For the exhaust pressure range between p_d and p_g flow discontinuities (shock) must occur in the nozzle, followed by diffusion (pressure rise) from and after the shock point.

7-6. Effect of Back Pressure on Nozzle Flow. In the discussions so far it was assumed that the static pressure in the exit plane of the nozzle is the same as the pressure in the reservoir into which the nozzle exhausts. This is called the *design pressure* (p_d in Fig. 7-5). It is, of course, desirable that the nozzle be served by a reservoir, the pressure of which just equals the design pressure. There are many conditions under which the flow will not be in design balance and thus the pressure in the exit plane will be either less or greater than the pressure in the reservoir. If the receiver pressure is greater than the design pressure, the nozzle is said to be *overexpanding*, and if it is less the nozzle is said to be *underexpanding*.

As before, consider a convergent-divergent nozzle connecting a reservoir and a receiver. If the flow is isentropic, the pressure distributions shown by curves a, b, g, and d in Fig. 7-5 may result. Experimental evidence indicates that when the back pressure is slightly less than the exit pressure, small standing waves occur outside the nozzle. These waves, which are oblique, are reflected by the boundary of the free jet because at the boundary of the free jet density discontinuities occur. Figure 7-7 shows a sketch of the standing waves when the back pressure is less than the exit pressure. The configuration of the waves, when the back pressure is greater than the exit pressure, is shown in Fig. 7-8.

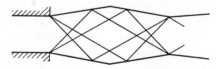

FIG. 7-7. Standing waves—underexpanding nozzle.

As the back pressure becomes more greatly different from the design pressure, the waves outside the nozzle shift from their position as depicted in Figs. 7-7 and 7-8, and their shapes also change. Thus when the pressure is between (g) and (d) in Fig. 7-5, the waves will move upstream into the nozzle. For an exhaust pressure such as at (e) the pressure at the throat will still be the critical value and the velocity at the throat sonic. Downstream from the throat the velocity increases in supersonic magnitude up

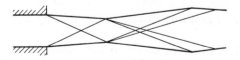

FIG. 7-8. Standing waves—overexpanding nozzle.

to a certain point, such as position f in Fig. 7-5. When the pressure at (e) in Fig. 7-5 is thus in the range of values between (d) and (g), normal and oblique waves will occur downstream from the throat in the vicinity of (f).

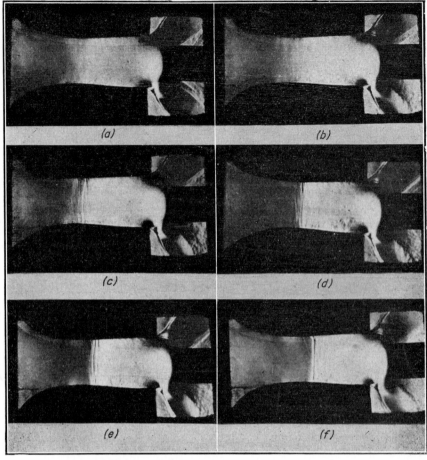

FIG. 7-9. Schlieren photographs of flow through a two-dimensional nozzle showing the development of a shock. The flow is from left to right. The obstacle at the atmospheric end of the nozzle is moved slightly backward in each picture, raising the throat Mach number. (*NACA photo.*)

In such cases, the flow will seem to separate from the walls and the velocity will become subsonic, and if the position f is far in the nozzle, the latter will act as a diffuser and further reduce the velocity as the medium leaves the nozzle.

As the disturbance moves closer to the throat, the tendency for flow separation will diminish. Where the shock wave forms downstream from the throat, there is always an increase of entropy. However, the flow will be closely isentropic from the entrance to (f). At this point a drastic rise in pressure is experienced to point h. From point g to e the flow may proceed isentropically again. Because across a normal shock the velocity becomes subsonic, it follows that the downstream velocity must become subsonic. In the sequence pictures of Fig. 7-9 the formation of shock in a two-dimensional nozzle is shown.

7-7. Isothermal Flow.   The flow through nozzles is generally considered to be adiabatic because the time of passage is too rapid to permit very significant transfer of heat.   Although this assumption is reasonably valid, there are indications that this may be an oversimplification.   For example, Saenger[1] has shown that isothermal flow may occur in rocket nozzles because of dissociation at high temperatures.   Isothermal expansion has some desirable aspects, as was shown by Randolph,[2] Cambel,[3] and Seifert and Altman.[4]   Their conclusions stem from the observation that isothermal flow may produce high thermal efficiencies in gas-turbine installations and produce increased thrust in rocket nozzles.

Basically, isothermal expansion of gases proceeds in accordance with two patterns.   The first is the arrangement in which heat is added—either through the duct walls or by virtue of a chemical reaction taking place within the flow—thereby preventing the usual drop of temperature accompanying adiabatic expansion.   The second pattern is to use a gas of extremely high specific heat so that it expands isothermally as well as isentropically.   Although the first technique is easy to conceive, the latter requires explanation.

7-8. Isothermal-Isentropic Flow.   For every gas the number of degrees of freedom f is defined by the principle of equipartition of energy.   At high temperatures, vibration may be set up along the axis of the molecule which results in an additional manner of exchanging energy, thus increasing the degrees of freedom by one.   Experience indicates that the number of degrees of freedom as predicted by theory does not always agree with the actual number determined by experiment.   In general, the agreement between theory and experiment is good at room temperature, although deviations become appreciable for complicated molecules.   One could imagine a complex molecule which could have a very large number of degrees of freedom f, even an infinite number.   For such a gas the specific-heat ratio k will approach unity.   If we recall from kinetic theory that k is defined by

$$k = 1 + \frac{2}{f} \qquad (7\text{-}24)$$

then as $f \rightarrow \infty$, $k \rightarrow 1$.   For a reversible, adiabatic process the polytropic equation is $p/\rho^k = $ constant.   In employing this equation we merely substitute the numerical value for k corresponding to the gas under consideration, and thus for a gas with an infinitely large specific heat the polytropic relation becomes $p/\rho = $ constant.   Therefore, it follows that for such a gas undergoing a reversible process the expansion will be both isothermal and isentropic.

For steady, one-dimensional flow in the absence of external forces such as gravity and magnetism, and when no shaft work is done, the energy balance between the two stations 1 and 2 is given by Eq. (4-3) as

$\dfrac{kR}{k-1} = c_p$ $Q_{1 \to 2} = \dfrac{kR}{k-1}(T_{02} - T_{01})$ (4-3)

It can be seen by Eq. (4-3) that in diabatic gas flow, the stagnation temperature changes during the heat-transport process, and accordingly, one stagnation state is not sufficient to define the flow conditions. Equation (4-3) is general and applies equally well to isothermal and to isothermal-isentropic flow. However, although in the former case the stagnation temperature changes, in the latter case the stagnation temperature remains the same because no heat is being added. Thus, just as for isentropic conditions, one reservoir is sufficient to define the flow. In summary, for isentropic flow, the free-stream temperature varies, but the stagnation temperature remains the same; for reversible isothermal flow, the static temperature remains the same but the stagnation temperature changes; and for isentropic-isothermal flow both the static and the stagnation temperatures remain the same.

7-9. Isothermal-flow Functions. The most effective approach to flow problems of this type is to express ratios of the gas properties and flow parameters between any two points in the flow stream as functions of the Mach number and of the specific-heat ratio k of the gas. Using these ratios, a reference state is defined, and the ratios of the variables at any Mach number to those at the reference state are tabulated. Three basic equations and two definitions are used. These are Euler's equation (thus imposing the limitation of reversibility), the continuity equation, the perfect-gas equation of state, the definition of Mach number, and the definition of the thrust function. Respectively, these are

Eulers EQ. $\dfrac{dp}{\rho} + V\,dV = 0$ (2-29)

Cont. Eq. $\rho A V = \text{constant}$ (2-2)

Perfect gas Eq. of state $p = \rho R T$ (1-11)

Defin. of Mach No. $V = M\sqrt{kRT}$ (3-11)

THRUST FUNCTION $F = pA + \rho V^2 A$ (2-7)

For isothermal flow, from Eq. (1-11),

$$\frac{p_2}{p_1} = \frac{\rho_2}{\rho_1}$$

and from Eq. (3-11),

$$\frac{V_2}{V_1} = \frac{M_2}{M_1}$$ — isothermal flow only

Substituting these into Eq. (2-2), we find

$$\frac{\rho_2 A_2 V_2}{\rho_1 A_1 V_1} = \frac{p_2 A_2 M_2}{p_1 A_1 M_1} = 1 \tag{7-25}$$

Substitution of Eq. (1-11) into Eq. (2-29) yields

$$V\, dV + RT \frac{dp}{p} = 0 \tag{7-26}$$

Equation (7-26) is applicable to reversible isothermal flow in the same manner that Eq. (3-14) is applicable to adiabatic flow. When integrated between limit points 1 and 2, Eq. (7-26) becomes

$$\frac{V_2^2 - V_1^2}{2} + RT \ln \frac{p_2}{p_1} = 0 \tag{7-27}$$

isothermal or $T_{static} = const$

Equation (7-27) can be solved for the exit velocity V_2; thus

$$V_2 = \sqrt{2\left(RT \ln \frac{p_1}{p_2} + \frac{V_1^2}{2}\right)} \tag{7-28}$$

$T_{static} = Const$

If in Eq. (7-28) the term $V_1^2/2$ is negligible, then at any section

$$V = \sqrt{2RT \ln \frac{p_1}{p_2}} \tag{7-29}$$

This equation, written for reversible isothermal flow, is analogous to Eq. (7-7).

Substituting the defining Mach-number relationship in Eq. (7-27) and rearranging,

$$\frac{M_2^2 kRT_2 - M_1^2 kRT_1}{2} = RT \ln \frac{p_2}{p_1}$$

but $T = T_1 = T_2$ in an isothermal process, so that

$$\ln \frac{p_2}{p_1} = \frac{(M_1^2 - M_2^2)k}{2} \tag{7-30}$$

Note method

Thus

$$\frac{p_2}{p_1} = \frac{\rho_2}{\rho_1} = \left(\frac{e^{M_1^2}}{e^{M_2^2}}\right)^{k/2} \tag{7-31}$$

Upon combining Eq. (7-31) with the continuity equation we obtain

$$\frac{A_2}{A_1} = \frac{M_1 p_1}{M_2 p_2} = \frac{M_1}{M_2}\left(\frac{e^{M_2^2}}{e^{M_1^2}}\right)^{k/2} \tag{7-32}$$

The stagnation-temperature and pressure ratios may be evaluated from Eqs. (3-30) and (3-34), which apply regardless of whether the flow is isentropic, isothermal, or isentropic-isothermal, because in all cases the flow may be assumed to come to rest isentropically.

It follows that the stagnation-temperature ratio is

[handwritten: isothermal only]

$$\frac{T_{02}}{T_{01}} = \frac{1 + \frac{1}{2}(k - 1)M_2^2}{1 + \frac{1}{2}(k - 1)M_1^2} \tag{7-33}$$

Similarly, the stagnation-pressure ratio may be found by substituting from Eq. (7-31). Thus,

[handwritten: $\frac{P_2}{P_1} = \left(\frac{e^{M_1^2}}{e^{M_2^2}}\right)^{k/2}$]

$$\frac{p_{02}}{p_{01}} = \left(\frac{e^{M_1^2}}{e^{M_2^2}}\right)^{k/2}\left[\frac{1 + \frac{1}{2}(k - 1)M_2^2}{1 + \frac{1}{2}(k - 1)M_1^2}\right]^{k/(k-1)} \tag{7-34}$$

By (2-7) the thrust-function ratio is

$$\frac{F_2}{F_1} = \frac{p_2A_2 + \rho_2V_2^2A_2}{p_1A_1 + \rho_1V_1^2A_1}$$

Dividing through by p_2A_2/p_1A_1, and substituting from Eq. (1-11), we find that

$$\frac{F_2}{F_1} = \frac{p_2A_2}{p_1A_1}\frac{1 + V_2^2/RT}{1 + V_1^2/RT}$$

But from (3-11), $V^2/RT = kM^2$, and from Eq. (7-25), $p_2A_2/p_1A_1 = M_1/M_2$. Hence

$$\frac{F_2}{F_1} = \frac{M_1\left[1 + kM_2^2\right]}{M_2\left[1 + kM_1^2\right]} \tag{7-35}$$

One may now establish the reference state as that state at which the Mach number is unity. The critical section, rather than the reservoir, is used as a reference because in isothermal flow the stagnation temperature may change. Denoting the station at which the Mach number is equal to unity by an asterisk, the various ratios already discussed become

$$\frac{V}{V^*} = M \tag{7-36}$$

$$\frac{T}{T^*} = 1 \tag{7-37}$$

[handwritten: do not need brackets since $M^* = 1$]

$$\frac{p}{p^*} = \frac{\rho}{\rho^*} = \left[e^{(1-M^2)k/2}\right] \tag{7-38}$$

$$\frac{A}{A^*} = \frac{1}{M}e^{(M^2-1)k/2} \tag{7-39}$$

[handwritten: $\frac{dp}{p^*} = MKe^{(1-M^2)K/2}\left(M^2K - 1\right)dM$]

[handwritten: $\frac{dA}{A^*} = \frac{e^{(1-M^2)K/2}}{M^2}$]

$$\frac{dT_0}{T_0^*} = \frac{(k-1)M\,dM}{k+1}$$

take
after.

$$\frac{T_0}{T_0^*} = \frac{2[1 + \frac{1}{2}(k - 1)M^2]}{k + 1} \tag{7-40}$$

$$\frac{p_0}{p_0^*} = e^{(1-M)k/2} \left\{ \frac{2[1 + \frac{1}{2}(k - 1)M^2]}{k + 1} \right\}^{k/(k-1)} \tag{7-41}$$

$$\frac{F}{F^*} = \frac{1}{M} \frac{1 + kM^2}{1 + k} \tag{7-42}$$

Equations (7-37) to (7-42) have been plotted by Romer and Cambel [7] in Fig. 7-10 for a diatomic gas ($k = 1.4$) such as air undergoing a reversible isothermal process.

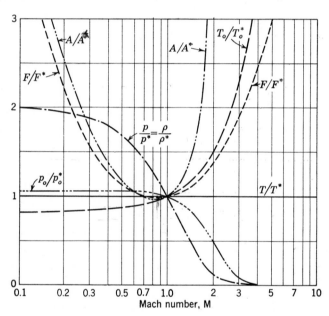

FIG. 7-10.   Reversible isothermal flow functions for a perfect gas ($k = 1.4$).

The various curves depicted in Fig. 7-10 have characteristics which merit comment. Thus for isothermal flow the temperature-ratio T_0/T_0^* curve is rather different than would be the case for isentropic flow. Also of considerable interest are the minima of the area and the thrust-ratio curves. As may be seen in Fig. 7-10, these curves reach low values at less than unity at the section where the Mach number is equal to $1/\sqrt{k}$, which for the diatomic gases with $k = 1.4$ is 0.85. However, at the usual throat section the ratios are equal to unity. To understand this, consider the minimum section or throat of a convergent-divergent nozzle. Here, the ratio $A/A*$ becomes a minimum, and thus

$$\frac{d(A/A*)}{d\mathrm{M}} = \frac{k\mathrm{M}^2 e^{(\mathrm{M}^2-1)k/2} - e^{(\mathrm{M}^2-1)k/2}}{\mathrm{M}^2} = 0$$

This reduces to

$$k\mathrm{M}^2 - 1 = 0$$

or

$$\mathrm{M} = \frac{1}{\sqrt{k}}$$

If on account of the characteristics of the gas the expansion is both isothermal and isentropic, then the minimum section will occur at the throat corresponding to the isentropic nozzle.

It becomes of interest now to determine the velocity at the throat of an isothermal nozzle. By definition, the throat velocity is

$$V_t = \mathrm{M}\sqrt{kRT_g} = \sqrt{RT_g} \tag{7-43}$$

The throat-pressure ratio (referred to the reservoir where $\mathrm{M} = $ zero) becomes

$$\frac{p_t}{p_R} = e^{-\mathrm{M}_t^2 k/2}$$

$$= e^{-(1/k)(k/2)} = e^{-\frac{1}{2}} = 0.607 \tag{7-44}$$

Equation (7-44) is of considerable interest because the critical-pressure ratio is seen to be a definite constant which is completely independent of the particular gas undergoing the expansion process. This is in contrast to isentropic flow, where the specific-heat ratio influences the critical pressure. It follows further that because the adiabatic speed of sound is greater than the isothermal speed of sound, isothermal flow may be supercritical without being necessarily supersonic. This is in sharp contrast to isentropic flow, in which supercritical conditions result invariably in supersonic flow. It should be recalled that regardless of the flow being isothermal, small disturbances will be propagated with the adiabatic speed of sound.

In Fig. 7-11, reproduced here from Romer and Cambel,[7] are plotted the area and the thrust-function ratios for isothermal and isentropic flow through nozzles, using data from reference 5 at $k = 1.4$. It may be seen from this figure that for the same Mach number in the supersonic domain $A/A*$ for isothermal flow is higher than $A/A*$ for isentropic flow. Thus it follows that for the same nozzle length, separation is more likely to occur in an isothermal nozzle than in an isentropic nozzle. However, it should be noted that separation in the divergent part of rocket nozzles is not detrimental but actually desirable, as has been shown by Summerfield.[6]

Therefore, peripheral injection to control separation and increase thrust seems to be advantageous in isothermal nozzles. Actually this would be an added improvement because, as Fig. 7-11 indicates, the isothermal nozzle already has a higher thrust-function ratio at the same Mach number when compared with the isentropic nozzle.

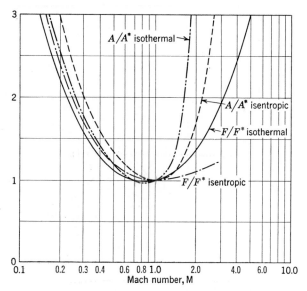

FIG. 7-11. Comparison of area and thrust function variations between reversible isothermal flow and isentropic flow ($k = 1.4$, perfect gas).

7-10. Comparison of Flow in Nozzles. In Fig. 7-12 are plotted[7] velocity, density, and Mach number along a hypothetical nozzle when the flow is isentropic and when it is reversibly isothermal. In either case the specific-heat ratio is 1.4. The density is seen to decrease at the same rate in the convergent section of the nozzle, but not so in the divergent section. The Mach number in isentropic flow is greater at each section, with the velocity curves crossing one another in the divergent section. This may be explained as follows: For isentropic flow, the maximum or limiting velocity (defined as the velocity which exists at absolute vacuum) is given by Eq. (3-21) as

$$V_{\max} = 109.7\sqrt{T_0}$$

and is thus determined by the reservoir temperature. It follows that for any practical case $V_{\max}$ is of finite value. That this is not so for isothermal flow may be seen from Eq. (7-38), which indicates that the Mach number, and hence the velocity, tend to infinity if the pressure at the exit goes to zero.

Finally, in Fig. 7-13 are plotted [7] the pressure and temperature ratios for the two types of flow. It is evident that for the same reservoir and nozzle, the pressure and the temperature are lower at each section when the flow is proceeding isentropically rather than isothermally.

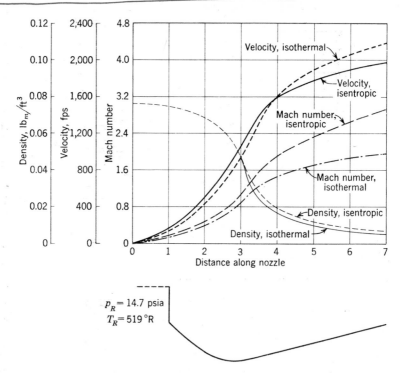

FIG. 7-12. Comparison of velocity, density, and Mach number in a hypothetical nozzle between reversible isothermal flow and isentropic flow ($k = 1.4$, perfect gas, $T_R = 519°$R, $p_R = 1$ atm).

7-11. Generalized One-dimensional Flow. In Chaps. 4 and 5, and in Secs. 7-1 to 7-10 of this chapter, three types of flow, namely, flow with heat exchange, flow with friction, and flow in variable-area ducts, were discussed separately to the exclusion of other complicating phenomena. However, very frequently several phenomena occur simultaneously in flow applications. To study such multiple processes, Shapiro and Hawthorne [8] have developed a method for treating generalized, one-dimensional continuous flow. Using this method it is possible to consider many configuration types occurring simultaneously. By this method it is possible to account for area change, wall friction, drag of internal bodies, external-heat exchange, chemical reactions, phase changes, mixing of streams, and changes in specific heat and in molecular weight.

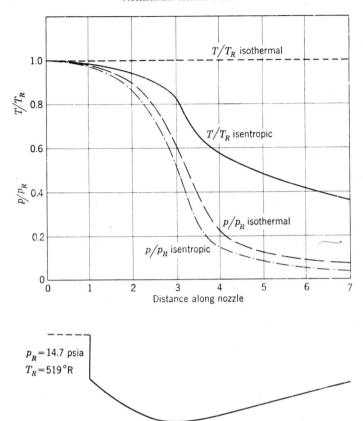

FIG. 7-13.   Comparison of temperature and pressure ratios in a hypothetical nozzle between reversible isothermal flow and isentropic flow ($k = 1.4$, perfect gas).

The assumptions made by Shapiro and Hawthorne are as follows: (1) The flow is one-dimensional; (2) the flow is steady; (3) changes in stream properties are continuous; and (4) the gas properties vary with temperature only.

The basic model of the flow system to be utilized with this analysis is depicted in Fig. 7-14. The model might represent a combustion chamber or a rocket motor into which there may be injected a fuel stream. It may also include evaporated liquid entering the control volume. It is important to note that any liquid

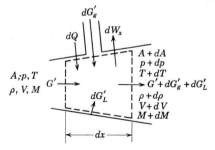

FIG. 7-14.   Flow model for generalized flow.

entering the control volume or traveling through it is considered to lie outside the control volume. The equation of continuity applicable to Fig. 7-14 can be written as follows:

$$dG' = dG'_L + dG'_g \qquad (7\text{-}45)$$

in which dG'_g represents the injected gas and dG'_L is the evaporated liquid entering the control volume. The latter may be positive or negative, depending on whether liquid is evaporated or condensed. In logarithmic differential form the continuity equation is

$$\frac{dG'}{G'} = \frac{d\rho}{\rho} + \frac{dA}{A} + \frac{dV}{V} \qquad (7\text{-}46)$$

The energy equation is written by Shapiro and Hawthorne in the following manner:

$$\frac{dQ - dW_s + dH}{c_p T} = \frac{dT}{T} + \frac{k-1}{2} M^2 \frac{dV^2}{V^2} \qquad (7\text{-}47)$$

in which dH is an energy term defined as

$$dH = dh_{pr} - \left[\bar{c}_{pg}(T - T_{og}) + \frac{V^2}{2} \right] \frac{dG'_g}{G'} - \left(h_L - h_v + \frac{V^2 - V_L^2}{2} \right) \frac{dG'_L}{G}$$

where T_{og} = stagnation temperature of injected gas
T = temperature
$\bar{c}_{pg}$ = specific heat at constant pressure of injected gas

$$\bar{c}_{pg} = \frac{1}{T - T_{og}} \int_{T_{oe}}^{T} c_{pg}\, dT$$

h_{pr} = heat of reaction at constant pressure $(dh = -dh_{pr} + c_p\, dT)$
h_L = enthalpy of liquid about to evaporate as it enters control volume
h_v = enthalpy of evaporated liquid at temperature T
V = velocity of stream
V_L = velocity of injected fluid changing phase

Finally, the momentum equation is expressed as

$$\frac{dp}{p} + \frac{kM^2}{2}\frac{dV^2}{V^2} + \frac{kM^2}{2}\left(4f\frac{dx}{D} + \frac{dX}{\frac{1}{2}kpAM^2} \right)$$

$$+ kM^2(1 - y)\frac{dG'}{G'} = 0 \qquad (7\text{-}48)$$

where D = mean hydraulic diameter

X = drag force

$$(1 - y)\frac{dG'}{G'} = (1 - y_g)\frac{dG'_g}{G'} + (1 - y_L)\frac{dG'_L}{dG'}$$

$$y_g = \frac{V'_g}{V}$$

$$y_L = \frac{V'_L}{V}$$

V'_g, V'_L = forward-velocity components

Two avenues of approach are now possible. The first takes into consideration possible variations in molecular weight and specific heat. The second assumes constant molecular weight and specific heat. Although the former is in a way more general, it has the disadvantage that for this case there are no simple algebraic relations between the local properties and the stagnation properties.

Consider the general case when in addition to friction, heat exchange, area change, chemical phenomena, shaft work, phase change, injection, the molecular weight, and the specific heat may vary. Using the basic gas-dynamic equations and definitions, one may write 8 equations relating 14 differential variables. It is desirable now to choose among these the six which are most easily controlled in practice as the independent ones. Using methods of simultaneous linear algebraic equations we can then solve for the various dependent variables. Shapiro and Hawthorne have solved these equations and have compiled the solutions in Table 7-1. In this table, the differential variables in the heads are the independent variables, and the dependent variables are listed in the first column. This table is most convenient in solving for the dependent variables. If it is assumed that we wish to determine the logarithmic differential of the acoustic speed for generalized flow, we can simply write, by the use of Table 7-1,

$$\frac{da}{a} = \frac{[(k-1)/2]M^2}{1-M^2}\frac{dA}{A} + \frac{1-kM^2}{2(1-M^2)}\frac{dQ - dW_x + dH}{c_p T}$$

$$- \frac{k(k-1)M^4}{4(1-M^2)}\left(4f\frac{dx}{D} + \frac{dX}{\frac{1}{2}kpAM^2} - 2y\frac{dw}{w}\right)$$

$$- \frac{[(k-1)/2]M^2(1+kM^2)}{1-M^2}\frac{dW}{W} + \frac{kM^2-1}{2(1-M^2)}\frac{dW}{W} + \frac{1}{2}\frac{dk}{k}$$

The parameters making up the table are called the *influence coefficients*. Each influence coefficient is the partial derivative of the variable in the

TABLE 7-1. TABLE OF INFLUENCE COEFFICIENTS; †

	$\dfrac{dA}{A}$	$\dfrac{dQ - dW_x + dH}{c_p T}$	$4f\dfrac{dx}{D} + \dfrac{dX}{\frac{1}{2}kp A M^2} - 2y\dfrac{dw}{w}$
$\dfrac{dM^2}{M^2}$	$-\dfrac{2\left(1 + \dfrac{k-1}{2}M^2\right)}{1 - M^2}$	$\dfrac{1 + kM^2}{1 - M^2}$	$\dfrac{kM^2\left(1 + \dfrac{k-1}{2}M^2\right)}{1 - M^2}$
$\dfrac{dV}{V}$	$-\dfrac{1}{1 - M^2}$	$\dfrac{1}{1 - M^2}$	$\dfrac{kM^2}{2(1 - M^2)}$
$\dfrac{dc}{c}$	$\dfrac{\dfrac{k-1}{2}M^2}{1 - M^2}$	$\dfrac{1 - kM^2}{2(1 - M^2)}$	$-\dfrac{k(k-1)M^4}{4(1 - M^2)}$
$\dfrac{dT}{T}$	$\dfrac{(k-1)M^2}{1 - M^2}$	$\dfrac{1 - kM^2}{1 - M^2}$	$-\dfrac{k(k-1)M^4}{2(1 - M^2)}$
$\dfrac{d\rho}{\rho}$	$\dfrac{M^2}{1 - M^2}$	$-\dfrac{1}{1 - M^2}$	$-\dfrac{kM^2}{2(1 - M^2)}$
$\dfrac{dp}{p}$	$\dfrac{kM^2}{1 - M^2}$	$-\dfrac{kM^2}{1 - M^2}$	$-\dfrac{kM^2[1 + (k-1)M^2]}{2(1 - M^2)}$
$\dfrac{dF}{F}$	$\dfrac{1}{1 + kM^2}$	0	$-\dfrac{kM^2}{2(1 + kM^2)}$
$\dfrac{ds}{c_p}$ ‡	0	1	$\dfrac{(k-1)M^2}{2}$

† Tables of numerical values of the influence coefficients appear in the Design Data Section of *J. Appl. Mechanics*, vol. 14, no. 4, December, 1947, in the paper Tables for Numerical Solution of Problems in the Mechanics and Thermodynamics of Steady One-

VARIABLE SPECIFIC HEAT AND MOLECULAR WEIGHT

	$\dfrac{dw}{w}$	$\dfrac{dW}{W}$	$\dfrac{dk}{k}$
$\dfrac{d\mathrm{M}^2}{\mathrm{M}^2}$	$\dfrac{2(1 + k\mathrm{M}^2)\left(1 + \dfrac{k-1}{2}\mathrm{M}^2\right)}{1 - \mathrm{M}^2}$	$-\dfrac{1 + k\mathrm{M}^2}{1 - \mathrm{M}^2}$	-1
$\dfrac{dV}{V}$	$\dfrac{1 + k\mathrm{M}^2}{1 - \mathrm{M}^2}$	$-\dfrac{1}{1 - \mathrm{M}^2}$	0
$\dfrac{dc}{c}$	$-\dfrac{\dfrac{k-1}{2}\mathrm{M}^2(1 + k\mathrm{M}^2)}{1 - \mathrm{M}^2}$	$\dfrac{k\mathrm{M}^2 - 1}{2(1 - \mathrm{M}^2)}$	$\tfrac{1}{2}$
$\dfrac{dT}{T}$	$-\dfrac{(k-1)\mathrm{M}^2(1 + k\mathrm{M}^2)}{1 - \mathrm{M}^2}$	$\dfrac{(k-1)\mathrm{M}^2}{1 - \mathrm{M}^2}$	0
$\dfrac{d\rho}{\rho}$	$-\dfrac{(k+1)\mathrm{M}^2}{1 - \mathrm{M}^2}$	$\dfrac{1}{1 - \mathrm{M}^2}$	0
$\dfrac{dp}{p}$	$-\dfrac{2k\mathrm{M}^2\left(1 + \dfrac{k-1}{2}\mathrm{M}^2\right)}{1 - \mathrm{M}^2}$	$\dfrac{k\mathrm{M}^2}{1 - \mathrm{M}^2}$	0
$\dfrac{dF}{F}$	0	0	0
$\dfrac{ds}{c_p}$ ‡	$(k-1)\mathrm{M}^2$	0	0

dimensional Gas Flow without Discontinuities, by G. M. Edelman and A. H. Shapiro.
‡ For unaltered chemical composition only, and referring to entropy change of main stream.

TABLE 7-2. TABLE OF INFLUENCE COEFFICIENTS; †

	$\dfrac{dA}{A}$	$\dfrac{dT_0}{T_0}$
$\dfrac{d\mathrm{M}^2}{\mathrm{M}^2}$	$-\dfrac{2\left(1 + \dfrac{k-1}{2}\,\mathrm{M}^2\right)}{1 - \mathrm{M}^2}$	$\dfrac{(1 + k\mathrm{M}^2)\left(1 + \dfrac{k-1}{2}\,\mathrm{M}^2\right)}{1 - \mathrm{M}^2}$
$\dfrac{dV}{V}$	$-\dfrac{1}{1 - \mathrm{M}^2}$	$\dfrac{1 + \dfrac{k-1}{2}\,\mathrm{M}^2}{1 - \mathrm{M}^2}$
$\dfrac{dc}{c}$	$\dfrac{\dfrac{k-1}{2}\,\mathrm{M}^2}{1 - \mathrm{M}^2}$	$\dfrac{\dfrac{1 - k\mathrm{M}^2}{2}\left(1 + \dfrac{k-1}{2}\,\mathrm{M}^2\right)}{1 - \mathrm{M}^2}$
$\dfrac{dT}{T}$	$\dfrac{(k-1)\mathrm{M}^2}{1 - \mathrm{M}^2}$	$\dfrac{(1 - k\mathrm{M}^2)\left(1 + \dfrac{k-1}{2}\,\mathrm{M}^2\right)}{1 - \mathrm{M}^2}$
$\dfrac{d\rho}{\rho}$	$\dfrac{\mathrm{M}^2}{1 - \mathrm{M}^2}$	$-\dfrac{1 + \dfrac{k-1}{2}\,\mathrm{M}^2}{1 - \mathrm{M}^2}$
$\dfrac{dp}{p}$	$\dfrac{k\mathrm{M}^2}{1 - \mathrm{M}^2}$	$-\dfrac{k\mathrm{M}^2\left(1 + \dfrac{k-1}{2}\,\mathrm{M}^2\right)}{1 - \mathrm{M}^2}$
$\dfrac{dp_0}{p_0}$	0	$-\dfrac{k\mathrm{M}^2}{2}$
$\dfrac{dF}{F}$	$\dfrac{1}{1 + k\mathrm{M}^2}$	0
$\dfrac{ds}{c_p}$	0	$1 + \dfrac{k-1}{2}\,\mathrm{M}^2$

† Tables of numerical values of the influence coefficients appear in the Design Data Section of *J. Appl. Mechanics*, vol. 14, no. 4, December, 1947, in the paper Tables for

CONSTANT SPECIFIC HEAT AND MOLECULAR WEIGHT

	$4f\dfrac{dx}{D} + \dfrac{dX}{\frac{1}{2}kpAM^2} - 2y\dfrac{dw}{w}$	$\dfrac{dw}{w}$
$\dfrac{dM^2}{M^2}$	$\dfrac{kM^2\left(1 + \dfrac{k-1}{2}M^2\right)}{1 - M^2}$	$\dfrac{2(1 + kM^2)\left(1 + \dfrac{k-1}{2}M^2\right)}{1 - M^2}$
$\dfrac{dV}{V}$	$\dfrac{kM^2}{2(1 - M^2)}$	$\dfrac{1 + kM^2}{1 - M^2}$
$\dfrac{dc}{c}$	$-\dfrac{k(k-1)M^4}{4(1 - M^2)}$	$-\dfrac{\dfrac{k-1}{2}M^2(1 + kM^2)}{1 - M^2}$
$\dfrac{dT}{T}$	$-\dfrac{k(k-1)M^4}{2(1 - M^2)}$	$-\dfrac{(k-1)M^2(1 + kM^2)}{1 - M^2}$
$\dfrac{d\rho}{\rho}$	$-\dfrac{kM^2}{2(1 - M^2)}$	$-\dfrac{(k+1)M^2}{1 - M^2}$
$\dfrac{dp}{p}$	$-\dfrac{kM^2[1 + (k-1)M^2]}{2(1 - M^2)}$	$-\dfrac{2kM^2\left(1 + \dfrac{k-1}{2}M^2\right)}{1 - M^2}$
$\dfrac{dp_0}{p_0}$	$-\dfrac{kM^2}{2}$	$-kM^2$
$\dfrac{dF}{F}$	$-\dfrac{kM^2}{2(1 + kM^2)}$	0
$\dfrac{ds}{c_p}$	$\dfrac{(k-1)M^2}{2}$	$(k-1)M^2$

Numerical Solution of Problems in the Mechanics and Thermodynamics of Steady One-dimensional Gas Flow without Discontinuities, by G. M. Edelman and A. H. Shapiro.

first column with respect to the variable in the head.   There is no need to use an influence coefficient in its entirety if some of the phenomena accounted for are not involved in the problem at hand.

In most problems the initial conditions are given as well as certain prescribed variations of the various parameters.   In turn it is desired to determine the properties at some point in the stream.   In order to accomplish the latter we can integrate the differential equation either analytically, numerically, or graphically, depending on which is most convenient.   For a complicated equation, this is obviously not a simple matter, and it may be necessary to use an electronic computer.

Fortunately, in many gas-dynamic problems, the specific heat and the molecular weight remain essentially constant.   For these, Shapiro and Hawthorne have compiled another table incorporating influence coefficients for the logarithmic differential of the stagnation temperature.   This table is reproduced here in Table 7-2 and its use is similar to the preceding one.

In order to facilitate the numerical-integration process mentioned above, tables for numerical solutions developed by Edelman and Shapiro [9, 10] are also available in the literature.   Another generalized approach to the solution of compressible-fluid-flow problems has been developed by Kestin and Oppenheim [11] utilizing an entropy chart.   The effect of viscosity in one-dimensional flow is discussed by Kestin and Zaremba.[12]

PROBLEMS

7-1. If the velocity of approach is not negligible, will the critical pressure exist at the throat of a well-insulated, frictionless nozzle?

7-2. For isentropic flow in a convergent-divergent nozzle, will the Mach number be equal to unity at the throat if the velocity of approach is large?

7-3. Using Eqs. (7-7) and (7-10), carry out the steps leading to Eq. (7-11).

7-4. Using Eq. (7-7), prepare a graph using the flux as ordinate and the pressure ratio as abscissa for the range $0 < p/p_0 < 1$.   Does this computed curve agree with the Reynolds criterion?   Explain.

7-5. Would it be possible to use a converging nozzle as a flow regulator for applications in which the supply pressure is about twice the outlet pressure?   Explain.

7-6. Air expands adiabatically in a convergent-divergent nozzle from a pressure of 73.5 psig to a pressure of 35.2 psia.   The temperature of the air entering the nozzle is 1200°R.   The nozzle efficiency is 0.90.   Using the air tables, find (a) the velocity at the mouth of the nozzle, (b) the temperature at the mouth of the nozzle, (c) the change in entropy across the nozzle, and (d) the Mach number at the mouth of the nozzle.

7-7. One pound of dry air expands isothermally at 1000°R through a pressure ratio of 6:1.   (a) Find the change in entropy.   (b) Find the enthalpy.   (c) Find the volume.

7-8. One pound of air expands isentropically through a nozzle.   The initial temperature is 1600°R and the pressure ratio is 6:1.   Find the final temperature.

7-9. Referring to Fig. 7-5 of this chapter, discuss qualitatively the velocity (subacoustic, acoustic, superacoustic) for the case when the exit pressure is at (e), (e'), and

(e''). Will the velocity be supersonic anywhere in the nozzle? What will it be at the exit?

7-10. Show that for reversible adiabatic expansion in a nozzle

$$- V\,dV = dh$$

in which h is the enthalpy, $h = u + pv$.

7-11. Show that for isothermal flow in a nozzle

$$- V\,dV = dF$$

in which F is the Gibbs free-energy function, $F = h - Ts$.

7-12. Explain why there will be efflux from a nozzle which exhausts into a pressure higher than the design exit pressure.

7-13. In the derivation of Eq. (7-10), explain why the ratio G'/A has a maximum and not a minimum.

7-14. Outline the requirements for flow acceleration or deceleration for convergent sections, for divergent sections, and for subsonic and supersonic flow when the flow is isothermal.

REFERENCES

1. Saenger, E.: "Raketen-flugtechnik," R. Oldenbourg, Berlin, 1933.
2. Randolph, J. R.: Isothermal Expansion in Nozzles, *J. Am. Rocket Soc.*, no. 74, p. 71, June, 1948.
3. Cambel, Ali Bulent: Gas-turbine Power Plant for Aircraft, *J. Aeronaut. Sci.*, vol. 19, no. 11, p. 791, November, 1952.
4. Seifert, H. S., and D. Altman: A Comparison of Adiabatic and Isothermal Expansion Processes in Rocket Nozzles, *J. Am. Rocket Soc.*, vol. 22, no. 3, p. 159, May–June, 1952.
5. Keenan, Joseph H., and Joseph Kaye: "Gas Tables," p. 139, John Wiley & Sons, Inc., New York, 1948.
6. Summerfield, Martin: Fundamental Problems in Rocket Research, *J. Am. Rocket Soc.*, no. 81, p. 79, June, 1950.
7. Romer, I. Carl, Jr., and Ali Bulent Cambel: Analysis of Isothermal Variable Area Flow, *Aircraft Eng.*, vol. 27, no. 322, p. 398, December, 1955.
8. Shapiro, A. H., and W. R. Hawthorne: The Mechanics and Thermodynamics of Steady, One-dimensional Gas Flow, *J. Appl. Mechanics*, vol. 14, no. 4, p. A-317, 1947.
9. Edelman, G. M., and A. H. Shapiro: Tables for Numerical Solution of Problems in the Mechanics and Thermodynamics of Steady One-dimensional Gas Flow without Discontinuities, *J. Appl. Mechanics*, vol. 14, p. A-344, 1947.
10. Shapiro, A. H., and G. M. Edelman: Tables for Numerical Solutions of Problems in Compressible Gas Flow with Energy Effects, *J. Appl. Mechanics*, vol. 15, p. A-169, 1948.
11. Kestin, J., and A. K. Oppenheim: The Calculation of Compressible Fluid Flow by the Use of a Generalized Entropy Chart, *Inst. Mech. Engrs. (London), Proc.*, vol. 159, WEP no. 43, p. 313, 1948.
12. Kestin, J., and S. K. Zaremba: One-dimensional High-speed Flows, *Aircraft Eng.*, June, 1953.

CHAPTER 8

THERMOCHEMISTRY

8-1. Introduction. Combustion may be defined as a chemical reaction during which thermal energy is liberated. It is therefore an exothermic reaction in contrast to an endothermic reaction, which is one during which heat is absorbed. An explosion is a combustion process usually taking place so rapidly as to be uncontrolled. Its inception may take place by design or by mischance.

An exothermic reaction may be written in symbolic form as

$$aA + bB \rightleftharpoons cC + dD + \Delta_r \qquad (8\text{-}1)$$

In this equation the capital letters indicate the symbol of the compound or element whereas the lower-case letters represent the number of moles. In turn Δ_r denotes the heat of reaction. The number of moles need not remain constant in a process. Thus in the combustion reaction

$$CO + \tfrac{1}{2}O_2 \rightarrow CO_2$$

there are $1\tfrac{1}{2}$ moles of reactants and only 1 mole of product, resulting in a decrease in the number of moles. The heat of reaction is equal to the change in enthalpy during combustion processes which take place at constant pressure. If the reaction is a combustion process, the heat of reaction is called the *heat of combustion*. For a constant-pressure process the heat of combustion is equal to the difference of the enthalpy of the products and the enthalpy of the reactants. If a conventional fuel is participating in the combustion process, the heat of combustion is the same as the heating value of the fuel, but although these are numerically equal to one another, their signs are opposite. The heating value is always a positive number, whereas the change in enthalpy for a combustion reaction which begins and ends at standard temperature and pressure is always negative.

In using tabulated data, care must be taken that no inconsistencies are introduced because of different reference points. In general, chemists use 25°C (77°F) and 1 atm pressure as the standard, whereas engineers frequently use 59 or 60°F and 1 atm pressure as the standard condition. This difference is liable to cause an error if an inconsistent basis is taken and the heating value for a certain fuel is set equal to the heat of reaction or the

148

change in enthalpy for the reaction. However, such inconsistencies can be remedied by applying a correction keeping in mind that both the temperature and the pressure must be the same before and after the reaction. It should be realized, however, that in combustion processes not only is the state defined by pressure and temperature, but in addition the composition must be specified. Furthermore, the composition may require the definition of several additional variables.

The heat of combustion can be determined by experiment or by computation. If the latter method is to be employed it is necessary to know the heats of formation of the reactants and the products. The heat of formation, to be denoted by Δ_f, is the heat absorbed or released when a compound is formed from its constituents. It is the change in enthalpy taking place during the formation reaction. It may be positive or negative, depending on the compound under consideration. Using the heats of formation, the heat of reaction may be found by the following equation:

$$\Delta_r = \Sigma n(\Delta_f)_{\text{products}} - \Sigma n(\Delta_f)_{\text{reactants}} \qquad (8\text{-}2)$$

in which n denotes the number of moles. The heat of formation may be based on almost any arbitrary datum, but it is customary to specify it at 77°F. Table A-6 (from reference 1) lists heats of formation and heats of combustion for various chemical species. In the literature, tables list the thermodynamic properties in either Btu per pound mole or calories per gram mole, or kilocalories per kilogram mole. Note that

$$1 \text{ cal/g mole} = 1.8 \text{ Btu/lb mole}$$

A chemical reaction will carry to completion only if certain definite ratios of reactants are involved. This follows from the *law of definite proportions* (also called the *law of combining weights*), which states: Different elements combine in fixed and definite proportions by weight. The weight ratios involved are rarely whole numbers but the ratios of the atoms or molecules reacting are always integers.

8-2. Heating Values. Two important heating values are in use, the higher or gross heating value (HHV), and the lower or net heating value (LHV). In a combustion process, the fuel may contain moisture and hydrogen. When hydrogen combines with oxygen, water vapor is formed. If the temperature is such that the water vapor can condense, then the heat of condensation (latent heat of evaporation) will also be liberated, and the higher heating value is released; whereas if the temperature is so high that the moisture does not condense, then the heat of vaporization (condensation) cannot be realized. The higher heating value differs from the lower heating by a latent heat of vaporization which in many engineering problems can be rounded off to 1050 Btu/lb of water vapor condensed. In constant-pressure calorimeters where much of the moisture does not condense, the LHV or a hybrid value is obtained. In constant-volume calorimeters like the oxygen-bomb calorimeter, essentially all of the moisture condenses and the HHV is obtained directly from the readings.

In computing heats of formation and heats of reaction, the enthalpies for various species must be known, and some of these are listed in Table A-7 (from reference 1).

Example 1. Find the heat of formation of H_2O (liquid) at $300°K$.
Solution. The combustion equation for gaseous hydrogen is

$$H_2(g) + \tfrac{1}{2}O_2(g) \rightarrow H_2O(g) + \Delta_f$$

At $300°K$ the enthalpy of H_2 is 59,145, the enthalpy of $\tfrac{1}{2}O_2$ is $\tfrac{1}{2} \times 2,077 = 1,038$, and the enthalpy of H_2O is 2,380. Then

$$59,145 + 1,038 \rightarrow 2,380 + \Delta_f$$

Then the heat of formation of H_2O is $\Delta_f = 57,803$ cal/g mole for gaseous reactants and products.

To convert to engineering units, $57,803 \times 1.8 = 104,000$ Btu/lb mole for gaseous reactants and products. For H_2O in condensed or liquid state add the latent heat of condensation for the 18 lb in a mole, or $1,050 \times 18 = 18,900$ Btu/lb mole, and $104,000 + 18,900 = 122,900$ Btu/lb mole $H_2O(l)$.

Also, $122,900/1.8 = 68,300$ cal/g mole $H_2O(l)$, which agrees with Table A-6.

For combustion products such as CO_2 and H_2O, the respective heats of formation and the heats of combustion are equal numerically but are opposite in sign. The heat of formation is considered negative, and the heat of combustion is positive.

Example 2. Find the heat of combustion from the heat of formation for ethyl alcohol at $300°K$ and 1 atm.
Solution. At $300°K$ the enthalpy of C_2H_5OH is computed as follows, using Table A-7:

$$2C + 3H_2 + \tfrac{1}{2}O_2 \rightarrow C_2H_5OH$$

Enthalpy of 2C is $2 \times 94,224$............ 188,448
Enthalpy of $3H_2$ is $3 \times 59,145$............. 177,435
Enthalpy of $\tfrac{1}{2}O_2$ is $\tfrac{1}{2} \times 2,077$............ 1,038

                                                   _____
                                                   366,921

From this we must subtract the heat of formation of C_2H_5OH, which is 67,140, or

$$366,921 - 67,140 = 299,781 \text{ cal/g mole}$$

which equals the enthalpy of C_2H_5OH at $300°K$.

$$C_2H_5OH + 3O_2 \rightarrow 2CO_2 + 3H_2O$$

Heat of combustion $= \Sigma\,H_{\text{products}} - \Sigma\,H_{\text{reactants}}$

Enthalpy of $3O_2$ is $3 \times 2,077$................ 6,231
Enthalpy of $2CO_2$ is $2 \times 2,256$.............. 4,512
Enthalpy of $3H_2O$ is $3 \times 2,380$.............. 7,140

$299,781 + 6,231 = 306,012$ enthalpy of reactants

$4,512 + 7,140 = 11,652$ enthalpy of products

Thus

$$306,012 - 11,652 = 294,360 \text{ cal/g mole}$$

is the net heat of combustion.

Gross heat of combustion = net heat + latent heat

The latent heat of 3 moles of H_2O is $3 \times 18 \times 1,050$ Btu/lb mole, or $56,700/1.8 = 31,500$ cal/g mole. Thus

$$\text{Gross heating value} = 294,360 + 31,500$$

$$= 325,860 \text{ cal/g mole}$$

Example 3. Find the heat of formation of C_2H_5OH from its heat of combustion.
Solution

$$C_2H_5OH + 3O_2 \rightarrow 2CO_2 + 3H_2O(g) + 294,360$$

Enthalpy of C_2H_5OH at $300°K$............ 366,921
Enthalpy of $3O_2$ at $300°K$................. 6,231
Enthalpy of $2CO_2$ at $300°K$............... 4,512
Enthalpy of $3H_2O$ at $300°K$............... 7,140

$$366,921 + 6,231 = 4,512 + 7,140 + 294,360 + \Delta_f$$

$$\Delta_f = 67,140 \text{ cal/g mole}$$

In actual engines the enthalpy with which the reactants enter the combustion chamber may be higher than the enthalpy computed from tables. This is because the enthalpy increase due to pumping is not included in the theoretical calculations.

The heating value of fuels is determined by calorimetric experiments and these may be made either at constant pressure or at constant volume. Consider first a constant-volume calorimeter in which no work of any kind occurs; then the first law of thermodynamics can be written as

$$Q_v = \Delta E \tag{8-3}$$

The change in internal energy is determined if the internal energy is known for the mixture (reactants) and the products. The energy of the mixture is the sum of the sensible internal energy E_{sm} and the chemical energy E_{ch}, namely,

$$E = E_{sm} + E_{ch} \tag{8-4}$$

The internal energy of the products is made up of the sensible internal energy, namely, E_{sp}. Therefore, the heat liberated in a constant-volume process is

$$Q_v = E_{sp} - (E_{sm} + E_{ch}) \tag{8-5}$$

For constant-pressure combustion similar relations may be written, but enthalpies must be used instead of the internal energies. Thus the heat liberated in a constant-pressure reaction is

$$Q_p = H_{sp} - (H_{sm} + U_{ch}) \tag{8-6}$$

$$Q_p = U_{sp} + (pv')_p - [U_{sm} + (pv')_m + U_{ch}] \tag{8-7}$$

where v' is the molar volume. (It can be demonstrated that the heat liberated in a steady-flow combustion process is expressed by an equation like the one defining constant-pressure combustion. The proof of this is left to the student in Prob. 8-22.)

The difference in the two heating values would be

$$Q_p - Q_v = (pv')_p - (pv')_m \tag{8-8}$$

which for a perfect gas becomes

$$Q_p - Q_v = (nRT)_p - (nRT)_m \tag{8-9}$$

where n is the number of moles.

8-3. Equilibrium Constant. When a thermochemical reaction is initiated it takes place at a certain rate which gradually decreases as the concentration of the reactants decreases. The relation between the rate of a reaction and the concentration of the reactants is expressed by the law of mass action enunciated by Guldberg and Waage in 1879. This law is usually stated: "The rate of a reaction is proportional to the active concentration of the constituents." By concentration is meant the number of moles in a unit volume. It should be noted that the active concentration is usually less than the molar concentration. The concentrations of the reactants and products at the equilibrium point are called the *equilibrium concentrations*. Certain reactions which may take place in either direction, depending on how they are driven, are said to be reversible.

The thermodynamic function known as *free energy* (F) and also as the *Gibbs thermodynamic potential* is of value in developing basic equilibrium theory. By definition

$$F = H - TS \tag{8-10}$$

and

$$dF = dH - T\,dS - S\,dT \tag{8-11}$$

where H = enthalpy (total)
$\quad\quad\ T$ = temperature
$\quad\quad\ S$ = entropy (total)

For a closed system, in which $p\,dv$ work but no shaft work is involved, the first law of thermodynamics appears as

$$dQ = dU + p\,dv$$

and for a reversible process this can be written as

$$T\,dS = dU + p\,dv \tag{8-12}$$

Introducing enthalpy $H = U + pv$,

$$T\,dS = dH - p\,dv - v\,dp + p\,dv \tag{8-13}$$

$$T\,dS = dH - v\,dp$$

Using this in Eq. (8-11),

$$dF = dH - T\,dS - S\,dT$$

$$= T\,dS + v\,dp - T\,dS - S\,dT$$

$$dF = v\,dp - S\,dT \tag{8-14}$$

For an isothermal process

$$dF = v\,dp \tag{8-15}$$

Consider the change in free energy for a perfect gas in an isothermal process, where with

$$v = \frac{RT}{p}$$

$$dF = RT\frac{dp}{p} \tag{8-16}$$

Integration between states 1 and 2 yields

$$F_2 - F_1 = \Delta F = RT\ln\frac{p_2}{p_1} \tag{8-17}$$

Considering the chemical reaction

$$aA + bB \rightleftharpoons cC + dD$$

we can write an expression for the free-energy change of each constituent, respectively, as

$$\Delta F_A = aRT\ln\left(\frac{p_2}{p_1}\right)_A \tag{8-18}$$

$$\Delta F_B = bRT\ln\left(\frac{p_2}{p_1}\right)_B \tag{8-18a}$$

$$\Delta F_C = cRT\ln\left(\frac{p_2}{p_1}\right)_C \tag{8-18b}$$

and

$$\Delta F_D = dRT\ln\left(\frac{p_2}{p_1}\right)_D \tag{8-18c}$$

The total change in free energy will be the net change between the component F_2 values (ΔF_2) and the component F_1 values (ΔF_1):

$$F_2 - F_1 = \Delta F_C + \Delta F_D - \Delta F_A - \Delta F_B \qquad (8\text{-}19)$$

$$= \Delta F_2 - \Delta F_1$$

and hence

$$\Delta F_2 - \Delta F_1 = cRT \ln\left(\frac{p_2}{p_1}\right)_C + dRT \ln\left(\frac{p_2}{p_1}\right)_D$$

$$- aRT \ln\left(\frac{p_2}{p_1}\right)_A - bRT \ln\left(\frac{p_2}{p_1}\right)_B. \qquad (8\text{-}20)$$

Rearranging terms, the following result is obtained:

$$\Delta F_2 - \Delta F_1 = RT\left[\ln \frac{(p_{2C})^c (p_{2D})^d}{(p_{2A})^a (p_{2B})^b} - \ln \frac{(p_{1C})^c (p_{1D})^d}{(p_{1A})^a (p_{1B})^b}\right] \qquad (8\text{-}21)$$

In searching for a standard state, let us arbitrarily take the reference state to be at point 1; then also let

$$p_{1A} = p_{1B} = p_{1C} = p_{1D} = 1$$

where 1 may be 1 atm, 1 psi, 1 mm Hg, or any convenient and consistent datum pressure. Accordingly,

$$\ln \frac{(p_{1C})^c (p_{1D})^d}{(p_{1A})^a (p_{1B})^b} = 0 \qquad (8\text{-}22)$$

Thus we can write, for a perfect gas undergoing an isothermal process, that

$T = \text{Const}$

$$\Delta F_2 - \Delta F_1 = RT \ln \frac{(p_{2C})^c (p_{2D})^d}{(p_{2A})^a (p_{2B})^b} \qquad (8\text{-}23)$$

If a reversible process takes place isothermally and no shaft work is involved there will be no change in the free energy; thus $\Delta F_2 = 0$. Further, since we are considering the equilibrium state to be at point 2, then ΔF_2 must necessarily also equal zero. Thus ΔF_1 or, as it is more usually called, ΔF^0 appears as

$$-\Delta F^0 = RT \ln \frac{(p_{2C})^c (p_{2D})^d}{(p_{2A})^a (p_{2B})^b} \qquad (8\text{-}24)$$

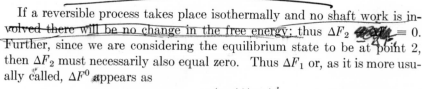

$$e^{-\Delta F^0/RT} = \frac{(p_{2C})^c (p_{2D})^d}{(p_{2A})^a (p_{2B})^b} = K_p = K_2 \qquad (8\text{-}25)$$

Now ΔF^0 or ΔF_1 was set at a constant-pressure state and thus Eq. (8-25) represents what is called the pressure-equilibrium constant. It has been evaluated for numerous chemical species at various temperatures, and data can be found in Fig. 8-1 (from reference 2) as well as many places in the technical literature.

Nearly all processes are controlled in some manner by what might be called *rate equations.* Thus we might say that a certain process proceeds

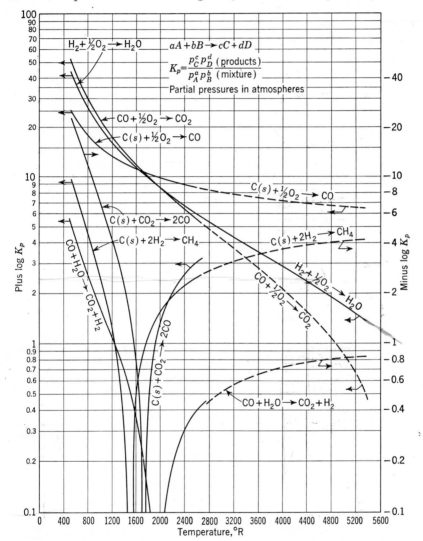

FIG. 8-1. Equilibrium constants. (*E. F. Obert, "Thermodynamics," McGraw-Hill Book Company, Inc., New York, 1948. Solid lines—American Petroleum Institute Research Project 44, table 1y, 0y, National Bureau of Standards, Washington, D.C., Aug. 31, 1944, and Aug. 31, 1946. Dashed lines—B. Lewis and G. von Elbe, "Combustion Flames and Explosions of Gases," table II, Cambridge University Press, New York, 1938.*)

at a rate which is directly proportional to the available potential and indirectly proportional to the resistance hindering the progress of the process. For the linear case, this can be written as follows:

$$\text{Rate} \propto \frac{\text{potential}}{\text{resistance}} \qquad (8\text{-}26)$$

Introduce a proportionality constant k, and

$$\text{Rate} = k \frac{\text{potential}}{\text{resistance}} \qquad (8\text{-}27)$$

It should be recalled that not all cases are linear. In Eq. (8-27), k is called the _specific-reaction-rate constant_.† For many thermal processes, k is a function of temperature. In general, chemical reactions proceed in both directions. Accordingly, consider now a reversible reaction as follows:

$$aA + bB \rightleftharpoons cC + dD \qquad (8\text{-}28)$$

At the start the reaction may progress rapidly from left to right under the influences represented by the law of mass action. However, as soon as products form, a reaction in the opposite direction also develops. Eventually the corresponding rates of both reactions become equal and the reaction process is said to be in equilibrium. At equilibrium, the rate of formation of products and of decomposition is the same, and we can write

$$\text{Rate} = \text{rate}$$
$$\xrightarrow{\hspace{1cm}} \qquad \xleftarrow{\hspace{1cm}}$$

Then

$$\overset{}{\underset{\rightarrow}{(k)}} \frac{(\text{potential})_{A \text{ and } B}}{\underset{\longrightarrow}{\text{Resistance}}} = \overset{}{\underset{\leftarrow}{(k)}} \frac{(\text{potential})_{B \text{ and } C}}{\underset{\longleftarrow}{\text{resistance}}}$$

$$\frac{\underset{\rightarrow\leftarrow}{k \text{ resistance}}}{\underset{\leftarrow\longrightarrow}{k \text{ resistance}}} = \frac{(\text{potential})_{B \text{ and } C}}{(\text{potential})_{A \text{ and } B}} = K \qquad (8\text{-}29)$$

The free-energy function F is called a _potential function_, because when its value decreases a change in that direction would be spontaneous. For example, if we know the value of F in state 1 (F_1), and also know the value of F in state 2 (F_2), we can say that a reaction may spontaneously occur from 1 to 2 if $F_1 > F_2$, that is, in the direction of free-energy decrease. Note that $dF = 0$ at constant temperature and pressure from Eq. (8-14).

† The specific-reaction-rate constant is sometimes called the _velocity coefficient_ or simply the _coefficient_.

To extend the scope of Eqs. (8-21) and (8-24) to cases where the perfect-gas concept is not applicable, Lewis † introduced the concepts of *fugacity* and *activity*.   For an isothermal process

SKIP

$$dF = v \, dp \qquad (8-15)$$

and with a perfect gas, by Eq. (8-16),

$$dF = RT \frac{dp}{p} = RT \, d(\ln p) \qquad (8-16)$$

For the general case of a nonideal gas, Lewis introduced the fugacity f, defined thus:

$$dF = RT \, d(\ln f) = v \, dp \qquad (8-30)$$

Integrating at constant temperature between two states at different pressures and taking p^0 as the pressure in an arbitrary standard state,

$$F - F^0 = RT \ln \frac{f}{f^0} = \int_{p^0}^{p} v \, dp \qquad (8-31)$$

For convenience we consider fugacity to be equal to pressure when the substance is at sufficiently low pressure to be in the state of an ideal gas.   A reference point can nearly always be taken under these conditions, and then $f^0 = p^0$.   The pressure selected is frequently assumed to be 1 atm, although 0.1 atm or 0.01 atm would be more rigorously correct.   When $f^0 = p^0 = 1$, Eq. (8-30) becomes

$$\ln f = \frac{1}{RT} \int v \, dp \qquad (8-32)$$

Lewis defined the term *activity* as

$$a = \frac{f}{f^0} \qquad (8-33)$$

and in terms of activity, Eq. (8-31) becomes

$$F - F^0 = RT \ln a \qquad (8-34)$$

Start with Eq. (8-24) and consider the problem of equilibrium at constant pressure and temperature.   For this equilibrium to hold, the total free-energy change must be zero, and in terms of the number of reactants and products, namely, a, b and c, d, we can write as follows:

$$aF_A + bF_B - cF_C - dF_D = 0 \qquad (8-35)$$

† See, for example, reference 3, 4, or 5.

By Eq. (8-33) if we refer to a standard state $F_i{}^0$ for each reactant and product, then

$$(F - F^0)_i = RT \ln a_i \qquad (8\text{-}36)$$

$$F_i = RT \ln a_i - F_i{}^0 \qquad (8\text{-}37)$$

Substituting in Eq. (8-29),

$$a(RT \ln a_A - F_A{}^0) + b(RT \ln a_B - F_B{}^0) - c(RT \ln a_C - F_C{}^0)$$

$$- d(RT \ln a_D - F_D{}^0) = 0$$

$$RT(a \ln a_A + b \ln a_B - c \log a_C - d \log a_D) + aF_A{}^0 + bF_B{}^0$$

$$- cF_C{}^0 - dF_D{}^0 = 0 \quad (8\text{-}38)$$

This can be reduced to the following form if the F^0 product terms are represented symbolically by ΔF^0:

$$\frac{a_C{}^c a_D{}^d}{a_A{}^a a_B{}^b} = e^{-\Delta F^0/RT} \qquad (8\text{-}39)$$

The value F^0 is based on a definite pressure and concentration state and is thus a function of temperature only. As stated before, it is called the *equilibrium constant* at constant pressure:

$$e^{-\Delta F^0/RT} = \frac{a_C{}^c a_D{}^d}{a_A{}^a a_B{}^b} = K_a \qquad (8\text{-}40)$$

$$\Delta F^0 = -RT \ln K_a \qquad (8\text{-}41)$$

If Eq. (8-40) is compared with Eq. (8-24) it can be seen that for the ideal gas the partial pressures and activities are equivalent, and $K_p = K_2 = K_a$. For many cases involving combustion the equivalence of K_p and K_a is assumed to hold.

8-4. Spontaneity of Thermochemical Reactions. In thermochemical computations the engineer is concerned with whether or not a reaction is feasible, or whether it will proceed in a stipulated manner. In searching for useful criteria on the spontaneity of a reaction, the application of certain thermodynamic functions appears to be a good starting point.

Consider first internal energy as a criterion for the spontaneity of a reaction which proceeds from state 1 to state 2. Because internal energy is a point function we might write $\Delta E_{1 \to 2} = -\Delta E_{2 \to 1}$. This states that the internal-energy change has a certain value in some direction, but it does not state in which direction the reaction will take place. We cannot depend on the sign of the internal-energy change because in some reactions it is positive and in others it is negative. The same stipulations are true of the enthalpy change, because in some processes it is positive and in others it is negative. Hence, like internal energy, enthalpy is not a suitable criterion in determining the spontaneity of a reaction. At this point it might be observed that the above conclusion could have been surmised a priori because both the internal energy and the enthalpy are consequences of the first law. This law is obeyed in all applications, but it never supplies information regarding possible direction of change.

The entropy of the system and the surroundings taken together can yield invaluable information about direction of change. Thus if the change in entropy is positive in a certain reaction, the reaction can take place in that direction. However, although it is possible for the reaction to take place if the entropy change is positive, it does not mean that the reaction must take place.

The Gibbs, or free-energy, function is also most useful in studies of chemical equilibrium. In this connection, for preliminary analyses of the feasibility of a reaction proceeding under conditions of the same temperature and pressure at the initial and final conditions, the following tabulation can be used as a guide:

1. If $\Delta F^0 < 0$, the reaction is possible spontaneously.

2. If $\Delta F^0 = 0$, the reaction is reversible.

3. If $\Delta F^0 > 0$, the reaction is impossible, except that a reaction which is impossible at standard conditions may, in certain cases, be made to proceed by altering the equilibrium point as by superposition of a higher temperature or pressure.

Chemical equilibrium is that condition at which a chemical reaction and its reverse take place at the same speed, and thus the concentrations of the reactants and of the products remain the same. The state of chemical equilibrium is essentially a final stage rather than an initial one, and truly is reached asymptotically. Chemical equilibrium and the rate of chemical reactions have certain things in common, but they are not the same. Equilibrium is a state, and hence can be treated by thermodynamic laws and principles. On the other hand, the rate of a reaction cannot be treated thermodynamically because it does not constitute equilibrium. Whether or not equilibrium can be reached within a practicable period of time depends on the rate of the reaction. A chemical reaction may or may not be practicable depending on whether or not it is too close to the equilibrium state, and also depending on its rate. The proximity to equilibrium may be varied by changing the pressure, the temperature, or the relative concentration of the constituents. These same variables may be altered to vary the reaction rate, and in addition catalysts may be used to accelerate the reaction. Further reference will be made to possible variants later in this chapter.

8-5. Stoichiometry. The equilibrium constant may be used to great advantage in many instances. One application is in stoichiometric calculations. In general, these must precede energy balances. To illustrate this application of the equilibrium constant consider the explosion of cellulose nitrate. Write its chemical reaction as follows:

$$C_{24}H_{30}O_{20}(NO_2)_{10} \rightleftharpoons aCO_2 + bCO + cH_2O + dH_2 + eN_2 \quad (8\text{-}42)$$

In order to solve the equation completely it is necessary to find a, b, c, d, and e. For this purpose write respectively a carbon balance, an oxygen balance, a hydrogen balance, and a nitrogen balance. Thus

$$a + b = 24$$

$$a + \frac{b}{2} + \frac{c}{2} = 20$$

$$c + d = 15$$

$$e = 5$$

There are now four equations but five unknowns. The necessary fifth equation may be obtained by writing the water-gas reaction. Thus

$$CO_2 + H_2 \rightleftharpoons H_2O + CO \quad (8\text{-}43)$$

for which the equilibrium constant K_p would appear from Eq. (8-25) as

$$K_p = \frac{p_{CO}p_{H_2O}}{p_{CO_2}p_{H_2}} \quad (8\text{-}44)$$

or, as partial pressures in a gas are proportional to molal concentrations,

$$K_p = \frac{bc}{ad} \quad (8\text{-}45)$$

The value of K_p is easily found from Fig. 8-1 as soon as the reaction temperature is stated, and then with five equations the five unknowns can be determined with relative ease by solving the simultaneous equations.

Example 4. Find the molal products resulting from the explosion of cellulose nitrate, if the explosion is considered to take place at 4000°F.

Solution. Use the four simultaneous equations involving a, b, c, d, and e which follow Eq. (8-42).

For water-gas reaction [Eqs. (8-43) and (8-44)], log K_p from Fig. 8-1 at 4460°R is −0.78.

$$\log K_p = -0.78 = 9.2200 - 10$$

$$K_p = 0.1657 \equiv 0.166$$

Then from Eq. (8-45)

$$bc = 0.166ad$$

Solving the five equations simultaneously it is found that

$$a = 13.41 \qquad b = 10.59 \qquad c = 2.59 \qquad d = 12.41 \qquad e = 5$$

Thus

$$C_{24}H_{30}O_{20}(NO_2)_{10} \rightleftharpoons 13.41CO_2 + 10.59CO + 2.59H_2O + 12.41H_2 + 5N_2$$

The stoichiometry of hydrocarbon fuels may be determined similarly, but it is necessary that one know the resulting products of combustion in order to be able to set up the stoichiometric equations. For a chemically correct mixture of a hydrocarbon fuel and air the following chemical equation can be written:

$$\text{Hydrocarbon} + bO_2 + 3.76 \times bN_2 \rightarrow cCO_2 + dH_2O + b \times 3.76N_2$$

There are actually two unknowns in this reaction although four elements take part in it. Consequently, the stoichiometric calculations may be performed with ease. In the case of lean and rich mixtures the calculations, though still easy, are a little bit more complicated. Thus, for a rich mixture of hydrocarbon fuel and air the chemical equation will probably be

$$\text{Hydrocarbon} + bO_2 + 3.76 \times bN_2$$

$$\rightarrow cCO_2 + dH_2O + eCO + fH_2 + 3.76 \times bN_2$$

There are then five unknowns, namely, b, c, d, e, and f, but only four elements enter the reaction. Thus a fifth equation is necessary, and one may use the water-gas reaction as before if its equilibrium constant is known. In the case of lean mixtures the chemical reaction will probably be as follows:

$$\text{Hydrocarbon} + bO_2 + 3.76 \times bN_2$$

$$\rightarrow cCO_2 + dH_2O + eCO + fH_2 + gO_2 + 3.76 \times bN_2$$

There are still four elements and thus four equations, but the number of unknowns has risen to six. Therefore it is expedient to consider other auxiliary reactions for which the equilibrium constants are known. One may choose for this particular case any two of the following three, for example:

$$CO + \tfrac{1}{2}O_2 \rightleftharpoons CO_2 \tag{8-46}$$

$$H_2 + \tfrac{1}{2}O_2 \rightleftharpoons H_2O \tag{8-47}$$

and the water-gas reaction which has already been mentioned,

$$H_2O + CO \rightleftharpoons CO_2 + H_2 \tag{8-43}$$

At high temperatures, such as those commonly encountered in rocket motors and other jet-propulsive devices, the above equations are no longer

valid because the products of combustion contain not only the more important components but also traces of other reaction products such as free
carbon, C; methane, CH_4; ammonia, NH_3; cyanogen, C_2N_2; ozone, O_3; hydroxyl, OH; and monatomic hydrogen and oxygen, H and O, respectively.
They may also contain nitrous and nitric oxide, NO and NO_2, respectively.
Although the procedure to be followed in computing the stoichiometry of
such reactions is essentially the same as before, it is much more tedious.
Such calculations may be facilitated by first considering only the important products, thus reaching an approximate solution. The minor components are then considered to yield more refined results.

8-6. Gibbs-Helmholtz, Planck Equations and Dissociation. In considering changes in free energy it is usually implied that the process takes
place in such a manner that the pressure and temperature are the same at
the initial and final states. This reminder and Eqs. (8-39) and (8-40), derived in Sec. 8-3, suggest that the equilibrium constant should depend on
the temperature. In this section it will be established that the equilibrium
constant is a function of temperature only. Let us develop this by noting
that the free energy F is

$$F = H - TS = E + pv - TS \qquad (8\text{-}10)$$

Differentiating,

$$dF = dE + p\,dv + v\,dp - T\,dS - S\,dT$$

but in a reversible process

$$dE + p\,dv = T\,dS$$

Therefore

$$dF = -S\,dT + v\,dp$$

and under conditions of constant pressure

$$\left(\frac{\partial F}{\partial T}\right)_p = -S$$

This equation is one of the so-called *Gibbs-Helmholtz relations*, and from
Eq. (8-10) it also follows that

$$\left(\frac{\partial F}{\partial T}\right)_p = -S = \frac{F - H}{T}$$

The so-called *Planck potential* ϕ is defined as

$$\phi = \frac{F}{T} = \frac{H - TS}{T} \qquad (8\text{-}48)$$

Differentiating the right-hand members of Eq. (8-48),

$$\frac{dF}{T} - \frac{F\,dT}{T^2} = \frac{dH}{T} - \frac{H\,dT}{T^2} - dS$$

$$T\,dF - F\,dT = T\,dH - H\,dT - T^2\,dS$$

$$= -H\,dT + T(dH - T\,dS)$$

But for a reversible process at constant pressure

$$dH - T\,dS = 0$$

and

$$T\,dF - F\,dT = (-H\,dT)_p$$

Dividing by T^2,

$$\frac{T\,dF - F\,dT}{T^2} = \left(-\frac{H\,dT}{T^2}\right)_p$$

$$\left[\frac{\partial}{\partial T}\left(\frac{F}{T}\right)\right]_p = -\frac{H}{T^2} = \left(\frac{\partial}{\partial T}\phi\right)_p \qquad (8\text{-}49)$$

By extension of Eq. (8-49),

$$\frac{\partial}{\partial T}(\Delta\phi)_p = -\frac{\Delta H}{T^2} \qquad (8\text{-}50)$$

For the Planck potential, using Eq. (8-41) or (8-25),

$$\Delta\phi^0 = \frac{\Delta F^0}{T} = -R\ln K_a \qquad (8\text{-}51)$$

Referring to Eq. (8-50),

$$\frac{\partial}{\partial T}(\Delta\phi^0)_p = \left[\frac{\partial}{\partial T}(-R\ln K_a)\right]_p = -\frac{\Delta H^0}{T^2}$$

Integration gives

$$\ln K = \int \frac{\Delta H^0}{RT^2}\,dT + I \qquad (8\text{-}52)$$

where I is a constant of integration.

The enthalpy of a gas integrated over a constant-pressure path is

$$H = \int c_p\,dT + H^0 \qquad (8\text{-}53)$$

As c_p for gases is primarily a function of temperature (see Table A-8) essentially independent of pressure at low and moderate values, say up to 300 psi, then it follows that H is a function of temperature. Similarly, H^0 (and

ΔH^0 for a collection of gases) should be a function of temperature. The value of ΔH^0 (and of ΔF^0) can be determined from heats of reaction and the value of the constant of integration I in Eq. (8-52) determined from such values of ΔH^0 and ΔF^0. Thus as the variables in Eq. (8-52) are functions of temperature, the equilibrium constant is also a function of temperature.

Example 5. Find the temperature at which H_2O becomes 5 per cent dissociated into hydrogen and oxygen at a pressure of 5 atm. The reaction is

$$H_2 + \tfrac{1}{2}O_2 \rightleftharpoons H_2O$$

Solution. Let x be the fraction of 1 mole of original H_2O which is dissociated. Then

$$xH_2 + \frac{x}{2}O_2 \rightleftharpoons (1-x)H_2O$$

and at equilibrium the total number of moles is

$$x + \frac{x}{2} + 1 - x = 1 + \frac{x}{2}$$

Accordingly, one may write for this problem

$$0.05H_2 + 0.025O_2 \rightleftharpoons 0.95H_2O$$

and the total number of moles is 1.025. The partial pressures of the constituents are

$$p_{H_2} = 5 \times \frac{0.05}{1.025} = 0.244 \text{ atm}$$

$$p_{O_2} = 5 \times \frac{0.025}{1.025} = 0.122 \text{ atm}$$

$$p_{H_2O} = 5 \times \frac{0.95}{1.025} = 4.64 \text{ atm}$$

The constant-pressure equilibrium constant is

$$K_p = \frac{p_{H_2O}}{(p_{H_2})(p_{O_2})^{1/2}} = \frac{4.64}{(0.244)(0.122)^{1/2}} = 54.3$$

and $\log 54.3 = 1.7348$. From Fig. 8-1 this corresponds to a temperature of about $4890°R$.

It was seen that the percentage dissociation of a reaction is found from the equilibrium constant. The larger the equilibrium constant, the greater will be the dissociation. On the other hand, the equilibrium constant increases with increasing temperature. Thus there is a temperature below which dissociation is not too important. Commonly this is considered to be below $4800°F$.

In a dissociation process, heat will be absorbed. Accordingly, dissociation requires energy, and therefore decreases the available energy. This results in a lowering of the exhaust velocity in the case of nozzles. On the other hand, the molecular weight of the products is lowered in dissociation, resulting in an increase of available energy. The former effect is more pronounced than the latter.

8-7. Order of Chemical Reactions. It has been stated that at least in principle all reactions are reversible, and further, that processes take place according to a rate equation. It has also been shown that in the equilibrium state, an equilibrium constant K_p can be defined as a consequence of the rate equation and the law of mass action.

According to the law of mass action, there is a definite relation between the concentration of the reactants and the rate of the reaction. The form of the relation is defined by the *order* of the reaction and the rate of a reaction taking place is related to the order of the reaction. Thus, a reaction is said to be of the nth order if it can be expressed by the expression

$$\frac{dc}{dt} = \pm kc^n \tag{8-54}$$

where c = molar concentration in moles per unit volume
$\quad t$ = time
$\quad k$ = reaction-rate constant

The negative sign holds when dc/dt is the time rate of decrease of the concentration, and the positive sign applies when dc/dt represents an increasing concentration.

There is little need to consider reactions of higher than third order because it is exceedingly improbable that more than three molecules would collide. If more than three molecules come into the picture one may divide the reaction into steps. Because many hydrocarbon reactions are approximately of the first order, these will be treated in brief detail here.

Consider a first-order reaction as follows:

$$A \rightarrow D + \cdots$$

According to Eq. (8-54) it follows that

$$\frac{d[A]}{dt} = -k[A]^1$$

Integrating,

$$\ln \frac{[A]}{[A_0]} = -kt \tag{8-55}$$

Equation (8-55) may be used to determine any of the terms k, t, or $[A]$.

In any decomposition relation, the half-time is of interest. Because the half-time decomposition refers to the time at which the actual concentration is one-half the original concentration we can write by Eq. (8-55)

$$t_{\frac{1}{2}} = \frac{1}{k} \ln 2$$

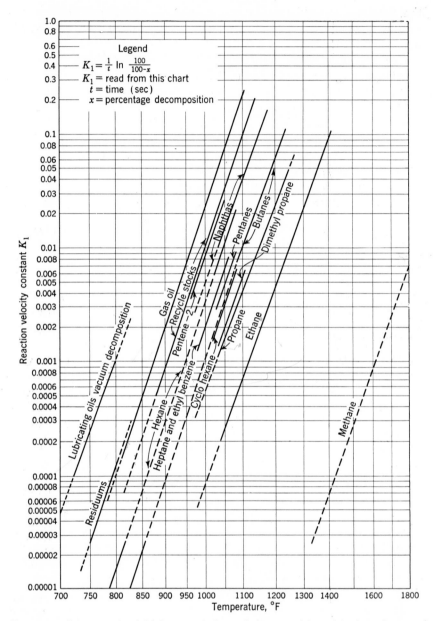

FIG. 8-2. Constants for initial rates of thermal decomposition of hydrocarbons and petroleum fractions. (*John Griswold, "Fuels, Combustion and Furnaces," McGraw-Hill Book Company, Inc., New York*, 1946.)

Now let $[X]$ be the concentration of a reagent stoichiometrically consistent with the amount of the product at time t. It follows from Eq. (8-55) that

$$\frac{d[X]}{dt} = k[A_0 - X]$$

Integration between $A_0 - X$ and A_0 yields

$$\ln \frac{[A_0]}{[A_0 - X]} = kt$$

Denoting A_0 by 100 per cent we can write

$$k = \frac{1}{t} \ln \frac{100}{100 - X} \tag{8-56}$$

Figure 8-2, reproduced from reference 6, shows the velocity coefficient for various hydrocarbons and may be used conveniently.

8-8. Reaction Kinetics. In order for a reaction to take place, collision between molecules is necessary. The probable frequency with which collisions take place depends on the molar concentration.

Arrhenius showed experimentally that there is a relation between rate of reaction and temperature. This is corroborated by the equilibrium constant, which is a function of temperature. Arrhenius expressed his law by the relation

$$\frac{d(\ln k)}{dT} = \frac{E}{RT^2} \tag{8-57}$$

where T = temperature, °R
$\quad\quad R$ = molar gas constant
$\quad\quad E$ = energy of activation, a constant which is characteristic of the reaction
$\quad\quad k$ = velocity coefficient

Integration of the Arrhenius equation yields

$$k = ae^{-E/RT} \tag{8-58}$$

where a = the so-called *frequency factor*.

In Eq. (8-58), $e^{-E/RT}$ represents the fraction of collisions that are successful. One can integrate the Arrhenius equation [Eq. (8-57)] between limits and thereby obtain

$$\ln \frac{k_2}{k_1} = \frac{E}{R}\left(\frac{1}{T_1} - \frac{1}{T_2}\right) \tag{8-59}$$

If values of k at various temperatures are given for a reaction, Eq. (8-59) may be used to calculate the appropriate energy of activation.

Table 8-1 lists the activation energies and the frequency factor for two hydrocarbons. It appears that since the energy of activation of propane is lower than that of methane, propane will react more easily. This is significant because when it is necessary to supply energy by means of a spark plug, for example, less energy need be supplied by an outside device for the material with lower activation energy. It should also be noted that the

TABLE 8-1.   ACTIVATION ENERGY

	Formula	a	E, cal/g mole
Methane.......	CH_4	1.0×10^{12}	79,385
Propane........	C_3H_8	6.4×10^{13}	62,100

frequency factor a for propane is higher than it is for methane. Thus the rate of the propane reaction will be greater than that of a methane reaction.

Farrington Daniels and his associates have shown that

$$k = \frac{TR}{Nh} e^{\Delta S/R} e^{-\Delta H/RT} \tag{8-60}$$

where N = Avogadro's number and h = Planck constant.

In any combustion reaction we would like to have k large so that the time of the reaction could be small. We may shorten the reaction time if we keep the temperature constant, or we may lower the temperature if we keep the rate constant. We have three alternatives: (1) increase T, (2) increase ΔS, or (3) decrease ΔH. Since we usually run the reaction at some particular temperature, only the last two alternatives are of major effect. This we do by using suitable catalysts. The effects of catalysts may be twofold: (1) to increase the entropy of activation, and (2) to decrease the energy (enthalpy) of activation. If a reaction is slow, the heat liberated is disposed of by convection and conduction. However, if the reaction is very fast, the heat may not be disposed of easily, resulting in a temperature rise in the system, and the reaction may become explosive.

We know that in order for a molecule to react it must have a certain minimum energy. The energy of activation is a measure of this. The catalyst lowers the necessary energy of activation and thus lowers the resistance to a reaction. In other words, it makes it easier for the reaction to take place. A catalyst does take part in a reaction, but actually it often causes an intermediate reaction. Thus for ethyl alcohol with a copper catalyst one would write

$$C_2H_5OH \xrightarrow{Cu} CH_3CHO + H_2$$

Actually, what happens is that

$$C_2H_5OH + Cu \rightarrow Cu \cdot C_2H_5OH \rightarrow CH_3CHO + H_2 + Cu$$

It follows that by using a catalyst the energy needed to activate the reaction is reduced. For example, consider the decomposition of diethyl ether,

$$C_2H_5OC_2H_5 \rightarrow C_2H_5OH + C_2H_4 \tag{8-61}$$

It is found that without any catalyst the energy of activation is 53,000 cal/g mole, and if iodine is used as a catalyst, the energy of activation is 34,300 cal/g mole.

8-9. Chain Reactions. In any reaction we have reactant(s) and product(s). If one or more of the first products act as a reagent to continue the reaction in further steps, we call the reaction a *chain reaction*. Such a first product is called a *chain carrier*. Chain carriers are usually free atoms of diatomic gases such as O and H. Other chain carriers are free radicals such as OH, CHO, CH or organic compounds such as formaldehyde. A free radical consists of a group of atoms carrying one or more unpaired electrons, or in other words it has a free valence bond. It is estimated that billions of chain carriers are formed and destroyed within an exceedingly short period of time.

Consider the reaction

$$H_2 + Br_2 \rightarrow 2HBr \tag{8-62}$$

Actually this reaction proceeds as a chain and does not occur directly. Thus

$$Br_2 \rightarrow 2Br \qquad k_1$$
$$Br + H_2 \rightarrow HBr + H \qquad k_2$$
$$H + Br_2 \rightarrow HBr + Br \qquad k_3$$
$$H + HBr \rightarrow H_2 + Br \qquad k_4$$
$$Br + Br \rightarrow Br_2 \qquad k_5$$

where k_1, k_2, etc., are the velocity coefficients corresponding to each step. This reaction will continue until either the hydrogen or the bromine is exhausted.

Chain reactions are of great importance because practical combustion processes, like the combustion in a spark-ignition or compression-ignition engine, are chain reactions. Obviously, we must be able to control these chain reactions for proper combustion processes.

Most combustion processes (one exception is the combustion of pure carbon) take place in the gaseous phase. One such reaction about which we have relatively sufficient information is the reaction between hydrogen and oxygen,

$$2H_2 + O_2 \rightarrow 2H_2O \tag{8-63}$$

which has been investigated by Lewis and von Elbe.[7] When hydrogen and oxygen react one observes the following sequence of reactions. First, certain dissociation reactions take place as follows:

$$H_2 \rightarrow 2H$$

$$O_2 \rightarrow 2O$$

$$H_2O \rightarrow OH + H$$

The chain reactions resulting from these are then

$$OH + H_2 \rightarrow H_2O + H \qquad k_1 \qquad\qquad (a)$$

$$H + O_2 \rightarrow OH + O \qquad k_2 \qquad\qquad (b)$$

$$O + H_2 \rightarrow OH + H \qquad k_3 \qquad\qquad (c)$$

We may then have a chain-breaking process brought about by the presence of a chain breaker, to be denoted by M, which may be any body or wall of a container. Thus,

$$OH + H + M \rightarrow H_2O + M \qquad k_4 \qquad\qquad (d)$$

It has been found that chain-breaking mechanisms are more effective at low pressures, and that high temperatures are more conducive to chain propagation. Cold surfaces adsorb chain carriers and thus have an impeding effect on the reaction. Cold surfaces also receive appreciable amounts of heat from combustion waves, resulting in quenching. Quenching is affected by several factors such as pipe diameter, mixture composition, pressure, configuration of combustion chamber, and temperature.

In reactions a, b, and c we have the following considerations: Reaction a is *chain-propagating* in that it produces one molecule of final product and one chain carrier; reactions b and c are called *branching reactions* because each radical which is destroyed results in two new ones. If reactions b and c predominate over reaction d, then the rate of reaction will increase, and an explosion may occur although the reaction mixture might not have heated up spontaneously. In order for a reaction to proceed at a practicable rate it is necessary that the effect of chain carriers supersede that of the chain breakers. Thus let us consider the reaction velocity of the combustion of hydrogen.

$$\frac{d[H]}{dt} = k_1[OH][H_2] - k_2[H][O_2] + k_3[O][H_2] - k_4[OH][H][M] \qquad (a)$$

$$\frac{d[O]}{dt} = k_2[H][O_2] - k_3[O][H_2] \qquad\qquad (b)$$

$$\frac{d[OH]}{dt} = -k_1[OH][H_2] + k_2[H][O_2] + k_3[O][H_2] - k_4[OH][H][M] \qquad (c)$$

Consider now the case where the differential quotients are zero. Then solving Eq. (b) for [O],

$$[O] = \frac{k_2[H][O_2]}{k_3[H_2]} \tag{8-64}$$

Equation (a) gives

$$k_1[OH][H_2] + k_3[O][H_2] = k_2[H][O_2] + k_4[OH][H][M] \tag{a}$$

$$k_3[O][H_2] = k_2[H][O_2] \tag{b}$$

$$k_1[OH][H_2] - k_3[O][H_2] = k_2[H][O_2] - k_4[OH][H][M] \tag{c}$$

Equations (a) and (c) give

$$2k_1[OH][H_2] = 2k_2[H][O_2]$$

Solving for [OH], one obtains

$$[OH] = \frac{k_2[H][O_2]}{k_1[H_2]} \tag{8-65}$$

Substituting above,

$$k_2[H][O_2] = \frac{k_4 k_2}{k_1} \frac{[H][H][O_2][M]}{[H_2]}$$

$$[H] = \frac{k_1}{k_4} \frac{[H_2]}{[M]} \tag{8-66}$$

Then

$$[O] = \frac{k_2}{k_3} \frac{k_1}{k_4} \frac{[H_2][O_2]}{[M][H_2]}$$

$$[O] = \frac{k_1 k_2}{k_3 k_4} \frac{[O_2]}{[M]}$$

and

$$[OH] = \frac{k_2}{k_1} \frac{k_1}{k_4} \frac{[H_2]}{[M]} \frac{[O_2]}{[H_2]}$$

$$[OH] = \frac{k_2}{k_4} \frac{[O_2]}{[M]}$$

$$\frac{d[H_2O]}{dt} = k_1[OH][H_2] + k_4[OH][H][M]$$

$$\frac{d[H_2O]}{dt} = k_1 \frac{k_2}{k_4} \frac{[O_2]}{[M]} [H_2] + k_4 \frac{k_2}{k_4} \frac{[O_2]}{[M]} \frac{k_1}{k_4} \frac{[H_2]}{[M]} [M]$$

$$\frac{d[H_2O]}{dt} = 2 \frac{k_1 k_2}{k_4} \frac{[O_2][H_2]}{[M]} \tag{8-67}$$

This equation is an expression for the rate of H_2O formation.

8-10. Transport Phenomena. In classical thermodynamics it is customary to consider systems as undergoing reversible processes. In reality there are no practical processes which are truly reversible, but quite frequently the premise of processes which are reversible does not introduce serious errors if one selects equilibrium end-states. Most technological applications involve phenomena which are highly irreversible and hence any treatment of these phenomena based on thermodynamic equilibrium and reversibility is inadequate.

An example of a process for which conventional thermodynamic methods are ill suited is the diffusion of two gases when brought together. This is a typical example of transport phenomena and is far from equilibrium in most instances. From the numerous types of transport phenomena there are several which are of particular interest to gas dynamics. These involve thermal transport, momentum transport, mass transport, and chemical diffusion. Although they are different phenomena, they may be treated in basically the same manner. Let us assume that a portion of gas is bounded by two horizontal planes AA' and BB' and divided by another horizontal plane CC' as shown in Fig. 8-3. We may assume then that the "transport" occurs across the plane CC' and further we should note that the transport is not necessarily steady but can vary with time. In other words, we are concerned with a rate problem. Let us further assume that along the plane CC' we can select an appropriate generalized functional magnitude. If the process proceeds from plane CC' to plane AA' in linear manner, it is easily possible to find the gradient of the generalized function. The transported magnitude will be different in each transport phenomenon. Thus for thermal phenomena the transported magnitude is kinetic energy of the molecules. Consider that the gas between AA' and CC' is at a higher temperature than that between CC' and BB'. By the kinetic theory we know that the temperature of a gas is defined by the kinetic energy of its constituent particles. It follows that the particles coming from AA' and crossing CC' will possess higher kinetic energy than those coming from BB' and crossing CC'. Eventually the gas between AA' and BB' will tend to equalize in temperature, but this will happen only when sufficient kinetic energy has been transported across CC'. Thus we conclude that in the case of thermal conductivity in gases, the transported magnitude is kinetic energy.

We may reason in a similar manner about viscosity. For this we might

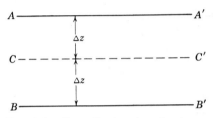

FIG. 8-3. Generalized system for transport phenomena.

presumably assume that the layer BB' is stationary while layer AA' is in motion. Thus the momenta of the particles above layer CC' are greater than the momenta of the particles below it. Hence the particles moving downward across CC' will have greater momenta in the horizontal direction than those crossing CC' in the upward direction. Since faster molecules lose momentum and slower ones gain momentum, it follows that viscosity can be considered as momentum transport.

Quite frequently we deal with coupled transport phenomena where occurrence of one transport phenomenon gives rise to another and the reverse also applies. For example, in a thermocouple an electric current in a circuit incorporating dissimilar metallic conductors will cause absorption or evolution of heat at respective junctions. Conversely, when the junctions are kept at different temperatures an electromotive force will appear in the circuit.

Thus in transport phenomena it can be considered that there is a flux, denoted by J, and a driving potential or force X causing the flux. The force and the flux are related through a phenomenological coefficient L, and in a simple transport process

$$J = LX \qquad (8\text{-}68)$$

It should be mentioned that techniques are available to treat nonlinear cases also, but a study of these is outside the scope of this text.

However, if we have coupled transport phenomena, we must consider several forces, fluxes, and coefficients. Suppose we have a coupled transport of two phenomena. We must then have two fluxes J_1 and J_2, two forces X_1 and X_2, and four coefficients L_{11}, L_{12}, L_{21}, and L_{22}, where L_{11} and L_{22} are the coefficients for a specific transport, and L_{12} and L_{21} are the constants concerned with the cross effects. We would write for this a set of two simultaneous equations, namely,

$$J_1 = L_{11}X_1 + L_{12}X_2 \qquad (8\text{-}69)$$

and

$$J_2 = L_{21}X_1 + L_{22}X_2 \qquad (8\text{-}70)$$

Or in general we can write, using symbolic notation,

$$J_i = \sum_{k=1}^{n} L_{ik}X_k \qquad \begin{array}{l} i = 1, 2, \ldots, n \\ k = 1, 2, \ldots, n \end{array} \qquad (8\text{-}71)$$

By the application of the concept of microscopic reversibility, Onsager derived reciprocal relations, namely,

$$L_{ik} = L_{ki} \qquad (8\text{-}72)$$

The subject of irreversible thermodynamics and transport phenomena is beyond the appropriate scope of this text except in regard to the Onsager relations, but references 8 to 13 should be considered by those interested in this field.

The reciprocal relationship of Onsager presents a most powerful tool in combustion phenomena, and therefore we will discuss it in some detail. The reciprocal relations are good only for molecular processes which take place not far from equilibrium conditions. Onsager, however, assumed that the same thermodynamic equations of motion for molecular processes are valid for macroscopic processes too, and therefore concluded that the reciprocal relations are applicable in the macroscopic domain.

Let us consider a homogeneous, single-phase substance, which exists in three different forms, namely, A, B, and C. At equilibrium, there might be interconversion of one form into the other, but the total macroscopic state does not change. Such a transformation can be represented by the cycle

$$\begin{array}{c} B \\ \nearrow \quad \downarrow \\ A \\ \nwarrow \quad \searrow \\ C \end{array}$$

For each individual reaction the rate of flow has to be such as to maintain constant concentration for each component.

However, the principle of microscopic reversibility requires that each individual, independent reaction has to be in balance. In other words, $A \rightarrow B$ and $B \rightarrow A$, etc., must take place, on the average, at the same rate. The above system in equilibrium is represented then by the cycle

Let k_1 be the velocity constant for the transformation $A \rightarrow B$, and k_1' the velocity constant for the transformation $B \rightarrow A$, etc. This can be represented diagrammatically as follows:

$$\begin{array}{c} B \\ k_1 \nearrow \quad \Big\downarrow k_2 \\ A \\ k_3 \nwarrow \quad \searrow \\ C \end{array} \qquad\qquad \begin{array}{c} B \\ k_1' \swarrow \quad \Big\uparrow k_2' \\ A \\ k_3' \searrow \quad \downarrow \\ C \end{array}$$

Let us assume such reactions for which the reaction velocities are pro portional to the first degree of concentrations (c_A, c_B, c_C); then,

$$\frac{dc_A}{dt} = -(k_1 + k_3')c_A + k_1'c_B + k_3c_C$$

$$\frac{dc_B}{dt} = k_1c_A - (k_1' + k_2)c_B + k_2'c_C \qquad (8\text{-}73)$$

$$\frac{dc_C}{dt} = k_3'c_A + k_2c_B - (k_3 + k_2')c_C$$

At the equilibrium state the reaction velocities are zero. Hence,

$$-(k_1 + k_3')\bar{c}_A + k_1'\bar{c}_B + k_3\bar{c}_C = 0$$

$$k_1\bar{c}_A - (k_1' + k_2)\bar{c}_B + k_2'\bar{c}_C = 0 \qquad (8\text{-}74)$$

$$k_3'\bar{c}_A + k_2\bar{c}_B - (k_3 + k_2')\bar{c}_C = 0$$

where the bar denotes the concentration at the state of equilibrium.

Suppose that the system is not yet in equilibrium, but close to it, and let us denote this condition mathematically as

$$Y_A = c_A - \bar{c}_A \qquad c_A = Y_A + \bar{c}_A$$

$$Y_B = c_B - \bar{c}_B \qquad c_B = Y_B + \bar{c}_B \qquad (8\text{-}75)$$

$$Y_C = c_C - \bar{c}_C \qquad c_C = Y_C + \bar{c}_C$$

as deviations in concentrations from equilibrium concentrations.

Since

$$\frac{dc_A}{dt} = \frac{dY_A}{dt} \qquad \frac{dc_B}{dt} = \frac{dY_B}{dt} \qquad \frac{dc_C}{dt} = \frac{dY_C}{dt}$$

Eq. (8-73) can be written in the form

$$\frac{dY_A}{dt} = -(k_1 + k_3')(Y_A + \bar{c}_A) + k_1'(Y_B + \bar{c}_B) + k_3(Y_C + \bar{c}_C)$$

$$\frac{dY_B}{dt} = k_1(Y_A + \bar{c}_A) - (k_1' + k_2)(Y_B + \bar{c}_B) + k_2'(Y_C + \bar{c}_C)$$

$$\frac{dY_C}{dt} = k_3'(Y_A + \bar{c}_A) + k_2(Y_B + \bar{c}_B) - (k_3 + k_2')(Y_C + \bar{c}_C)$$

or

$$\frac{dY_A}{dt} = -(k_1 + k_3')Y_A + k_1'Y_B + k_3Y_C$$
$$\qquad - (k_1 + k_3')\bar{c}_A + k_1'\bar{c}_B + k_3\bar{c}_C$$

$$\frac{dY_B}{dt} = k_1Y_A - (k_1' + k_2)Y_B + k_2'Y_C$$
$$\qquad + k_1\bar{c}_A - (k_1' + k_2)\bar{c}_B + k_2'\bar{c}_C$$

$$\frac{dY_C}{dt} = k_3'Y_A + k_2Y_B - (k_3 + k_2')Y_C$$
$$\qquad + k_3'\bar{c}_A + k_2\bar{c}_B - (k_3 + k_2')\bar{c}_C$$

According to Eq. (8-74), the above equations become

$$\frac{dY_A}{dt} = \dot{Y}_A = -(k_1 + k_3')Y_A + k_1'Y_B + k_3Y_C$$

$$\frac{dY_B}{dt} = \dot{Y}_B = k_1Y_A - (k_1' + k_2)Y_B + k_2'Y_C \qquad (8\text{-}76)$$

$$\frac{dY_C}{dt} = \dot{Y}_C = k_3Y_A + k_2Y_B - (k_3 + k_2')Y_C$$

The deviations in concentrations Y_A, Y_B, and Y_C can be expressed in terms of chemical potentials, μ_A, μ_B, μ_C, where the chemical potential represents the partial molal free energy and equilibrium concentrations. For dilute, ideal solutions, it is shown in chemical thermodynamics that

$$\mu_A - \bar{\mu}_A = RT \ln \frac{c_A}{\bar{c}_A}$$

$$\mu_B - \bar{\mu}_B = RT \ln \frac{c_B}{\bar{c}_B} \qquad (8\text{-}77)$$

$$\mu_C - \bar{\mu}_C = RT \ln \frac{c_C}{\bar{c}_C}$$

where the bar has the same meaning as before. The above equations can be written also in the form

$$\mu_A - \bar{\mu}_A = RT \ln \frac{Y_A + \bar{c}_A}{\bar{c}_A} = RT \ln \left(1 + \frac{Y_A}{\bar{c}_A}\right)$$

$$\mu_B - \bar{\mu}_B = RT \ln \frac{Y_B + \bar{c}_B}{\bar{c}_B} = RT \ln \left(1 + \frac{Y_B}{\bar{c}_B}\right)$$

$$\mu_C - \bar{\mu}_C = RT \ln \frac{Y_C + \bar{c}_C}{\bar{c}_C} = RT \ln \left(1 + \frac{Y_C}{\bar{c}_C}\right)$$

For small deviations in Y, we can use the mathematical expansion series

$$\ln(1 + Y) = Y - \frac{Y^2}{2} + \frac{Y^3}{3} - \frac{Y^4}{4} + \cdots - 1 < Y \leq 1$$

and the above equations, if the first term is employed, become

$$\mu_A - \bar{\mu}_A = RT \frac{Y_A}{\bar{c}_A}$$

$$\mu_B - \bar{\mu}_B = RT \frac{Y_B}{\bar{c}_B}$$

$$\mu_C - \bar{\mu}_C = RT \frac{Y_C}{\bar{c}_C}$$

and hence

$$Y_A = - \frac{\bar{c}_A}{RT} (\bar{\mu}_A - \mu_A)$$

$$Y_B = - \frac{\bar{c}_B}{RT} (\bar{\mu}_B - \mu_B) \qquad (8\text{-}78)$$

$$Y_C = - \frac{\bar{c}_C}{RT} (\bar{\mu}_C - \mu_C)$$

Substituting these expressions in Eq. (8-76), we obtain

$$\dot{Y}_A = \frac{(k_1 + k_3')\bar{c}_A}{RT} (\bar{\mu}_A - \mu_A) - \frac{k_1'\bar{c}_B}{RT} (\bar{\mu}_B - \mu_B) - \frac{k_3\bar{c}_C}{RT} (\bar{\mu}_C - \mu_C)$$

$$\dot{Y}_B = - \frac{k_1\bar{c}_A}{RT} (\bar{\mu}_A - \mu_A) + \frac{(k_1' + k_2)\bar{c}_B}{RT} (\bar{\mu}_B - \mu_B) - \frac{k_2'\bar{c}_C}{RT} (\bar{\mu}_C - \mu_C)$$

$$\dot{Y}_C = - \frac{k_3'\bar{c}_A}{RT} (\bar{\mu}_A - \mu_A) - \frac{k_2\bar{c}_B}{RT} (\bar{\mu}_B - \mu_B) + \frac{(k_3 + k_2')\bar{c}_C}{RT} (\bar{\mu}_C - \mu_C)$$

$$(8\text{-}79)$$

The last step is now to apply the principle of microscopic reversibility. This implies that at equilibrium each individual reaction is balanced in both directions, $A \rightleftharpoons B$, or, mathematically expressed,

$$k_1\bar{c}_A = k_1'\bar{c}_B = LRT \qquad k_2\bar{c}_B = k_2'\bar{c}_C = MRT$$

$$k_3\bar{c}_C = k_3'\bar{c}_A = NRT \qquad L, M, N = \text{constant}$$

Equations (8-79) now become

$$\dot{Y}_A = \frac{(k_1 + k_3')\bar{c}_A}{RT} (\bar{\mu}_A - \mu_A) - L(\bar{\mu}_B - \mu_B) - N(\bar{\mu}_C - \mu_C)$$

$$\dot{Y}_B = -L(\bar{\mu}_A - \mu_A) + \frac{(k_1' + k_2)\bar{c}_B}{RT} (\bar{\mu}_B - \mu_B) - M(\bar{\mu}_C - \mu_C) \qquad (8\text{-}80)$$

$$\dot{Y}_C = -N(\bar{\mu}_A - \mu_A) - M(\bar{\mu}_B - \mu_B) + \frac{(k_3 + k_2')\bar{c}_C}{RT} (\bar{\mu}_C - \mu_C)$$

The comparison of Eqs. (8-80) with Eqs. (8-69) and (8-70) shows clearly that, for this chemical system, the reciprocal relations

$$L_{12} = L_{21} \qquad L_{13} = L_{31} \qquad L_{23} = L_{32} \tag{8-81}$$

are valid. In Eqs. (8-80) the thermodynamic forces are the chemical potentials, and the fluxes are the velocities of formation dc/dt.

8-11. Combustion of Hydrocarbons. It was indicated already that the chain of events in a chemical reaction is very difficult to determine. This is especially so for more complex reactants such as the hydrocarbons. For an example, consider the combustion of pentane. For this,

$$C_5H_{12} + 8O_2 \rightleftharpoons 5CO_2 + 6H_2O$$

there are nine molecules which at the start take part in the reaction. Indications are that the reaction must consist of steps, in each of which there can be no more than three initial molecules reacting at one time. This is so because, as stated already, it is highly improbable that more than three molecules will interact at one time.

It is obvious, then, that it is indeed exceedingly difficult to write the various chain reactions, and it becomes necessary to rely heavily on experimental observations. There are in principle two methods for such experimental studies. One is called the *static method*, and the other is called the *continuous-flow method*. When employing the static method, the reacting media are introduced into a closed vessel which is maintained at the desirable temperature. The progress of the oxidation may then be followed visually through quartz windows located suitably in the walls of the chamber. Chemical analyses as well as the rate of pressure rise may be determined by the use of appropriate instrumentation. In the continuous-flow method the reacting media are passed at constant velocity through a uniformly heated tube and samples of the products are analyzed at suitable intervals. In the case of solid fuels one might use a tube made of the solid propellant and pass oxygen through this tube.

Because of the many variables involved it is presently necessary to study the combustion of each hydrocarbon individually. Notwithstanding this there are certain similarities among the various hydrocarbons. One scheme which has been proposed [14, 15] to explain the combustion of hydrocarbons is called the *aldehyde-degradation mechanism*, which is based on the observation that there is a tendency to shorten the length of the alkyl radical in the aldehyde. This mechanism may be explained as follows: Consider any hydrocarbon of the paraffin family such as propane, for example. Propane, C_3H_8, is represented symbolically as

$$\begin{array}{ccccccc} & H & & H & & H & \\ & | & & | & & | & \\ H - & C & - & C & - & C & - H \\ & | & & | & & | & \\ & H & & H & & H & \end{array}$$

In order for the propane to react it is necessary that it lose one of the hydrogen atoms, becoming an alkyl radical, thus making it possible for oxygen to attack the free carbon valence. There are various schools of thought regarding which hydrogen will be lost initially, but the discussion of this is beyond the scope of this book. The alkyl radical of propane would be

$$\begin{array}{ccc} H & H & H \\ | & | & | \\ H-C-C-C- \\ | & | & | \\ H & H & H \end{array}$$

Because most alkyl radicals act alike we may denote them by R in general. A paraffin hydrocarbon is then RH. Other intermediate products which may occur in a hydrocarbon combustion process are shown in Table 8-2.

TABLE 8-2. INTERMEDIATE PRODUCTS

Alcohols.....................	ROH
Aldehydes....................	RCHO
Acids........................	RCOOH
Peracids.....................	RCO(OOH)
Ketones.....................	RCOR
Hydroperoxides..............	ROOH
Dialkyl peroxides............	ROOR
Carbonyl....................	RCO

The aldehyde-degradation mechanism may be outlined as follows: A free radical like the hydroxyl OH may react with a hydrocarbon, giving an alkyl radical and water. Thus

$$RH + OH \rightarrow R + H_2O$$

The alkyl radical is oxidized by reacting with oxygen and gives an aldehyde:

$$R + O_2 \rightarrow R'CHO$$

where R' is the next lower alkyl radical. The aldehyde now reacts with hydroxyl, yielding a carbonyl:

$$R'CHO + OH \rightarrow R'CO$$

The carbonyl may oxidize giving a peracid in two steps; thus

$$R'CO + O_2 \rightarrow R'CO(OO)$$

$$R'CO(OO) + RH \rightarrow R'CO(OOH) + R$$

Peracids are very unstable at high temperatures and decompose readily to the aldehyde of the next lower alkyl radical which we will denote by R''. Thus,

$$R'CO(OOH) \rightarrow R''CHO + CO + H_2O$$

From the above it may be seen that the kinetics of hydrocarbon combustion is rather complex. Rapid strides are being made in this field, and concepts are altered frequently as new scientific evidence becomes available.

8-12. Explosion Limits. By *explosion limit* is meant the temperature above which autoignition sets in at constant pressure. Conversely, it may be the pressure (at constant temperature) above which explosion sets in.

A second meaning of explosion limit is based on mixture properties. Thus it may also be defined as the limits of the composition outside of which an explosion (externally ignited) may not propagate at a given temperature and pressure. This mixture explosion limit will depend on both temperature and pressure. In general, an increase in temperature and/or pressure will hasten the explosion and thus the critical range will have been extended. The container dimensions will also have an effect on the mixture explosion limit as the dimensions of the system will have thermal effects.

Any mixture of fuel and air is not combustible. A theoretically correct mixture or a stoichiometric mixture is combustible and falls between two limiting fuel-air ratios, one each on the lean and on the rich sides.

Table 8-3 lists the air-fuel ratios at approximate limits of inflammability for representative gases and liquids.

TABLE 8-3. APPROXIMATE LIMITS OF INFLAMMABILITY †

Pounds of air per pound of fuel

Fuel	Symbol	Low	High
Hydrogen	H_2	346	5.1
Carbon monoxide	CO	7.3	0.28
Methane	CH_4	34.3	10.2
Propane	C_3H_8	26.8	6.3
Benzene	C_6H_6	26.0	5.1
Methyl alcohol	CH_3OH	12.6	1.6
Ethyl alcohol	C_2H_5OH	18.6	2.7

† Abstracted from M. L. Smith and K. W. Stinson, "Fuels and Combustion," McGraw-Hill Book Company, Inc., New York, 1952.

Experiments indicate that for downward flame travel the limits are closer than for horizontal travel. In turn, they are closer for horizontal than for upward flame travel. Furthermore, it is found that the larger the tube diameter, the wider the inflammability limits.

PROBLEMS

8-1. Compute the heat of formation of carbon dioxide at 300°K.

8-2. Find the heat of combustion at 300°K of each of the following species: (a) methane, (b) hydrogen, (c) ethylene, (d) water, (e) n-octane, (f) furfural, (g) propane.

8-3. Show that the heats of reaction at constant pressure and at constant volume differ by $\Delta n\, RT$.

8-4. For a first-order chemical reaction show that the time required for 75 per cent reaction is twice that required for 50 per cent.

8-5. How long will it take for 30 per cent decomposition of hexane at 1100°F?

8-6. At what temperature will propane be decomposed 20 per cent in 3 sec?

8-7. Determine the temperature at which 10 per cent of H_2O may dissociate into H_2 and O_2 at a pressure of 10 atm.

8-8. Complete the stoichiometric equation when nitroglycerine, $(C_3H_5NO_3)_3$, explodes at 4000°F. $CO \qquad H_2O \qquad H_2 \qquad N_2$

8-9. How much H_2O is dissociated at 4000°F when the pressure is (a) 1 atm, (b) 5 atm, (c) 10 atm?

8-10. The following data are given in the literature for the decomposition of nitromethane at 209.8°C $(CH_3NO_2 \rightarrow NO + \frac{1}{2}HCHO + \frac{1}{2}CH_3OH)$:

Time, min	Partial pressure, mm
0	230.1
7	184.2
11	163.6
16	139.7
20	123.6

Is this a first-order reaction?

8-11. Write an expression for the rate change of concentration of a zero-order reaction. Would you expect the rate of the concentration to be dependent on the concentration?

8-12. Find the enthalpy of n-octane at 300°K.

8-13. Find the heat of formation of n-octane from its heat of combustion.

8-14. Find the enthalpy of propane at 300°K.

8-15. Find the heat of formation of propane from its heat of combustion.

8-16. Find the heat of combustion of hydrogen at 400°K.

8-17. Given the reaction

$$C_6H_6 + 15\frac{1}{2}O_2 \rightarrow 6CO_2 + 3H_2O$$

find (a) the entropy, (b) the enthalpy, (c) the free energy, all at 300°K.

8-18. What is the approximate decomposition of propane at 1300°F during a period of 2 sec?

8-19. The Fischer-Tropsch process for the production of synthetic fuel is

$$C + H_2O \xrightarrow{\text{Co}} CH_2 + H_2O$$

in which the catalyst used is cobalt. Write the stepwise reaction which actually gives the above chemical equation.

8-20. Will the decomposition of water vapor at normal temperature and pressure be appreciable?

8-21. Carbon dioxide is dissociated into carbon monoxide and oxygen at various pressures and temperatures. Determine the per cent dissociated for the pressures and temperatures shown in the table below:

°R	Atmospheres			
	½	1	2	4
3000				
5000				

8-22. Derive an expression defining the heat which is liberated in a combustor operating with steady-flow combustion.

REFERENCES

1. Hottel, H. C., G. C. Williams, and C. N. Satterfield: "Thermodynamic Charts for Combustion Processes," vol. I, John Wiley & Sons, Inc., New York, 1949.
2. Obert, E. F.: "Thermodynamics," McGraw-Hill Book Company, Inc., New York, 1948.
3. Dodge, Barnett F.: "Chemical Engineering Thermodynamics," McGraw-Hill Book Company, Inc., New York, 1944.
4. Klotz, I. M.: "Chemical Thermodynamics," Prentice-Hall, Inc., Englewood Cliffs, N.J., 1950.
5. Rossini, F. D.: "Chemical Thermodynamics," John Wiley & Sons, Inc., New York, 1950.
6. Griswold, John: "Fuels, Combustion and Furnaces," McGraw-Hill Book Company, Inc., New York, 1946.
7. Lewis, B., and G. von Elbe: "Combustion, Flames and Explosions of Gases," Academic Press, Inc., New York, 1951.
8. Prigogine, I.: "Introduction to Thermodynamics of Irreversible Processes," Charles C Thomas, Publisher, Springfield, Ill., 1955.
9. Bosworth, R. C. L.: "Heat Transfer Phenomena," Associated General Publications Pty. Ltd., Sydney, Australia, 1952.
10. Hirschfelder, J. O., C. F. Curtiss, and R. B. Bird: "Molecular Theory of Gases and Liquids," John Wiley & Sons, Inc., New York, 1954.
11. Richardson, John M., and Stuart R. Brinkley, Jr.: Mechanics of Reaction Continua, in B. Lewis, R. N. Pease, and H. S. Taylor (eds.), "Combustion Processes," vol. II, "High Speed Aerodynamics and Jet Propulsion," pp. 203–215, Princeton University Press, Princeton, N.J., 1956.
12. Penner, S. S.: Introduction to Chemical Kinetics for Aeronautical Engineers, in 1952 Rome AGARD Combustion Panel, Palais de Chaillot, Paris.
13. DeGroot, S. R.: "Thermodynamics of Irreversible Processes," North Holland Publishing Co., Amsterdam, 1952.
14. Jost, W.: "Explosion and Combustion Processes in Gases" (trans. by H. O. Croft), McGraw-Hill Book Company, Inc., New York, 1946.
15. Smith, M. L., and K. W. Stinson: "Fuels and Combustion," McGraw-Hill Book Company, Inc., New York, 1952.

CHAPTER 9

INTRODUCTION TO FLAMES AND COMBUSTION

9-1. Introduction. In the process of rapid, high-temperature oxidation, otherwise called *combustion*, the liberation of chemical energy usually produces luminous gases which are called *flames*. Thus a flame represents a region of fast, high-temperature oxidation. The flame front is an area of rapid chemical reaction and is the boundary between the burned and the unburned portions of the mixture. The flame front, in moving from the burning portion of the mixture into the unburned portion, produces progressive ignition of the unburned portion. This results as the large amounts of heat which progress forward into the mixture initiate the rapid chemical reaction. In controlled combustion, the unburned portion of the mixture is timed generally to ignite only after it has been ignited by the flame front. The flame front is thinner in fast reactions than it is in slow reactions. Although many factors are involved, in general the rate of flame propagation is primarily a function of (1) mixture composition, (2) temperature, and (3) total pressure.

The flames encountered in technological applications may be classified as either stationary flames or nonstationary flames. Stationary flames are those in which the flame front is stationary in space and the unburned mixture travels toward the burning zone. For any particular set of conditions such as fuel-air ratio, inlet temperature, duct diameter, etc., there is a limiting velocity which the flow must not exceed if the flame is to remain stationary.† A stationary flame is analogous to a standing wave. Most combustion-engineering applications utilize stationary flames.

Stationary flames can appropriately be classified in two different ways. One is on the basis of mixing with air, and the other is on the basis of flow pattern. Thus respectively we might find:

1. Premixed flames or laminar flames
2. Diffusion flames or turbulent flames

Premixed flames are those in which the fuel and the air are mixed prior to arriving in the burning zone. In the case of diffusion flames, the fuel and the oxygen arrive at the combustion area separately and mixing occurs in

---

† It will be seen in Chap. 13 that flames may be stabilized in high-velocity gas streams by the use of so-called *flame holders*.

the reaction zone. In general, a premixed flame will be connected to a burning zone which is shorter than the burning zone of a diffusion flame. Stationary flames exist at various pressure levels, from below atmospheric and ranging above atmospheric depending on the particular application.

Nonstationary flames exist when the flame front itself moves through the mixture. If this takes place with great rapidity, an explosion may occur. Nonstationary flames are often associated with

1. Isobaric (constant-pressure) conditions
2. Isometric (constant-volume) conditions

Consider as an example a mine explosion. In general, this is the case of an isobaric nonstationary flame. Here the combustion is essentially completed at the flame front with little burning taking place after the flame has passed through the region.

Constant-volume, nonstationary flames occur in spark-ignition engines. Experimental evidence indicates that the flame front is usually less regular than is the case with nonstationary, isobaric flames.

If combustion occurs at relatively low temperatures, say below 1000°F, the resulting flame is said to be a cool flame. Cool flames emit little light and heat because a temperature of about 1200°F is necessary for most physical substances to emit light. A cool flame is sustained because of chain branching and may leave as a residue aldehydes and/or peroxides.

9-2. Flame Propagation. Several different velocities may be associated with flame propagation. These velocities are very important because they have a marked effect on the amount of heat which may be liberated during a combustion process. Consider a flame front in a horizontal tube as sketched in Fig. 9-1. The flame front, which may or may not be symmetrical, separates the burned gases and the fresh mixture. Several velocities can be defined as follows: The gas velocity V_g is the velocity of the fresh mixture relative to a fixed observer (this velocity is sometimes called the *mixture velocity*); the flame velocity V_f (also called the *spatial velocity*) is the velocity of the flame front relative to a fixed observer; finally, the burning velocity V_b (also called the *transformation velocity*) is the velocity of the burned gases relative to the unburned gases. It follows that the flame velocity is equal to the vector sum of the gas velocity and the burning velocity. In other words

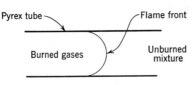

Fig. 9-1. Flame front.

$$\mathbf{V}_f = \mathbf{V}_g + \mathbf{V}_b \qquad (9\text{-}1)$$

We may use two different coordinate systems. In one we can assume that the observer is outside the tube and observes the flame as it goes by. In the other we assume that the observer travels with the flame.

Relative to a fixed observer we find from Eq. (9-1) that the flame velocity is equal to the burning velocity, because we consider that the fresh mixture is stationary until the arrival of the flame front. On the other hand, if our observer travels with the flame front the relative flame velocity will be zero and in accordance with Eq. (9-1) the burning velocity will be equal numerically to the gas velocity, but will be in the opposite direction.

Consider a flame front perpendicular to the axis of the pipe. Because of combustion, the gas temperature is raised and hence the mixture volume increases. This has the effect of pushing the burned gas back and the unburned gas forward. Because of greater friction at the wall, the flame proceeds faster at the center and a parabolic flame front is formed. However, the flame experiences buoyancy effects and thus is frequently asymmetric, as shown in Fig. 12-40, which is a photograph taken in a 7/8-in.-ID horizontal Pyrex tube. The propane-air flame traveled from left to right. This increases the flame-front area and a greater amount of gas is burned. Turbulence and eddies also encourage flame travel. Experiments indicate that the flame travel is faster in large tubes than it is in small tubes. The faster the flame, the higher will be the rate of increase of pressure of the mixture. Experiments indicate that in controlled-combustion processes the combustion is fairly complete in the regions through which the flame front has passed.

In detonation, the unburned mixture is ignited without the action of the flame front and essentially an uncontrolled combustion occurs. With detonation, the disturbance is so intense that a resulting shock wave or waves pass through the mixture at supersonic speed. Contrary to combustion of the flame-front type, in detonation the passing of the wave does not mean that the combustion in the particular region is completed. In fact, several waves may be supported by the same region.

Consider a tube which contains a combustible mixture and is provided with a spark plug at one end. This tube may be filled with a combustible mixture. If a spark is passed, the mixture in its immediate vicinity will be ignited and a flame will travel downstream. At the beginning, only a small portion of the gas is luminous, the rest being dark. As the flame travels forward more and more of the gas becomes luminous, and the extent of the dark region decreases. In the combustion of gaseous mixtures, this demarcation between the luminous and the dark, unburned regions exists, and this surface is the flame front. The characteristics of the flame front are governed by chemical as well as aerodynamic laws. When there is no other means of ignition (no detonation, autoignition, or other spark plug) in the tube, the unburned mixture must wait until the arrival of the flame front for any unburned portion to be ignited. Thus in a way the flame front is analogous to a weak compression wave. The unburned gases do not become luminous immediately upon the arrival of the flame front because there is an ignition delay. Thus it is customary to consider two regions in the burning zone. One is the luminous and the other is the reaction zone. Ignition takes place in the reaction zone, but the completion of burning takes place in the luminous zone. A clear-cut distinction between the two zones is difficult to make because the thickness of the burning zone

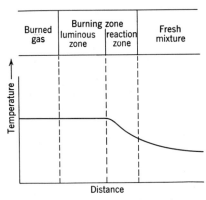

is something about which little is known, because different conditions will result in different thicknesses. In general, the faster the combustion process, the thinner will be the flame front. These phenomena may be summarized in Fig. 9-2, which represents a section of the tube in Fig. 9-1. In Fig. 9-2 the temperature-distribution curve indicates the flame temperature along the tube.

FIG. 9-2.   Zones of combustion.

Observations indicate that the same combustible mixture will travel faster in a vessel such as a tube than it would in unconfined space.

9-3. Diffusion Flames.   We noted in Sec. 9-1 that stationary flames may be either premixed or diffused. In general, premixed flames have received considerably more attention than have diffusion flames although the latter are encountered frequently in technological applications. For example, when producer gas is burned with air in steel furnaces, the ensuing flame is a turbulent diffusion flame. Probably the most familiar diffusion flame is a candle flame.

The classical work describing diffusion flames is that by Burke and Schumann.[1] These investigators contributed greatly to an understanding of diffusion flames although in recent years some of their assumptions have been shown to be questionable. However, their basic argument that the rate of diffusion is the rate setting the phenomenon is accepted. One important difficulty which does arise is the determination of the diffusion coefficient which is to be used in the mathematical analysis.

A diffusion flame commonly starts on the rim of the burner. However, it is possible to lift a flame as has been done by Kippenhan and Croft.[2] In the latter case the flame is suspended at some distance above the burner rim causing some air entrainment and thus resembling a premixed flame.

Anyone who has watched the smoke emanating from a lighted cigarette resting in quiet surroundings has probably observed that the smoke pattern is laminar close to the tip of the cigarette, but is then transformed into a turbulent pattern. The transition from open laminar flames to open turbulent flames manifests a similar picture. Experimental observations indicate that the length of a laminar diffusion flame depends on the type of fuel burned and the rate of fuel flow, but is not affected to a marked degree by the diameter of the burner. In contrast, the flame length of a fully developed turbulent-diffusion flame depends not on the fuel-flow rate but on the burner configuration.

There are several theories which attempt to establish the structure of diffusion flames, but there exist certain conflicts among these. Barr [3] sug-

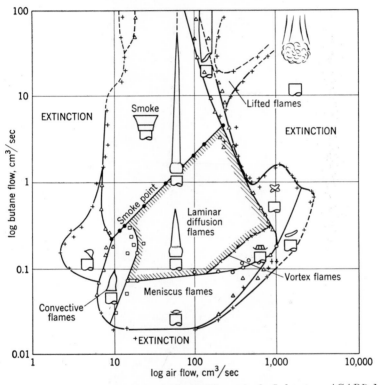

Fig. 9-3. Transitions. (*John Barr, Diffusion Flames in the Laboratory, AGARD Mem. AG 11/M7, Scheveningen Conference, May 3–7, 1954.*)

gests that any successful theory should take into consideration, among other factors, the width of the reaction zone, the radiation heat losses, carbon formation, the convective flow pattern, momentum transfer, the diffusion coefficient, and the stoichiometric air-fuel ratio. Barr has studied the many factors which must be considered in any study of diffusion flames, and some of his findings are shown here pictorially in Fig. 9-3, which is self-explanatory.

9-4. Premixed Flames. The premixed flame with which the engineer is most familiar is the bunsen flame. In a bunsen burner, gaseous fuel issuing from an orifice inside the burner entrains primary air, and the mixture burns at the top of the burner tube where it also receives secondary

FIG. 9-4.   Propane-air flame on a Smithsell separator.   (*Gas Dynamics Laboratory, Northwestern University.*)

air which further assists the combustion process.   Premixed flames generally result in rather intense combustion and do not pose much difficulty as far as sooting is concerned.

In observing a bunsen burner flame one can notice two cones, an inner one and an outer one, which may be separated conveniently by the use of a

Smithsell's separator as shown in Fig. 9-4. The inner cone corresponds to the flame front for the combustion of the fuel and the primary air and is the true premixed flame. The outer cone is formed by the combustion of the existing mixture and the secondary air, and is actually a diffusion flame.

FIG. 9-5.   Photograph of laminar flame.   (*Reproduced from B. Lewis and G. von Elbe, "Combustion, Flames and Explosions of Gases," p. 480, Academic Press, Inc., New York, 1951.*)

A premixed flame may be laminar or it may be turbulent, depending on the Reynolds number of the flow in the tube. Figure 9-5 shows a laminar flame; Fig. 9-6 shows a turbulent flame. It can be noticed that the laminar flame is tall and has a thin zone of combustion of the fuel and primary air. A turbulent flame on the other hand has a thick zone of primary combustion, and the flame front becomes blurred as the turbulence increases. The zone in which the primary combustion occurs in a turbulent flame is sometimes called the *flame brush*. Lengthening the burner tube is conducive to obtaining a laminar flame. The turbulence in flames can best be observed by the use of schlieren photography, the principles of which are described in a later chapter. Schlieren photographs of a laminar and a turbulent flame are shown in Figs. 9-7 and 9-8 respectively.

By increasing the gas flow, and thus the gas velocity, it is possible to lift the flame above the burner rim. A stable flame will be possible as long as the gas velocity and the burning velocity are substantially the same. The

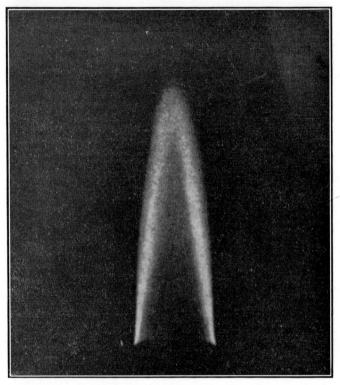

FIG. 9-6. Photograph of turbulent flame. (*Reproduced from B. Lewis and G. von Elbe, "Combustion, Flames and Explosions of Gases," p. 480, Academic Press, Inc., New York, 1951.*)

mixture-flow lines will diverge outside the burner rim, and thus the gas velocity will be reduced, but on the other hand, the burning velocity will be increased because flame quenching due to the relatively cool burner walls will be reduced. As the flame is lifted off the burner rim diffusion of secondary air reduces the burning velocity. As long as these three effects occur in proper magnitude the flame will be stable. However, if the burning-velocity decrease due to secondary air diffusion exceeds the increase in burning velocity due to reduced quenching, the flame will blow off, and this condition is called the blowout limit.

If the gas velocity is less than the burning velocity, the flame will flash back into the tube. In the same burner, all fuels do not behave in the same manner as far as blowoff and flashback are concerned, and hence the burner design must take into consideration the kind of fuel to be used.

There are certain distinctions between premixed flames and diffusion flames, although in practice there is evidence of overlapping. For a true premixed flame the ratio of fuel to oxygen is not changed by the addition of oxygen as from diffusion into the flame from the outside. Again, in a

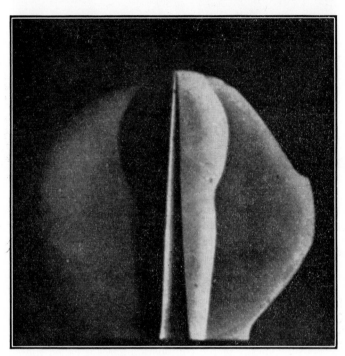

Fig. 9-7. Schlieren photograph of laminar flame. (*Reproduced from B. Lewis and G. von Elbe, "Combustion, Flames and Explosions of Gases," p. 480, Academic Press, Inc., New York, 1951.*)

premixed flame an explosion wave travels through a mixture, but in a diffusion flame there is no burning velocity which can be defined adequately. It is also difficult to define a true mixture strength (fuel-air ratio) for diffusion flames. Carbon formation is less pronounced in premixed flames in comparison with diffusion flames. In premixing, preignition reactions occur, and the reaction can start at low temperatures, whereas in diffusion flames, the average temperature of the reaction zone is close to the theoretically possible maximum temperature.

In combustion processes we would like to have as high a temperature as possible, because with higher temperature more heat can be transferred.

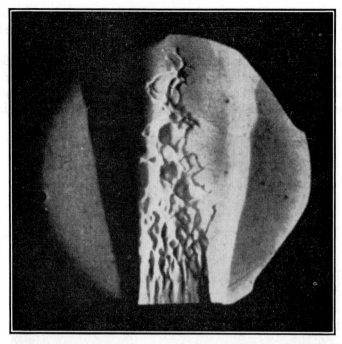

Fig. 9-8.   Schlieren photograph of turbulent flame.   (*Reproduced from B. Lewis and G. von Elbe, "Combustion, Flames and Explosions of Gases," p. 480, Academic Press, Inc., New York, 1951.*)

Thus, a smaller and lighter engine can be built for the same power in the case of high-temperature, heat-transfer power units.

9-5. Combustion Temperature.   The temperature calculated for conditions in which a fuel is burned so that all of its heat of combustion goes into raising the sensible energy of the combustion gases is called the *adiabatic-combustion* or the *adiabatic-flame temperature*.   This theoretical temperature is the highest temperature for which a combustion chamber need be designed.   Actually the term *flame temperature* is a misnomer because thermodynamically temperature connotes an equilibrium state which does not exist in a zone of rapid combustion.   Experiments indicate that the temperature at different points of a flame varies widely.   Thus, for example, in a bunsen burner the highest local temperature is encountered a short distance above the inner cone.   In general, the temperature obtained by measurements in a flame is somewhat lower than the calculated temperature primarily because of heat-loss and dissociation effects which are not always accounted for in the theoretical calculations.   The highest temperature measured on a particular burner is usually obtained when the mixture is slightly lean.

In calculating the adiabatic-flame temperature a variety of simplifying assumptions may be made, but caution must be exercised so as not to over-simplify the problem under consideration. The two basic assumptions generally made are: (1) No shaft work accompanies the combustion process, and (2) the combustion process proceeds adiabatically. Additional simplifications which may be imposed at the discretion of an investigator are: (1) The air used in the combustion is dry, (2) the entire chemical reaction goes to completion at the temperature of the fuel-air mixture, and (3) there is no dissociation. These assumptions are fairly valid for present-day jet-engine and gas-turbine design practice. However, when temperatures appreciably higher than 2500°F are maintained, as in some rocket motors, dissociation must be taken into consideration. It may be expected that with the rapid progress under way in jet propulsion, the temperatures employed will progressively rise in future years. If dissociation is taken into consideration, the calculated temperature will be somewhat less than for combustion without dissociation because dissociation reactions are endothermic in nature. For example, in complete combustion carbon dioxide appears as the end product from the combustion of carbon, which is an exothermic reaction. However, when the carbon dioxide dissociates to carbon monoxide and oxygen the process is endothermic. As is known, dissociation at any particular temperature is offset or at least diminished by increasing the pressure. Consider the isobaric combustion process

$$\text{Fuel} + \text{air} \rightarrow \text{condensable products} + \text{dry products}$$

The energy balance (neglecting changes in potential and kinetic energy) will be

$$m_f h_f + m_a h_a + Q = W_s + m_c h_c + m_d h_d \qquad (9\text{-}2)$$

where m = mass
 h = specific enthalpy
 Q = heat transfer to or from surroundings
 W_s = thermodynamic mechanical work
f, a, c, d = subscripts denoting respectively fuel, air, condensable products,
   and dry products
It should be recalled that the enthalpy in this energy balance includes both the sensible enthalpy and the chemical enthalpy.

Consider the enthalpies h_1 and h_2 at two state points 1 and 2 respectively. These may be defined as

$$h_1 = f_1(T,p) + h_1^0$$
$$h_2 = f_2(T,p) + h_2^0$$

where h_1^0 and h_2^0 are constants of integration and as yet have not been defined. As long as the engineer deals with one particular medium, such as steam or air for example, and is concerned with enthalpy differences only, there is no need to know the actual numerical value of the reference enthalpies, which are the same for any particular medium undergoing a process limited by state points 1 and 2. However, in problems involving combustion the reactants and the products are drastically different, and hence $h_1^0 \neq h_2^0$ and $f_1(T,p) \neq f_2(T,p)$. Thus it becomes desirable to know the absolute values of the enthalpy function, and we must take into consideration the reference enthalpies. The form for expressing the enthalpy could appear as $h = f(p,T, \text{composition})$.

This concept will now be applied to the isobaric-combustion process under consideration. In doing this we add and subtract the reference enthalpies for the fuel, the air, and the products of combustion in one energy balance. Thus the energy balance becomes

$$m_f(h_f - h_f^0) + m_a(h_a - h_a^0) \pm Q = W_s + m_c(h_c - h_c^0)$$
$$+ m_d(h_d - h_d^0) - (m_f h_f^0 + m_a h_a^0 - m_c h_c^0 - m_d h_d^0) \quad (9\text{-}3)$$

The last term represents the enthalpy of the components at the reference state. It is defined as the reference enthalpy of combustion thus:

$$-\frac{m_f}{M} H^0 = m_f(-h^0) = m_f h_f^0 + m_a h_a^0 - m_c h_c^0 - m_d h_d^0 \quad (9\text{-}4)$$

where $-H^0$ is used on a mole basis and $-h^0$ on a mass basis. The energy balance can thus be written as

$$m_f(h_f - h_f^0) + m_a(h_a - h_a^0)$$
$$= \pm Q + W_s m_c(h_c - h_c^0) + m_d(h_d - h_d^0) - \left(-\frac{m_f}{M} H^0\right) \quad (9\text{-}5)$$

Sometimes different authors may assign different signs to the enthalpy of combustion, that is, some use a plus sign and others use a minus sign. It should be remembered that in the exothermic-combustion process under adiabatic conditions, the difference in total enthalpy of the reactants represents the heat liberated during the combustion process, or the heating value. Thus, for example, the heating value of propane is 19,929 Btu/lb$_m$. This means that

$$-h^0 = 19{,}929$$

and the absolute numerical value of this is added on the right-hand side of the energy-balance equation (9-5).

The analysis discussed above is applicable to steady-flow or isobaric processes when changes in kinetic energy and in potential energy are negligible. The same type of analysis may be applied to isometric processes by using the internal energy (sensible and chemical) instead of the enthalpy.

So far we have discussed the energy balance on a general basis. Let us now apply the two basic assumptions commonly used in the calculation of the flame temperature, namely, that no shaft work is done, and that the process proceeds adiabatically. The internal energy E is composed of internal energy E_s and chemical energy E_{ch}, namely,

$$E = E_s + E_{ch} \tag{9-6}$$

By our basic assumptions

$$Q = W_s = 0$$

Therefore, by the first law of thermodynamics,

$$\Delta E = 0$$

Also, $$E = E_{pT_2} - E_{mT_1} = 0 \tag{9-7}$$

where the subscripts p and m refer to products and mixture respectively, and 1 and 2 refer to the initial and final temperatures. It follows that

$$E_{pT_2} = E_{mT_1}$$

Recall from Eq. (9-6) that

$$E = E_s + E_{ch}$$

But after the chemical energy has been released it follows that

$$E_p = E_{sp} \tag{9-8}$$

and we recognize that

$$E_{spT_2} = E_{smT_1} + E_{ch} \tag{9-9}$$

Now consider a constant-volume calorimeter. Because no mechanical work is realized, the heat delivery for a constant-volume combustion process Q_v is

$$Q_v = E = E_p - E_m \tag{9-10}$$

$$Q_v = E_{sp} - E_{sm} - E_{ch} \tag{9-11}$$

Similarly, for a constant-pressure calorimeter,

$$Q_p = H_{sp} - H_{sm} - E_{ch} \tag{9-12}$$

For a perfect gas, and using the definition of enthalpy, the difference $Q_p - Q_v$ is

$$Q_p - Q_v = (nRT)_p - (nRT)_m \tag{8-9}$$

In calculating the adiabatic-flame temperature the following reasoning is followed in principle: The equilibrium constant for any reaction is a function of the temperature, as was shown in the preceding chapter. In turn, the value of the equilibrium constant determines the equilibrium composition obtained because a particular amount of energy released raises the temperature. Moreover, the energy release is represented by a change in enthalpy. Again we know that for any enthalpy change there corresponds a certain change in temperature, and this is the difference between the final or flame temperature and the initial temperature. Therefore, for any particular case we compute the equilibrium temperature, and then determine by trial and error whether or not the energy released corresponds to the temperature change. Let us now demonstrate this procedure by an example.

Example 1. Calculate the theoretical (adiabatic) flame temperature for the combustion of propane with 120 per cent of dry theoretical air at 4 atm pressure. Assume that no dissociation takes place and that the initial temperature is 77°F. The enthalpy of combustion of propane at 77°F is 876,876 Btu/lb mole.

Solution. We write first the combustion equation for the problem and do this by assuming that the combustion is complete. Thus we write

$$C_3H_8 + 6O_2 + 22.56N_2 \rightarrow 3CO_2 + 4H_2O + O_2 + 22.56N_2$$

By Eq. (9-5) it follows that, for adiabatic combustion in the absence of shaft work,

$$\Sigma H_m = \Sigma H_p$$

We now evaluate the enthalpies of the various components at 77°F. In doing this we may use (1) specific-heat equations or (2) tables of enthalpies. Let us use the former and in doing so let us assume that we are dealing with a semiperfect gas. In other words, the specific heat is a function of temperature only. Thus,

$$c_p = f(T) \quad \text{and} \quad c_p \, dT = dH$$

Using the data in Table A-8 and assuming an arbitrary reference temperature of 460°F, we have, for the oxygen,

$$(H - H^0)_{O_2} = \int_{460}^{537} \left(11.515 - \frac{172}{\sqrt{T}} + \frac{1,530}{T} \right) dT$$

$$= 504 \text{ Btu/lb mole}$$

$$6(H - H^0)_{O_2} = 504 \times 6 = 3024 \text{ Btu}$$

For the nitrogen,

$$(H - H^0)_{N_2} = \int_{460}^{537} \left(9.47 - \frac{3.47 \times 10^3}{T} + \frac{1.16 \times 10^6}{T^2} \right) dT$$

$$= 602 \text{ Btu/lb mole}$$

$$22.56(H - H^0)_{N_2} = 22.56 \times 602 = 13,581.12 \text{ Btu}$$

We have found the enthalpies of the reactants. We must determine now the temperature at which the summations of the enthalpies of the reactants and of the products are equal. Thus for the respective constituents we write

$$(H - H^0)_{CO_2} = \int_{460}^{T} \left(16.2 - \frac{6.53 \times 10^3}{T} + \frac{1.41 \times 10^6}{T^2} \right) dT$$

$$(H - H^0)_{H_2O} = \int_{460}^{T} \left(19.86 - \frac{597}{\sqrt{T}} + \frac{7,500}{T} \right) dT$$

$$(H - H^0)_{O_2} = \int_{460}^{T} \left(11.515 - \frac{172}{\sqrt{T}} + \frac{1,530}{T}\right) dT$$

$$(H - H^0)_{N_2} = \int_{460}^{T} \left(9.47 - \frac{3.47 \times 10^3}{T} + \frac{1.16 \times 10^6}{T^2}\right) dT$$

The following equality can then be set up for solution:

$$876,876 + 3024 + 13,581.12 = 3\int_{460}^{T} \left(16.2 - \frac{6.53 \times 10^3}{T} + \frac{1.41 \times 10^6}{T^2}\right) dT$$

$$+ 4\int_{460}^{T} \left(19.86 - \frac{597}{\sqrt{T}} + \frac{7,500}{T}\right) dT + \int_{460}^{T} \left(11.515 - \frac{172}{\sqrt{T}} + \frac{1,530}{T}\right) dT$$

$$+ 22.56\int_{460}^{T} \left(9.47 - \frac{3.47 \times 10^3}{T} + \frac{1.16 \times 10^6}{T^2}\right) dT$$

Integrating, expanding, and using a trial-and-error solution, $T = 3800°R = 3340°F$ is found to be the answer.

Example 2. Solve Example 1 taking the effects of dissociation into consideration.

Solution. The following dissociation reactions are applicable:

$$CO_2 \rightarrow CO + \tfrac{1}{2}O_2 \tag{a}$$

$$H_2O \rightarrow H_2 + \tfrac{1}{2}O_2 \tag{b}$$

First, treat dissociation reaction (a), and let x be the moles dissociated per mole of CO_2. Thus we have from Eq. (a),

$$(1 - x)CO_2 \rightarrow xCO + \frac{x}{2}O_2$$

The total number of moles dissociated will be

$$\Sigma N_i = N_{CO_2} + N_{CO} + N_{O_2} = 1 - x + x + \frac{x}{2} = 1 + \frac{x}{2} \quad \text{moles}$$

The partial pressures will be given by

$$p_i = p \frac{N_i}{\Sigma N_i}$$

where p is the total pressure in atmospheres, namely 4 in this particular problem. Thus we have

$$p_{CO_2} = 4 \frac{1 - x}{1 + x/2} = 8 \frac{1 - x}{2 + x}$$

$$p_{O_2} = 4 \frac{x/2}{1 + x/2} = \frac{4x}{2 + x}$$

$$p_{CO} = 4 \frac{x}{1 + x/2} = \frac{8x}{2 + x}$$

The constant-pressure equilibrium constant K_p for the dissociation equation (a) is defined as

$$K_p = \frac{(p_{CO})(p_{O_2})^{1/2}}{p_{CO_2}} = \frac{[8x/(2 + x)][4x/(2 + x)]^{1/2}}{8[(1 - x)/(2 + x)]} = \frac{2x\sqrt{x}}{(1 - x)\sqrt{2 + x}} \tag{c}$$

In order to find the dissociation in terms of x, we must employ the value of the equilibrium constant, which depends on the temperature. As the temperature being sought is not known, it becomes necessary to assume a temperature and use a double trial-and-error solution. In assuming this temperature we can be guided by the answer found in the previous example. Actually the adiabatic-combustion temperature when dissociation occurs must be lower than that when no dissociation occurs. However, because the temperature found in Example 1 is low as far as dissociation effects are concerned, we can predict that the amount of dissociation will be small, thus resulting in only slight lowering of the temperature. Let us assume then that $T = 3760°R$, and from Fig. 8-1 at this temperature the equilibrium constant is $K_p = 0.0025$. Solving Eq. (c) for this value we find $x = 0.0145$. Now let y be the moles dissociated from each mole of H_2O and, proceeding as before, we find $y = 0.005$.

The combustion reaction with dissociation is

$$C_3H_8 + 6O_2 + 22.56N_2 \rightarrow 3(1 - x)CO_2 + 4(1 - y)H_2O + O_2 + 3xCO$$

$$+ 3\frac{x}{2} O_2 + 4yH_2 + 4\frac{y}{2} O_2 + 22.56N_2 \quad (d)$$

Substituting for x and y in Eq. (d), we get

$$C_3H_8 + 6O_2 + 22.56N_2 \rightarrow 2.96CO_2 + 3.98H_2O + 1.032O_2$$

$$+ 0.0435CO + 0.02H_2 + 22.56N_2 \quad (e)$$

In order to obtain the adiabatic-combustion temperature we must ascertain that $\Sigma H_m = \Sigma H_p$. From here we proceed with a trial-and-error solution as we did in Example 1 and find $T = 3770°R = 3310°F$. This deviates only slightly, in particular by $10°F$, from our original assumption and hence may be accepted as satisfactory. If the accuracy is not sufficient, we repeat the solution starting with values of the equilibrium constant at $3770°R$ until the enthalpy-summation equality is satisfied in accordance with our desire.

In general, the thermodynamic properties of gases are given without dissociation. Actually, at high temperatures a portion of the gas is not in the form of pure molecular species but may be broken up into atoms or molecules of intermediate size. For more information concerning this, the reader is referred to Wooley.[4]

Example 3. Repeat Example 1 but assume that the specific humidity of the air supplied is 0.03 lb of H_2O per pound of dry air.

Solution. The combustion equation in the case of dry air is from Example 1.

$$C_3H_8 + 6O_2 + 22.56N_2 \rightarrow 3CO_2 + 4H_2O + O_2 + 22.56N_2$$

The mass of dry air m_a is

$$m_a = 6 \times 32 + 22.56 \times 28 = 824 \text{ lb/mole of fuel}$$

The mass of water vapor m_w is

$$m_w = 824 \times 0.03 = 24.75 \text{ lb/mole of fuel}$$

The moles of water vapor $N_w = 24.75/18.016 = 1.374$ moles of H_2O per mole of C_3H_8. The combustion equation becomes

$$C_3H_8 + 6O_2 + 22.56N_2 + 1.374H_2O \rightarrow 3CO_2 + 5.374H_2O + O_2 + 22.56N_2$$

We must satisfy the enthalpy balance for this equation as before. We find by trial and error that $T = 3647°R = 3187°F$.

In the preceding three examples the final temperature was found by using the specific-heat equations. An alternative method using tabular data of enthalpy values listed as a function of temperature would be considerably less cumbersome. Such data are available in the literature and the reader is referred to the gas tables of Keenan and Kaye [5] or the tables of Huff, Gordon, and Morrell.[6] By use of tabular data the method is not changed, but the operations of the trial-and-error solution are less burdensome.

Because of the rapid technological developments in jet propulsion, many studies have been made concerning flame and combustion temperatures.

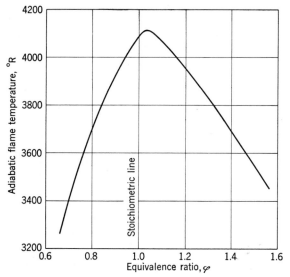

FIG. 9-9.   Theoretical flame temperatures of propane-air mixtures including dissociation effects.

Some of these present very accurate data in tabular as well as graphical form, and also offer time-saving short cuts without sacrificing accuracy. Because a thorough discussion of these is beyond the scope of this text we will merely call attention to references 7 to 10. The variation of flame temperature with mixture strength for propane at atmospheric pressure is shown in Fig. 9-9.

9-6. Ignition. The ignition of a combustible mixture is accomplished by several means. The spark plug, so common in automobile engines and gas-turbine combustors, may be used to supply the necessary energy; or the mixture can be compressed adiabatically with resultant temperature rise as in a diesel engine. Finally, the mixture may be heated externally until it ignites. In these methods two parameters are of considerable interest. One is the energy of activation discussed in a previous chapter, and the other is the ignition temperature. The latter is the lowest temperature at which a fuel may be ignited and kept burning. It is questionable whether or not the ignition temperature of a fuel is really one of its true properties. Experience indicates that many variables affect the ignition temperature, among which are the pressure, the mixture strength, and combustion-chamber configuration, as well as the wall surface and its heat-transfer characteristics. Thus different results are obtained under different conditions. Table 9-1 lists the minimum ignition temperature of selected

TABLE 9-1. MINIMUM IGNITION TEMPERATURES OF SELECTED COMPOUNDS †

Name	Formula	Ignition temperature, °F
Acetone....................	C_3H_6O	1042
Acetylene..................	C_2H_2	581
Benzene...................	C_6H_6	1078
Isobutane..................	C_4H_{10}	1010
Isobutyl alcohol............	$C_4H_{10}O$	813
Carbon monoxide...........	CO	1128
Cyclopropane..............	C_3H_6	928
Ethane....................	C_2H_6	882
Ethyl alcohol..............	C_2H_6O	738
Ethylene..................	C_2H_4	914
Gasoline..................	100 octane	804
Hydrogen.................	H_2	1065
Methane..................	CH_4	1170
Naphtha..................	...	450–531
Octane...................	C_8H_{18}	446
Oil, lubricating............	...	711
Paraffin wax..............	...	473
Propane..................	C_3H_8	898
Turpentine...............	$C_{10}H_{16}$	464

† Compiled by G. W. Jones, *U.S. Bur. Mines Bull.*, 1946.

substances and is adapted here from G. W. Jones in a U.S. Bureau of Mines Bulletin of 1946. Various characteristics of hydrocarbon ignition have been studied by Swarts and Frank.[11] Caution should be exercised in using the spontaneous-ignition temperature as a significant criterion in combustion studies as it has no definite value but changes with varying conditions.

Spark ignition can be explained according to two schools of thought. According to the thermal theory, the spark raises the temperature of a small volume of the mixture to the ignition temperature, thus initiating the ignition. According to the electrical theory, the spark supplies a certain amount of energy to the mixture, thereby exciting the molecules to an energy level at which ignition may occur. Experience indicates that the manner in which a spark is fired is quite important. Thus, for example, the discharge of a condenser is more efficient than an inductive discharge although the amount of energy generated may be the same. It has been shown by Swett [12] that the spark energy necessary for ignition decreases with increasing pressure. On the other hand, increasing mixture velocities require an increase of the ignition energy. Although the size and configuration of electrodes have an appreciable effect on ignition energy, in general less energy is needed as the electrode spacing is increased.[13] It should be remembered that a mixture does not ignite immediately upon reaching its spontaneous-ignition temperature but actually experiences an ignition delay. This is probably because of the fact that it is necessary to generate a certain concentration of active particles before rapid combustion can start. Experiments by Jackson and Brokaw [14] show that ignition lag tends to decrease with increasing temperature as well as with increasing fuel concentration.

9-7. Quenching. An important phenomenon to be considered in conjunction with flame propagation is flame quenching. It is well known that a flame can be prevented from striking back in a tube by the use of a flame trap in the form of a wire screen. Other effects such as cold walls or elbows and restrictions tend to quench a flame either by removing a sufficient amount of chain carriers or by lowering the temperature of the mixture. If we investigate flame propagation within a rectangular chamber having movable walls, we find that although we can ignite a mixture we may not maintain a flame unless the distance between the walls has a definite value. We define the quenching distance as the distance between two plates below which a flame will not propagate. Numerous and frequently conflicting studies of flame quenching have been undertaken, but it is beyond the scope of this text to deal in detail with flame quenching. Instead, the reader is referred to the studies by Lewis and von Elbe,[15] by Gaydon and Wolfhard,[16] and to many NACA publications as, for example, Potter and Berlad.[17]

9-8. General Remarks. In the preceding sections various aspects of phenomena involving flames and combustion have been considered. A careful reader will realize the subject of flames and combustion in many ways is still an art, and there are many gaps which need to be filled before it becomes a science grounded on general theories. In this introductory text it has been meant merely to survey this broad field. For detailed studies of combustion the reader can study with profit many of the references listed at the end of the chapter, including reference 18.

In regard to combustion in general it should be mentioned that the spectrum of temperatures encountered in nature varies over an exceedingly wide range. These range from close to absolute zero temperature, where the oddities of cryogenics occur, and upwards. The surface of the sun is estimated to be about 6000°K, and temperatures encountered with hydrogen bombs may be of the order of several million degrees. In this extremely wide range it is interesting to note that the spectrum of temperatures encountered with most flames is really rather narrow. Thus the flame of a gas kitchen stove is about 1500°C, whereas most molecules dissociate at temperatures less than 6000°C. When compared with the previously mentioned spectrum this is indeed a very narrow band, and yet the engineer is faced with some very difficult problems. The temperature of the oxygen-hydrogen flame is of the order of 3000°C; an oxygen-aluminum torch delivers temperatures of the order of 3500°C. Most other fuel-oxidizer combinations give temperatures which are relatively low and quite similar. As new fuels are developed the temperatures may be expected to rise appreciably. Temperatures encountered in hypersonic flight tend to be much higher than the commonly encountered flame temperatures.

Research concerning flames and combustion is physicochemical in nature and a good portion of it is done on bunsen burners. Certain aspects of the flame cannot be studied chemically because some of the intermediary products of chemical reactions are very short-lived. Using spectroscopic studies, intermediary products like OH, HC, and C_2 have been noticed.[19] These species react with one another and other molecules to form stable compounds. The energy of a molecule is made up of several types of energy, namely, translational, vibrational, rotational, and electronic. These energies may be studied in considerable detail from the radiations they emit.[20, 21] In the reaction zone of a flame it is meaningless to discuss temperature because there no equilibrium exists.

PROBLEMS

9-1. Calculate the theoretical flame temperature for the combustion of propane with 80 per cent of (dry) theoretical air at 4 atm. Neglect dissociation. The initial temperature is 77°F. Assume that the enthalpy of complete gaseous combustion of propane is 19,929 Btu/lb at 77°F. With 80 per cent air, only 80 per cent thermal-combustion energy is released.

9-2. (a) Together with the answer found in Example 1 and Prob. 9-1 above, plot the temperature as ordinate and the equivalence ratio ϕ (the equivalence ratio ϕ is defined as the ratio of the actual fuel-air ratio to the stoichiometric fuel-air ratio) between 80 per cent and 120 per cent theoretical air. (b) Explain the shape of the curve. (c) Where does the maximum temperature occur? Explain. (d) Would you expect the same trend for most hydrocarbons? (e) Would you expect the same trend for other fuels such as alcohol? (f) What fuel-oxidant combination might not act in this manner? Explain.

9-3. Repeat Prob. 9-1, taking dissociation into consideration.

9-4. Repeat Prob. 9-1, except that the air is moist and contains 0.02 lb of H_2O per pound of dry air.

9-5. Repeat Prob. 9-4, taking into consideration the effect of dissociation.

9-6. A mixture of 80 per cent of theoretical air and propane is burned at an altitude of 100,000 ft where the nitrogen-oxygen ratio is approximately 4.18 ÷ 1. Calculate the adiabatic-flame temperature if the pressure is 0.25 psia. Assume no dissociation.

9-7. Repeat Prob. 9-6, taking into account the effects of dissociation.

9-8. Repeat Prob. 9-1 if the initial temperature is 1000°F.

9-9. Repeat Prob. 9-3 if the initial temperature is 1000°F.

9-10. Repeat Prob. 9-4 if the initial temperature is 1000°F.

9-11. Repeat Prob. 9-5 if the initial temperature is 1000°F.

9-12. Repeat Prob. 9-6 if the initial temperature is 1000°F.

9-13. Repeat Prob. 9-7 if the initial temperature is 1000°F.

9-14. Solve Probs. 9-1 to 9-13 using data given in the gas tables by Keenan and Kaye.

9-15. Solve Probs. 9-1 to 9-13 using the data given in *NACA Rept.* 1037.

9-16. Consider the flames resulting from two different fuels one of which has a larger kinematic viscosity. In which flame will turbulence tend to set in at lower velocities provided the same burner is used?

9-17. Find the constant-volume heat of combustion of carbon monoxide at 25°C and 1 atm.

9-18. For the same fuel, will Q_p vary at different temperatures? Prove your answer by (*a*) the derivation of pertinent equations, and (*b*) the explanation of the physical concepts involved.

9-19. Repeat Prob. 9-18 for Q_v.

9-20. Explain why, in general, a lean mixture burns hotter.

9-21. Why does a mixture diluted with nitrogen tend to give a cooler flame?

REFERENCES

1. Burke, S. P., and T. E. W. Schumann: Diffusion Flames, *Ind. Eng. Chem.*, vol. 20, no. 10, p. 998, 1928.
2. Kippenhan, C. J., and H. O. Croft: The Effect of High-frequency Sound Waves on an Air-Propane Flame, *Trans. ASME*, vol. 74, pp. 1151–1155, October, 1952.
3. Barr, John: Diffusion Flames in the Laboratory, *AGARD Mem.* AG 11/M7, Scheveningen Conference, May 3–7, 1954.
4. Wooley, H. W.: Effect of Dissociation on Thermodynamic Properties of Pure Diatomic Gases, *NACA TN* 3270, April, 1955.
5. Keenan, J. H., and J. Kaye: "Gas Tables," John Wiley & Sons, Inc., New York, 1945.
6. Huff, V. N., S. Gordon, and V. E. Morrell: General Method and Thermodynamic Tables for Computation of Equilibrium Composition and Temperature of Chemical Reactions, *NACA Rept.* 1037, 1951.
7. Turner, L. R., and D. Bogart: Constant-pressure Combustion Charts Including Effects of Diluent Addition, *NACA Rept.* 937, 1949.
8. Vichnievsky, R., B. Sale, and J. Marcadet: Combustion Temperatures and Gas Composition, *Jet Propulsion*, vol. 3, no. 25, p. 105, 1955.
9. Powell, H. N., and S. N. Suciu: Survey of the Thermodynamic Properties of C_nH_{2n}: Air Combustion Gases, *Proc. Gas Dynamics Symposium on Aerothermochemistry*, Northwestern University–American Rocket Society, 1955.
10. Noeggerath, W.: General Enthalpy-Temperature-Entropy Diagram for Ideal Gases and Gas Mixtures, Up to 5000°K, paper presented at Ninth Annual Meeting, American Rocket Society, 1954.
11. Swarts, D. E., and C. E. Frank: Effect of Hydrocarbon Structure on Reaction Processes Leading to Spontaneous Ignition, *NACA TN* 3384, July, 1955.

12. Swett, C. C., Jr.: Spark Ignition of Flowing Gases. IV. Theory of Ignition in Non-turbulent and Turbulent Flow Using Long-duration Discharges, *NACA* RME 54F29a, 1954.

13. Swett, C. C., Jr.: Spark Ignition of Flowing Gases. II. Effect of Electrode Parameters on Energy Required to Ignite a Propane-Air Mixture, *NACA* RME 51J12, 1951.

14. Jackson, J. L., and R. S. Brokaw: Variation of Spontaneous Ignition Delays with Temperature and Composition for Propane-Oxygen-Nitrogen Mixtures at Atmospheric Pressure, *NACA* RM E54B19, 1954.

15. Lewis, B., and G. von Elbe: "Combustion, Flames and Explosions of Gases," Academic Press, Inc., New York, 1951.

16. Gaydon, A. G., and H. G. Wolfhard: "Flames," Chapman and Hall, Ltd., London, 1953.

17. Potter, A. E., Jr., and A. L. Berlad: A Thermal Equation for Flame Quenching, *NACA TN* 3398, 1955.

18. Jost, W.: "Explosion and Combustion Processes in Gases" (trans. by H. O. Croft), McGraw-Hill Book Company, Inc., New York, 1946.

19. Gaydon, A. G.: "Spectroscopy and Combustion Theory," 2d ed., Chapman and Hall, Ltd., London, 1948.

20. Penner, S. S.: "Spectroscopic Studies of Premixed Laminar Flames, Selected Combustion Problems," AGARD, Butterworth's Scientific Publications, London.

21. Dyne, P. J., and S. S. Penner: Survey of Optical Methods for the Determination of Temperatures in Rocket Engines, *J. Am. Rocket Soc.*, vol. 23, p. 165, 1953.

CHAPTER 10

INTRODUCTION TO MULTIDIMENSIONAL FLOW

10-1. Introduction. In most of the preceding discussions it was assumed that the flow is one-dimensional and steady. The limitations of one-dimensional flow were discussed in Chap. 2, and it was also noted that with flow phenomena such as shock waves and circulation it is necessary to consider flow in at least two directions. In this chapter an attempt will be made to summarize the fundamentals of multidimensional flow. The approach chosen is based on cartesian coordinates, but it should be mentioned that another system, such as one using cylindrical coordinates, could have been employed. The discussions here do not constitute a detailed treatise on the subject, and for a more comprehensive treatment the reader is referred to the excellent treatises listed in the bibliography at the end of this chapter.

10-2. The Equation of Continuity. The first law of thermodynamics is a mathematical statement of the principle of the conservation of energy. Similarly, the equation of continuity is the mathematical statement of the principle of the conservation of mass. In Chap. 2 the equation of continuity was derived for steady, one-dimensional flow. Here, an equation of continuity, which will be applicable to both steady and unsteady flow and which will be useful when properties change in more than one direction, will be developed. For this purpose, consider a fluid element in the form of a parallelepiped as shown in Fig. 10-1. Assume that the various properties of pressure, density, temperature, and velocity have values p, ρ, T, and V at the geometric center of the figure. These properties may be different at various points in the region defined by the parallelepiped. Also, depending on the characteristics of the system, the properties may change at different rates in each direction of the coordinate system.

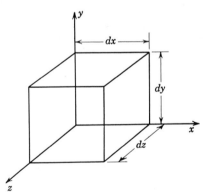

Fig. 10-1. Fluid element.

For convenience, the positive directions along the axes are taken in the directions of the axis arrows. Thus in the x direction the density at the center of the left face of the parallelepiped having dimensions dy and dz will be

$$\rho - \frac{1}{2} \frac{\partial \rho}{\partial x} dx$$

The negative increment is introduced to show the apparent decrease in density toward the left. Similarly, on the opposite face the density is greater than at the center and hence appears as

$$\rho + \frac{1}{2} \frac{\partial \rho}{\partial x} dx$$

The density can have similar variations in the y and the z directions. Of course, if the flow is one-dimensional the y and z directions do not affect the problem, and $\partial \rho / \partial x = d\rho / dx$. Thus at the two faces already discussed, the density will be

$$\rho - \frac{1}{2} d\rho \qquad \text{and} \qquad \rho + \frac{1}{2} d\rho$$

respectively.

Although the density can vary as discussed above, it is a scalar quantity and does not have components along each of the coordinate axes. This is not so in the case of velocity, which is a vector quantity and thus in cartesian coordinates has components V_x, V_y, and V_z. Thus,

$$V^2 = V_x{}^2 + V_y{}^2 + V_z{}^2$$

In vectorial notation one may write

$$\mathbf{V} = \mathbf{i}V_x + \mathbf{j}V_y + \mathbf{k}V_z$$

in which $\mathbf{i}$, $\mathbf{j}$, and $\mathbf{k}$ are unit vectors in the x, y, and z directions respectively.

Let the velocity and the density of the fluid be denoted by $\mathbf{V} = \mathbf{i}V_x + \mathbf{j}V_y + \mathbf{k}V_z$ and ρ respectively at the geometric center of the parallelepiped control volume. It should be noted that the velocity is a function of the coordinates only, regardless of time. It follows that the mass rate of flow or the flux entering the control volume through the left-hand face and in the x direction will be

$$\left[\rho V_x - \frac{1}{2} \frac{\partial}{\partial x} (\rho V_x)\, dx \right] dy\, dz$$

Similarly, the mass rate of flow leaving the control volume through its right-hand face will be

$$\left[\rho V_x + \frac{1}{2} \frac{\partial}{\partial x} (\rho V_x)\, dx \right] dy\, dz$$

For the steady flow and considering the x direction only, the influx and efflux will be the same. However, for unsteady flow the fluid within the central volume may be increased or depleted. For the general case, then, the amount of fluid stored within the control volume will be the difference of the amounts of fluid entering and leaving, namely,

$$-\frac{\partial}{\partial x} (\rho V_x) \, dx \, dy \, dz$$

Similarly, the storage due to flow in the y direction will be

$$-\frac{\partial}{\partial y} (\rho V_y) \, dx \, dy \, dz$$

and in the z direction it will be

$$-\frac{\partial}{\partial z} (\rho V_z) \, dx \, dy \, dz$$

The total amount of fluid stored within the control volume will be the sum of these, namely,

$$-\left[\frac{\partial}{\partial x} (\rho V_x) + \frac{\partial}{\partial y} (\rho V_y) + \frac{\partial}{\partial z} (\rho V_z)\right] dx \, dy \, dz$$

On the other hand, the rate of increase of the mass of the parallelepiped is

$$\frac{\partial \rho}{\partial t} \, dx \, dy \, dz$$

Equating this to the expression for the storage of fluid within the parallelepiped and dividing by $dx \, dy \, dz$ throughout, the general form of the continuity equation is obtained, namely,

$$\frac{\partial}{\partial x} (\rho V_x) + \frac{\partial}{\partial y} (\rho V_y) + \frac{\partial}{\partial z} (\rho V_z) + \frac{\partial \rho}{\partial t} = 0 \qquad (10\text{-}1)$$

Equation (10-1) may be written in vectorial notation as follows:

$$\text{div } \rho \mathbf{V} = -\frac{\partial \rho}{\partial t} \qquad (10\text{-}2)$$

By virtue of vector identities

$$\text{div } \rho \mathbf{V} = \rho \text{ div } \mathbf{V} + \mathbf{V} \cdot \text{grad } \rho$$

Therefore, Eq. (10-2) becomes

$$\rho \text{ div } \mathbf{V} + \mathbf{V} \cdot \text{grad } \rho + \frac{\partial \rho}{\partial t} = 0 \qquad (10\text{-}3)$$

208 GAS DYNAMICS

Equations (10-1) to (10-3) are all expressions of the equation of continuity and are valid for both steady and unsteady flow.

In the case of steady flow there can be no increase of mass within the control volume and accordingly $\partial \rho / \partial t = 0$. Hence, for steady flow the continuity equation becomes

$$\text{div } \rho \mathbf{V} = 0 \tag{10-4}$$

which by vector identities is

$$\rho \text{ div } \mathbf{V} + \mathbf{V} \cdot \text{grad } \rho = 0 \tag{10-5}$$

If, further, the flow is incompressible, ρ remains constant during the process, and hence the continuity equation assumes the form

$$\text{div } \mathbf{V} = 0 \tag{10-6}$$

10-3. The Momentum Equations. Various viewpoints hold in considering the motion of fluids. One of these, the momentum principle, will be discussed in this section, and the Lagrangian and the Eulerian approaches will be considered in the next two sections. The momentum considerations derive from Newton's second law of motion. The momentum theorem is of particular interest when the dynamic equilibrium of a finite volume of fluid particles is under consideration, and is related to Euler's equation as the next two sections will show.

Consider a system as shown in Fig. 10-2, and assume that this system lies within the fixed control volume $\mathcal{V}$ at time t_1. Let the area of the con-

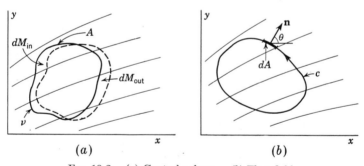

Fig. 10-2. (a) Control volume. (b) Flow field.

trol volume be denoted by A, and assume that fluid flow proceeds in the x direction. Because of the flow process, the boundary of the fluid system will no longer coincide with the boundary of the control volume after a time lapse dt. Thus, if $t_2 = t_1 + dt$, then at time t_2 there will lie within the system boundary, but outside the control volume, a certain amount of fluid, the momentum increment of which may be denoted by dM_{out}. Similarly, the momentum increment of the fluid within the control volume, but not part of the system, may be denoted by dM_{in}. Accordingly, the rate of change of momentum of the fluid inside the control volume will be given by

$$\frac{dM}{dt} = \frac{dM'_2 - dM'_1}{dt} + \frac{dM_{out} - dM_{in}}{dt} \tag{10-7}$$

in which the superscript refers to the fluid inside the control volume.

In the case of steady flow, Eq. (10-7) reduces to

$$\frac{dM}{dt} = \frac{dM_{out} - dM_{in}}{dt} \tag{10-8}$$

Now consider Fig. 10-2, in which is shown the control volume $\mho$ having the surface area under consideration. An increment of the control-volume area may be denoted by dA and represented by a unit vector $\mathbf{n}$ which forms an angle θ with the horizontal direction.

The force on the fluid within the control volume is

$$-\iint_A p \cos \theta \, dA$$

The velocity of the fluid is in vectorial form $\mathbf{V} = \mathbf{i}V_x + \mathbf{j}V_y$, and the unit vector $\mathbf{n} = \mathbf{i} \cos \theta + \mathbf{j} \sin \theta$. The net force acting on the boundary must be equal both in magnitude and in direction to the momentum flux (time rate of momentum exchange) across the boundary.

In accordance with the equation of continuity, the mass rate of flow through dA is $\rho \mathbf{V}\mathbf{n} \, dA$, which may be written in the form

$$\rho(V_x \cos \theta + V_y \sin \theta) \, dA$$

It follows that the total rate change of momentum considered in the x direction is

$$\rho \iint_A V_x(V_x \cos \theta + V_y \sin \theta) \, dA$$

On the other hand, the force on the fluid within the control volume is

$$-\iint_A p \cos \theta \, dA$$

Therefore, by Newton's second law of motion, the momentum flux in the x direction is

$$\iint_A \rho V_x(V_x \cos \theta + V_y \sin \theta) \, dA = -\iint_A p \cos \theta \, dA \tag{10-9}$$

If external forces F such as those due to gravity are to be accounted for, Eq. (10-9) may be written in the form

$$\iint_A V_x(V_x \cos \theta + V_y \sin \theta)\, dA = F_x - \iint_A p \cos \theta\, dA \qquad (10\text{-}10)$$

Similar equations can be derived for the y and z directions.

Equations (10-9) and (10-10) are two versions of the so-called *momentum equation* which is valid for both reversible and irreversible processes. In Eq. (10-10), the force F is positive denoting the force which an object such as an airfoil inside the control boundary exerts *on* the fluid. The momentum equation is used to calculate forces on a body moving relative to an unbounded fluid. It may also be used in determining skin friction.

10-4. Lagrange's Method. As implied in the last section, the equations of fluid motion can be expressed in the form of both Lagrange and Euler. In Lagrange's form, the motion is described in terms of the paths followed by the individual fluid particles, but in Euler's form the motion is described at all points of space occupied by the fluid at various values of the time t. In other words, in Lagrange's form the coordinates are assumed to be moving with the fluid particles, and in Euler's form the coordinates are fixed in space.

Both in Lagrange's form and in Euler's form certain restrictions are imposed on the system. These are:

1. The principle of conservation of mass holds.
2. The principle of conservation of momentum holds.
3. The flow is frictionless.
4. External forces such as gravity, magnetism, and electricity do not exist.†
5. No shaft work is done.

For analysis, a set of cartesian coordinates with x, y, and z axes will be used, and $\mathbf{V}$ will be considered the velocity vector representing the flow such that

$$\mathbf{V} = \mathbf{i}V_x + \mathbf{j}V_y + \mathbf{k}V_z$$

$$V^2 = V_x{}^2 + V_y{}^2 + V_z{}^2$$

Let the rectangular coordinates x, y, and z be functions of the time t and write $V = V(x,y,z,t)$. At $t = 0$ the original position of a fluid particle is fixed by ξ, η, and ζ. Then ξ, η, and ζ are independent variables, and x, y, and z are dependent variables of ξ, η, ζ, and t.

† The imposing of restriction 4 on Euler's equation is to some extent a matter of conjecture. Thus, although in the very true sense external forces should be considered in the "dynamic equations of motion" (general) rather than in Euler's equations, some sources nevertheless include external forces in the Eulerian analysis.

The velocity components of the fluid particle will be

$$V_x = \frac{\partial x}{\partial t} \qquad V_y = \frac{\partial y}{\partial t} \qquad V_z = \frac{\partial z}{\partial t}$$

and the acceleration components will be

$$\alpha_x = \frac{\partial^2 x}{\partial t^2} \qquad \alpha_y = \frac{\partial^2 y}{\partial t^2} \qquad \alpha_z = \frac{\partial^2 z}{\partial t^2}$$

V_x, V_y, and V_z are finite and continuous functions of x, y, and z. α_x, α_y, and α_z are also everywhere finite. Accordingly, in the absence of external forces the equations of motion must be

$$\frac{\partial^2 x}{\partial t^2} = -\frac{1}{\rho}\frac{\partial p}{\partial x} \qquad \frac{\partial^2 y}{\partial t^2} = -\frac{1}{\rho}\frac{\partial p}{\partial y} \qquad \frac{\partial^2 z}{\partial t^2} = -\frac{1}{\rho}\frac{\partial p}{\partial z} \qquad (10\text{-}11)$$

This can be written in vectorial notation as

$$\frac{dV}{dt} = -\frac{1}{\rho}\,\mathrm{grad}\,p \qquad (10\text{-}12)$$

Equations (10-11) and (10-12) express the conservation of momentum and are restatements of Newton's law. In these relations the partials of pressure are expressed with respect to the dependent variables and can be written also with respect to ξ, η, and ζ. Multiplying Eqs. (10-11) by $\partial x/\partial \xi$, $\partial x/\partial \eta$, $\partial x/\partial \zeta$, $\partial y/\partial \xi$, $\partial y/\partial \eta$, etc., and adding, it is found that

$$\frac{\partial^2 x}{\partial t^2}\frac{\partial x}{\partial \xi} + \frac{\partial^2 y}{\partial t^2}\frac{\partial y}{\partial \xi} + \frac{\partial^2 z}{\partial t^2}\frac{\partial z}{\partial \xi} = -\frac{1}{\rho}\frac{\partial p}{\partial \xi}$$

$$\frac{\partial^2 x}{\partial t^2}\frac{\partial x}{\partial \eta} + \frac{\partial^2 y}{\partial t^2}\frac{\partial y}{\partial \eta} + \frac{\partial^2 z}{\partial t^2}\frac{\partial z}{\partial \eta} = -\frac{1}{\rho}\frac{\partial p}{\partial \eta} \qquad (10\text{-}13)$$

$$\frac{\partial^2 x}{\partial t^2}\frac{\partial x}{\partial \zeta} + \frac{\partial^2 y}{\partial t^2}\frac{\partial y}{\partial \zeta} + \frac{\partial^2 z}{\partial t^2}\frac{\partial z}{\partial \zeta} = -\frac{1}{\rho}\frac{\partial p}{\partial \zeta}$$

Equations (10-13) are known as the Lagrangian form of the dynamical equations.

In a closed channel a fluid of mass m may be expressed as

$$m = \int_{\upsilon} \rho \, dx \, dy \, dz$$

in which υ denotes that the integral is to be calculated for the control volume υ.

This may be written in terms of the variables ξ, η, and ζ by Jacobian transformation. Thus the Jacobian

$$ J = \frac{\partial(x,y,z)}{\partial(\xi,\eta,\zeta)} $$

is by definition the determinant

$$ \begin{vmatrix} \dfrac{\partial x}{\partial \xi} & \dfrac{\partial y}{\partial \xi} & \dfrac{\partial z}{\partial \xi} \\[2ex] \dfrac{\partial x}{\partial \eta} & \dfrac{\partial y}{\partial \eta} & \dfrac{\partial z}{\partial \eta} \\[2ex] \dfrac{\partial x}{\partial \zeta} & \dfrac{\partial y}{\partial \zeta} & \dfrac{\partial z}{\partial \zeta} \end{vmatrix} da\, db\, dc $$

Accordingly,

$$ m = \iiint \rho\, \frac{\partial(x,y,z)}{\partial(\xi,\eta,\zeta)}\, d\xi\, d\eta\, d\zeta $$

and for steady flow from the equation of continuity

$$ \frac{\partial}{\partial t}\left[\rho\, \frac{\partial(x,y,z)}{\partial(\xi,\eta,\zeta)} \right] = 0 $$

The Eqs. (10-13) are cumbersome to solve and therefore the Lagrangian form is not commonly used, but Euler's method is employed.

10-5. Euler's Method. A velocity function $\mathbf{V} = f(x,y,z,t)$ may undergo change in two ways: change due to time, and change due to variation of position. The former is expressed by the local differential quotient, and the latter is expressed by the spatial or convective differential quotient. The total change is caused by the superimposition of the two changes, provided they both exist, and is expressed by the substantial differential quotient. Accordingly,

$$ \frac{d\mathbf{V}}{dt} = \frac{\partial \mathbf{V}}{\partial t} + \frac{\partial \mathbf{V}}{\partial x}\frac{dx}{dt} + \frac{\partial \mathbf{V}}{\partial y}\frac{dy}{dt} + \frac{\partial \mathbf{V}}{\partial z}\frac{dz}{dt} \tag{10-14} $$

or

$$ \frac{d\mathbf{V}}{dt} = \frac{\partial \mathbf{V}}{\partial t} + \mathbf{V}\cdot\mathrm{grad}\ \mathbf{V} \tag{10-15} $$

The local differential $\partial \mathbf{V}/\partial t$ is a measure of unsteadiness; the spatial differential $\mathbf{V}\cdot\mathrm{grad}\ \mathbf{V}$ indicates nonuniformity. In steady-flow relations the local differential will be nonexistent since there is no change of properties at each state point with respect to time. The acceleration of an elementary fluid volume will be equal to and in the direction of the force acting upon it.

Euler's equation for one-dimensional flow [Eq. (2-29)] is

$$\mathbf{V} \, d\mathbf{V} + \frac{dp}{\rho} = 0$$

Also for steady one-dimensional flow,

$$\frac{d\mathbf{V}}{dt} = \frac{\partial \mathbf{V}}{\partial x} \frac{dx}{dt} = V_x \frac{\partial \mathbf{V}}{\partial x}$$

and Euler's equation becomes

$$V_x \frac{\partial \mathbf{V}}{\partial x} + \frac{1}{\rho} \frac{\partial p}{\partial x} = 0 \tag{10-16}$$

In three directions, then,

$$\underbrace{V_x \frac{\partial \mathbf{V}}{\partial x} + V_y \frac{\partial \mathbf{V}}{\partial y} + V_z \frac{\partial \mathbf{V}}{\partial z}}_{\frac{d\mathbf{V}}{dt}} + \frac{1}{\rho} \underbrace{\left(\frac{\partial p}{\partial x} + \frac{\partial p}{\partial y} + \frac{\partial p}{\partial z} \right)}_{\text{grad } p} = 0$$

and

$$\frac{d\mathbf{V}}{dt} + \frac{1}{\rho} \text{grad } p = 0 \tag{10-17}$$

or, in equivalent form,

$$\frac{dV}{dt} = - \frac{1}{\rho} \left(\frac{\partial p}{\partial x} \mathbf{i} + \frac{\partial p}{\partial y} \mathbf{j} + \frac{\partial p}{\partial z} \mathbf{k} \right) \tag{10-18}$$

In Eq. (10-14) appear the terms

$$\frac{\partial V}{\partial x} = \frac{\partial}{\partial x} (V_x \mathbf{i} + V_y \mathbf{j} + V_z \mathbf{k})$$

$$\frac{\partial V}{\partial x} = \frac{\partial V_x}{\partial x} \mathbf{i} + \frac{\partial V_y}{\partial x} \mathbf{j} + \frac{\partial V_z}{\partial x} \mathbf{k}$$

$$\frac{\partial V}{\partial y} = \frac{\partial V_x}{\partial y} \mathbf{i} + \frac{\partial V_y}{\partial y} \mathbf{j} + \frac{\partial V_z}{\partial y} \mathbf{k} \tag{10-19}$$

and

$$\frac{\partial V}{\partial z} = \frac{\partial V_x}{\partial z} \mathbf{i} + \frac{\partial V_y}{\partial z} \mathbf{j} + \frac{\partial V_z}{\partial z} \mathbf{k}$$

Also

$$(\mathbf{V} \cdot \text{grad})\mathbf{V} = V_x \frac{\partial V}{\partial x} + V_y \frac{\partial V}{\partial y} + V_z \frac{\partial V}{\partial z} \tag{10-20}$$

Using Eqs. (10-19) and (10-20),

$$(\mathbf{V}\cdot\text{grad})\mathbf{V} = V_x\left(\frac{\partial V_x}{\partial x}\mathbf{i} + \frac{\partial V_y}{\partial x}\mathbf{j} + \frac{\partial V_z}{\partial x}\mathbf{k}\right)$$

$$+ V_y\left(\frac{\partial V_x}{\partial y}\mathbf{i} + \frac{\partial V_y}{\partial y}\mathbf{j} + \frac{\partial V_z}{\partial y}\mathbf{k}\right)$$

$$+ V_z\left(\frac{\partial V_x}{\partial z}\mathbf{i} + \frac{\partial V_y}{\partial z}\mathbf{j} + \frac{\partial V_z}{\partial z}\mathbf{k}\right) \quad (10\text{-}21)$$

Using Eqs. (10-10) and (10-21), Eq. (10-17) becomes

$$-\frac{1}{\rho}\left(\frac{\partial p}{\partial x}\mathbf{i} + \frac{\partial p}{\partial y}\mathbf{j} + \frac{\partial p}{\partial z}\mathbf{k}\right) = \frac{\partial V_x}{\partial t}\mathbf{i} + \frac{\partial V_y}{\partial t}\mathbf{j} + \frac{\partial V_z}{\partial t}\mathbf{k}$$

$$+ V_x\left(\frac{\partial V_x}{\partial x}\mathbf{i} + \frac{\partial V_y}{\partial x}\mathbf{j} + \frac{\partial V_z}{\partial x}\mathbf{k}\right) + V_y\left(\frac{\partial V_x}{\partial y}\mathbf{i} + \frac{\partial V_y}{\partial y}\mathbf{j} + \frac{\partial V_z}{\partial y}\mathbf{k}\right)$$

$$+ V_z\left(\frac{\partial V_x}{\partial z}\mathbf{i} + \frac{\partial V_y}{\partial z}\mathbf{j} + \frac{\partial V_z}{\partial z}\mathbf{k}\right) \quad (10\text{-}22)$$

Collecting terms with the same unit vector and canceling this unit vector, we find that the equations can be written as

$$\frac{\partial V_x}{\partial t} + V_x\frac{\partial V_x}{\partial x} + V_y\frac{\partial V_x}{\partial y} + V_z\frac{\partial V_x}{\partial z} = -\frac{1}{\rho}\frac{\partial p}{\partial x}$$

$$\frac{\partial V_y}{\partial t} + V_x\frac{\partial V_y}{\partial x} + V_y\frac{\partial V_y}{\partial y} + V_z\frac{\partial V_y}{\partial z} = -\frac{1}{\rho}\frac{\partial p}{\partial y} \quad (10\text{-}23)$$

$$\frac{\partial V_z}{\partial t} + V_x\frac{\partial V_z}{\partial x} + V_y\frac{\partial V_z}{\partial y} + V_z\frac{\partial V_z}{\partial z} = -\frac{1}{\rho}\frac{\partial p}{\partial z}$$

Equations (10-23) represent another way of expressing Euler's equations of motion. As before, they are valid only in the case of reversible flow of an inviscid fluid in the absence of friction and external forces such as gravity. Of course, there are no thermal restrictions imposed on the flow, and accordingly it may or may not be adiabatic. More general dynamic equations of motion will be developed in later sections of this chapter.

In vectorial notation Euler's equations are written as

$$\frac{\partial \mathbf{V}}{\partial t} + \mathbf{V}\cdot\text{grad } \mathbf{V} = -\frac{1}{\rho}\text{grad } p \quad (10\text{-}24)$$

However, by the identity of vectors

$$\mathbf{V} \cdot \text{grad } \mathbf{V} = \text{curl } \mathbf{V} \times \mathbf{V} + \text{grad } \frac{V^2}{2}$$

so that Eq. (10-24) becomes

$$\frac{\partial \mathbf{V}}{\partial t} + \text{curl } \mathbf{V} \times \mathbf{V} + \text{grad } \frac{V^2}{2} = -\frac{1}{\rho} \text{grad } p \qquad (10\text{-}25)$$

In Eqs. (10-23) there are five unknowns, V_x, V_y, V_z, p, and ρ and only three equations. Another relation may be added without introducing any new unknown variables by using the continuity principle as expressed by Eq. (10-3). As a fifth relation, the equation state or the definition of the acoustic velocity can be used. Also, another equation, accompanied by only one additional variable, could have been added to the system considering the substantial differential of the entropy for the adiabatic case. Thus

$$\frac{\partial s}{\partial t} + V_x \frac{\partial s}{\partial x} + V_y \frac{\partial s}{\partial y} + V_z \frac{\partial s}{\partial z} = 0 \qquad (10\text{-}26)$$

10-6. Bernoulli's Equation. The definition of irrotational flow holds regardless of whether the flow is compressible or incompressible.

For steady, irrotational flow Euler's equation [Eq. (10-25)] becomes

$$\text{grad } \frac{V^2}{2} + \frac{1}{\rho} \text{grad } p = 0 \qquad (10\text{-}27)$$

However, by the definition of enthalpy,

$$\mathbf{V} \text{ grad } p = \frac{1}{\rho} dp = dh - T \, ds$$

and therefore Eq. (10-27) becomes

$$\text{grad } \frac{V^2}{2} + \text{grad } h = T \text{ grad } \mathbf{s} \qquad (10\text{-}28)$$

which for an isentropic flow is

$$\text{grad } \frac{V^2}{2} + \text{grad } h = 0 \qquad (10\text{-}29)$$

10-7. The Energy Equation. According to the first fundamental law of thermodynamics, when the shaft work and the change in potential energy need not be considered the first-law equation can be expressed as

$$dQ = du + d\left(\frac{p}{\rho}\right) + d\left(\frac{V^2}{2}\right) \qquad (10\text{-}30)$$

Let us introduce time in differential form and set an equality between the change in heat transport and the other variable factors. We may express this statement as follows:

$$\frac{d}{dt}(Q) = \frac{d}{dt}(u) + \frac{d}{dt}\left(\frac{p}{\rho}\right) + \frac{d}{dt}\left(\frac{V^2}{2}\right) \tag{10-31}$$

In Eq. (10-31), Q may be the sum of the heat transported across the boundaries and also represents irreversibility effects resulting from mechanical-energy dissipations in the system. The term Q may vary with both coordinates and time, the latter variable entering the considerations if the heat flow is unsteady. Considering the heat transport only, we can express the conduction-heat transfer by the well-known Fourier equation,

$$\alpha \nabla^2 T = \frac{\partial T}{\partial t}$$

in which ∇^2 is the Laplacian operator defined as

$$\nabla^2 = \frac{\partial^2}{\partial x^2} + \frac{\partial^2}{\partial y^2} + \frac{\partial^2}{\partial z^2}$$

and α is the thermal diffusivity $= k/c\rho$, where k is the coefficient of thermal conductivity. By employing suitable vector identities the Fourier equation may be rewritten as follows:

$$c\frac{\partial T}{\partial t} = \frac{1}{\rho}\,\text{div}\,(k\,\text{grad}\,T)$$

which upon expansion becomes

$$\frac{\partial Q}{\partial t} = \frac{1}{\rho}\left[\frac{\partial}{\partial x}\left(k\frac{\partial T}{\partial x}\right) + \frac{\partial}{\partial y}\left(k\frac{\partial T}{\partial y}\right) + \frac{\partial}{\partial z}\left(k\frac{\partial T}{\partial z}\right)\right] \tag{10-32}$$

The internal energy is of course a property of the system under consideration. It may vary with time, and in many cases it does not need to be considered as a function of the coordinates x, y, and z. On the other hand, it sometimes is convenient to express the change in internal energy in component form, and this may be accomplished easily for a perfect gas for which the internal energy is a function of temperature only, namely, $du = c_v\,dT$. Thus we can write

$$\frac{du}{dt} = \frac{d}{dt}(c_v T) = \frac{\partial}{\partial t}(c_v T) + \frac{\partial}{\partial x}(c_v T)\frac{dx}{dt} + \frac{\partial}{\partial y}(c_v T)\frac{dy}{dt} + \frac{\partial}{\partial z}(c_v T)\frac{dz}{dt}$$

$$\tag{10-33}$$

Remembering that the time rate of distance is the velocity, Eq. (10-33) becomes

$$\frac{du}{dt} = \frac{d}{dt}(c_v T) = \frac{\partial}{\partial t}(c_v T) + V_x \frac{\partial}{\partial x}(c_v T) + V_y \frac{\partial}{\partial y}(c_v T) + V_z \frac{\partial}{\partial z}(c_v T)$$

$$(10\text{-}34)$$

The change with time of the kinetic energy is found by recalling that

$$|\mathbf{V}| = \sqrt{V_x^2 + V_y^2 + V_z^2}$$

Thus
$$\frac{d}{dt}\left(\frac{V^2}{2}\right) = \frac{d}{dt}\left(\frac{V_x^2 + V_y^2 + V_z^2}{2}\right)$$

$$= V_x \frac{\partial V_x}{\partial t} + V_y \frac{\partial V_y}{\partial t} + V_z \frac{\partial V_z}{\partial t}$$

$$+ V_x \frac{\partial V_x}{\partial x}\frac{dx}{dt} + V_y \frac{\partial V_y}{\partial y}\frac{dy}{dt} + V_z \frac{\partial V_z}{\partial z}\frac{dz}{dt}$$

$$\frac{d}{dt}\left(\frac{V^2}{2}\right) = V_x \frac{\partial V_x}{\partial t} + V_y \frac{\partial V_y}{\partial t} + V_z \frac{\partial V_z}{\partial t}$$

$$+ V_x^2 \frac{\partial V_x}{\partial x} + V_y^2 \frac{\partial V_y}{\partial y} + V_z^2 \frac{\partial V_z}{\partial z} \qquad (10\text{-}35)$$

The change in the flow energy p/ρ is derived by applying the equation of continuity. The derivation is especially easy to develop when one direction only is considered and then equations for the remaining directions are written similarly. Thus in the x direction

$$\frac{d}{dt}\left(\frac{p}{\rho}\right) = \frac{\partial}{\partial t}\left(\frac{p}{\rho}\right) + \frac{1}{\rho}\frac{\partial p}{\partial x}\frac{dx}{dt} - \frac{p}{\rho^2}\frac{\partial \rho}{\partial x}\frac{dx}{dt}$$

The change in the p/ρ term is found as follows:

$$\frac{d}{dt}\left(\frac{p}{\rho}\right) = \frac{\partial}{\partial t}\left(\frac{p}{\rho}\right) + \frac{1}{\rho}\frac{\partial p}{\partial x}V_x - \frac{p}{\rho^2}\frac{\partial \rho}{\partial x}V_x$$

$$+ \frac{1}{\rho}\frac{\partial p}{\partial y}V_y - \frac{p}{\rho^2}\frac{\partial \rho}{\partial y}V_y + \frac{1}{\rho}\frac{\partial p}{\partial z}V_z - \frac{p}{\rho^2}\frac{\partial \rho}{\partial z}V_z$$

However, by the equation of continuity for steady flow we have in the x direction

$$\frac{\partial}{\partial x}(\rho V_x) = 0 = V_x \frac{\partial \rho}{\partial x} + \rho \frac{\partial V_x}{\partial x}$$

and hence

$$V_x \frac{\partial \rho}{\partial x} = -\rho \frac{\partial V_x}{\partial x}$$

Similarly,

$$V_y \frac{\partial \rho}{\partial y} = -\rho \frac{\partial V_y}{\partial y}$$

and

$$V_z \frac{\partial \rho}{\partial z} = -\rho \frac{\partial V_z}{\partial z}$$

Substituting and recognizing that

$$\frac{\partial}{\partial x}(pV_x) = p \frac{\partial V_x}{\partial x} + V_x \frac{\partial p}{\partial x}$$

$$\frac{\partial}{\partial y}(pV_y) = p \frac{\partial V_y}{\partial y} + V_y \frac{\partial p}{\partial y}$$

$$\frac{\partial}{\partial z}(pV_z) = p \frac{\partial V_z}{\partial z} + V_z \frac{\partial p}{\partial z}$$

we get

$$\frac{d}{dt}\left(\frac{p}{\rho}\right) = \frac{\partial}{\partial t}\left(\frac{p}{\rho}\right) + \frac{1}{\rho}\left[\frac{\partial}{\partial x}(pV_x) + \frac{\partial}{\partial y}(pV_y) + \frac{\partial}{\partial z}(pV_z)\right] \quad (10\text{-}36)$$

Equations (10-32), (10-34), (10-35), and (10-36) can now be incorporated into the energy equation as the situation warrants.

Should the flow be an irreversible process, work in overcoming the losses will be dissipated from the mechanical form. In such cases the so-called *dissipation function* is defined as follows:

$$\phi = -\tfrac{2}{3}\mu \left(\frac{\partial V_x}{\partial x} + \frac{\partial V_y}{\partial y} + \frac{\partial V_z}{\partial z}\right)^2$$

$$+ \mu \left\{2\left[\left(\frac{\partial V_x}{\partial x}\right)^2 + \left(\frac{\partial V_y}{\partial y}\right)^2 + \left(\frac{\partial V_z}{\partial z}\right)^2\right] + \left(\frac{\partial V_z}{\partial y} + \frac{\partial V_y}{\partial z}\right)^2\right.$$

$$\left. + \left(\frac{\partial V_x}{\partial z} + \frac{\partial V_z}{\partial x}\right)^2 + \left(\frac{\partial V_y}{\partial x} + \frac{\partial V_x}{\partial y}\right)^2\right\} \quad (10\text{-}37)$$

and for flow with losses this is added (see reference 1, for example) to the energy equation.

10-8. Navier-Stokes Equations. In Sec. 10-5, dynamic equations were developed for inviscid fluids undergoing reversible processes in the absence of external forces. In this section an attempt will be made to develop the so-called *Navier-Stokes equations* which constitute the momentum equations for viscous fluids. The effects of external forces such as gravity or magnetism will be taken into consideration also.

In a fluid at rest, particles of fluid exert a pressure on each other which is caused only by the hydrostatic pressure. At each point within the fluid, the hydrostatic pressure has some value which is affected by the height of the fluid above it. In treatments of ideal fluids it is assumed that there are no forces except the hydrostatic one that act on the different portions of the flow. The flow of real or actual fluids indicates that this is an over-simplification, and that actually there are internal forces within the fluid, due to relative motion of fluid layers, which motion is caused by internal friction between fluid particles. This is called *viscosity*. Euler's equations, which apply to inviscid fluids, cannot be applied to viscous fluids.

Viscous flow is one manifestation of transport phenomena and hence is related to the coefficients of conductivity and diffusion. However, there is one complication in the case of viscous flow because the momentum which is transported is a vector quantity, whereas most other types of transport phenomena deal with scalar quantities.

The student of gas dynamics will recall that in Eqs. (10-23), namely, the Eulerian equations, the terms on the left-hand sides constitute the inertia forces in the x, y, and z directions respectively. In turn, the terms on the right-hand sides are the pressure forces. In developing the Navier-Stokes equations these terms will of course continue to exist, but terms for viscous effects and for external forces must be taken into consideration also. The latter will be denoted by $\mathbf{F}$, in general, and will have, of course, components along the cartesian axes, namely, F_x, F_y, and F_z.

In determining the shearing forces due to viscosity, consider a fluid element as shown in Fig. 10-3. Two types of stress forces may act on the faces of this element. These forces are internal forces, and are caused by the existence of external forces which act on the body. If the stress resulting from the stress force is normal to the face, it is called a normal stress, and is usually denoted by σ, but if it is tangential it is called a shear stress, and is usually denoted by τ. Now let the stresses at the geometric center of the parallelepiped shown in Fig. 10-3 be σ_x, σ_y, σ_z, τ_{xy}, τ_{yz}, and τ_{zx}. The normal stresses σ_x, σ_y, and σ_z are, respectively, those in the direction of the x, y, and z axes or respectively normal to the y-z, x-z, and x-y planes. Because we are considering a three-dimensional fluid element there will be three normal stresses, namely, σ_x, σ_y, and σ_z, and six shearing stresses τ_{xy}, τ_{yx}, τ_{yz}, τ_{zy}, τ_{zx}, and τ_{xz}. The normal stresses are said to be positive whenever they point outward or when the element is in tension. They

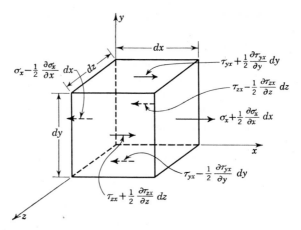

FIG. 10-3.   Normal and shearing stresses on fluid element in x direction.

are said to be negative whenever the fluid element is in compression.   The direction of the shearing stresses is expressed by the order of the subscripts. Thus the shear stress τ_{yx} is perpendicular to the y axis and parallel to the x axis, and at the same time is in the plane perpendicular to the y axis as shown in Fig. 10-3.   It may be noticed from Fig. 10-4 that

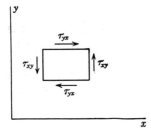

FIG. 10-4.   Shearing stresses in xy plane.

$$\tau_{xy} = \tau_{yx}$$

because they are the only stresses which can cause moments about an axis in the z direction. Similarly,

$$\tau_{yz} = \tau_{zy} \quad \text{and} \quad \tau_{zx} = \tau_{xz}$$

In Fig. 10-4, if we consider the shear stress in the x direction on the face of the parallelepiped normal to the y axis we will have on the top face a stress

$$\tau_{yx} + \frac{1}{2}\frac{\partial \tau_{yx}}{\partial y}dy$$

and on the lower face

$$\tau_{yx} - \frac{1}{2}\frac{\partial \tau_{yx}}{\partial y}dy$$

In order to obtain the respective shear forces it is necessary merely to multiply each stress by the area of the face, which is $dx\,dz$ in this case.

Thus the shear forces are

$$\left(\tau_{yx} + \frac{1}{2}\frac{\partial \tau_{yx}}{\partial y}\,dy\right) dx\,dz$$

and

$$\left(\tau_{yx} - \frac{1}{2}\frac{\partial \tau_{yx}}{\partial y}\,dy\right) dx\,dz$$

There will be two other shear forces in the x direction, namely,

$$\left(\tau_{zx} + \frac{1}{2}\frac{\partial \tau_{zx}}{\partial z}\,dz\right) dx\,dy$$

and

$$\left(\tau_{zx} - \frac{1}{2}\frac{\partial \tau_{zx}}{\partial z}\,dz\right) dx\,dy$$

Having determined the shearing forces in the x direction we may now proceed to the other forces in this direction. Thus we have first the normal stress forces

$$\left(\sigma_x + \frac{1}{2}\frac{\partial \sigma_x}{\partial x}\,dx\right) dy\,dz \qquad \text{and} \qquad \left(\sigma_x - \frac{1}{2}\frac{\partial \sigma_x}{\partial x}\,dx\right) dy\,dz$$

The x component of the force due to acceleration is $\rho\alpha_x\,dx\,dy\,dz$, in which α_x is the acceleration in the x direction. Similarly, external forces may be lumped together as $\mathbf{F}$ and will have an x component F_x. Addition of all forces and division by the mass $\rho\,dx\,dy\,dz$ yields, for the x direction,

$$\frac{1}{\rho\,dx\,dy\,dz}F_x + \frac{1}{\rho}\frac{\partial \sigma_x}{\partial x} + \frac{1}{\rho}\frac{\partial \tau_{yx}}{\partial y} + \frac{1}{\rho}\frac{\partial \tau_{zx}}{\partial z} = \alpha_x$$

Similarly,

$$F_y + \frac{1}{\rho}\frac{\partial \sigma_y}{\partial y} + \frac{1}{\rho}\frac{\partial \tau_{xy}}{\partial x} + \frac{1}{\rho}\frac{\partial \tau_{zy}}{\partial z} = \alpha_y \qquad (10\text{-}38)$$

$$F_z + \frac{1}{\rho}\frac{\partial \sigma_z}{\partial z} + \frac{1}{\rho}\frac{\partial \tau_{xz}}{\partial x} + \frac{1}{\rho}\frac{\partial \tau_{yz}}{\partial y} = \alpha_z$$

Letting $F_x/(\rho\,dx\,dy\,dz) = F'_x$, one may write

$$F'_x + \frac{1}{\rho}\frac{\partial \sigma_x}{\partial x} + \frac{1}{\rho}\frac{\partial \tau_{yx}}{\partial y} + \frac{1}{\rho}\frac{\partial \tau_{zx}}{\partial z} = \alpha_x \qquad (10\text{-}39)$$

The partial differentials of the velocity components in angular deformation represent the angular velocities. The angular deformation corresponding to the shearing stress τ_{xy} is, for example, $\partial V_x/\partial y + \partial V_y/\partial x$. Thus the shear stresses may be written as

$$\tau_{xy} = \tau_{yx} = \mu\left(\frac{\partial V_x}{\partial y} + \frac{\partial V_y}{\partial x}\right)$$

$$\tau_{yz} = \tau_{zy} = \mu\left(\frac{\partial V_y}{\partial z} + \frac{\partial V_z}{\partial y}\right) \qquad (10\text{-}40)$$

$$\tau_{zx} = \tau_{xz} = \mu\left(\frac{\partial V_z}{\partial x} + \frac{\partial V_x}{\partial z}\right)$$

It may be shown [2] further that the normal stresses are

$$\sigma_x = -p - \tfrac{2}{3}\mu\left(\frac{\partial V_x}{\partial x} + \frac{\partial V_y}{\partial y} + \frac{\partial V_z}{\partial z}\right) + 2\mu\frac{\partial V_x}{\partial x}$$

$$\sigma_y = -p - \tfrac{2}{3}\mu\left(\frac{\partial V_x}{\partial x} + \frac{\partial V_y}{\partial y} + \frac{\partial V_z}{\partial z}\right) + 2\mu\frac{\partial V_y}{\partial y} \qquad (10\text{-}41)$$

$$\sigma_z = -p - \tfrac{2}{3}\mu\left(\frac{\partial V_x}{\partial x} + \frac{\partial V_y}{\partial y} + \frac{\partial V_z}{\partial z}\right) + 2\mu\frac{\partial V_z}{\partial z}$$

Combining Eqs. (10-38), (10-40), and (10-41), the Navier-Stokes equations, which follow, are obtained:

$$F_x' - \frac{1}{\rho}\frac{\partial p}{\partial x} + \frac{\nu}{3}\frac{\partial}{\partial x}\left(\frac{\partial V_x}{\partial x} + \frac{\partial V_y}{\partial y} + \frac{\partial V_z}{\partial z}\right) + \nu V^2 V_x = \frac{DV_x}{Dt}$$

$$F_y' - \frac{1}{\rho}\frac{\partial p}{\partial y} + \frac{\nu}{3}\frac{\partial}{\partial y}\left(\frac{\partial V_x}{\partial x} + \frac{\partial V_y}{\partial y} + \frac{\partial V_z}{\partial z}\right) + \nu V^2 V_y = \frac{DV_y}{Dt} \qquad (10\text{-}42)$$

$$F_z' - \frac{1}{\rho}\frac{\partial p}{\partial z} + \frac{\nu}{3}\frac{\partial}{\partial z}\left(\frac{\partial V_x}{\partial x} + \frac{\partial V_y}{\partial y} + \frac{\partial V_z}{\partial z}\right) + \nu V^2 V_z = \frac{DV_z}{Dt}$$

in which D/Dt is an operator defined as follows:

$$\frac{D}{Dt} = V_x\frac{\partial}{\partial x} + V_y\frac{\partial}{\partial y} + V_z\frac{\partial}{\partial z} + \frac{\partial}{\partial t}$$

It was explained in Chap. 1 that the dynamic viscosity is defined for laminar or streamline flow and that for turbulent flow it is necessary to take into consideration the eddy viscosity ϵ. The force in the x direction due to eddy viscosity is, for example,

$$\frac{\partial}{\partial x}\left(\epsilon\frac{dV_x}{dx}\right) dx\, dy\, dz$$

Accordingly, in the presence of eddy viscosity the Navier-Stokes equations can be written as follows:

$$\rho \left(\frac{\partial V_x}{\partial t} + V_x \frac{\partial V_x}{\partial x} + V_y \frac{\partial V_x}{\partial y} + V_z \frac{\partial V_x}{\partial z} \right) = F''_x - \frac{\partial p}{\partial x} + \frac{\partial}{\partial x} (\mu + \epsilon) \frac{dV_x}{dx}$$

$$\rho \left(\frac{\partial V_y}{\partial t} + V_x \frac{\partial V_y}{\partial x} + V_y \frac{\partial V_y}{\partial y} + V_z \frac{\partial V_y}{\partial z} \right) = F''_y - \frac{\partial p}{\partial y} + \frac{\partial}{\partial y} (\mu + \epsilon) \frac{dV_y}{dy}$$

$$\rho \left(\frac{\partial V_z}{\partial t} + V_x \frac{\partial V_z}{\partial x} + V_y \frac{\partial V_z}{\partial y} + V_z \frac{\partial V_z}{\partial z} \right) = F''_z - \frac{\partial p}{\partial z} + \frac{\partial}{\partial z} (\mu + \epsilon) \frac{dV_z}{dz}$$

$$(10\text{-}43)$$

in which $F''_{x,y,z} = F_{x,y,z}/(dx\, dy\, dz)$.

The Navier-Stokes equations, it should be noted, are nonlinear partial differential equations which are complicated and for which there exist no general solutions. It should be noted that in deriving the Navier-Stokes equations the viscosity was assumed to be constant. This is not always the case.

10-9. Potential Flow. Regardless of what their order is,† differential equations may be classified as being either linear or nonlinear. A first-order linear differential equation by definition is, therefore, one which is of the first degree in the differential or partial differentials. However, the dependent variable itself may occur in any manner. A partial differential equation of order m is linear if the dependent variable and its derivatives are of the first degree. The following equation is linear:

$$x^3 \frac{d^3y}{dx^3} + x^2 \frac{d^2y}{dx^2} + x \frac{dy}{dx} + y = \text{constant}$$

and

$$y^3 \frac{d^3y}{dx^3} + y^2 \frac{d^2y}{dx^2} + y \frac{dy}{dx} + x = \text{constant}$$

is nonlinear, because in the former the dependent variable y is of the first degree, but in the latter it is not. Again, let A, B, C, D, E, F, and G be functions of x and y only. Then

$$A \frac{\partial^2 z}{\partial x^2} + B \frac{\partial^2 z}{\partial x\, \partial y} + C \frac{\partial^2 z}{\partial y^2} + D \frac{\partial z}{\partial x} + E \frac{\partial z}{\partial y} + F_2 = G(x,y)$$

is a second-order partial differential equation.

† The *order* and the *degree* are described as follows: In a partial derivative $(\partial^m z/\partial x^m)^n$, m denotes the order and n the degree.

Euler's equations are not linear, because, for example, in the x direction

$$V_x \frac{\partial V_x}{\partial x} + V_y \frac{\partial V_x}{\partial y} + V_z \frac{\partial V_x}{\partial z} + \frac{\partial V_x}{\partial t} = -\frac{1}{\rho}\frac{\partial p}{\partial x} \qquad (10\text{-}44)$$

in which V_x is a dependent variable and hence the first term on the left-hand side, namely, $V_x(\partial V_x/\partial x)$, contributes to the nonlinearity.

Physically it is possible to visualize linearization if we assume that the flow velocity consists of a uniform, parallel velocity upon which are superposed small perturbation velocities. This viewpoint simplifies the necessary mathematical manipulations.

In this chapter the method of characteristics, which is applicable to flow in the supersonic regime and closely related to linearized flow, will be discussed. The method of characteristics is used extensively in designing the convergent portion of supersonic wind tunnels. The following assumptions must be accepted a priori if the method of characteristics is to apply:

1. The flow is two-dimensional.
2. The flow is irrotational.
3. The flow proceeds isentropically.
4. The flow is steady.
5. The flow velocity is supersonic.
6. External forces such as gravity and magnetism are negligible.
7. The fluid medium acts like a perfect gas.

It follows, then, that in analyzing the flow around bodies it is convenient to apply the so-called *potential functions*. The necessary and sufficient condition for irrotational flow, namely, curl $\mathbf{V} = 0$, implies the existence of a velocity potential (analogous to a force potential) which describes the velocity field of the flow. The velocity potential will be denoted by the function φ, such that $\varphi = \varphi(x,y,z,t)$ and $\mathbf{V} = \text{grad } \varphi$. For irrotational flow, curl $(T \text{ grad } s)$ must vanish. Therefore, it would also have been possible to assign a potential φ to the vector field $T \text{ grad } s$ such that $T \text{ grad } s = \text{grad } \varphi$.

By definition,

$$\text{grad } \varphi = \mathbf{i}\frac{\partial \varphi}{\partial x} + \mathbf{j}\frac{\partial \varphi}{\partial y} + \mathbf{k}\frac{\partial \varphi}{\partial z}$$

Because the velocity potential is defined $\mathbf{V} = \text{grad } \varphi$, it follows that

$$V_x = \frac{\partial \varphi}{\partial x} = \varphi_x \qquad V_y = \frac{\partial \varphi}{\partial y} = \varphi_y \qquad V_z = \frac{\partial \varphi}{\partial z} = \varphi_z \qquad (10\text{-}45)$$

Furthermore,

$$\frac{\partial V_x}{\partial x} = \frac{\partial^2 \varphi}{\partial x^2} = \varphi_{xx} \qquad \frac{\partial V_y}{\partial y} = \frac{\partial^2 \varphi}{\partial y^2} = \varphi_{yy} \qquad \frac{\partial V_z}{\partial z} = \frac{\partial^2 \varphi}{\partial z^2} = \varphi_{zz} \qquad (10\text{-}46)$$

Example 1. At a certain point in a three-dimensional-flow field the three velocity components are $V_x = 5$ fps, $V_y = 12$ fps, and $V_z = 8$ fps. Find the potential function.

Solution. The potential function at this point is the sum of the potential functions in each direction. By definition of the velocity potential, integration yields

$$\varphi_x = 5x \qquad \varphi_y = 12y \qquad \text{and} \qquad \varphi_z = 8z$$

Thus the flow pattern is represented by the equation

$$\varphi = 5x + 12y + 8z$$

By the equation of continuity, for steady flow,

$$\text{div } (\rho V_x \mathbf{i} + \partial V_y \mathbf{j} + \rho V_z \mathbf{k}) = 0$$

and it follows that

$$\rho(\varphi_{xx} + \varphi_{yy} + \varphi_{zz}) + \varphi_x \frac{\partial \rho}{\partial x} + \varphi_y \frac{\partial \rho}{\partial y} + \varphi_z \frac{\partial \rho}{\partial z} = 0 \qquad (10\text{-}47)$$

By Euler's equation,

$$\frac{1}{\rho} dp = -V \, dV$$

and by definition of the acoustic velocity a,

$$a^2 = \frac{dp}{d\rho}$$

Then
$$d\rho = -\frac{\rho}{2a^2} d\left[\left(\frac{\partial \varphi}{\partial x}\right)^2 + \left(\frac{\partial \varphi}{\partial y}\right)^2 + \left(\frac{\partial \varphi}{\partial z}\right)^2 \right]$$

The partials of this equation with respect to x, y, and z, respectively, are

$$\frac{\partial \varphi}{\partial x} = -\frac{\rho}{2a^2} \frac{\partial}{\partial x}\left[\left(\frac{\partial \varphi}{\partial x}\right)^2 + \left(\frac{\partial \varphi}{\partial y}\right)^2 + \left(\frac{\partial \varphi}{\partial z}\right)^2 \right]$$

$$\frac{\partial \varphi}{\partial y} = -\frac{\rho}{2a^2} \frac{\partial}{\partial y}\left[\left(\frac{\partial \varphi}{\partial x}\right)^2 + \left(\frac{\partial \varphi}{\partial y}\right)^2 + \left(\frac{\partial \varphi}{\partial z}\right)^2 \right] \qquad (10\text{-}48)$$

$$\frac{\partial \varphi}{\partial z} = -\frac{\rho}{2a^2} \frac{\partial}{\partial z}\left[\left(\frac{\partial \varphi}{\partial x}\right)^2 + \left(\frac{\partial \varphi}{\partial y}\right)^2 + \left(\frac{\partial \varphi}{\partial z}\right)^2 \right]$$

$$\varphi_{xx}\left(1 - \frac{\varphi_x^2}{a^2}\right) + \varphi_{yy}\left(1 - \frac{\varphi_y^2}{a^2}\right) + \varphi_{zz}\left(1 - \frac{\varphi_z^2}{a^2}\right)$$

$$= \frac{2}{a^2}\left(\varphi_x \varphi_y \varphi_{xy} + \varphi_x \varphi_z \varphi_{xz} + \varphi_y \varphi_z \varphi_{yz}\right) = 0 \qquad (10\text{-}49)$$

When second-order terms are neglected, Eq. (10-49) reduces to

$$\varphi_{xx}(1 - M^2) + \varphi_{yy} + \varphi_{zz} = 0 \qquad (10\text{-}50)$$

For two-dimensional flow, all streamlines lie in parallel planes and no property changes occur at right angles to these planes. The two-dimensional case may be solved in single terms by the effecting of a linearization, and Eq. (10-50) becomes

$$\varphi_{xx}(1 - M^2) + \varphi_{yy} = 0 \tag{10-51}$$

Equations (10-50) and (10-51) are called the *linearized flow equations*.

A second-order linear differential equation with variable coefficients is generally expressed by

$$Rr + Ss + Tt + Pp + Qq + Zz = F \tag{10-52}$$

in which

$$r = \frac{\partial^2 z}{\partial x^2} \qquad s = \frac{\partial^2 z}{\partial x\, \partial y} \qquad t = \frac{\partial^2 z}{\partial y^2} \qquad p = \frac{\partial z}{\partial x} \qquad q = \frac{\partial z}{\partial y}$$

and $z = z(x,y)$. R, S, T, P, Q, Z, and F are functions of x and y only.

Equation (10-52) may express one of three forms, which may be determined by the following test conditions:

Case 1, $S^2 - 4RT < 0$. Relation (10-52) is of the elliptic form.

Case 2, $S^2 - 4RT = 0$. Relation (10-52) is of the parabolic form.

Case 3, $S^2 - 4RT > 0$. Relation (10-52) is of the hyperbolic form.

Example 2. In the supersonic domain what form does two-dimensional flow assume?
Solution. Two-dimensional linearized flow is represented by Eq. (10-51) in which only the partials r and t exist. The coefficients R and T are, respectively, $R = 1 - M^2$, $T = 1$, and $S = 0$. Because for supersonic flow $M > 1$, it follows that $R < 0$, or negative. Accordingly, the test condition is

$$S^2 - 4RT > 0$$

and it follows that Eq. (10-51) is of the hyperbolic form in this case.

In the hyperbolic form two real curves may be defined on the x,y plane by the relation

$$R\, dy^2 - 2S\, dx\, dy + T\, dx^2 = 0$$

These are called the characteristic curves, or characteristics of the fundamental relation (10-50). The characteristics of Eq. (10-51) are

$$(M^2 - 1)\, dy^2 - dx^2 = 0$$

Hence,

$$\frac{dy}{dx} = \pm \frac{1}{\sqrt{M^2 - 1}}$$

However, $1/\sqrt{M^2 - 1} = \tan \alpha$, in which α is the Mach angle. Thus it follows that the characteristics and the Mach lines are the same thing. It may also be noted from this that the characteristics are real for supersonic flow only. It is customary to speak of the Mach line in the physical sense of the characteristic line in the mathematical sense. Because the Mach line is an infinitely small shock wave across which the entropy does not increase, the gas stream does not experience any irreversible changes as it moves across a Mach line. The characteristic line forms the Mach angle with the streamlines corresponding to the local Mach number at that point.

10-10. The Method of Characteristics. In subsonic flow a sudden expansion in the wall is felt over the whole flow field. This is not so in supersonic flow. Suppose that there is a sudden expansion as shown in Fig. 10-5. The disturbance will cause a standing wave at the corner which will form an angle β with the original flow direction and this will result in deflecting the flow by an angle of $d\theta$. The original flow velocity V_1 will not be affected by the disturbance upstream of the standing wave, but it is changed to V_2 downstream of the wave. In the method of characteristics, the disturbances downstream from the standing wave are superposed but do not influence the flow upstream. In a smoothly expanding section an infinite number of standing waves are generated. The method of characteristics is a numerical approximation which reduces the infinite number of waves to a finite one. This can be done simply by replacing a curved boundary by a relatively large number of straight-line segments. In so

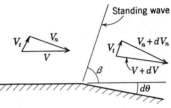

FIG. 10-5.   Expansion wave.

doing it is assumed that in the areas bounded by the straight-line segment, the two standing waves at each of its corners and the centerline, the magnitude, and direction of the velocity are constant.

It was explained that when a sudden expansion occurs in a wall bounding a supersonic flow field, the flow is deflected through an angle $d\theta$. In doing so the flow velocity and thus the pressure also change. By the continuity equation we can write

$$\rho V_n = (\rho + d\rho)(V_n + dV_n)$$

which simplifies to

$$V_n\, d\rho + \rho\, dV_n = 0 \qquad (10\text{-}53)$$

The momentum equation is written in the direction normal to the wave; thus,

$$\rho V_n\, dV_n + dp = 0 \qquad (10\text{-}54)$$

Eliminating dV_n in Eqs. (10-53) and (10-54) one may solve for V_n, obtaining

$$V_n = \sqrt{\frac{dp}{d\rho}}$$

From the definition of the acoustic velocity it follows that

$$V_n = a$$

It may be concluded therefore that

$$4\beta = 4\alpha$$

where the latter is the so-called *Mach angle*.

By study of Fig. 10-5, the incremental change in velocity through the wave is

$$dV = dV_n \sin \beta \tag{10-55}$$

Similarly, the change in the flow direction is given by

$$d\theta = \frac{dV_n}{V} \cos \beta \tag{10-56}$$

Combining Eqs. (10-55) and (10-56) there results

$$\frac{dV}{V} = \tan \beta \, d\theta$$

Recall that

$$\sin \alpha = \frac{1}{M} = \sin \beta$$

Then

$$\frac{dV}{V} = \frac{d\theta}{\sqrt{M^2 - 1}} \tag{10-57}$$

Equation (10-57) is the basis for the method of characteristics. However, it is necessary to develop a relation between V, a^*, and the Mach number. This is easily accomplished by combining Eqs. (3-13) and (3-16), namely,

$$\frac{a^2}{k-1} + \frac{V^2}{2} = \frac{a_0{}^2}{k-1} \qquad a^{*2} = \frac{2}{k+1} a_0{}^2$$

Thus we obtain

$$\left(\frac{V}{a^*}\right)^2 = \frac{k+1}{k-1+2/M^2} \tag{10-58}$$

Letting $\overline{V} = V/a^*$ and combining Eqs. (10-57) and (10-58), we find that

$$d\theta = \sqrt{\frac{\overline{V}^2 - 1}{1 - [(k-1)/(k+1)]\overline{V}^2}} \, \frac{d\overline{V}}{\overline{V}} \tag{10-59}$$

Equation (10-59) expresses the "strength of the reflected waves," namely, $d\theta$.

It follows from Eq. (10-59) that

$$\theta = \theta(\overline{V})$$

and by Eq. (10-58)

$$\overline{V} = \overline{V}(M)$$

Therefore,

$$\theta = \theta(M)$$

Equation (10-59) may be integrated [3] choosing the limits so that $\theta = 0$ when $M = 1$. Thus we obtain

$$\theta = \sqrt{\frac{k+1}{k-1}} \arctan\left[\sqrt{\frac{k-1}{k+1}} \sqrt{M^2 - 1} \right] - \arctan^{-1} \sqrt{M^2 - 1} \quad (10\text{-}60)$$

For each θ angle there corresponds a certain Mach number, or conversely, for every Mach number to be obtained there is a maximum angle θ_{max} beyond which flow without compression waves cannot be obtained. This angle is the maximum permissible angle and will result in the shortest nozzle for any particular-design Mach number. If an angle less than θ_{max} is chosen the same Mach number may be obtained in a longer nozzle. Whether or not the maximum permissible divergence angle is to be chosen depends on various conditions. A short wind tunnel will save space, which in certain installations can be a major consideration. It will also be advantageous if boundary-layer growth and frictional losses are to be prevented. However, a longer nozzle will be more conducive to a parallel and uniform flow.

If the standing waves resulting from some supersonic flow form on the lower wall of the flow section they are said to constitute the *lower family*, and those formed on the upper boundary are called *upper family*. It is obvious that the directions of the two families are opposite to one another.

If the upper and lower walls of a divergent section are symmetric about the axis then the upper and lower families should intersect one another along the centerline. However, it is possible that they are not. Consider the configuration depicted in Fig. 10-6.

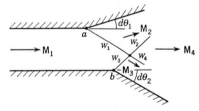

Fig. 10-6.   Asymmetric divergence.

At point a a wave will originate which will cause the flow to be deflected upward; the wave emanating from point b will cause the flow to be deflected downward. In all probability M_1 will be given, and to it will correspond an angle θ_1 in the table so that M_2 and M_3 will be determined by $d\theta_1$ and $d\theta_2$. In turn, M_4 will correspond to the angle

$$\theta_1 + d\theta_1 + d\theta_2$$

and the direction of flow will be that which has been deflected by $d\theta_1 - d\theta_2$

relative to the original flow. It should be noted that wave W_4 will cause the flow to be deflected by an angle $d\theta_1$, which is the same as the deflection caused by W_1 even though it has been intersected by another wave.

When a lower-family wave hits the upper wall as in Fig. 10-7, it will be reflected, but the angle of incidence and reflection will not be the same. The angle of reflection will be such that the final flow will have the same direction as the original flow. If the upper wall has a deflection angle $d\theta$ which corresponds to the angle by which the flow is deflected as it passes through the wave W_1, then there will result no reflected wave because the incident wave W_1 will end at the upper wall, or be *canceled*.

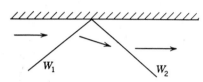

FIG. 10-7. Reflection from upper boundary.

10-11. Nozzle Design. The preceding discussions lead to a very convenient graphical procedure which, when applied to supersonic nozzle design, will result in waves canceling out. Such a graphical procedure actually includes many considerations which cannot be answered simply. Here a very simplified version of the so-called *method of characteristics* will be outlined to serve as an introduction. For a more rigorous approach the reader should consult the references listed at the end of this chapter.

1. Decide on the Mach number to be obtained. Decide on the test-section height to accommodate the model or test item.

2. From Table A-9 [4] find the maximum angle θ which corresponds to this Mach number.

3. For a symmetrical nozzle only one side, the upper or the lower boundary, need be drawn because by symmetry the center streamline is the centerline. It is generally easier to draw the upper boundary about the horizontal centerline.

4. The angle of divergence of one wall will be one-half of the angle found in step 2.

$$\nu = \frac{\theta_{\max}}{2}$$

5. Assume that at the start of the divergence the Mach number is unity. Then the height at the entrance will be given by

$$\frac{A_1}{A_2} = \frac{M_2}{M_1} \left\{ \frac{1 + [(k-1)/2]M_1^2}{1 + [(k-1)/2]M_2^2} \right\}^{(k+1)/2(k-1)}$$

$$A_1 = A_n M_2 \left\{ \frac{(k+1)/2}{1 + [(k-1)/2]M_2^2} \right\}^{(k+1)/2(k-1)}$$

6. The height at the entrance will be proportional to

$$\frac{\text{Height (test section)}}{2A_2/A_1} = \text{height (entrance)}$$

7. Draw a short arbitrary horizontal line OA at the beginning as in Fig. 10-8. At A draw a short divergent line AB making an angle of about $2°$ with the horizontal. For greater accuracy, an angle of $1°$ may be chosen. From A a standing wave AC will emanate. Now there are individual flow fields which may be denoted by a set of coordinates (a,b) where a is the number of degrees produced so far by upper-family waves and b the number of degrees produced so far by lower-family curves. Then the local flow angle ν is

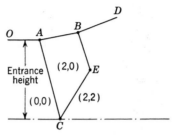

$$\nu = a - b$$

FIG. 10-8.   Nozzle design.

the flow being horizontal when $a = b$.

8. Immediately downstream of wave AC there will be a zone represented by 2,0. From Table A-9 it may be found that the Mach number here is 1.1328. To this Mach number there corresponds a Mach angle of $\alpha = 61.96$. Then the wave angle which AC will make is

$$\frac{61.96 + 90.00}{2} - 1 = 74.98°$$

9. At B draw another divergent section BD making an additional angle of $2°$. The flow has now undergone a total deflection of $4°$ and hence its Mach number is 1.2170 to which corresponds a Mach angle of $55.25°$. The angle which the wave at B makes with the mean flow is

$$\frac{55.25 + 61.96}{2} = 58.60°$$

The wave emanating at B makes an angle of

$$\frac{55.25 + 61.96}{2} - 3 = 55.60°$$

with the horizontal.

10. The wave emanating from B will not reach the centerline without deflection because a wave passing through C will intersect it at some point E. The flow downstream from CE will have been deflected twice: once upward $2°$ by AC and once downward $2°$ by CE, thus making it horizontal. The total deflection is $2 + 2 = 4$. This procedure is continued until one

obtains the conditions which give the same local Mach number as was desired, so that all expansion waves are canceled. This may entail several trials. The shape of the nozzle which is actually built should consist of a curve faired through all the points where the waves intersect with the wall. A supersonic nozzle so designed will then consist of a convergent section (diffuser, not discussed), a throat, a divergent section, and a parallel wall section. A supersonic wind-tunnel nozzle designed by Petersen [5] for a test-section Mach number of 1.37 is shown in Fig. 10-9.

Supersonic nozzle $m = 1.37$

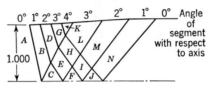

Line between region	α, deg †	Line between region	α, deg †
AB	101.90	HI	55.53
BC	65.33	IJ	52.20
BD	105.52	GK	110.85
CE	120.43	HL	128.47
DE	61.56	IM	129.80
EF	57.23	JN	130.81
DG	108.41	KL	57.53
EH	124.77	LM	54.20
FI	126.47	MN	51.13
GH	59.23	NO	48.43

† α is the angle (with respect to the zero angle of the axis) of the lines between the given regions.

FIG. 10-9.   Nozzle-design diagram.

Nozzle design by the method of characteristics just described is simple but somewhat tedious. It should be remembered further that there will exist a boundary layer at the wall which will have the tendency to reduce the effective area unless provision is made to accommodate the boundary layer by shifting the walls outward. A detailed description of this is beyond the scope of this book, and accordingly, the reader is referred to reference 3.

A nonlinear partial differential equation may be linearized by two different approaches. The simple technique is to assume that the nonlinear terms are negligible; the other is to transform by mathematical means the exact nonlinear partial differential equation into an exact linear partial differential equation. One such approach is the hodograph transformation out of which may be developed the hodograph characteristics. For the transformation there exist various types which use the velocity component rather than the x coordinate as an independent variable. Thus the angle θ and the velocity are plotted on polar coordinates. A thorough discussion of the hodograph characteristics is beyond the scope of this text because of the many ramifications involved. For details the reader is referred to references 6 to 12.

PROBLEMS

10-1. Show that $\mathbf{V}(\rho\mathbf{V}) = \mathbf{V}\,\text{grad}\,\rho + \rho\,\text{div}\,\mathbf{V}$.

10-2. Show that in cylindrical coordinates the circulation is given by $\Gamma = \oint \mathbf{V}\cdot d\mathbf{r}$, in which $\mathbf{r}$ is a length element along the integration contour.

10-3. What is the form of the two-dimensional flow if (a) $M = 1$, and (b) $M < 1$?

10-4. What is the form of the equation expressing detonation in a spark-ignition engine?

10-5. Show that $\mathbf{V}\,\text{div}\,\mathbf{V} = \text{curl}\,\mathbf{V} \times \mathbf{V} + \text{grad}\,\mathbf{V}^2/2$.

10-6. What would be the form of the equations of motion if the effects of gravity and magnetism were considered?

10-7. Show that for irrotational flow $\oint dp/\rho = 0$.

10-8. Starting with Euler's equations derive Lagrange's equations.

10-9. Show that for incompressible flow $\text{div}\,\mathbf{V} = 0$.

10-10. For what type of flow is the circulation $\Gamma = 0$?

10-11. For what type of flow is the circulation $\Gamma = \text{constant}$?

10-12. For what type of flow is the circulation $\Gamma = \text{variable}$?

10-13. Can the flow be isentropic for rotational flow?

10-14. Derive an expression for the acoustic velocity in three-dimensional form. Use cartesian coordinates.

10-15. Show that at each point in a flow field, the projection of the velocity on the normal to a characteristic is the speed of sound at that point.

10-16. Using the method of characteristics, design the divergent portion of a convergent-divergent nozzle for exit Mach numbers of 1.2, 1.8, and 3.0.

10-17. Can the method of characteristics be applied to three-dimensional flow?

10-18. Discuss the uses of the hodograph characteristics.

10-19. Determine the form of the second-order linear partial differential equation at a point where the velocity is 800 fps and the temperature is 59°F.

10-20. Can the method of characteristics be applied to the convergent part of a DeLaval nozzle?

10-21. Supersonic flow having a Mach number of 1.5 is accelerated in a divergent section to a Mach number of $M = 2.5$. Assuming symmetry, find the angle of divergence which each wall of a two-dimensional nozzle will make with the horizontal.

REFERENCES

1. Ackeret, J.: "Handbuch der Physik," vol. VII, Springer-Verlag OHG, Berlin, 1927.
2. Hopf, L.: "Handbuch der Physik," vol. VII, Springer-Verlag OHG, Berlin, 1927.
3. Puckett, A. E.: "Supersonic Nozzle Design," *J. Appl. Mechanics*, December, 1946, p. A-264.
4. Shapiro, A. H.: "The Dynamics and Thermodynamics of Compressible Fluid Flow," The Ronald Press Company, New York, 1953.

5. Petersen, M. W.: "Preliminary Design of a Supersonic Wind Tunnel Using a Steam Jet Exhauster," M.S. thesis in Mechanical Engineering, State University of Iowa, August, 1953.
6. Liepmann, H. W., and A. E. Puckett: "Introduction to Aerodynamics of a Compressible Fluid," John Wiley & Sons, Inc., New York, 1947.
7. Busemann, A.: "Handbuch der Experimental Physik," vol. 4, pt. 1, "Gas Dynamik," Akademische Verlagsgesellschaft, Leipzig, 1931.
8. Streeter, V. L.: "Fluid Dynamics," McGraw-Hill Book Company, Inc., New York, 1948.
9. Sauer, R.: "Theoretische Einfuhrung in die Gasdynamik," Springer-Verlag OHG, Berlin, 1943.
10. Courant, R., and D. Friedrichs: "Supersonic Flow and Shock Waves," Interscience Publishers, Inc., New York, 1948.
11. Hunsaker, J. C., and B. G. Rightmire: "Engineering Applications of Fluid Mechanics," McGraw-Hill Book Company, Inc., New York, 1947.
12. Kuethe, A. M., and J. D. Schetzer: "Foundations of Aerodynamics," John Wiley & Sons, Inc., New York, 1950.

CHAPTER 11

DIMENSIONAL ANALYSIS AND SIMILITUDE

11-1. Introduction. Equations of applied mathematics may differ from those of pure mathematics in that they should always conform to the *principle of dimensional homogeneity*. This principle affirms that each and every term of a dimensionally correct engineering equation must have the same units. The mathematical practice related to developing engineering equations which are dimensionally correct is called *dimensional analysis*.

Besides the determination of correct units, dimensional analysis is useful in the prediction of engineering equations and the study of phenomena by means of models. If the problem under consideration is a simple one, dimensional analysis may indicate the form of the appropriate equation. However, it should be emphasized that it alone will never give the exact equation. Dimensional analysis is used primarily as a tool to supplement other data. If the basic law underlying a certain phenomenon is well known for the desired range of application, the outcome of events should be computed from the fundamental laws or other well-established relations, and except for consistency, dimensional analysis is not needed. But if the interrelation of the variables affecting the behavior of a system is complex or uncertain a study based on similitude may be justified. For certain problems the differential equation can be written, but its solution may be very laborious or unattainable. In such cases the use of dimensional analysis is often indicated. Thus in some ways dimensional analysis is analogous to statistical theory, because like statistics it need not be used if more precise and well-established principles are known about the events under consideration.

11-2. System of Units. In engineering work two types of units may be defined, *fundamental units* and *derived units*. Fundamental units are those which are considered basic for a given field of utilization and are used as the building blocks for other units. For example, *time, length,* and *temperature* are generally considered to be fundamental units. Derived units are those which are formed by the combining of fundamental units as, for example, velocity, which is dimensionally length over time, i.e., feet per second, miles per hour, etc. The concept of the fundamental unit is in some

TABLE 11-1. DIMENSIONS OF GAS-DYNAMIC QUANTITIES

Quantity	Units in F, T, t, L	Units in H, T, t, L
Acceleration	$\dfrac{L}{t^2}$	$\dfrac{L}{t^2}$
Area	L^2	L^2
Coefficient of compressibility	$\dfrac{L^2}{F}$	$\dfrac{L^3}{H}$
Coefficient of expansion	$\dfrac{1}{T}$	$\dfrac{1}{T}$
Coefficient of thermal conductivity	$\dfrac{F}{Tt}$	$\dfrac{H}{LtT}$
Convection-film coefficient	$\dfrac{F}{tLT}$	$\dfrac{H}{tL^2T}$
Density	$\dfrac{Ft^2}{L^4}$	$\dfrac{Ht^2}{L^5}$
Energy, specific	$\dfrac{L^2}{t^2}$	$\dfrac{L^2}{t^2}$
Energy, total	FL	H
Enthalpy, specific	$\dfrac{L^2}{t^2}$	$\dfrac{L^2}{t^2}$
Enthalpy, total	FL	H
Entropy, specific	$\dfrac{L^2}{t^2T}$	$\dfrac{L^2}{t^2T}$
Entropy, total	$\dfrac{FL}{T}$	$\dfrac{H}{T}$
Force	F	$\dfrac{H}{L}$
Gas constant	$\dfrac{FL}{t}$	$\dfrac{H}{t}$
Joule-Thomson coefficient	$\dfrac{TL^2}{F}$	$\dfrac{TL^3}{H}$
Length	L	L
Mass	$\dfrac{Ft^2}{L}$	$\dfrac{Ht^2}{L^2}$
Mass rate of flow	$\dfrac{Ft}{L}$	$\dfrac{Ht}{L^2}$
Momentum	Ft	$\dfrac{Ht}{L}$

TABLE 11-1. DIMENSIONS OF GAS-DYNAMIC QUANTITIES (*Continued*)

Quantity	Units in F, T, t, L	Units in H, T, t, L
Power, horsepower...............	$\dfrac{FL}{t}$	$\dfrac{H}{t}$
Pressure.......................	$\dfrac{F}{L^2}$	$\dfrac{H}{L^3}$
Revolutions per minute............	$\dfrac{1}{t}$	$\dfrac{1}{t}$
Specific heat....................	$\dfrac{L^2}{t^2 T}$	$\dfrac{L^2}{t^2 T}$
Specific volume..................	$\dfrac{L^3}{F}$	$\dfrac{L^4}{H}$
Specific weight..................	$\dfrac{F}{L^3}$	$\dfrac{H}{L^4}$
Surface tension..................	$\dfrac{F}{L}$	$\dfrac{H}{L^2}$
Temperature....................	T	T
Time..........................	t	t
Velocity.......................	$\dfrac{L}{t}$	$\dfrac{L}{t}$
Viscosity, absolute...............	$\dfrac{Ft}{L^2}$	$\dfrac{Ht}{L^3}$
Viscosity, kinematic..............	$\dfrac{L^2}{t}$	$\dfrac{L^2}{t}$
Work..........................	FL	H

ways an arbitrary one. In thermodynamics there are several classes of fundamental units. One class is the set of fundamental units which employs *thermal energy H, temperature T, time t,* and *length L.* A second, equally valid set of fundamental units employs *force F, temperature T, time t,* and *length L.* It is evident that although thermal energy H is a fundamental unit in the first set, it is a derived unit in the second set. In turn the force F, which is a derived unit in the first classification, is a fundamental unit in the second classification. Thus if one visualizes H as a derived unit defined in terms of work, where work is evidenced by force acting through distance, then

$$H = FL \qquad\qquad (11\text{-}1)$$

However, if the force H is considered as a fundamental unit, it is evident that force F can be defined as

$$F = \frac{H}{L} \tag{11-2}$$

Table 11-1 lists the units of quantities most commonly encountered in thermodynamics. It is interesting to note in Table 11-1 that all fundamental units and some of the thermodynamic quantities such as the specific heat have the same units in both the F, T, t, L and the H, T, t, L systems. Another frequently used pattern of units employs M, T, t, and L, where M is mass.

Certain other frequently met dimensionless products are listed in Table 11-2.

TABLE 11-2. COMMON DIMENSIONLESS QUANTITIES

Angle	Pressure ratio
Coefficient of friction	Specific-heat ratio
Compression ratio	Sine of an angle
Efficiency	Temperature ratio
Molecular weight	Work ratio

In the solution of a particular problem it is advisable to choose the set of fundamental units which can furnish the most convenient means of measurement or analysis. Similarly, the fundamental units in which tabular data are already available should be utilized. In certain problems, such as in the derivation of Nusselt-type equations, it may be convenient to use two sets of fundamental units concurrently. Although this procedure is acceptable, it may be more confusing than helpful.

In discussing engineering units, it is interesting to note that zero may have dimensions. For example, the first law of thermodynamics can be written as

$$dQ = du + dW$$

and with each term representing energy the units of the equation may be energy per unit mass. By transposing terms, it can be seen that

$$dQ - du - dW = 0 \tag{11-3}$$

Thus in order to agree with the principle of homogeneity, the dimensions of zero must be energy units per unit mass.

Several systems of units are encountered in engineering and these have been discussed in Sec. 1-6 of this text.

11-3. Dimensionless Ratios. It is realized that in engineering work many dimensionless ratios, such as the trigonometric functions, the thermal efficiency, and the compression ratio, are commonly used. Numerous other dimensionless parameters can be developed on the basis of dimensional analysis. The use of such dimensionless parameters or products is of particular interest in research work, because by the proper combination of variables the amount of laboratory work to correlate miscellaneous data can be reduced.

Suppose that some variable X_1 is a function of some other variable X_2. Consequently,

$$X_1 = \phi(X_2) \tag{11-4}$$

The function ϕ may be determined conveniently by conducting experiments in which the effect of X_2 on X_1 is studied. The results thus obtained may be sketched as in Fig. 11-1. The above case is an elementary one

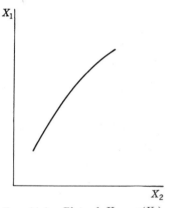

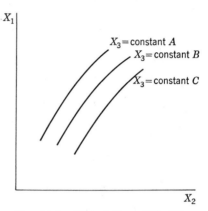

FIG. 11-1. Plot of $X_1 = \phi(X_2)$. FIG. 11-2. Plot of $X_1 = \phi(X_2, X_3)$.

and its solution will not pose undue difficulty. As a second possibility, consider that some variable X_1 is dependent on two variables X_2 and X_3. This can be written as

$$X_1 = \phi(X_2, X_3) \tag{11-5}$$

Here the determination of ϕ is more involved because we have to study the influence of both X_2 and X_3 on X_1. This means that in conducting the experiments we might first study the influence of X_2 on X_1 while maintaining a certain value of X_3. At the completion of this set of experiments we might repeat the investigation at some other value of X_3. This might have to be done many times. The experimental values thus obtained could conceivably be plotted as shown in Fig. 11-2.

As most research problems in engineering involve two or more influencing variables, it stands to reason that a technique for reducing the required number of measurements is desirable. This may be accomplished by the combination of several variables into dimensionless products. Another useful application of dimensional analysis is measuring several items and plotting the resulting data in dimensionless form. As will be discussed in later sections, such curves may be used in predicting the characteristics of similar devices which have not been studied experimentally.

Consider a certain thermodynamic phenomenon which is controlled by the quantities X_1, X_2, X_3, ..., X_n, in which $n = 1, 2, \ldots$. We can write this in functional form as

$$\phi(X_1, X_2, X_3, \ldots, X_n) = 0 \tag{11-6}$$

or

$$X_1 = \phi'(X_2, X_3, \ldots, X_n) \tag{11-7}$$

It is possible to put Eq. (11-6) into the form of an equivalent-power series. Thus,

$$C_1 X_1^{a_1'} X_2^{a_2'} \cdots X_n^{a_n'} + C_2 X_1^{b_1'} X_2^{b_2'} \cdots X_n^{b_n'} + \cdots = 0 \tag{11-8}$$

In Eq. (11-8) the C's, the a''s, and the b''s are dimensionless constants. In summation notation, Eq. (11-8) may be written as

$$\sum_{}^{n} (C_1 X_i^{a_i'} + C_2 X_i^{b_i'} + \cdots) = 0 \qquad i = 1 \tag{11-9}$$

Dividing Eq. (11-8) by $C_1 X_1^{a_1'} \cdots X_n^{a_n'}$, one obtains

$$1 + \frac{C_2}{C_1} X_1^{b_1'-a_1'} X_2^{b_2'-a_2'} \cdots X_n^{b_n'-a_n'} + \cdots = 0 \tag{11-10}$$

Since each term in Eq. (11-8) has the same dimension, it follows by the principle of dimensional homogeneity that the product of the X terms in Eq. (11-10) must be dimensionless. Therefore, we can write

$$X_1^{a_1} X_2^{b_1} X_3^{c_1} \cdots = F^0 T^0 t^0 L^0 = 1 \tag{11-11}$$

in which a_1, b_1, c_1, ... are as yet unknown coefficients.

The desirability as well as the possibility of combining several variables into dimensionless products has been observed. The dimensionless products which are obtained in a dimensional analysis are called π *terms*. In this usage of π there is no connection with the use of $\pi = 3.14159$ as the dimensionless geometric ratio.

The number of π terms obtained in a dimensional analysis will be less than the number n of original variables. Thus, if in an analysis one determines π_1, π_2, π_3, ..., π_i, then $i < n$.

Because each π term is dimensionless by itself, any combination of π terms will be dimensionless also. Consequently, we can write

$$\frac{C_2}{C_1} X^{b_1'-a_1'} X_2^{b_2'-a_2'} \cdots X^{b_n'-a_n'} = D\pi_1^{w_1} \pi_2^{w_2} \cdots \pi_i^{w_i} \tag{11-12}$$

in which D and the w's are pure numbers. It follows from Eq. (11-12) that Eq. (11-6) may be replaced by another function, namely,

$$\psi(\pi_1, \pi_2, \ldots, \pi_i) = 0 \tag{11-13}$$

Consequently, Eqs. (11-6) and (11-13) are equivalent.

It also follows that if in any assumed engineering equation there exists a variable X which cannot be combined with other X terms into a dimensionless product, X cannot exist in the original equation.

Table 11-3 lists some of the dimensionless products most frequently encountered in thermodynamics. Table 11-3 for these π terms under prescribed conditions also indicates types of applications.

TABLE 11-3. LIST OF DIMENSIONLESS GROUPS

Name	Symbols		Defining terms	Application
	Usual	ASA Z10.7		
Cauchy number.....	Cau	N_{Cau}	$\dfrac{F}{L^2\rho V^2}$	Elastic effect
Froude number.....	Fr	N_{Fr}	$\dfrac{V^2}{Lg}$	Gravitational effect
Mach number.......	M	N_M	$\dfrac{V}{a}$	Compressibility effect
Reynolds number....	Re	N_{Re}	$\dfrac{\rho VL}{\mu}$	Viscosity effect
Pressure coefficient..	N_P	N_P	$\dfrac{P}{V^2\rho}$	Pressure drop
Weber number......	We	N_{We}	$\dfrac{\rho V^2 L}{\sigma}$	Capillary action
Peclet number......	Pe	N_{Pe}	$\dfrac{c\rho VL}{k}$	Temperature field
Grashof number.....	Gr	N_{Gr}	$\dfrac{\beta(\Delta T)gL^3\rho^2}{\mu^2}$	Gravitational effect in free convection
Nusselt number.....	Nu	N_{Nu}	$\dfrac{hL}{k}$	Heat flow
Prandtl number.....	Pr	N_{Pr}	$\dfrac{c\mu}{k}$	Temperature

where β = coefficient of expansion, $1/T$
$\quad\mu$ = coefficient of viscosity, Ft/L^2
$\quad\rho$ = density, Ft^2/L^4
$\quad h$ = coefficient of heat transfer, H/tL^2T
$\quad k$ = thermal conductivity, H/tLT
$\quad\sigma$ = surface tension, F/L

Several of the π terms listed in Table 11-3 find their original derivations in the field of heat transfer. They are also included in this text because they frequently appear in gas-dynamics studies.

11-4. Buckingham's Pi Theorem.   The fact that a dimensionally homo-geneous equation is reducible to a relation among dimensionless parameters was indicated in the previous section.

Let a phenomenon be represented in functional form as

$$\phi(X_1, X_2, X_3, \ldots, X_n) = 0$$

in which f fundamental units Y_1, Y_2, ..., Y_f are to be considered.   Every X term may be written as a product of the fundamental units.   Thus

$$X_1 = Y_1^{\alpha_1} Y_2^{\alpha_2} \cdots Y_f^{\alpha_f}$$
$$X_2 = Y_1^{\beta_1} Y_2^{\beta_2} \cdots Y_f^{\beta_f}$$

$$\cdots \cdots \cdots \cdots$$

$$X_n = Y_1^{v_1} Y_2^{v_2} \cdots Y_f^{v_f} \tag{11-14}$$

On the other hand, each π term can be given by relations written as follows:

$$\pi_1 = X_1^{a_1} X_2^{b_1} \cdots X_n^{n_1}$$
$$\pi_2 = X_1^{a_2} X_2^{b_2} \cdots X_n^{n_2}$$

$$\cdots \cdots \cdots \cdots$$

$$\pi_i = X_1^{a_i} X_2^{b_i} \cdots X_n^{n_i} \tag{11-15}$$

Using Eqs. (11-14), the individual π terms may be written as

$$\pi_1 = [Y_1^{\alpha_1} Y_2^{\alpha_2} \cdots Y_f^{\alpha_f}]^{a_1} [Y_1^{\beta_1} Y_2^{\beta_2} \cdots Y_f^{\beta_f}]^{b_1} \cdots [Y_1^{v_1} Y_2^{v_2} \cdots Y_f^{v_f}]^{n_1} = 1$$
$$\pi_2 = [Y_1^{\alpha_1} Y_2^{\alpha_2} \cdots Y_f^{\alpha_f}]^{a_2} [Y_1^{\beta_1} Y_2^{\beta_2} \cdots Y_f^{\beta_f}]^{b_2} \cdots [Y_1^{v_1} Y_2^{v_2} \cdots Y_f^{v_f}]^{n_2} = 1$$

$$\cdots \cdots \cdots \cdots \cdots \cdots \cdots \cdots \cdots \cdots$$

In solving for the exponents on the brackets, namely, the a's, the b's, etc., one may use simultaneous equations.   For example, in the determination of the terms with subscript 1 write

$$\alpha_1 a_1 + \beta_1 b_1 + \cdots + v_1 n_1 = 0$$
$$\alpha_2 a_1 + \beta_2 b_1 + \cdots + v_2 n_1 = 0$$

$$\cdots \cdots \cdots \cdots \cdots \cdots \tag{11-16}$$

$$\alpha_f a_1 + \beta_f b_1 + \cdots + v_f n_1 = 0$$

Call f the number of fundamental dimensions involved and n the num-ber of variables which appear; then in connection with Eqs. (11-16), one of three cases may occur.

Case 1, $n < f$.   No solution is possible except the trivial one, in which all of the subscript-1 terms are equal to zero.

Case 2, $n = f$. Solutions other than the trivial zero solution exist and a unique dimensionless ratio is obtained.

Case 3, $n > f$. There are solutions other than the trivial zero, and $n - f$ dimensionless ratios are obtained.

In the solving of the simultaneous equations at least f steps must be undertaken. Consequently, each π term will include $(f + 1)$ X terms, and the number of π terms will be

$$i = n - f \qquad (11\text{-}17)$$

Equation (11-17) is the formulation of Buckingham's π theorem.[1]

Example 1. In turbulent flow with a viscous fluid, the resistance per unit area p is controlled by the pipe diameter D, the fluid velocity V, the fluid density ρ, and the fluid viscosity μ. Find the probable π terms in the problem.

Solution. In functional form we can write

$$p = \phi(D,V,\rho,\mu)$$

and by using Table 11-1, we can form a dimensional matrix as follows:

	F	L	T	t
p	1	-2	0	0
D	0	1	0	0
V	0	1	0	-1
ρ	1	-4	0	2
μ	1	-2	0	1

This matrix indicates that the temperature need not be considered in the problem because in the manner that it has been set up, thermal phenomena are not involved. It follows that only three fundamental units need to be considered. The total number of variables in this problem is five, and therefore in accordance with Buckingham's theorem there are $i = 5 - 3$ or 2 π terms. In each of the two π terms there may be as many as $3 + 1 = 4$ terms. It should be noted that there is no set rule which standardizes the choice of the variables to be assigned to each dimensionless ratio. This indicates that the same physical problem can be served by several different but nevertheless correct π terms. In the choice of elements entering the various π terms it is advisable to keep the experimental facilities in mind. Furthermore, it should be ascertained that each π term includes all of the fundamental units involved in the problem. Finally, the π terms should be arranged so that, whenever possible, standard dimensionless parameters such as those listed in Table 11-3 result. By using standard parameters, the investigator can more readily compare his results with those of other workers.

In the determination of the two dimensionless ratios one might assign the five variables as follows:

$$\pi_1 = V^{a_1}\rho^{b_1}D^{c_1}p = F^0L^0t^0 = 1$$

$$\pi_2 = V^{a_2}\rho^{b_2}D^{c_2}\mu = F^0L^0t^0 = 1$$

A combination other than V, ρ, and D could have been used as the basis for the dimensionless parameter. In deciding on the basic f variables (V, ρ, and D as used in this case) we must keep in mind the following criteria:

1. The f variables chosen will be the same in each π term. If possible, they should collectively incorporate all of the fundamental units entering the problem under study.

2. The f variables should be such that when combined with an additional one a desired π term may be obtained. For example, in fluid-flow problems the Reynolds number is a most common one and many data are given as a function of the Reynolds number. By choosing V, ρ, and D, the Reynolds number cannot be obtained unless viscosity is also brought into the picture. With V, D, and p as the basic variables, it would be impossible to arrive at the Reynolds number although two dimensionless parameters could be obtained.

Consider first π_1, and introduce the units of the variables. Thus

$$\left(\frac{L}{t}\right)^{a_1} \left(\frac{Ft^2}{L^4}\right)^{b_1} L^{c_1} \frac{F}{L^2} = F^0 L^0 t^0 = 1$$

The exponents a_1, b_1, and c_1 are found by dimensional analysis by the balancing of the exponents on the fundamental units. The procedure is to collect the exponents for each of the dimensions as follows:

For F: $b_1 + 1 = 0$

For t: $-a_1 + 2b_1 = 0$

For L: $a_1 - 4b_1 + c_1 - 2 = 0$

Solving by the equation for F,

$$b_1 = -1$$

Solving by the equation for t,

$$a_1 = 2b_1$$

$$a_1 = -2$$

Solving by the equation for L,

$$c = 0$$

Thus $\pi_1 = V^{-2}\rho^{-1}D^0 p = \dfrac{p}{V^2\rho}$

Carrying through similar steps for π_2 with

$$\left(\frac{L}{t}\right)^{a_2} \left(\frac{Ft^2}{L^4}\right)^{b_2} L^{c_2} \frac{Ft}{L^2} = 1$$

it can be shown that

$$\pi_2 = V^{-1}\rho^{-1}D^{-1}\mu = \frac{\mu}{VD\rho}$$

Dimensionally $\mu/VD\rho$ and $VD\rho/\mu$ are the same and it will be noted that the latter is the Reynolds number (Re).

Therefore, in dimensionless form, resistance per unit area is expressible by

$$\psi\left(\frac{p}{V^2\rho}, \frac{V\rho D}{\mu}\right) = 0$$

or $\psi(N_p, \mathrm{Re}) = 0$

Solving for p it is found that

$$p = V^2\rho\psi'(\mathrm{Re})$$

The function ψ' remains to be determined experimentally.

11-5. Van Driest's Theorem. According to Eq. (11-17) the number of π terms in a problem is equal to the total number of variables minus the number of fundamental units involved. Although this is generally correct, it is not always so. Therefore, it is suggested that the student employ Eq. (11-17) with caution. Bridgman [2] and Van Driest [3] have demonstrated that in some cases the number of necessary π terms may be greater than the number predicted by Eq. (11-17).

In any problem the number of π terms depends on the total number of variables and the greatest number of these variables which will not form a dimensionless product. If the greatest number of variables which cannot be combined into a dimensionless product is denoted by κ, then $\kappa \leqq f$. According to Van Driest, the number of dimensionless products in a complete set is equal to the total number of variables minus the maximum number of these variables that will not form a dimensionless product. It follows that Eq. (11-17) should be modified to read

$$i = n - \kappa \qquad (11\text{-}18)$$

Equation (11-18) is the formulation of Van Driest's theorem. The determination of κ may be accomplished by trial. Though this is tedious at times, it is nevertheless advisable to consider the possibility in which $\kappa < f$. Such cases arise when the same combination of units appears in more than one variable of the same problem.

Example 2. A classical problem in which $\kappa < f$ occurs when a steel rod loses heat to ambient air. In the solving of the problem let k be thermal conductivity, and T the temperature. Further, let the subscript s denote the steel and subscript a the air. If the rod having a diameter d and a length l rejects heat amounting to Q per unit time we can write

$$Q = \phi(T_s - T_a,\, l,\, d,\, k_s,\, k_a)$$

In this problem none of the variables considered depends on force or mass and hence it is more convenient to use the $HLTt$ system rather than the $FLTt$ system.

Accordingly, the dimensional matrix becomes

	H	L	T	t
Q	1	0	0	-1
$T_s - T_a$	0	0	1	0
l	0	1	0	0
d	0	1	0	0
k_s	1	-1	-1	-1
k_a	1	-1	-1	-1

Therefore, by dimensional analysis

$$\frac{H}{t} = C T^a l^b L^c \left(\frac{H}{LTt}\right)^d \left(\frac{H}{LTt}\right)^e$$

Equate the exponents of H to obtain

$$1 = d + e \qquad \text{and} \qquad d = 1 - e$$

Equate the exponents of t to obtain

$$-1 = -d - e \quad \text{and} \quad d = 1 - e$$

Equate the exponents of T to find

$$0 = a - d - e$$

and as $d = 1 - e$,

$$a = 1$$

Equating the exponents of L gives

$$0 = b + c - d - e$$

and by substituting from the preceding,

$$b = 1 - c$$

It is noticed at once that the exponents a, b, c, d, and e have been solved in terms of c and e because in this problem there are a greater number of unknowns than there are equations available. Thus,

$$Q = C[T^1 l^{1-c} d^c (k_s)^{1-e} (k_a)^e]$$

$$Q = C \left\{ [(T_s - T_a) l k_s]^1 \left(\frac{d}{l}\right)^c \left(\frac{k_a}{k_s}\right)^e \right\}$$

There are three π terms in this solution, namely,

$$\pi_1 = \frac{Q}{(T_s - T_a) l k_s}$$

$$\pi_2 = \frac{d}{l}$$

and

$$\pi_3 = \frac{k_a}{k_s}$$

In contrast, the prediction of the Buckingham theorem is that the number of π terms is equal to two. It will be evident to the student that as before, pure numbers C, c, and e remain to be determined by experimental means. When Van Driest's theorem is applied, the number of quantities in a π term is equal to $\kappa + 1$ rather than $f + 1$. The case $\kappa < f$ occurs when the number of independent equations in the exponential balancing is less than the number of fundamental units entering the problem.

To determine which theorem is applicable, namely, that of Buckingham or that of Van Driest, Langhaar [4] suggests the following procedure: Upon preparing the dimensional matrix for a particular problem one finds the highest-ranking determinant other than zero. The number of π terms i is then obtained by subtracting the rank r of this determinant from the total number of variables n. In other words $r = \kappa$. Let us apply this method to the preceding example. The matrix which we prepared has six rows and four columns. The highest-ranking determinant which would be obtainable from this matrix would be a four by four matrix or a determinant of rank four. We can obtain this determinant by deleting any two of the six

rows. Upon evaluating the determinants of rank four we find that they
are zero. Therefore, we go to the next-lower rank, namely, three. We find
that we can have a determinant of rank three which when evaluated is
other than zero. Thus according to Langhaar's method the number of
dimensionless terms is $6 - 3 = 3$, which we found already. Langhaar's
method relies upon trial and error, but it nevertheless systematizes the
solution and thus is a powerful adjunct to Van Driest's theorem.

The number of π terms i, is the smallest number of π terms which will
satisfy Eq. (11-13). Also i is the greatest number of dimensionless products which can be formed from the given number of X terms. It should
be noted that i is not the total number of dimensionless ratios which may
be formulated. The total number of possible π terms is given by the combination

$$C^n_{\kappa+1} = \frac{n!}{(\kappa + 1)!(n - \kappa - 1)!} \tag{11-19}$$

11-6. Descriptive Dimensional Analysis. Emphasis has already been
directed in this chapter to the idea that dimensional analysis is an engineering tool and many of the dimensionless parameters obtained for a physical
phenomenon have significant physical meaning. In descriptive dimensional analysis the concepts are extended further but at the same time
limited; for example, lengths in different directions cannot be canceled in-
discriminately.

Consider the units of viscosity. Viscosity was defined in Chap. 1 as the
ratio of the shearing stress to the rate of shearing strain. The shearing
stress is force/area and the rate of shearing strain is dV/dz. According to
conventional dimensional analysis the former has fundamental units of
F/L^2 and the latter is $(L/t)/L = 1/t$. Therefore, the units of viscosity are
Ft/L^2. For convenience let us here use mass M as a basic dimension and
continue using force F as well. As force equals mass times acceleration it
can be written as

$$F = M \frac{d^2 L_x}{dt^2}$$

Refer to Fig. 11-3, which pictures a slip plane used in defining viscosity, and
the shearing stress appears as

$$\frac{M \ d^2 L_x / dt^2}{L_x L_y}$$

The rate of shearing strain is

$$\frac{dV}{dz} = \frac{d(dL_x/dt) \ dt}{dL_z} = \frac{d^2 L_x \ dt}{dt^2 \ dL_z}$$

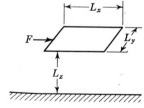

Fig. 11-3. Viscosity.

Therefore the coefficient of viscosity, again with reference to Fig. 11-3, becomes

$$\mu = \frac{M \ dL_z/dt}{L_x L_y} \qquad (11\text{-}20)$$

This expression for the viscosity in some ways is preferable to that obtained by conventional dimensional analysis—particularly so because it manifests a different physical meaning. In it the numerator is momentum, and viscosity can be considered as momentum transfer across unit area.

Kayser [5] has shown that descriptive dimensional analysis is helpful in establishing a mathematical as well as a physical relationship between two important transport phenomena, namely, viscosity and thermal conductivity. Considering Fig. 11-4, and recalling the Fourier heat-conduction equation, the coefficient of thermal conductivity can be written as

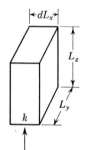

$$k = \frac{q}{A} \frac{dL}{dT} = \frac{(dH/dt) \ dL_z}{L_x L_y \ dT} \qquad (11\text{-}21)$$

The specific heat at constant pressure has the following dimensions:

$$c_p = \frac{dH}{M \ dT} \qquad (11\text{-}22)$$

Therefore,

$$\frac{k}{c_p} = \frac{(dH/dt) \ dL_z}{L_x L_y \ dt/(dH/M \ dt)} = \frac{M \ dL_z/dt}{L_x L_y} \qquad (11\text{-}23)$$

Fig. 11-4. Conduction.

It will be recognized at once that this ratio has the same dimensions as the viscosity coefficient. It follows that

$$k = c_p \mu \qquad (11\text{-}24)$$

an equation well known in kinetic theory and used extensively in the compilation of tables of thermodynamic properties. It is also a fact that von Kármán [6] established the relation between momentum and heat transfer in 1939 by the use of differential equations.

A distinct advantage of descriptive dimensional analysis is that two additional independent simultaneous equations may become available. Thus the formulation of a physical phenomenon may be solved completely by dimensional analysis, whereas heretofore it was often necessary to complete the study by additional analysis from experimentally obtained data curves. For a more stimulating discussion of descriptive dimensional analysis the reader is referred to Huntley.[7]

11-7. Dimensional Analysis of Differential Equations. In engineering phenomena it often happens that one is able to write an equation for a given

physical phenomenon even though there may be considerable difficulty or
even no possibility of solving it. One alternative in such cases is to reduce
the physical equation to a nondimensional form. Pertinent data for the
phenomenon under study may then be obtained by experimentation and
the results generalized by dimensional analysis. This technique is frequently employed in boundary-layer analysis or elsewhere where the solution of the dynamic equations meets with difficulty. Let us apply this
method of approach to the flow of a viscous fluid in the absence of external
forces such as gravity or magnetism. For multidimensional flow in cartesian coordinates one may write the Navier-Stokes equations as follows:

$$\frac{\partial V_x}{\partial t} + V_x \frac{\partial V_x}{\partial x} + V_y \frac{\partial V_x}{\partial y} + V_z \frac{\partial V_x}{\partial z}$$

$$= -\frac{1}{\rho}\frac{\partial p}{\partial x} + \nu \left(\frac{\partial^2 V_x}{\partial x^2} + \frac{\partial^2 V_x}{\partial y^2} + \frac{\partial^2 V_x}{\partial z^2} \right) \quad (11\text{-}25)$$

$$\frac{\partial V_y}{\partial t} + V_x \frac{\partial V_y}{\partial x} + V_y \frac{\partial V_y}{\partial y} + V_z \frac{\partial V_y}{\partial z}$$

$$= -\frac{1}{\rho}\frac{\partial p}{\partial y} + \nu \left(\frac{\partial^2 V_y}{\partial x^2} + \frac{\partial^2 V_y}{\partial y^2} + \frac{\partial^2 V_y}{\partial z^2} \right) \quad (11\text{-}25a)$$

$$\frac{\partial V_z}{\partial t} + V_x \frac{\partial V_z}{\partial x} + V_y \frac{\partial V_z}{\partial y} + V_z \frac{\partial V_z}{\partial z}$$

$$= -\frac{1}{\rho}\frac{\partial p}{\partial z} + \nu \left(\frac{\partial^2 V_z}{\partial x^2} + \frac{\partial^2 V_z}{\partial y^2} + \frac{\partial^2 V_z}{\partial z^2} \right) \quad (11\text{-}25b)$$

in which V is the velocity, t is the time, ρ is the density, and p is the pressure. The subscripts x, y, and z denote vector components in their respective directions. In order to make these equations dimensionless we divide
all velocities by a reference or characteristic velocity which will be desig-
nated V. Distances regardless of direction are divided by the characteristic
length l. The time is made dimensionless by dividing it by a characteristic
time. Because we have already used two characteristic terms, namely, V
and l, it follows that the appropriate characteristic time is equal to the
ratio l/V. Finally, the pressure is rendered dimensionless when it is
divided by twice the dynamic pressure of the reference velocity $2q = \rho V^2$
defined by Eq. (3-36). Thus the following dimensionless terms are
obtained:

$$V_x' = \frac{V_x}{V} \qquad V_y' = \frac{V_y}{V} \qquad V_z' = \frac{V_z}{V} \tag{11-26}$$

$$x' = \frac{x}{l} \qquad y' = \frac{y}{l} \qquad z' = \frac{z}{l} \tag{11-27}$$

$$t' = \frac{tV}{l} \tag{11-28}$$

$$p' = \frac{p}{\rho V_0{}^2} \tag{11-29}$$

Upon substituting these into the Navier-Stokes equations and multiplying by $1/V^2$ the following set of dimensionless equations is obtained:

$$\frac{\partial V_x'}{\partial t'} + V_{x'} \frac{\partial V_x'}{\partial x'} + V_{y'} \frac{\partial V_x'}{\partial y'} + V_{z'} \frac{\partial V_x'}{\partial z'}$$

$$= -\frac{\partial p'}{\partial x'} + \frac{1}{\mathrm{Re}} \left(\frac{\partial^2 V_x'}{\partial x'^2} + \frac{\partial^2 V_x'}{\partial y'^2} + \frac{\partial^2 V_x'}{\partial z'^2} \right) \tag{11-30}$$

$$\frac{\partial V_y'}{\partial t'} + V_{x'} \frac{\partial V_y'}{\partial x'} + V_{y'} \frac{\partial V_y'}{\partial y'} + V_{z'} \frac{\partial V_y'}{\partial z'}$$

$$= -\frac{\partial p'}{\partial y'} + \frac{1}{\mathrm{Re}} \left(\frac{\partial^2 V_y'}{\partial x'^2} + \frac{\partial^2 V_y'}{\partial y'^2} + \frac{\partial^2 V_y'}{\partial z'^2} \right) \tag{11-30a}$$

$$\frac{\partial V_z'}{\partial t'} + V_{x'} \frac{\partial V_z'}{\partial x'} + V_{y'} \frac{\partial V_z'}{\partial y'} + V_{z'} \frac{\partial V_z'}{\partial z'}$$

$$= -\frac{\partial p'}{\partial z'} + \frac{1}{\mathrm{Re}} \left(\frac{\partial^2 V_z'}{\partial x'^2} + \frac{\partial^2 V_z'}{\partial y'^2} + \frac{\partial^2 V_z'}{\partial z'^2} \right) \tag{11-30b}$$

These equations constitute the dimensionless form of the Navier-Stokes equations. They contain four unknowns, namely, the three dimensionless velocity components V_x', V_y', and V_z' and the dimensionless pressure p'. A fourth equation can be the multidimensional form of the equation of continuity. This introduces no additional unknowns, and accordingly V_x', V_y', V_z', and p' can be calculated. Further, the solutions can be represented graphically as functions of the dimensionless coordinates x', y', and z' and the Reynolds number. For further study of the dimensional analysis of differential equations the reader is referred to Birkhoff.[23]

11-8. Similitude and Model Study. In addition to being expensive, many of the devices designed by engineers are complicated or are large in size. Therefore it is desirable to study the performance of various devices by conducting tests on representative small-scale models. The advantages of such procedures are not difficult to see in terms of practicability, time, and expense. In order that a model represent its prototype properly, it is necessary that model and prototype be similar. This can be explained as follows: Suppose that the behavior of a prototype system is expressed in dimensionless form by

$$\psi(\pi_{p_1}, \pi_{p_2}, \ldots, \pi_{p_i}) = 0$$

and the behavior of its model is expressed by

$$\psi(\pi_{m_1}, \pi_{m_2}, \ldots, \pi_{m_i}) = 0$$

The prototype and its model constitute similar systems when the corresponding arguments within the function ψ are numerically equal to one another. In other words, one may write

$$\pi_{p_1} = \psi'(\pi_{p_2}, \pi_{p_3}, \ldots, \pi_{p_i}) \quad \text{and} \quad \pi_{m_1} = \psi'(\pi_{m_2}, \pi_{m_3}, \ldots, \pi_{m_i})$$

The function ψ' will be the same for the prototype and the model provided both are affected by the same variables in the same manner, or if $\pi_{p_2} = \pi_{m_2}$, $\pi_{p_3} = \pi_{m_3}$, ..., $\pi_{p_i} = \pi_{m_i}$. Consequently, $\pi_{p_1} = \pi_{m_1}$, or $\psi(\pi_{p_1}, \pi_{p_2}, \ldots, \pi_{p_i}) = \psi(\pi_{m_1}, \pi_{m_2}, \ldots, \pi_{m_i})$. This last equality is called a *prediction equation*, because for the existence of similitude $\pi_{p_i} = \pi_{m_i}$ one can write, alternatively,

$$\frac{\pi_{p_1}}{\pi_{m_1}} = 1 \qquad \frac{\pi_{p_2}}{\pi_{m_2}} = 1 \qquad \cdots \qquad \frac{\pi_{p_i}}{\pi_{m_i}} = 1 \qquad (11\text{-}31)$$

Although in similar systems the corresponding π terms are equal, the individual variables forming the various dimensionless products can be different. The ratio of a corresponding X variable in its various locations denotes the scale of the model and is called the scale ratio S. Thus

$$S_i = \frac{X_{p_i}}{X_{m_i}} \qquad (11\text{-}32)$$

For example, if every dimension of a model is one-fifth that of its prototype, then the scale ratio of the dimensions is equal to five. Because the fundamental unit involved in this case is the length

$$S_L = \frac{5}{1} = 5$$

The similitude of systems may be of four kinds. These are geometric similitude, kinematic similitude, dynamic similitude, and thermal similitude. *Geometric similitude* implies the existence of a single scale ratio of length between prototype and model. *Kinematic similitude* means that the corresponding motions of two systems are alike. *Dynamic similitude* exists when the forces acting at corresponding points of prototype and model have the same scale ratio. *Thermal similitude* means that a single scale ratio of temperatures exists at corresponding points of a prototype and its model.

In general it is desirable that the model and the prototype meet the requirements of all four kinds of similitude, because the results obtained by the testing of the model will better predict the behavior of the prototype. Models which represent the prototype in all aspects are called *true models*. However, it is not necessary that all four kinds of similitude coexist in a certain problem. For example, it can happen that two systems may be thermally similar without being geometrically similar.

Sometimes it is advantageous to use different scale ratios for the same quantity. For example, in certain studies of fluid flow the reduction of the pipe diameter may result in undue viscous effects. In such a case it may be advisable to reduce the pipe diameter and the pipe length according to different scale ratios of length. In the literature, such models are said to be distorted. The need for the existence or nonexistence of a certain type of similitude is often suggested by an analysis of how the fundamental units present in the various variables influence the phenomenon under study.

Let us now use scale factors in a manner outlined in the previous section. Again we write the Navier-Stokes equations. For purposes of illustration it will be sufficient to consider the equation in the x direction only, namely,

$$\frac{\partial V_x}{\partial t} + V_x\frac{\partial V_x}{\partial x} + V_y\frac{\partial V_x}{\partial y} + V_z\frac{\partial V_x}{\partial z}$$

$$= -\frac{1}{\rho}\frac{\partial p}{\partial x} + \nu\left(\frac{\partial^2 V_x}{\partial x^2} + \frac{\partial^2 V_y}{\partial y^2} + \frac{\partial^2 V_2}{\partial z^2}\right) \quad (11\text{-}25)$$

Let us now use scale factors for the various terms such that

$$V_x = \frac{V_x'}{s_V} \qquad V_y = \frac{V_y'}{s_V} \qquad V_z = \frac{V_z'}{s_V}$$

$$x = \frac{x'}{s_L} \qquad y = \frac{y'}{s_L} \qquad z = \frac{z'}{s_L}$$

$$\rho = \frac{\rho'}{s_\rho} \qquad p = \frac{p'}{s_p} \qquad \nu = \frac{\nu'}{s_\nu} \qquad t = \frac{t'}{s_t}$$

In applying these scale factors we will note, for example, that

$$\partial t = \frac{\partial t'}{s_t} \tag{11-33}$$

and that

$$\frac{s_L}{s_t} = s_V \tag{11-34}$$

Substituting in the Navier-Stokes equation and dividing throughout by the ratio S_t/S_V we get

$$\frac{\partial V_x'}{\partial t'} + V_{x'} \frac{\partial V_x'}{\partial x'} + V_{y'} \frac{\partial V_x'}{\partial y'} + V_{z'} \frac{\partial V_x'}{\partial z'}$$

$$= -\frac{S_\rho S_V^2}{p} \frac{1}{\rho'} \frac{\partial p'}{\partial x'} + \frac{S_L S_V}{S_\nu} \nu'^2 \left(\frac{\partial^2 V_x'}{\partial x'^2} + \frac{\partial^2 V_x'}{\partial y'^2} + \frac{\partial^2 V_x'}{\partial z'^2} \right) \quad (11\text{-}35)$$

In the above form of the Navier-Stokes equation there are two scale-ratio combinations, namely,

$$\frac{S_\rho S_V^2}{S_p} \quad (11\text{-}36)$$

and

$$\frac{S_L S_V}{S_\nu} \quad (11\text{-}37)$$

Inspection of Table 11-3 indicates that the first includes the terms used in the pressure-drop parameter, and the second includes the terms making up the Reynolds number. It follows from this that if these terms are the same for the model and the prototype dynamic similarity will exist between the two. Further interesting reading is found in references 24 to 26.

11-9. Analogic Techniques. Certain apparently un-related phenomena can often be expressed by the same type of equations. Thus it is frequently possible to asso-ciate a mechanical system with an electric system, an elec-tric system with a thermal or a hydraulic system, or a hydraulic system with an electrical system. The advan-tage of analogic techniques lies in overcoming the inherent difficulty which the measurement of certain quantities presents. Thus it may happen that by setting up an analogic technique the variables can be determined with greater facility. Consider a dynamic system as shown in Fig. 11-5, consisting of a spring, a weight, and a damping device. The equation † describing the response of this system is

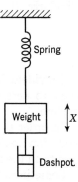

Fig. 11-5. Dy-namic system.

$$\frac{W}{g} \frac{d^2x}{dt^2} + C \frac{dx}{dt} + kx = 0 \quad (11\text{-}38)$$

where W = weight
$\quad x$ = displacement
$\quad t$ = time
$\quad C$ = damping constant
$\quad k$ = spring constant

† See, for example, S. Timoshenko, "Vibration Problems in Engineering," 2d ed., D. Van Nostrand Company, Inc., Princeton, N.J., 1937.

An analogous electric system may now be set up as shown in Fig. 11-6. The differential equation of this circuit is

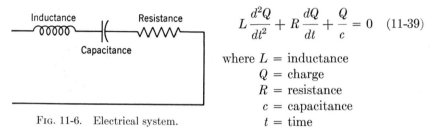

$$L\frac{d^2Q}{dt^2} + R\frac{dQ}{dt} + \frac{Q}{c} = 0 \quad (11\text{-}39)$$

where L = inductance
Q = charge
R = resistance
c = capacitance
t = time

FIG. 11-6. Electrical system.

A comparison of the equations representing, respectively, the vibrational and the electric systems indicates that the following corresponding quantities are analogic:

$$\frac{W}{g} \equiv L \qquad R \equiv C \qquad \frac{1}{c} \equiv k \qquad Q \equiv x \qquad (11\text{-}40)$$

Similarly, the respective differentials correspond as follows:

$$\frac{d^2x}{dt^2} \sim \frac{d^2Q}{dt^2} \qquad \frac{dx}{dt} \sim \frac{dQ}{dt} \qquad (11\text{-}41)$$

It is evident from this discussion that measurements in one system may be used to determine the variation of corresponding items in an analogous system.

In order to establish an analogic relation, it is necessary first to find an equation applicable to both systems. Second, it is desirable that measurements on the analogic system are easier to make than in the original system.

Sometimes two systems can be made analogic only after the equation describing one of them has been simplified. For example, Schneider and Cambel [8,9] have shown that steady-temperature fields in electrical coils can be studied by means of membrane analogy. Thus uniform heat generation in an electrical coil may be described by the following partial differential equation:

$$\frac{\partial^2}{\partial x^2} T(x,y) + \frac{\partial^2}{\partial y^2} T(x,y) + \frac{q}{k} = 0 \qquad (11\text{-}42)$$

in which T is the temperature, q is the unit volume heat generation in Btu per hour–cubic foot, k is the coefficient of thermal conductivity, and x and y are cartesian coordinates. It may also be shown that when a membrane having negligible weight and suspended on a continuous boundary such as the edge of a hole cut in a plate is dilated by a pressure p, the following equation is applicable:

$$\tau\left[1+\left(\frac{\partial z}{\partial x}\right)^2\right]\frac{\partial^2 z}{\partial x^2}+\tau\left[1+\left(\frac{\partial z}{\partial y}\right)^2\right]\frac{\partial^2 z}{\partial y^2}$$

$$-2\tau\frac{\partial z}{\partial x}\frac{\partial z}{\partial y}\frac{\partial^2 z}{\partial x\,\partial y}+p\left[1+\left(\frac{\partial z}{\partial x}\right)^2+\left(\frac{\partial z}{\partial y}\right)^2\right]^{3/2}=0\quad(11\text{-}43)$$

in which τ is the coefficient of surface tension, and x, y, and z are cartesian coordinates.

If the maximum slope of the film surface $z(x,y)$ is restricted to less than 30°, the second-degree derivatives $(\partial z/\partial x)^2$ and $(\partial z/\partial y)^2$, as well as the second-order derivative $\partial^2 z/(\partial x\,\partial y)$, are negligible. Therefore, an approximate equation describing the dilated membrane is

$$\frac{\partial^2}{\partial x^2}z(x,y)+\frac{\partial^2}{\partial y^2}z(x,y)+\frac{p}{\tau}=0\qquad(11\text{-}44)$$

and hence $T(x,y)$ and $z(x,y)$ are analogous. Therefore, the temperature-field variation can be related to measurements of the dilation distance of the membrane over its surface.

A water-channel analogue relative to high-velocity combustion has been developed by Oppenheim [10] by establishing certain nondimensional analogous functions between a gas-dynamic system and a closed-circuit hydraulic system.

People who have observed the flow of water in open channels have noticed the qualitative resemblance between supersonic gas flow and the subsonic flow of water. That this resemblance might be used for analogic technique was proposed by Jouguet.[17] Since then the method has been used quite extensively in gas dynamics, both in the presence of combustion [18] and in the absence of combustion.[19, 20]

In the absence of combustion, the analogy between a gas-dynamic system and a hydraulic system is because of the similarity among the equations of two-dimensional isentropic gas flow and the equations of two-dimensional open-channel flow of incompressible fluids. In order for the equations to be analogic it is necessary that the gas be treated as perfect, and that it have a specific-heat ratio $k = 2.0$. Qualitatively, the pressure waves observed in a gas-dynamic system and the water waves correspond to one another.

A small disturbance in a gas-dynamic system is propagated with the speed of sound. On the other hand, Lamb [21] has shown that long, gravity-surface waves in a shallow, horizontal, open channel propagate with a velocity $V_w = \sqrt{gz}$ provided the amplitude of the wave is considerably smaller than the depth of the water at that point. In turn, a shock wave is analogous to a hydraulic jump. In an open channel the depth of the stream will vary with changes in mass flow and thus the hydraulic-stream depth corresponds to density in the gas-dynamic stream.

We may now prepare Table 11-4.

TABLE 11-4

	Hydraulic system	Gas-dynamic system
Continuity equation..	$\dfrac{\partial z}{\partial t} + \dfrac{\partial (z V_x)}{\partial x} + \dfrac{\partial (z V_y)}{\partial y} = 0$	$\dfrac{\partial \rho}{\partial t} + \dfrac{\partial (\rho V_x)}{\partial x} + \dfrac{\partial (\rho V_y)}{\partial y} = 0$
Energy equation.....	$z + \dfrac{V^2}{2g} = z_0 + \dfrac{V_0^2}{2g}$	$\dfrac{kR}{k-1} T + \dfrac{V^2}{2} = \dfrac{kRT_0}{k-1} + \dfrac{V_0^2}{2}$
Gravity effect........	Froude number $\mathrm{Fr} \equiv \dfrac{V^2}{gz} = \dfrac{V}{V_w}$	
Compressibility effect	....	Mach number $\mathrm{M} \equiv \dfrac{V}{a}$

where z = height of water surface, vertical
  x,y = coordinates, horizontal
  V_x = velocity component in x direction
  V_y = velocity component in y direction
  V_w = water-wave velocity

Because V_0 is negligibly small, the energy equation for the hydraulic system becomes

$$z + \frac{V^2}{2g} = z_0 \tag{11-45}$$

Substituting the Froude number in this and solving for the ratio z_0/z we get

$$\frac{z_0}{z} = 1 + \tfrac{1}{2}\mathrm{Fr}^2 \tag{11-46}$$

We also recall from Chap. 3 that

$$\frac{T_0}{T} = 1 + \frac{k-1}{2} \mathrm{M}^2 \tag{3-31}$$

and

$$\frac{p_0}{p} = \left(1 + \frac{k-1}{2} \mathrm{M}^2\right)^{k/(k-1)} \tag{3-35}$$

Also, because for the isentropic process

$$\frac{\rho_0}{\rho} = \left(\frac{T_0}{T}\right)^{1/(k-1)}$$

it follows that

$$\frac{\rho_0}{\rho} = \left(1 + \frac{k-1}{2} \mathrm{M}^2\right)^{1/(k-1)}$$

Equation (11-46) will be similar to Eq. (3-31) when $k = 2.0$. Thus for a perfect gas having such a specific-heat ratio we get

$$\frac{T_0}{T} = 1 + \tfrac{1}{2}M^2 \tag{11-47}$$

$$\frac{p_0}{p} = (1 + \tfrac{1}{2}M^2)^2 \tag{11-48}$$

$$\frac{\rho_0}{\rho} = 1 + \frac{k-1}{2}M^2 \tag{11-49}$$

It follows at once that we have the following analogous quantities:

Gas-dynamic system, $k = 2$	Hydraulic analogue
$M = \dfrac{V}{a}$	$Fr = \dfrac{V}{V_w}$
$\dfrac{T}{T_0}$	$\dfrac{z}{z_0}$
$\dfrac{p}{p_0}$	$\left(\dfrac{z}{z_0}\right)^2$
$\dfrac{\rho}{\rho_0}$	$\dfrac{z}{z_0}$

Thus it is possible to study and design a gas-dynamic system such as a nozzle, rocket motor, venturi, etc. by setting up a hydraulic analogue and measuring the height of the free-water surface.

There are several factors which will influence the validity of the hydraulic analogue. The first that comes to mind is the value of the specific-heat ratio. In the analogue it is assumed that $k = 2$, but for most gases k is more nearly in the range 1.2 to 1.5. Fortunately this error is not too serious both in the subsonic and in the supersonic regimes.[22] Other errors that may be introduced are the boundary layer developed on the bottom of the water stream, viscosity, thermal conductivity, and surface tension. In the case of shock phenomena the analogy will fail if the experimenter does not replace the gas-dynamic equations by shock equations, and the steady-flow hydraulic equations by hydraulic-jump equations.

Proceeding in a similar manner Oppenheim [18] has developed analogous quantities between a high-speed combustion system and its hydraulic analogue.

11-10. Compressible Flow of Viscous Fluids. It was seen in Chap. 3 that when the velocity of gas flow is greater than one-half the speed of sound, or when thermal effects are appreciable, compressibility must be accounted for. In dealing with density variations it is necessary that thermal similitude be included in the derivations in addition to geometric, kinematic, and dynamic similitude. Therefore, the Reynolds number and the pressure coefficient which were found in the case of incompressible flow are not sufficient to define compressible flow.

In developing dimensionless parameters for compressible flow the following simplifying assumptions shall be made:

1. The flow is adiabatic.
2. The same medium is used.
3. Variations in the density are caused by pressure only.
4. The specific heats and the thermal conductivity of the gas are constants.

Therefore, the flow may be expressed by the function

$$\phi(\rho,L,V,\mu,g,a,p) = 0$$

where g = gravitational constant, and a = acoustic velocity. It is seen that in this function the specific heats and the thermal conductivity have not been included. This follows as a consequence of assumptions 2 and 4.

The dimensional matrix for the solution of this problem becomes

	F	L	T	t
ρ	1	-4	0	2
L	0	1	0	0
V	0	1	0	-1
μ	1	-2	0	1
g	0	1	0	-2
a	0	1	0	-1
p	1	-2	0	0

Applying Buckingham's theorem it follows that there are four π terms and these may be arranged as follows:

$$\pi_1 = \rho^{a_1}L^{b_1}V^{c_1}\mu = F^0L^0T^0t^0$$

$$\pi_2 = \rho^{a_2}L^{b_2}V^{c_2}g = F^0L^0T^0t^0$$

$$\pi_3 = \rho^{a_3}L^{b_3}V^{c_3}a = F^0L^0T^0t^0$$

$$\pi_4 = \rho^{a_4}L^{b_4}V^{c_4}p = F^0L^0T^0t^0$$

From dimensional analyses it may be found that the four dimensionless parameters are

$$\pi_1 = \frac{\rho L V}{\mu} = \text{Re}$$

$$\pi_2 = \frac{V^2}{Lg} = \text{Fr}$$

$$\pi_3 = \frac{V}{a} = \text{M}$$

$$\pi_4 = \frac{p}{\rho V^2} = \text{Cau}$$

It follows that

$$\psi(\text{Re,Fr,M,Cau}) = 0$$

It may be desirable to set up dimensionless ratios for the study of compressible-flow phenomena when different media are to be used. For example, supersonic wind tunnels using Freon gases such as dichlorodifluoromethane or steam have been proposed and constructed. In such cases assumptions 2 and 4 above do not apply, and other variables must be considered. The solution of this case is left to the student in Prob. 11-8 in this chapter.

In high-velocity problems the most important dimensionless parameters are the Reynolds number and the Mach number. The physical character of the process makes it impracticable to maintain similar Reynolds and Mach numbers concurrently. Therefore, in the incompressible domain the Reynolds number is the basic criterion of similarity, and in applications of compressible flow the Mach number is of paramount importance.

11-11. Further Applications of Dimensional Analysis. In the previous sections of this chapter the fundamentals of dimensional analysis have been discussed and some illustrations have been given. The concept of dimensionless parameters may be applied to many problems in gas dynamics and some of these are cited briefly.

Steam Turbines. Because of their universal use, steam turbines require detailed studies in making designs. However, the high rotational speeds, the high temperatures and pressures, as well as the small clearances in steam turbines, make many preliminary experimental studies impracticable. Ackeret [11] and his associates have developed a method for the investigation of turbine operation by the use of air as the working medium. Their analysis predicts that in a dimensionless study of steam turbines one may apply the function $\psi(\text{Re,M},k) = 0$.

Internal-combustion Engines. The application of dimensional analysis to internal-combustion engines has received considerable interest. Taylor and Taylor [12] describe data obtained on three similar engines constructed specifically for purposes of investigating dimensional-analysis criteria. One set of these similar engines has bores of 6, 4, and 2½ in., respectively, but in each case the stroke-bore ratio is 1.2. These engines are run under similar operating conditions, namely, the same inlet temperature and pressure, same inlet fuel-air ratio, same cooling-water-inlet temperature, same oil-inlet temperature, and the same best-power spark advance. The data indicate that when the volumetric efficiency of these three engines is plotted vs. the piston speed, one and the same curve may be used for all three engines to study performance. Taylor has compared the performance of a small model engine with that of a large diesel engine. The comparative results for these engines, which are both of the two-stroke variety, are tabulated in Table 11-5.

TABLE 11-5. MODEL STUDY OF TWO INTERNAL-COMBUSTION ENGINES

Item	Arden 1-cylinder airplane-model diesel	Nordberg 10-cylinder diesel
Bore, in.	0.495	29
Stroke, in.	0.516	40
Rpm	11,400	164
Cylinder displacement, cu in.	0.10	26,500
Horsepower per cubic inch of displacement	1.36	0.027
Pounds weight per horsepower	2.8	110
Brake mean effective pressure, psi	47	66
Piston speed, fpm	980	1,100
Horsepower per square inch of piston area	0.71	2.95
Pounds weight per cubic inch of displacement	3.78	2.9

It is rather interesting to note that two engines so drastically different in size may have characteristics so similar to one another. Thus, although the stroke and bore of the Nordberg are large, the brake mean effective pressure, the piston speed, and the weight per unit displacement volume are fairly similar for both engines.

Consider a gas-turbine cycle as shown in Fig. 11-7. It is customary to assume that the Joule-Brayton cycle shown in Fig. 11-8 is the closest prototype cycle. This consists of two isentropic and two isobaric processes. Actually, other arrangements may be more advantageous, at least thermodynamically. Two cycles will be discussed here with the help of two dimensionless ratios. Let a pressure ratio π be defined as follows:

$$\pi = \left(\frac{p_{max}}{p_{min}}\right)^{(k-1)/k} \tag{11-50}$$

where p_{max} and p_{min} are the maximum and minimum pressures respectively per power unit existing in the cycle. Thus p_{min} and p_{max} are the inlet and outlet pressures for each compressor and p_{max} is also the inlet pressure for

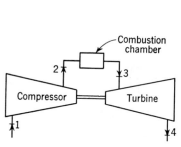

FIG. 11-7. Simple gas turbine.   FIG. 11-8. Joule-Brayton cycle.

each corresponding turbine, considering the combustion process to be isobaric. Similarly define a temperature ratio τ as follows:

$$\tau = \frac{T_{max}}{T_{min}} \tag{11-51}$$

Referring to Figs. 11-3 and 11-4 we can write, for the turbine work,

$$W_T = mc_p(T_3 - T_4) \tag{11-52}$$

Introducing the base or ambient temperature T_1,

$$W_T = mc_pT_1\left(\frac{T_3}{T_1} - \frac{T_4}{T_1}\right) \tag{11-53}$$

By definition,

$$\tau = \frac{T_{max}}{T_{min}} = \frac{T_3}{T_1} \tag{11-51a}$$

For a gas cycle consisting of pairs of isobaric and isentropic processes it can be shown that the products of the diagonal temperatures are equal. Thus,

$$T_1 \times T_3 = T_2 \times T_4$$

Therefore,

$$\frac{T_4}{T_1} = \frac{T_3}{T_2} \tag{11-54}$$

Divide and multiply the right-hand side by T_1, yielding

$$\frac{T_4}{T_1} = \frac{T_3}{T_1} \times \frac{T_1}{T_2} = \tau \frac{T_1}{T_2} \qquad (11\text{-}55)$$

For an isentropic process during compression

$$\frac{T_2}{T_1} = \left(\frac{p_2}{p_1}\right)^{(k-1)/k} \qquad (11\text{-}50a)$$

but

$$\frac{T_2}{T_1} = \pi$$

Therefore, the turbine work is

$$W_T = mc_p T_1 \left(\tau - \frac{\tau}{\pi}\right) \qquad (11\text{-}56)$$

It can be shown similarly that the compressor work is

$$W_c = mc_p T_1 (\pi - 1) \qquad (11\text{-}57)$$

and the heat supplied is

$$Q_s = mc_p T_1 (\tau - \pi) \qquad (11\text{-}58)$$

The thermal efficiency thus appears as

$$\eta_{th} = 1 - \frac{1}{\pi} \qquad (11\text{-}59)$$

According to this equation the efficiency will be increased by using a high T_2/T_1 ratio. Although this is true, of course it is not desirable just to raise the pressure ratio. To demonstrate this let us define the specific output (SO) as follows:

$$\text{SO} = \frac{W_T - W_c}{mc_p T_1} = \frac{W_N}{mc_p T_1} \qquad (11\text{-}60)$$

where W_N is the net output. Further,

$$\frac{W_N}{mc_p T_1} = \frac{1}{\pi} (\tau - \pi)(\pi - 1) \qquad (11\text{-}61)$$

From the viewpoint of the plant designer it is obviously desirable that $W_N/mC_p T_1$ be a maximum. Evidently, there will be some condition which will make the specific output a maximum and this is easily found by differentiating the specific output with respect to π. Thus,

$$\frac{d}{d\pi}\left(\frac{W_N}{mc_p T_1}\right) = \frac{\tau}{\pi^2} - 1 \qquad (11\text{-}62)$$

Setting this differential equal to zero to obtain a maximum and solving for π, there results

$$\pi = \pm\sqrt{\tau} \qquad (11\text{-}63)$$

In this solution only the plus sign has a physical meaning and therefore the plant will operate most productively when

$$\pi = \sqrt{\tau} \qquad (11\text{-}64)$$

This discussion indicates that a plant may operate at maximum productivity although it may not be operating most efficiently. Accordingly, it may be desirable in certain instances to cool the inlet air to the compressor.

Consider now a gas-turbine plant equipped with a regenerative heater, and further consider that the air passes through the compressor and the turbine reversibly and isothermally. Such a plant cycle is depicted in Fig. 11-9. For such a cycle heat must be rejected in the compressor and heat

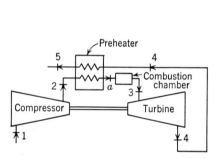

FIG. 11-9. Gas-turbine plant with regeneration.

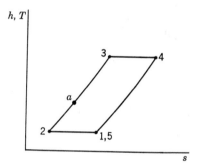

FIG. 11-10. $T,h\text{-}s$ diagram for isothermal gas turbine with regeneration.

must be supplied in the turbine to maintain the compression and expansion processes isothermal. Although this poses some practical difficulties it is in the realm of realization as a limiting condition. The cycle is depicted in Fig. 11-10.

For the isothermal expansion process in the turbine the process work is

$$W_T = mRT_3 \ln \frac{p_4}{p_1} \qquad (11\text{-}65)$$

Using definitions from Eqs. (11-50) and (11-51) and recalling that $c_p = kR/(k-1)$, this may be rewritten as

$$W_T = mc_pT_3 \ln \left(\frac{p_4}{p_1}\right)^{(k-1)/k}$$

$$= mc_pT_3 \ln \pi \qquad (11\text{-}66)$$

Similarly, the compressor work may be expressed by

$$W_c = mc_p T_1 \ln \pi \tag{11-67}$$

Therefore the net output is

$$W_N = W_T - W_c = mc_p T_1 (\tau - 1) \ln \pi \tag{11-68}$$

In order to compute the thermal efficiency it is necessary to know the heat supplied and this necessitates the determination of the temperature T_a. This can be accomplished by defining the preheater effectiveness e_R on the basis of a simple heat balance as follows:

$$e_R = \frac{T_a - T_2}{T_4 - T_2} \tag{11-69}$$

For an ideal cycle, $e_R = 100$ per cent and hence $T_a = T_4 = T_3$. It follows that at least theoretically there is no need for a combustion chamber. (For the actual plant there are losses, but nevertheless the combustion chamber will be limited in size.) The heat supplied to the ideal plant would consist merely of the heat supplied in the turbine. By the first law,

$$Q = \Delta u + W$$

and for perfect gases undergoing isothermal processes $\Delta u = 0$, and hence

$$Q = W = mc_p T_3 \ln \pi \tag{11-70}$$

Therefore, the thermal efficiency of the plant appears from Eqs. (11-68) and (11-70) as

$$\eta_{th} = 1 - \frac{1}{\tau}$$

This, it can be seen, is the same as the Carnot-cycle efficiency for the plant. Thus the most efficient gas-turbine cycle which may be arranged is regenerative and consists of isothermal compression and expansion processes. The practicality of this arrangement, however, is open to serious question because of pressure losses and the extent and weight of the heat-transfer surfaces required even to approach the end point indicated. However, the method itself is a powerful analytical tool and for that reason has much merit.

Other cycle arrangements may be analyzed by using the same technique. The performance curves of eight different arrangements calculated by Cambel [13] are shown in Fig. 11-11a and b.

Flame Stabilization. It has been learned from experiments that flame stabilization is affected by numerous factors and this is discussed in some detail in a later chapter. In an attempt to obtain a more general interpretation of flashback, Putnam and Jensen [14] have proposed the use of

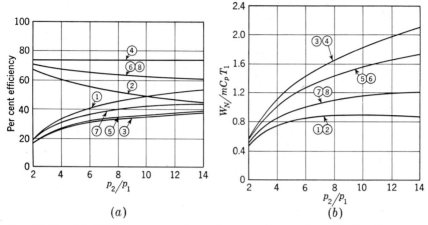

FIG. 11-11. (*a*) Efficiency curves of certain gas-turbine cycles. (*b*) Specific output parameter curves of certain gas-turbine cycles. Combustor temperature, 1500°F. No loss in available energy is considered. 1, adiabatic compression and adiabatic expansion. 3, isothermal compression and isothermal expansion. 5, adiabatic compression and isothermal expansion. 7, isothermal compression and adiabatic expansion. 2, adiabatic compression and adiabatic expansion with regeneration. 4, isothermal compression and isothermal expansion with regeneration. 6, adiabatic compression and isothermal expansion with regeneration. 8, isothermal compression and adiabatic expansion with regeneration.

dimensionless parameters. Basing their analysis on existing studies, these authors have shown that the Peclet number is a significant parameter.

A bluff-body flame-holding analogue proposed by Spalding has been described by Fenn,[27] and this has been studied by Anderson.[28]

11-12. Corrected Factors. Some of the potentialities for use of dimensionless parameters are evident from preceding discussions in this chapter. Dimensionless parameters are also useful in design. However, occasion frequently arises in the field of design for a more intimate knowledge of the manner in which physical quantities vary. This need, together with dimensional analysis, leads to the concept of the so-called *corrected factors* † which are not dimensionless and may even have fractional dimensions. An example of such a factor is the so-called *specific speed* used extensively in pump and blower design. This is defined as

$$n_s = \frac{n\sqrt{Q}}{z^{3/4}} \qquad (11\text{-}71)$$

where n_s = specific speed, rpm
n = impeller operating speed, rpm
Q = discharge, gpm
z = total head, ft

† Sometimes called *equivalent factors, reduced factors,* or *design parameters.*

Using the specific speed, impeller performance and configurations can be classified regardless of the size of impeller or its speed.

Another common example is the mean effective pressure, used in comparing internal-combustion engines. This is defined as the ratio of the cycle work to the piston displacement. Thus different automobile engines can be compared regardless of speed and number of cylinders. It is, of course, desirable that an engine have a high mean effective pressure.

TABLE 11-6. DERIVATION OF CORRECTED PARAMETERS FROM DIMENSIONLESS GROUPS FOR GAS TURBINES AND JETS

Designation	Dimensionless parameter	Constant of proportionality	Corrected parameter
Corrected airspeed.......	$\dfrac{V}{a}$	a_{std}	$\dfrac{V}{\sqrt{\theta}}$
Corrected engine speed....	$\dfrac{nL}{a}$	$\dfrac{a_{std}}{L}$	$\dfrac{n}{\sqrt{\theta}}$
Corrected air flow.......	$\dfrac{m_a a}{kL^2 p}$	$kL^2 \dfrac{p_{std}}{a_{std}}$	$\dfrac{m_a \sqrt{\theta}}{\delta}$
Corrected fuel-air ratio....	$(k-1)\dfrac{H}{a^2}\dfrac{m_f}{m_a}$	$\dfrac{a_{std}^2}{(k-1)H}$	$\dfrac{m_f/m_a}{\theta}$
Corrected temperature....	$\dfrac{T}{T_0}$	T_{std}	$\dfrac{T}{\theta}$
Corrected pressure.......	$\dfrac{p}{p_0}$	p_{std}	$\dfrac{p}{\delta}$

where a = speed of sound
H = heating value of fuel
k = ratio of specific heats of fluid
L = linear dimension
m_a = mass rate of air flow
m_f = mass rate of fuel flow
n = engine speed
p = pressure, total or static
V = linear velocity
δ = ratio of pressure to standard NACA sea-level pressure
θ = ratio of temperature to standard NACA sea-level temperature

Somewhat similar factors are used in the field of gas turbines and jet propulsion. In this field the corrected factors are actually a correction of experimentally obtained values by the use of standard values of pressure and temperature. To obtain these, dimensionless performance parameters are first derived. This was done by Sanders [15] and some of his values are listed in Table 11-6. These dimensionless parameters can be combined with suitable parameters to constitute constants of proportionality to bring out the relations between physical quantities. In finding the parameter, the product of the dimensionless parameter and its proportionality constant is multiplied or divided either by the standard sea-level temperature or pressure or by the square root of these, obtaining the so-called *corrected parameter* listed in column 4. A similar method has also been used by Pinkel [16] to determine combustion temperatures in ram-jet engines by means of total-pressure surveys.

PROBLEMS

11-1. An automobile manufacturer desires to determine the body characteristics of a new design in the wind tunnel. The height of the prototype is to be 4 ft 0 in. and its weight 3,000 lb. The height of the model is 2 ft 6 in. and the test section of the wind tunnel is 4 by 4 ft. What must be the wind velocity in the tunnel if a road speed of 60 mph is to be simulated? (Assume an air temperature of 76°F.)

11-2. A ship having an over-all length of 477 ft 6 in. and a speed of $18\frac{1}{2}$ knots is to be tested in the towing tank. At what speed will a 15 ft 0 in. model simulate the performance of the prototype?

11-3. A V-2 type rocket is to be tested in a supersonic wind tunnel having a test section 5 by 5 ft. The over-all length of the missile is 46 ft 0 in. and its cylindrical diameter is 5 ft 6 in. What must be the tunnel velocity if conditions at 3,400 mph and −49°F prototype velocity are to be investigated?

11-4. The flow of brine in a refrigeration system is to be investigated by the use of air but the same installation will be used for the tests. Find the air velocity if the brine velocity is 5 fps.

11-5. The quenching of a steel bar is to be investigated by dimensional analysis. Derive dimensionless parameters which may be useful.

11-6. Under what conditions will dimensional analysis fail if all the variables involved are not accounted for?

11-7. Show by dimensional analysis that the air standard efficiency of the Otto cycle is a function of the compression ratio and the ratio of the specific heats.

11-8. The phenomena taking place during supersonic flow in air are to be investigated by the use of a different gas. If the function $\phi(\rho, L, V, \mu, g, a, p, c_p, c_v, k) = 0$ is given, find the dimensionless parameters most convenient for experimental studies. Do these parameters apply to viscous or to inviscid fluids?

11-9. The adiabatic expansion of a gas in a piston-cylinder arrangement is to be studied by means of dimensional analysis. Determine dimensionless parameters which may be useful in such a study.

11-10. Using dimensional analysis, find an expression for the fluid resistance per unit area for laminar flow in a pipe.

11-11. The performance of a centrifugal blower used in air-conditioning work is to be studied by dimensional analysis. Find useful dimensionless parameters.

11-12. What dimensionless parameters may be meaningful in studying internal-combustion engines by means of models? Consider spark-ignition engines as well as compression-ignition engines.

11-13. What are some dimensionless parameters which may be used in analyzing gas-turbine combustion chambers?

11-14. A steam boiler is to be studied by means of a model using Freon-12. What dimensionless parameters would probably be necessary to determine the approximate scale ratio of length?

11-15. At sea level a turbosupercharger has an air flow of 3 lb/sec and its speed is 15,000 rpm. The inlet temperature is 85°F. Compute at least three corrected factors which may be determined from the given data.

11-16. The G.E. TG-180 turbojet engine has the following approximate characteristics: The thrust is 3,750 lb; the speed is 7,700 rpm; and the specific fuel consumption is 1.026 lb/(hr)(lb thrust). Find the corrected speed factor, the corrected air-flow factor, and the corrected fuel-air factor for the given conditions.

11-17. By the use of dimensional analysis show that for turbulent flow in a pipe one may write $\psi(p/V^2\rho,\ V\rho D/\mu) = 0$.

11-18. A perfect gas expands in a piston-cylinder arrangement. What are the variables which must be considered in a thermal study of this problem based on similitude? What are some useful dimensionless parameters?

11-19. Slightly superheated steam expands in a steam-engine cylinder and during the process some of it condenses. Suggest dimensionless parameters which may be used in studying such an engine by the use of models.

11-20. Repeat Prob. 11-8 for an inviscid fluid.

11-21. Repeat Prob. 11-10 for an inviscid fluid.

11-22. A missile is launched with a finite initial velocity in a horizontal direction. By the use of descriptive dimensional analysis show that its horizontal range L is

$$L = CV_0 \sqrt{\frac{h}{g}}$$

where C is a dimensionless constant, V_0 is the initial velocity, h is the initial launching height above the earth's surface, and g is the gravity-acceleration coefficient.

REFERENCES

1. Buckingham, E.: On Physically Similar Systems: Illustrations of the Use of Dimensional Equations, *Phys. Rev.*, vol. 4, p. 345, 1914.
2. Bridgman, P. W.: "Dimensional Analysis," 2d ed., Yale University Press, New Haven, Conn., 1931.
3. Van Driest, E. R.: On Dimensional Analysis and the Presentation of Data in Fluid Flow Problems, *J. Appl. Mechanics*, vol. 13, p. A-34, 1946.
4. Langhaar, H. L.: "Dimensional Analysis and Theory of Models," John Wiley & Sons, Inc., New York, 1951.
5. Kayser, R.: Analogy among Heat, Mass, and Momentum Transfer, *Ind. Eng. Chem.*, vol. 45, no. 12, p. 2634, 1953.
6. von Kármán, Th.: The Analogy between Fluid Friction and Heat Transfer, *Trans. ASME*, vol. 61, p. 705, 1939.
7. Huntley, H. E.: "Dimensional Analysis," MacDonald and Co., Ltd., London, 1952.
8. Schneider, P. J., and A. B. Cambel: Steady Temperature Fields in Electrical Coils by Membrane Analogy, Paper 53-SA-43, ASME Semiannual Meeting, 1953.
9. Schneider, P. J., and A. B. Cambel: Membrane Apparatus for Analogic Experiments, *Rev. Sci. Instr.*, vol. 24, no. 7, p. 513, 1953.
10. Oppenheim, A. K.: Water-channel Analog to High-velocity Combustion, *J. Appl. Mechanics*, March, 1953, p. 115.

11. Ackeret, J., C. Keller, and F. Salsman: *Schweiz. Bauz.*, vol. 104, pp. 259, 278, 292, 1934.

12. Taylor, C. F., and E. S. Taylor: "The Internal Combustion Engine," rev. ed., International Textbook Company, Scranton, Pa., 1948.

13. Cambel, A. B.: Gas Turbine Power Plane for Aircraft, *J. Aeronaut. Sci.*, vol. 19, no. 11, p. 791, 1952.

14. Putnam, A. A., and R. A. Jensen: Application of Dimensionless Numbers to Flashback and Other Combustion Phenomena, *3d Symposium on Combustion and Flame and Explosion Phenomena*, pp. 89–98, The Williams & Wilkins Company, Baltimore, 1949.

15. Sanders, N. D.: Performance Parameters for Jet-propulsion Engines, *NACA TN* 1106, July, 1946.

16. Pinkel, I. I.: Determination of Ram-jet Combustion Chamber Temperatures by Means of Total Pressure Surveys, *NACA TN* 2526, 1951.

17. Jouguet, E. J.: Quelques problèmes de hydrodynamique générale, *J. math. pure et appl.*, vol. 8, 1920.

18. Oppenheim, A. K.: Water-channel Analog to High-velocity Combustion, *J. Appl. Mechanics*, March, 1953, p. 115.

19. Shapiro, A. H.: An Appraisal of the Hydraulic Analogue to Gas Dynamics, *Mass. Inst. Technol. Meteor Rept.* 34, 1949.

20. Wuellner, N. H.: "A Study of the Hydraulic Analogy and a Demonstration of Its Application to the Study of Rectangular, Parallel-sided Passages Having Notches," M.S. thesis, Department of Mechanical Engineering, Northwestern University, 1953.

21. Lamb, H.: "Hydrodynamics," p. 245, Dover Publications, New York, 1945.

22. Shapiro, A. H.: Analogue Methods, p. 307 in "Physical Measurements in Gas Dynamics and Combustion," Princeton University Press, Princeton, N.J., 1954.

23. Birkhoff, G.: Dimensional Analysis of Partial Differential Equations, *Elec. Eng.*, vol. 67, p. 1185, 1948.

24. Murphy, G.: "Similitude in Engineering," The Ronald Press Company, New York, 1950.

25. Rayleigh, Lord: The Principle of Similitude, *Nature*, vol. 95, p. 66, 1915.

26. Duncan, W. J.: "Physical Similarity and Dimensional Analysis," Edward Arnold & Company, London, 1953.

27. Fenn, J. B.: Flame Holding Analog, *Office Naval Research, European Sci. Notes*, no. 10-3, p. 38, Mar. 1, 1956.

28. Anderson, T. P.: Informal Report, Gas Dynamics Laboratory, Northwestern University, Dec. 17, 1956.

CHAPTER 12

EXPERIMENTAL TECHNIQUES AND MEASUREMENTS

12-1. Introduction. In previous chapters of this book the major emphasis has been on analytical approaches to various phases of gas dynamics. However, there are many processes and conditions under which experimental approaches can yield information more quickly and effectively than can be hoped from analysis. It is also true, of course, that experimental data from a process may be needed to serve as a basis from which to make further analytical studies. In this chapter an effort has been made to include at least a brief mention of the more important measurement techniques and types of instrumentation pertinent to this field.

12-2. Temperature Measurement in High-velocity, High-temperature Streams. Engineers are frequently confronted with the necessity of measuring the temperature in high-velocity as well as high-temperature gaseous streams. In such streams a composite temperature indication is obtained. However, the determination of the static or free-stream temperature is of importance, because together with the static pressure it determines the thermodynamic state of the system. From it can be found the enthalpy, internal energy, specific heat, and the acoustic velocity. The velocity is also required as it is needed to describe the dynamics of the flow system. The only direct way to measure the free-stream or static temperature is by employing a thermometer traveling at the same speed as the fluid stream. This is obviously impractical and hence it is necessary to resort to indirect methods.

Imagine that a temperature-sensing element such as a thermocouple is inserted into a flow. (Because a number of different temperature-sensing instruments could be used, we will generically refer to all of them as thermometers.) The gas will flow by the thermometer, but a small portion of gas is brought to rest by the thermometer element as this obstructs the flow. If all of the gas around the thermometer is brought to rest, and the process is adiabatic with no heat exchange between the thermometer and its surroundings, the stagnation temperature as given by Eq. (3-29) would be realized, namely,

$$T_0 - T = \frac{V^2}{2c_p} \qquad (3\text{-}29)$$

270

For air with $c_p = 7.73$, there would be a temperature rise $T_0 - T$ of about 1°F when the flow velocity is 100 fps. In general we can assume that in measurements the stagnation-temperature rise must be taken into consideration if for gases having a similar c_p range, the Mach number is of the order of 0.3 or more.

It was shown in Chap. 3 that the stagnation-temperature rise, as defined by Eq. (3-29), is precise only if the gas is brought to rest at the thermometer in an isentropic manner. This of course is not realized in practice, although the assumption is often made. Actually, the temperature read on a thermometer immersed into a high-velocity gas stream is somewhat different than the reservoir temperature. The deviation arises from two causes. First, when a fluid passes over a surface a boundary layer is formed. In this boundary layer there will be a velocity and a temperature gradient. The velocity gradient gives rise to shearing forces which can be looked upon as fluid friction to be dissipated as heat. Thus there is a tendency to heat the thermometer over and above the heating caused when the kinetic energy of the gas is converted into thermal energy because of stagnation. There is still another boundary-layer phenomenon, and this is because of the temperature gradient. Thus the thermometer will tend to lose heat to the fluid if, as is usually the case, it is at a higher temperature than the gas. Thus there are two heat-transport phenomena having opposite directions. It is of course possible that they may be the same numerically and thus cancel one another out. Whether or not this will happen can be predicted by observing the Prandtl number $c_p\mu/k$, which represents the ratio of shearing effects to heat-transfer effects. If the Prandtl number is unity the two effects will cancel one another. If, however, the Prandtl number is less than unity, as it usually is for gases, then we can surmise that the thermal effects will exceed the viscous effect. The second reason for the deviation between the measured stagnation temperature and the isentropic stagnation temperature is the heat exchange between the probe and its surroundings. The thermometer may exchange heat with its surroundings by conduction via its stem and by radiant heat exchange with its surroundings.

The deviation of the actually measured stagnation temperature from the theoretical stagnation temperature is represented by a correction factor K as follows:

$$K = \frac{T_p - T}{T_0 - T} \tag{12-1}$$

where T_p is the measured temperature as read by the probe, T_0 is the theoretical stagnation temperature, and T is the free-stream temperature. If we use a calibrated thermometer for which K is known, T_p and the velocity are measured, the difference $T_0 - T$ can be found, and then the free-stream temperature T becomes known. It should be kept in mind that T_p, the temperature actually read by the thermometer, is affected by the boundary-layer transport as well as the heat losses. In a manner, K is a thermometer efficiency because it is the ratio of the actual temperature rise to the isentropic temperature rise.

Another correction factor is the so-called *recovery factor* $\Re$. Assume that the thermometer is so constructed that it experiences no heat exchange with its surroundings, either through its stem or by radiation. In other words the thermometer is considered to be a system which would undergo adiabatic processes only. Any deviation between the thermometer reading and the isentropic-stagnation temperature will be because of transport phenomena in the boundary layer. The temperature read by the thermometer is called the *adiabatic wall temperature* and is denoted by T_{aw}. The recovery factor $\Re$ is defined as

$$\Re = \frac{T_{aw} - T}{T_0 - T} \tag{12-2}$$

where T_0 and T are the reservoir (isentropic-stagnation) temperature and the free-stream temperatures respectively. After a substitution from Eq. (3-29) into the denominator of Eq. (12-2), we have

$$\Re = \frac{2c_p(T_{aw} - T)}{V^2} \tag{12-3}$$

If we multiply and divide Eq. (12-3) by the free-stream temperature T, and substitute in Eq. (3-30), we get

$$\frac{T_{aw}}{T} = 1 + \Re \frac{k-1}{2} M^2 \tag{12-4}$$

Frequently a thermometer can be designed in such a manner that heat losses are negligible, and thus it approximates an adiabatic thermometer. Under such circumstances it can be assumed that

$$K \approx \Re$$

We should like to emphasize that this is an approximation and that the correction factor K should not be considered synonymous with the recovery factor $\Re$.

Because the recovery factor is a measure of the transport phenomena in the boundary layer, it follows that it alters with the type of boundary layer (whether laminar or turbulent) and also with the shape of the thermometer. As a rather general rule of thumb it can be assumed that for a particular thermometer, both the recovery factor $\mathcal{R}$ and the correction factor K increase with increasing Reynolds number. A detailed study of this, which is beyond the scope of this text, appears in chaps. 26 and 27 of reference 4. In general, it can be said that for the same thermometer exposed to flows at the same Mach number, when an increase in Reynolds number occurs there will be an appreciable increase in the recovery factor. A comparison of numerous thermometers exposed to different Reynolds numbers has been compiled by Kaye.[5]

Figure 12-1 shows qualitatively the various factors under discussion. Assume that we introduce a thermometer with a recovery factor less than unity into a fluid stream, and plot the various temperatures as they vary with velocity. The reservoir temperature will be constant and will form the upper limiting curve. The free-stream temperature T decreases, the velocity increases, and thermal energy is converted into kinetic energy.

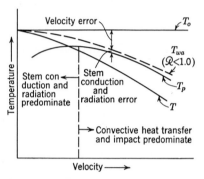

FIG. 12-1. Temperature in high-velocity, high-temperature gas streams.

Experiments indicate further that the temperature indicated by the probe, namely T_p, decreases also. The adiabatic wall temperature T_{aw} lies above the curve representing T_p. The difference between the two curves represents the error due to stem conduction and radiation (thermometer not adiabatic). In turn, the difference between the reservoir or isentropic-stagnation temperature and the adiabatic wall temperature is the velocity error due to the existence of a relative velocity between the thermometer and the gas. The maximum point on the T_p curve denotes a demarcation between the zone where radiation predominates and the zone where impact predominates.

Generally speaking, the walls of an engine or combustor housing are at an appreciably lower temperature than the gases contained therein. If a thermometric element is inserted into such a system, it loses heat by conduction, through its stem or connecting wires, and by radiation to the walls. In turn, it gains heat by convection from the gases, and may also absorb heat by radiation from regions of combustion, and by radiation from nonburning gases. However, the radiation sources can frequently be disregarded or if this is not the case the thermometer can be located in a position so that it is shielded. As far as the nonburning gases are concerned their emissivity is normally low, and as the temperature of the gases and the temperature of the thermometer are also usually not much apart this effect is trivial.

A complete heat balance for the thermometer would show the heat sources as equal to the heat-dissipation items after temperature equilibrium is reached; thus

$$q_{\text{gas radiation}} + q_{\text{convection}} = q_{\text{conduction}} + q_{\text{radiation to walls}} \qquad (12\text{-}5)$$

When we can disregard radiation effects from the gases and from combustion zones, the first term $q_{\text{gas radiation}}$ in the above equation disappears. It is also possible to minimize conduction losses $q_{\text{conduction}}$ if the experimental setup is so arranged that a portion of the thermocouple leads are kept at the same temperature as the junction, or if the thermometer bulb and stem are both immersed. Thus the simplified heat balance appears as

$$q_{\text{convection}} \approx q_{\text{radiation}} \qquad (12\text{-}6)$$

Using the basic equations of convection and radiation heat transfer, respectively, we have

$$hA(T_g - T_p) \approx \sigma \epsilon F_c A(T_p{}^4 - T_w{}^4) \qquad (12\text{-}7)$$

where h = convection film coefficient
A = thermocouple area
σ = Stefan-Boltzmann constant
ϵ = emissivity of thermocouple
F_c = percentage of total thermocouple area seen by surroundings, area configuration factor
T_g = gas temperature
T_p = observed thermocouple temperature
T_w = temperature of surroundings

This equation, when solved for the gas temperature, yields

$$T_g \approx T_p + \frac{\sigma \epsilon F_c(T_p{}^4 - T_w{}^4)}{h} \qquad (12\text{-}8)$$

The convection film coefficient h can be computed for the existing conditions from

$$h = \frac{\text{Nu}\,k}{d} \qquad (12\text{-}9)$$

where Nu = dimensionless Nusselt number, usually expressed as a function of Reynolds and Prandtl numbers, Nu = f(Re, Pr) (reference 6 gives data)
k = thermal conductivity of the gas film surrounding thermocouple, (Btu)(ft)/(hr)(ft^2)(°R)
d = a representative dimension (diameter) of thermocouple or thermometer

Nu, Pr, Re, and k are evaluated at the mean film temperature $T_g + T_p/2$

surrounding the element. Because in some cases T_p is vastly greater than T_w it is possible at times to simplify further the equation for T_g. Thus

$$T_g \approx T_p + \frac{\sigma \epsilon F_c T_p{}^4}{h} \qquad (12\text{-}10)$$

The emissivity of thermocouple junctions can be found from tables, but it should be recalled that an oxidized thermocouple has a vastly different emissivity than an unoxidized thermocouple. For unoxidized chromel Gilbert [7] suggests an emissivity of 0.35 and for oxidized chromel the emissivity is 0.87. For unoxidized and oxidized alumel his values are 0.37 and 0.87 respectively. Gilbert indicates that oxidation is ascertained after 4 hr of operation at high temperatures, with 1 or 2 hr probably sufficient. He recommends that either the unoxidized or the oxidized value be used, and not an intermediate one. Because Nu, Pr, Re, and k are to be evaluated at the mean film temperature $T_g + T_p/2$, it becomes necessary to use a trial-and-error solution in determining the gas temperature T_g in Eq. (12-8) or (12-10).

The design and construction of thermometers for high-velocity, high-temperature work is a complex field of instrumentation and many aspects must be considered. There are, however, certain general rules which have applicability. In order to exhibit rapid response characteristics, the thermometer should have a low heat capacity. Heat loss by conduction through the stem or thermocouple lead wires can be prevented, or at least reduced, by exposing a portion of the lead wires in the temperature region served by the sensing element. When a shield is used, care must be exercised in its design and choice, because fundamentally the shield will constitute a surface which itself emits or receives radiation from the sensing element. It has been shown by Emmons [8] that as many as eight concentric shields may be advisable to reduce the error introduced by radiation heat transfer. Because, in general, multiple shields are undesirable in any installation, the thermometer designer must often use single shields, choosing intelligently the shield material for proper conductivity and surface characteristics. High reflectivity and low emissivity are desirable.

The existence of a shock wave in front of a stagnation probe is not particularly bothersome. For one thing, the stagnation temperature is the same on each side of a shock wave. Experience indicates that stagnation-temperature measurements in the presence of shock waves are less prone to errors due to heat loss and flow direction.

The engineer is primarily interested in determining static temperature. This is the temperature which would be recorded by a thermometer traveling at the same speed as the gas or, in other words, having no relative velocity with respect to the gas stream. However, because a moving thermometer of this character is impractical, it is customary to measure the stagnation temperature, and from this the free-stream temperature can be determined.   Some of the factors which influence the stagnation-temperature readings have already been discussed, and consideration will now be given to practical thermometers.

The proper design of a thermometer for use in a gas stream depends first on whether or not the velocity is high, and second on whether or not there are appreciable radiation errors.   For the case of low temperatures at low Mach numbers, when radiation effects are negligible, a bare thermocouple or even a mercury-in-glass thermometer can be employed.

In high-velocity streams it is possible to achieve a correction factor of unity by locating the thermocouple inside a hollow streamlined body of aerodynamic shape.   This same type of housing can be utilized to shield the thermocouple junction against radiations.   A probe developed by Franz [9] is shown in Fig. 12-2.   In essence, the Franz probe consists of a

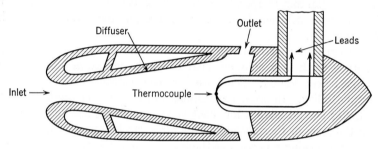

FIG. 12-2.   Franz-type pitot-thermocouple for measuring total temperature.   (*A. Franz, Pressure and Temperature Measurements in Supercharger Investigations, NACA TM 953, 1940.*)

diffuser which decelerates the velocity to a much-reduced value, so that the thermocouple is placed in a space which approximates a stagnation chamber.   Actually, the gas velocity is not zero because vent holes are drilled into the body to provide for the proper circulation of air.   If vent holes are not used, the air in the stagnation chamber cools because of heat loss and the stagnation probe indicates a false lower temperature.   Proper circulation thus improves the response characteristics of the probe.   The Franz probe is particularly suitable for high-temperature, compressible flow.   Probes of this type generally have the advantage of being relatively insensitive to yaw.   They are physically rugged, yet they can be constructed of very small size and thus have good response characteristics.   Types of temperature probes have also been studied extensively by Hottel and Kalitinski,[10] by Fiock and Dahl,[11] and by Stickney.[12]

Clark and Rohsenow [13] have proposed temperature instrumentation which principally measures pressure and the flow rate in a suction probe.   The static temperature is then computed from the data found using equations of gas dynamics. A different type of pneumatic probe for measuring exhaust-gas temperatures, proposed by Scadron,[14] is based on continuity of mass through two restrictions. Pinkel [15] has developed a graphical procedure to determine the temperature from total-pressure data. Vonnegut [16] has developed a thermometer which is housed in a Ranque or Hilsch tube and utilizes a heat balance between the vortex-flow cooling and aerodynamic heating. Hedge [17] has also developed designs of vortex tubes for measuring true free-air temperatures.

At low velocities it is possible to estimate the static temperature by using three thermocouple junctions located in very close proximity. The larger thermocouples will record higher temperatures than will the small thermocouple. The indicated temperature vs. the thermometer size can then be plotted to obtain the radiation-free temperature by extrapolating to zero size. This method is adequate at low velocities only because it assumes that all of the thermocouple junctions have the same recovery factor, which is not strictly true, because the recovery factor is influenced by the thermometer dimensions.

12-3. Surface-temperature Measurement. In most measurements involving gas temperature it is also desirable to know the temperature at the surface of the wall confining the gas. It was shown in Eq. (12-4) that together with the Mach number and recovery factor, the wall temperature leads to the free-stream temperature. The wall-surface temperature is useful also in relation to materials in high-velocity streams, whether or not the materials are at high temperature.

There are several methods of determining wall-surface temperatures, such as by use of thermocouples, by infrared radiation, and by phosphor luminescence. Here we shall describe the use of thermocouples only. In using thermocouples to determine wall-surface temperatures it is simple and expedient to peen a thermocouple to the surface of the wall. It is not always necessary to use two wires for the thermocouples because the wall itself may be used to serve as one of the two dissimilar metals constituting the thermocouple.

In constructing wall-surface thermocouples it is necessary to prevent the junction from protruding into the stream. If this is not done errors can result in determining the wall-surface temperature. For example, in supersonic flow a protrusion in the wall can cause a shock wave. The measurement of surface temperatures for metallic walls is relatively simple provided the thermocouple is in perfect thermal contact with the wall and provided the sensing point is at the surface. One arrangement which has been used in gun bores consists of pure nickel wire 0.2 mm in diameter which is oxidized electrically to a depth of 0.01 mm to form an insulating layer. This is then surrounded with a steel cylinder, and the ends of the nickel wire and the steel tubing are ground smooth. The end portion is then nickel-plated to a thickness of 0.002 mm, and the completed couple is inserted through a hole in the metal wall in such a manner that the couple rests flush with the surface under study. The active thermocouple junction would in this particular design be 0.002 mm away from the wall surface. For precise wall-temperature determinations, the wall temperature is determined by graphical procedures. Details concerning this method are considered by Hackemann.[18]

The determination of surface temperatures of nonmetallic walls offers some difficulty as the low conductivity of most nonmetals leads to the nonexistence of an isothermal zone in which the thermocouple can be placed. The technique commonly employed in such cases is to use a small insert made of copper or silver as is shown in Fig. 12-3.

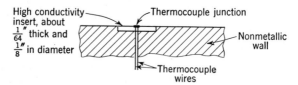

FIG. 12-3.   Surface (low-conductivity) thermocouple.

The errors which can arise in surface-temperature determinations from heat loss have been studied extensively by Boelter and Lockhart,[19] who have further outlined a method for predicting the magnitude of such error.

12-4. Pressure Measurement. The thermodynamic state of a system is defined by two or more independent properties. One such property, pressure, is highly significant in many gas-dynamics problems. Just as is true with temperature, both static pressure p and stagnation pressure p_0 must be considered. For isentropic flow these pressures bear a relation to the Mach number, as was indicated in Chap. 3, i.e.,

$$\frac{p_0}{p} = \left(1 + \frac{k-1}{2} M^2\right)^{k/(k-1)} \tag{3-35}$$

For Mach numbers not greatly in excess of 2 the expanded form represented by Eq. (3-40) is applicable,

$$p_0 - p = \tfrac{1}{2}V^2\rho\left(1 + \frac{M^2}{4} + \frac{2-k}{24} M^4 + \cdots\right) \tag{3-40}$$

For incompressible flow further simplification leads to Bernoulli's equation, namely,

$$p_0 - p = \tfrac{1}{2}V^2\rho \tag{3-41}$$

Thus in any determination of the dynamic-pressure rise $p_0 - p$, the density variation, if this exists, must be taken into consideration. The possible error which may be introduced by choosing the incorrect domain is shown graphically in Fig. 3-11. It is also necessary to consider the Mach number of the flow. For example, if the flow is supersonic a detached shock will be generated ahead of a pitot tube which might be introduced into the flow. Further, because the flow through a shock wave is not isentropic Eqs. (3-35) and (3-40) cannot apply, but it is necessary to use instead Eq. (6-46), the equation of Rayleigh-Pitot, namely,

$$\frac{p_{02}}{p_1} = \left[\frac{\left(M_1{}^2 \dfrac{k+1}{2} \right)^k}{\dfrac{2kM_1{}^2}{k+1} - \dfrac{k-1}{k+1}} \right]^{1/(k-1)} \tag{12-11}$$

Although in the case of temperature it is necessary in equivalent sense to devise a probe which should travel at the same speed as the gas if the static temperature is to be measured, this is not so for pressure. However,

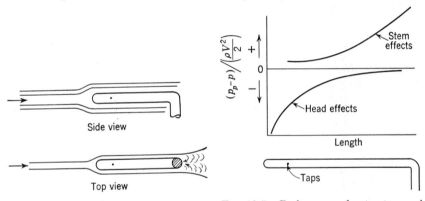

Side view

Top view

$\dfrac{(p_p - p)}{(\rho V^2 / 2)}$

Stem effects

Head effects

Length

Taps

FIG. 12-4. Pressure probe.   FIG. 12-5. Probe errors due to stem and head.

for pressure, transverse pressure gradients result only if there is a curvature of streamlines. Thus, by inserting a probe which does not distort the flow streamlines, it is possible to measure the static pressure. Consider a probe shown in Fig. 12-4. There are two effects on a pressure probe, the head effect and the stem effect. It is fortunate that these effects tend to have offsetting characteristics. Thus if there are taps in the probe, the indication of which we denote by p_p, then the errors introduced by the stem and the head are shown qualitatively by Fig. 12-5, where p is the static pressure in the undisturbed flow at the point to which the density ρ and the velocity V correspond. It is possible as was done by Prandtl to devise a probe which is so constructed that the head and stem effects cancel one another and thus enable the accurate determination of the stream pressure.

The dimensions of such a probe are given in Fig. 12-6. An improved version of the Prandtl probe has been developed by the National Physical Laboratory.

The stagnation pressure may be measured with a pressure probe which has a tapping at its tip. An improved Prandtl-type, pitot-static tube which can be used to measure both the stagnation and the static pressure is shown in Fig. 12-7. This same probe may be used for determination of the static pressure by simply omitting the tap at the front tip.

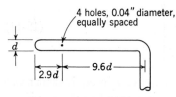

FIG. 12-6. Prandtl probe.   FIG. 12-7. Improved pitot-static tube.

Depending on its geometry, a stagnation probe may or may not be sensitive to yaw. In general, a probe made of a cylindrical tubing with a square leading edge is rather insensitive to yaw. Another insensitive stagnation probe is called the *Kiel probe*.[20] This consists of a small probe placed inside a venturi shroud and operates by taking advantage of the fact that in a yawed venturi, the interval streamlines remain parallel to the venturi axis to a great extent. Pressure probes of various configurations are discussed by Schulze, Ashby, and Erwin.[21]

The static pressure is determined quite frequently by wall taps. Rayle[22] has shown that the hole configuration of the tap must be taken into consideration for precise readings. Thus depending on the angle which the hole makes with the solid boundary, and depending on whether or not this hole has a sharp or rounded edge, the streamlines may be distorted. The stream pressure is affected to the extent that the streamlines are curved. This effect is obviously less if the hole is small. It is possible to make pressure taps self-compensating and Rayle suggests a hole 0.020 to 0.040 in. in diameter, countersunk to half a diameter.

12-5. Flow Direction. Velocity is a vector quantity, and it is important in many dynamic studies of gas flow to be cognizant of the direction of flow. Even when an asymmetric flow is to be straightened it may be important to know the prior velocity directions in order to design the straightening devices. In a following section on flow visualization several methods which can be used in determining the direction of flow are indicated. However, these techniques, which are applicable in the case of slow-speed flow, are open to question at high velocities. In these cases it is preferable to use directional probes. Various shapes of probes have been designed for this purpose [23] and are available commercially.   Most of these probes are operative because they sense pressure in different directions and the experimenter moves the probe in the flow field until the pressures in certain directions are equalized.   A protractor-type device can then be used to align the direction of the probe and thus of the gas stream relative to a fixed reference line.   Figure 12-8 shows the head of a conical-shaped probe having

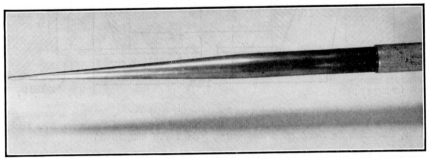

FIG. 12-8.   Conical-shaped directional probe with four radially located taps at 90° spacing. (*L. E. Bothell and the State University of Iowa.*)

four taps located radially, 90° apart.   Experience indicates that some of the conically shaped directional probes are not as sensitive as may be desired and a wedge of the design shown in Fig. 12-9 having pressure orifices at opposite sides may be preferable.   The existence of shock phenomena and compressibility do not change the angle indication provided the flow field and the shock are symmetrical about the probe.   Another type of probe used in determining flow direction in two planes resembles a claw.
There exist many types of combination probes which are available commercially.   Also, in many instances individual researchers or laboratories may design and construct probes for specific uses.

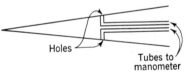

FIG. 12-9.   Directional wedge.

An ionization-tracer technique has been proposed to measure true air speed in the range $0.3 < M < 3.8$ by Boyd, Dorsch, and Brodie.[24]

12-6. Flow Measurement.   A knowledge of the mass-flow rates of gases entering into a gas-dynamic process is frequently required for purposes of analysis and design, or for control of the constituents entering into an experimental setup.   Basic considerations in relation to flow rates have been presented elsewhere in this book, but not primarily from a viewpoint of measurement.   Consequently, in this section the emphasis will be directed toward measurement techniques involved.   Basically, dynamic-flow-meas-

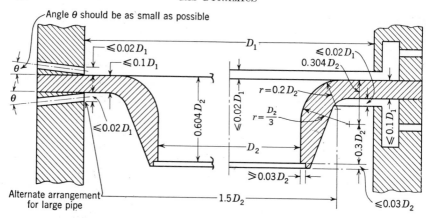

FIG. 12-10. Representative dimensions for standard flow nozzle. ("*Flow Measurement Power Test Codes*," pt. 5, chap. 4, *American Society of Mechanical Engineers, New York,* 1949, *Standards for Discharge Measurement, NACA TM 952,* 1940.)

urement techniques involve the placement in a flow stream of a partial obstruction such as a nozzle, orifice, venturi section, or a pitot or impact tube. By measurement of pressure change across the device it is possible to compute the flow pattern and the quantity of fluid passing. Particularly accurate results can be obtained if the flow devices are made and used in accordance with experimentally standardized patterns and techniques.

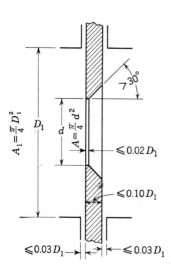

FIG. 12-11. Representative dimensions of standard sharp-edged orifice. (*Standards for Discharge Measurement, NACA TM 952,* 1940.)

The rounded-entry nozzle (Fig. 12-10) has discharge coefficients which are usually above 0.97. However, in large sizes, nozzles are awkward to construct and install. Consequently, the plate orifice (Fig. 12-11) with a sharp 90° leading edge is used extensively in test and field work. The coefficients of orifices are variable and some uncertainty arises if the leading edge is not carefully made or if it becomes rounded or otherwise damaged in use. The venturi is basically a rounded-entry nozzle followed by a carefully made diffusing (tapered) section. The diffusing section is used to reduce the high velocity at the throat of the venturi to a lower value and thereby produce a subsequent pressure rise. The over-all pressure loss across a venturi is smaller than would occur in a corresponding orifice or nozzle. Consequently the venturi is most frequently used in permanent installations such as pumping lines for gases or water, and in the measurement section of wind tunnels where dissipation of pressure is undesirable.

In compressible fluid flow, the Bernoulli equation is not broadly applicable, and the relations (6-2) and (6-3) developed from the steady-flow energy equation and the general gas laws must be employed.

Equation (7-3) can be transformed to appear as

$$\tfrac{1}{2}(V_2{}^2 - V_1{}^2) + \frac{k}{k-1}\frac{p_1}{\rho_1}\left[\left(\frac{p_2}{p_1}\right)^{(k-1)/k} - 1\right] = 0 \qquad (12\text{-}12)$$

Introduce the acoustic velocity from Eq. (3-6) or Eq. (3-6a). Using it in the form

$$a^2 = \frac{kp}{\rho}$$

Eq. (12-12) then appears as

$$\tfrac{1}{2}(V_2{}^2 - V_1{}^2) + \frac{a_1{}^2}{k-1}\left[\left(\frac{p_2}{p_1}\right)^{(k-1)/k} - 1\right] = 0 \qquad (12\text{-}13)$$

and by rearrangement

$$\frac{p_2}{p_1} = \left(1 - \frac{k-1}{a_1}\frac{V_2{}^2 - V_1{}^2}{2}\right)^{k/(k-1)} \qquad (12\text{-}14)$$

This gives the ratio of pressures at entry and exit from a reversible-adiabatic-flow device such as a nozzle or orifice in a pipe or duct.

By combination of the acoustic-velocity equation with

$$pv^k = \frac{p}{\rho^k} = \text{constant}$$

and

$$\frac{p}{\rho} = RT$$

it can be shown that

$$\left(\frac{a_2}{a_1}\right)^2 = \frac{T_2}{T_1} = \left(\frac{p_2}{p_1}\right)^{(k-1)/k} \qquad (12\text{-}15)$$

and therefore

$$\frac{k-1}{2}(V_2{}^2 - V_1{}^2) + a_2{}^2 - a_1{}^2 = 0 \qquad (12\text{-}16)$$

By eliminating the pressure ratios from Eqs. (12-14) and (12-15) it is possible to show that

$$\left(\frac{a_2}{a_1}\right)^2 = \frac{1 + [(k-1)/2](V_1/a_1)^2}{1 + [(k-1)/2](V_2/a_2)^2} \qquad (12\text{-}17)$$

Introducing the Mach number, Eq. (12-17) becomes

$$\left(\frac{a_2}{a_1}\right)^2 = \frac{T_2}{T_1} = \frac{1 + [(k-1)/2]M_1^2}{1 + [(k-1)/2]M_2^2} \tag{12-18}$$

and if pressure from Eq. (12-15) is employed, Eq. (12-18) becomes

$$\frac{p_2}{p_1} = \left\{\frac{1 + [(k-1)/2]M_1^2}{1 + [(k-1)/2]M_2^2}\right\}^{k/(k-1)} \tag{12-19}$$

Now solve for the Mach number at any point in the nozzle, and Eq. (12-19) is transformed to

$$M_2 = \sqrt{\frac{2}{k-1}\frac{1 + [(k-1)/2]M_1^2}{1 - (M_1/M_2)^2}\left[\left(\frac{p_1}{p_2}\right)^{(k-1)/k} - 1\right]} \tag{12-20}$$

and as $M_2 = V_2/a_2$,

$$V_{2s} = \sqrt{\frac{2kp_2}{\rho_2(k-1)}\frac{1 + [(k-1)/2]M_1^2}{1 - (M_1/M_2)^2}\left[\left(\frac{p_1}{p_2}\right)^{(k-1)/k} - 1\right]} \tag{12-21}$$

where the velocity V_2 is written V_{2s}, indicative of having the isentropic value, because the equation itself is true only for a reversible-adiabatic process. Equation (12-21) can be simplified for the rather usual case of M_1 much smaller than M_2, as for this condition the denominator term $(M_1/M_2)^2$ can be discarded, and if M_1 itself is small in magnitude its square can be eliminated in the numerator so that

$$V_{2s} = \sqrt{\frac{2kp_2}{\rho_2(k-1)}\left[\left(\frac{p_0}{p_2}\right)^{(k-1)/k} - 1\right]} \tag{12-22}$$

Here p_1 has been replaced by p_0 to indicate that, in neglecting the approach velocity, the situation is equivalent to inlet flow from a reservoir having indefinitely large dimensions. Equations (6-5), (6-6), and (6-7) are other convenient forms in which to express the value of V_{2s}.

The mass flow can be found, since the velocity is known, by combining the basic Eqs. (12-21), (6-5), or (6-7) with the equation of continuity of mass. This was done in Chap. 6 to yield Eqs. (6-8) and (6-9). For the most general case in which velocity of approach cannot be disregarded, the corresponding equation for the flow G' appears as

$$G' = A_2\sqrt{\frac{1 + [(k-1)/2]M_1^2}{1 - M_1^2/M_2^2}}\sqrt{\frac{2kp_2\rho_2}{k-1}\left[\left(\frac{p_1}{p_2}\right)^{(k-1)/k} - 1\right]} \tag{12-23}$$

As discussed in Chap. 7, it should be realized that there is a certain maximum flow which is not exceeded no matter how much the downstream pressure is decreased below a certain critical value $p_2 = p_c$. Equation (7-18) gives a basis for evaluating the magnitude of critical pressure. In most flow-measurement work, however, the pressure ratios used across the measuring device are so small that critical-pressure characteristics are not significant. When this is the case it is possible, by making use of a binomial-series expansion, to simplify the form of the pressure term in Eq. (12-23) as follows:

$$\frac{2k}{k-1}\left[\left(\frac{p_1}{p_2}\right)^{(k-1)/k} - 1\right] \equiv \frac{2(p_1 - p_2)}{p_2} = \frac{2\,\Delta p}{p_2} \qquad (12\text{-}24)$$

In the general case it is not desirable to disregard approach velocity, so further simplification can be made, based on the fact that for a small pressure drop $\rho_1 \cong \rho_2$, and with the continuity of mass applicable,

$$\frac{M_1}{M_2} = \frac{A_2}{A_1}$$

When applied to the first part of Eq. (12-20), realizing that M_1 is usually small, it can be seen that

$$\sqrt{\frac{1 + [(k-1)/2]M_1{}^2}{1 - M_1{}^2/M_2{}^2}} \equiv \sqrt{\frac{1}{1 - (A_2/A_1)^2}}$$

$$= \frac{1}{\sqrt{1 - (d_2/d_1)^4}} = \frac{1}{\sqrt{1 - \beta^4}} \qquad (12\text{-}25)$$

Up to this point it has been tacitly assumed that the flow conditions in the nozzle were reversible and adiabatic. This, of course, is not true, because friction, turbulence, and inadequate reconversion of energy from kinetic to other forms necessarily exist. Thus the flow through an orifice or nozzle should be modified by a coefficient of discharge C, and when this is done the flow equation appears as

$$G' = CA_2 \sqrt{\frac{1 + [(k-1)/2]M_1{}^2}{1 - M_1{}^2/M_2{}^2}} \sqrt{\frac{2kp_2\rho_2}{k-1}\left[\left(\frac{p_1}{p_2}\right)^{(k-1)/k} - 1\right]} \qquad (12\text{-}26)$$

$$G' = CA_2 \sqrt{\frac{1}{1 - \beta^4}} \sqrt{\frac{2kp_2\rho_2}{k-1}\left[\left(\frac{p_1}{p_2}\right)^{(k-1)/k} - 1\right]} \qquad (12\text{-}27)$$

For convenience in use, it is customary to combine the discharge coefficient and the approach-correction factor into a combined-flow coefficient K which is written as

$$K = \frac{C}{\sqrt{1 - \beta^4}} \qquad (12\text{-}28)$$

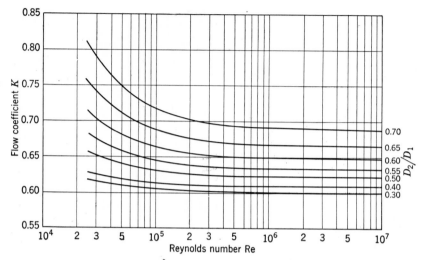

Fig. 12-12. Flow coefficients K corrected for velocity of approach for square-edged orifices employing flange taps. ("*Fluid Meters, Their Theory and Application,*" 4th ed., American Society of Mechanical Engineers, New York, 1937.)

In this form flow coefficients are given in Figs. 12-12 to 12-15, and these are applicable wherever standard nozzles and orifices are used as flow devices.

In the case of orifices, the location of the measuring taps is critical in connection with the magnitude of the flow coefficient. Three common

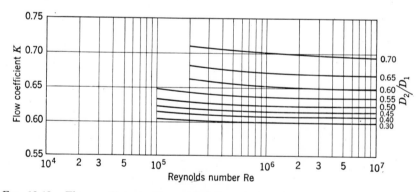

Fig. 12-13. Flow coefficients K corrected for velocity of approach for square-edged orifices employing radius taps. ("*Fluid Meters, Their Theory and Application,*" 4th ed., American Society of Mechanical Engineers, New York, 1937.)

locations are frequently used, and these are illustrated in Fig. 12-16. With the flange tap the pressure connections are made close and adjacent to the measuring orifice plate, that is, in the flanges which hold the plate in posi-

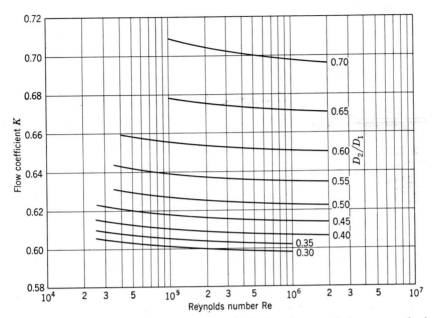

FIG. 12-14. Flow coefficients K corrected for velocity of approach for square-edged orifices employing vena contracta taps. (*"Fluid Meters, Their Theory and Application,"* 4th ed., American Society of Mechanical Engineers, New York, 1937.)

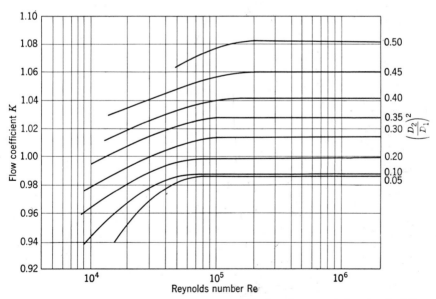

FIG. 12-15. Flow coefficients K corrected for velocity of approach for standard flow nozzles in terms of area ratio and Reynolds number. (*"Fluid Meters, Their Theory and Application,"* 4th ed., American Society of Mechanical Engineers, New York, 1937.)

tion. An equally common measuring arrangement employs the so-called *radius taps*. In using these, the pressure-measuring inlet point is located

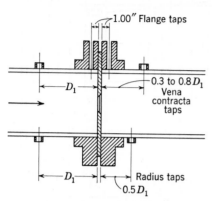

one pipe diameter or two pipe radii upstream, and the downstream pressure-measuring point is located one pipe radius away from the orifice. In using vena contracta taps, the inlet-pressure point is the same as for the inlet-radius tap, and the downstream tap is placed at varying locations with the thought of coinciding with the contraction point of the flow stream. This location is uncertain, and is in many ways the least satisfactory method to use, as the coefficients vary widely with the ratio of orifice diameter to pipe diameter. As a rough estimate, a downstream location 0.6 of a pipe diameter might be considered representative.

Fig. 12-16. Diagram showing representative locations of flange taps, radius taps, and vena contracta taps.

When the flow coefficient K is used with Eq. (12-27) this appears as

$$G' = KA_2 \sqrt{\frac{2kp_2\rho_2}{k-1}\left[\left(\frac{p_1}{p_2}\right)^{(k-1)/k} - 1\right]} \qquad (12\text{-}29)$$

or for small pressure changes with Δp not greater than $0.15p_1$,

$$G' = KA_2\sqrt{2\rho\,\Delta p} \qquad (12\text{-}30)$$

with the density $\rho = \rho_1 \cong \rho_2$.

In the preceding equations of this section note that

$\qquad G' = $ mass flow

$\qquad A_2 = $ orifice area

$\qquad K = $ flow coefficient (Figs. 12-13 to 12-16), dimensionless; see Eq. (12-8)

$\qquad \beta = $ ratio of minimum diameter of orifice (or nozzle) to pipe diameter

$\qquad \rho = $ density of gas flowing

$\qquad k = $ ratio of specific heats, c_p/c_v

$\qquad p_1, p_2 = $ respective pressures

$\qquad C = $ coefficient of discharge of flow device, dimensionless

$\qquad M = $ Mach number, V/a, dimensionless

$\qquad a = $ acoustic velocity

12-7. Flow Visualization. Before instruments are introduced into a flow stream to obtain quantitative data, it may be advisable to determine the flow configuration in a more qualitative manner. An informal publication of the National Advisory Committee for Aeronautics † attributes a pertinent statement in this connection to Anthony Fokker, that the airplane designer is at a disadvantage compared with a boat designer because he cannot see the spray that his airplane causes. Thus because the movement of an air stream cannot be easily observed it is expedient to make the flow artificially visible. Flow visualization may be accomplished by any of several methods. For example, we can introduce minute liquid or solid particles into the flow and study the reflections or scattering of light caused by these particles. Small particles such as opaque glass beads and aluminum flakes or even smokes are available for this purpose. The flow configuration can also be observed under some conditions by the use of somewhat elaborate optical instruments such as the shadowgraph, the Toepler-schlieren apparatus, and the interferometer. These will be discussed in a later section. They make use of changes in the refractive index of the gas with changes in the density. It is possible also to introduce into the flow particles of a fluid which have a different refractive index than that of the main fluid. Besides the methods mentioned, based on reflection and refraction, the flow configuration can be studied by the use of directional probes.

When small particles or filaments are introduced into a flow stream care must be exercised in the interpretation of the observations. Assume that a single particle is introduced into a fluid stream and travels a distance Δl in time Δt. The mean velocity of the particle will then be $\Delta l/\Delta t$. Suppose that a camera is directed into the flow field and the particle illuminated with proper lights. If a time exposure is now taken the photographic plate when developed will show a streak which can be called the *path line* in accordance with Prandtl. The path line may be a straight line or curve, or even cross itself depending on the manner in which the particle travels. Now consider introducing a number of reflecting particles into the fluid all at the same point but in a manner such that each particle enters the fluid alone; in other words let the particles be introduced in a time sequence. If the camera is aimed at the flow field, under adequate illumination, and a picture taken with a short time exposure, the film will show a number of short streaks. Each streak shows the travel of one particle during our short time exposure. If a line is drawn through these short streaks, we obtain a line which is called a *streamline* or a *filament line*. It is also called a streamline if the particles are of negligible mass. Most particles have mass, occupy volume, and so do not necessarily exactly show the motion of the fluid stream. In most cases, however, we assume

† NACA Elementary Smoke Flow Film.

that a filament line coincides with a streamline. The reader should recall that a streamline has no normal velocity component, and thus is strictly applicable to laminar flow. On the other hand, a filament path, in its general sense, may be useful in turbulent flow as well as in laminar flow.

When introducing actual particles into a flow configuration, particles with very small inertia should be used so that they closely follow the fluid. They should also be small so that they are not appreciably influenced by gravity. Smoke which consists of small particle suspensions has desirable characteristics and is suitable for flow visualization. One smoke commonly employed is titanium tetrachloride, which yields a dense, white cloud. The chemical titanium tetrachloride is a liquid at normal temperature and pressure, but reacts with moisture in the air to form titanium oxide and hydrochloride acid. Because of the acid formed, titanium tetrachloride has a corrosive effect on the apparatus used. It is also acrid and irritating to the observer. It can be used most effectively at relatively low velocities and introduced into the flow in a number of ways.[28] The components of the apparatus prone to corrosion should be provided with protective coatings or made from noncorrosive material.

Smoke is even often produced from the combustion of wood, tobacco, or hydrocarbons. Rotten wood is especially suitable if the tarry substances and the larger particles in the resulting smoke are distilled or filtered out. Cigars are suitable in a tobacco-burning smoke generator. Some persons prefer the smoke obtained from kerosene because carbon deposits resulting from the cracking of oil are not too cumbersome. Figure 12-17 shows

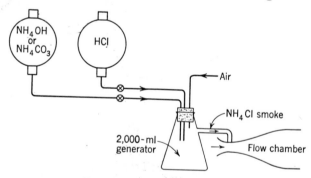

Fig. 12-17. Smoke generator.

schematically a smoke generator used in the Northwestern University Gas Dynamics Laboratory by M. Glaser and C. Smith.† This utilizes ammonium hydroxide and hydrochloric acid to produce ammonium chloride, a nontoxic, noncorrosive, white, dense smoke. About equal quantities of NH_4OH and HCl are used and the tubing is Tygon. The generator

† Private communication.

should preferably be made of Pyrex glass because the reaction is sufficiently exothermic to crack ordinary glass. The tunnel used in flow-visualization studies should be of the open-circuit type and should be provided with proper ventilation. The flow in the tunnel should be of low-turbulence design. The adjustable air speed should be high enough to prevent the smoke from sinking and the smoke should be introduced preferably in the convergent section.

In studying boundary-layer phenomena, smoke may be used as before by introducing it through holes located suitably in the surface creating the boundary layer. Sometimes it is desirable to study the boundary-layer transition. In such cases the surface can be coated with China clay in which a volatile liquid is sprayed. The tunnel is then started and the transition from the laminar- to the turbulent-boundary layer is determined by a transition near the surface where, because of turbulence, the rate of evaporation is greater. Lately, oil films have been proposed for the same purpose.

A simple expedient to study flow close to a solid boundary is to attach at one end threads of silk and cotton to the surface. These *tufts*, as they are usually called, may be of various lengths depending on the size of the model and the Reynolds number. The tuft technique gives a fair indication of flow separation as well as the transition region. In the laminar domain the tufts are steady but they flutter vigorously downstream from the transition point.

Particle paths can also be studied by creating small volumes of gas of different density. Thus small portions of the flow medium can be heated by the use of a very thin hot-wire filament introduced into the flow. Another method is to produce hot-gas pockets by means of a spark gap.

12-8. Determination of Density and Density Variation. Three optical instruments used in studying the density or its variations in gaseous-flow stream are the *shadowgraph*, the *schlieren apparatus*, and the *interferometer*. These three instruments are all based on the characteristic phenomenon that changes in the density of a gas produce a change in the refractive index of the gas. A common feature of the three instruments is that they are optical devices and consequently do not need to have other components introduced into the flow stream. Thus, they can be used to study flow patterns without disturbing the flow stream in any way. In spite of common characteristics, it should be noted that each instrument serves a different function. The shadowgraph gives an indication of change in density gradients or, in other words, the second differential of the density. The schlieren system is useful in studying density gradients themselves, and the interferometer is used if the density is to be determined.

In a homogeneous medium, and in the absence of very intense gravitational fields, light is propagated in straight lines. However, if light travels through a system which contains two zones having different densities it will be refracted as it passes from one zone into the other. Consider that two zones 1 and 2 of a system are separated by a boundary AA' as shown in Fig. 12-18, in which i is the angle of incidence and r the angle of refraction. The extent of the refraction is defined by the index of refraction n, which is defined as the ratio of the speed of light in a vacuum to the speed of light in the medium for which the index is being considered. The speed of light depends on the index of refraction of the medium through which it passes. Because the speed of light is greatest in a vacuum, the index of

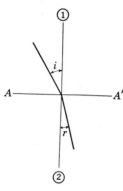

FIG. 12-18.   Incidence and refraction.

refraction is always greater than unity. The index of refraction varies with the wavelength of the light. For air at a temperature of 32°F at a pressure of 14.7 psia through which light with a wavelength of 589.3 $m\mu$ is passing, the index of refraction n is 1.0002926. For carbon monoxide at the same conditions $n = 1.000346$; for carbon dioxide note that $1.000448 < n < 1.000454$; for water vapor note that $1.000249 < n < 1.000259$; for molecular hydrogen $n = 1.000132$; for molecular oxygen $n = 1.000271$; for molecular nitrogen note that $1.000296 < n < 1.000298$; and for benzene note that $1.001700 < n < 1.001823$. The indices of refraction of liquids and solids at the same wavelength are generally higher than those listed above. According to the law of refraction, or Snell's law, and using the notation of Fig. 12-18, we can write

$$\frac{\sin i}{\sin r} = \frac{n_2}{n_1} \tag{12-31}$$

If the index of refraction is close to unity, as it is for most gases, the empirical Gladstone-Dale equation is applicable. This can be written as

$$\frac{n - 1}{\rho} = \frac{n_1 - 1}{\rho_1} = \frac{n_2 - 1}{\rho_2} = \text{constant} \tag{12-32}$$

where ρ is the density of the medium, with the subscripts 1 and 2 denoting different conditions. The density of a gas-dynamic system can vary with location and/or time. The index of refraction of air for sodium light is represented approximately by

$$n \cong 1 + 0.2267\rho \tag{12-33}$$

where ρ is the density of air in grams per cubic centimeter. These relations between the index of refraction of a medium and its density present powerful techniques for the study of flow fields through the use of the schlieren method, the shadowgraph, and the interferometer.

12-9. The Schlieren System. Consider a gas-flow system enclosed in transparent (glass) walls and exposed to a light ray as shown in Fig. 12-19. Assume originally that the glass boundary walls contain a medium at the same conditions as on the medium outside. A light beam passing through them will strike the screen at some point p_1. However, if the medium in the test section is now disturbed so that its density differs from that of the same medium on the outside, the light will be deflected through some angle $d\theta$ and will strike the screen at the point p_2. Because the path followed by the light in going to p_2 is different from that in going to p_1, there

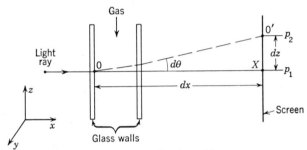

FIG. 12-19.   Deflection of light.

will be a difference in elapsed time for the light from its source to arrival at the screen. Let this time difference be dt and let the distance between p_1 and p_2 be dz. Depending on the arrangement of the same basic components, it is possible to measure $d\theta$ by the schlieren method, dz by the shadowgraph, and dt by the interferometer. Note that the changes dz, $d\theta$, and dt are all due to changes in the refractive index.

To develop the basic schlieren equation, consider the two-dimensional field shown in Fig. 12-19. Let us assume that OX is the path of a light ray in an undisturbed flow field. Let us assume further that at time $t = t_1$ the wave is located along the axis. At some time $t = t_2$, the wave will have moved to a new position and will have rotated because the velocities at various points along the wave differ because of different refractive indices. Thus after the time interval $dt = t_2 - t_1$ the deflected beam will be at OO' making an angle $d\theta$ with the original line.

In most cases the deflections are small, since for most gases the refractive index is very close to unity. Because of this it follows that

$$\theta_z \cong \frac{\partial n}{\partial z}\, dx \tag{12-34}$$

where θ_z is the total deflection in a plane normal to OY. According to electromagnetic-light theory, the specific refraction r is defined by the Lorenz-Lorentz equation as

$$r = \frac{1}{\rho}\frac{n^2 - 1}{n^2 + 2} \qquad (12\text{-}35)$$

where r may be treated as a constant. Differentiating Eq. (12-35) and evaluating the differential for $n = 1$ we obtain

$$\frac{\partial n}{\partial \rho} = \tfrac{3}{2}r \qquad (12\text{-}36)$$

If we combine this with Eq. (12-34) we obtain the schlieren equation, namely,

$$\theta_z = \tfrac{3}{2}r\frac{\partial \rho}{\partial z}\,dx \qquad (12\text{-}37)$$

Consider a parallel beam of light passing through a glass chamber divided into two parts C_1 and C_2 as shown in Fig. 12-20. Let each compart-

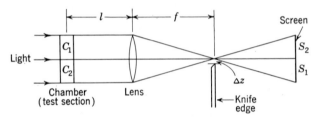

FIG. 12-20. Basic schlieren system.

ment contain the same gas at the same pressure and temperature so that the densities are exactly the same in each. At some distance l let us place a lens having a focal length f and also let us locate a screen in the system. At the focal point of the lens a knife edge is placed which can be moved up or down. First, if the knife edge is pulled out of the way the light rays falling on the screen will illuminate it brightly. Next, if the knife edge is moved upward it will start to obstruct the light rays. If moved so far that it completely obstructs the light rays, the screen will be dark. However, let us assume that the knife edge is so positioned that it obstructs some of the light, but permits part to pass by it and illuminate the screen partially but uniformly. The screen could be divided into two parts S_1 and S_2, S_1 bearing the outline of C_1, and S_2 the outline of C_2. However, because the densities are the same in C_1 and C_2, the images on S_1 and S_2 will be the same.

Now let us change the density of the gas in chamber C_2 slightly while maintaining it the same as before in C_1. Because of the change in density, the index of refraction will change also. Let us assume that this change has the effect of refracting the light ray through C_2 in a clockwise direction. Because of the refraction, the light ray passing through C_2 will be obstructed appreciably by the knife with the result that S_2 will appear to be dark while S_1 remains as before. Now assume the refractive index of C_2 is changed so that the light ray is refracted in a counterclockwise direction. In this case the light passing through C_2 will pass over the knife with the result that the screen S_2 is further illuminated. If there is no disturbance in the test section we would expect the screen to be illuminated uniformly. Whenever we introduce the knife edge at the focus of the lens into the path of light we reduce the illumination on the screen. The screen is still illuminated uniformly, but the intensity of the illumination bears a close proportionality on the up or down distance Δz that the knife edge is displaced from the focal point. When we introduce a disturbance in the test section the light will be refracted so that the image of the source is displaced a distance Δz from the original position of the knife edge. The displacement angle is small; so we can write

$$\Delta z = f\theta \qquad (12\text{-}38)$$

Also, because the illumination I is proportional to the distance from the knife edge, we have

$$\frac{\Delta I}{I} = \frac{\Delta z}{z} \qquad (12\text{-}39)$$

Combining Eqs. (12-38) and (12-39) and substituting into the integral of Eq. (12-34) we get

$$\frac{\Delta I}{I} = \frac{f}{z} \int \frac{1}{n} \frac{\partial n}{\partial z} \, dx \qquad (12\text{-}40)$$

A Toepler-schlieren system is shown in Fig. 12-21. The system consists of a light source, a condensing lens L_1, a slit S_1, two identical lenses L_2 and L_3, a knife edge S_2, and a screen. The light source commonly used is an air-cooled or a water-cooled mercury lamp.[29] The light source may be operated with alternating current or direct current. The former is suitable for visual observations but cannot be used if motion pictures are to be taken. Sharp, still photographs are best obtained by incorporating a flash circuit into the power supply. Such a flash may have a duration of about 2 to 10 μsec. The photograph of the screen pattern is obtained by using a simple camera having its shutter synchronized with the flash. The condensing lens L_1 is not necessary, but may be used to advantage to increase the effective size of the source. The slit S_1 controls the light passing through it to lens L_1. The second lens L_2 forms a parallel beam of light which passes through the test section. The third lens L_3 focuses the image of the light source at the knife edge. The knife edge is used to control the light intensity. The screen may be a ground glass for visual observation or it may be a photosensitive plate if photographic recording is preferred.

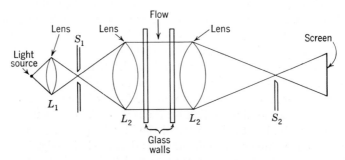

FIG. 12-21.   Toepler-schlieren system.

Because large-diameter lenses of high optical quality are difficult to obtain, large parabolic mirrors are commonly used. In this case the schlieren setup may be arranged as in Fig. 12-22. The mirrors to be used should be of high optical quality, free of chromatic and spherical aberration. In addition the inherent astigmatism should be small. The two mirrors should be a matched pair and should be correct to within one-tenth of a wavelength of light. The angle β which the mirror axis makes should be small, and in order to prevent coma the screen and the light source should be placed on opposite sides of the light beam between the two mirrors.

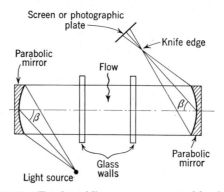

FIG. 12-22.   Toepler-schlieren arrangement with mirrors.

The distance between the mirrors should be at least twice the focal length of the mirrors. A schlieren system can be arranged in a variety of ways and there are numerous improvements which may be incorporated into such a system. Thus although there are some stringent requirements in the design of a schlieren system, the investigator has latitude and freedom to arrange the system most useful to his work. In general, schlieren systems are used for qualitative studies. Figure 12-23 shows a schlieren photograph of a spiral vortex developed by Waldron [30] on a wedge placed in a shock tube. References 31 to 37 treat various aspects of schlieren systems and several of these also include excellent lists of references.

FIG. 12-23. Schlieren photograph of supersonic flow at a wedge. (*From H. F. Waldron, An Experimental Study of a Spiral Vortex Formed by Shock-wave Diffraction, Univ. Toronto, Inst. Aerophysics Tech. Note 2, September, 1954.*)

12-10. The Shadowgraph. The schlieren system is used most advantageously when the refractive index varies gradually. However, in many applications the refractive index varies rapidly, as in certain combustion phenomena and in intense shock waves. For these applications the shadowgraph can be used to better advantage than can the schlieren system. This is so because the shadowgraph gives a representation of the second derivative of the density. Thus it can be shown [38] that for a shadowgraph

$$\frac{\Delta I}{I} = l \int \left(\frac{\partial^2 n}{\partial x^2} + \frac{\partial^2 n}{\partial y^2} \right) \log n \, dz \qquad (12\text{-}41)$$

where l is the distance of the screen from the disturbance, all other quantities being the same as before.

A shadowgraph may be obtained most simply as in Fig. 12-24. Thus imagine three points a, b, and c in the test section. If the density gradient is the same at these three points the rays will be deflected by the same amount, and the screen will be illuminated uniformly because there is no change in light intensity. Thus if the gradient $\partial n/\partial x$ does not experience a change, the second derivative $\partial^2 n/\partial x^2$ will have to be zero. Now assume that the density gradient is different at the three points. It follows that the second derivative $\partial^2 n/\partial x^2$ will have to be other than zero. Assume for convenience that the gradient $\partial n/\partial x$ at b is greater than that at a and c. Thus the rays will be deflected a greater amount so that b'' will no longer lie between a' and c'. Thus the region between a' and c' will become darker, while the region between c' and b'' is lighter. As in the case of the schlieren system, different arrangements may be used in setting up a shadowgraph. Figure 12-25 is a shadowgraph of the same phenomena already

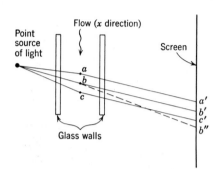

Fig. 12-24.   Simple shadowgraph.

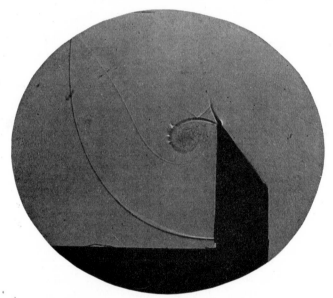

Fig. 12-25. Shadowgraph photograph of supersonic flow around a wedge. (*From H. F. Waldron, An Experimental Study of a Spiral Vortex Formed by Shock-wave Diffraction, Univ. Toronto, Inst. Aerophysics Tech. Note 2, September, 1954.*)

shown in Fig. 12-23 and was taken by Waldron [30] under the same conditions as those used in Fig. 12-23. In general a shadowgraph may be obtained from the same components that are used for the schlieren. It should be noted, however, that a shadowgraph is not a substitute for a schlieren system. The two systems cannot be used interchangeably; they should be used to complement one another.

12-11. The Interferometer. So far we have discussed instruments which can be used to determine the first and the second density gradients. Theoretically, it is possible then to arrive at the density itself by integrating the results obtained by the schlieren system or the shadowgraph. Although this approach is possible it is not the most advisable, and hence in determining the density it may be preferable to utilize an interferometer

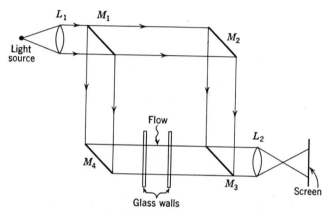

FIG. 12-26.   Mach-Zehnder interferometer.

which gives an indication of the refractive index itself. There are different arrangements of interferometers, one of which, namely, the Mach-Zehnder type, is shown in diagrammatic form in Fig. 12-26 (references 33, 38, and 39).

The interferometer uses four plane mirrors. Two of these, M_1 and M_3, are half-silvered mirrors. In other words these mirrors have been silvered only to such an extent that they reflect but half of the incident light while passing the other half. Mirrors M_2 and M_4 are fully silvered mirrors. The light from the light source passes through the collimating lens L_1 and then encounters the half-silvered mirror M_1. One-half of the light is reflected to the fully silvered mirror M_4 while one-half is passed to the fully silvered mirror M_2. The light from mirror M_4 is reflected fully and passing through the test section arrives at the half-silvered mirror M_3. The light from the fully silvered mirror M_2 also is reflected on the half-silvered mirror M_3 so that the original light beam after having been split by mirror M_1 is now brought together at M_3 and then reaches the screen.

Assume that there is no flow through the test section and that the pressure and temperature of the air in the test section are the same as those of the surrounding air. The screen will now be illuminated uniformly and brightly because there is no phase difference between the two light beams meeting at M_3. Now let us increase the pressure in the test section uniformly while there is no flow. As we increase the pressure, the illumination on the screen will diminish as the screen darkens uniformly. The screen will be darkest when the pressure has been increased, corresponding to the condition where the upper and lower beams are out of phase by half

Fig. 12-27. Supersonic flow pattern around a wedge taken with an interferometer. (*From H. F. Waldron, An Experimental Study of a Spiral Vortex Formed by Shock-wave Diffraction, Univ. Toronto, Inst. Aerophysics Tech. Note 2, September, 1954.*)

a wavelength. If we continue to increase the pressure in the test section the screen will become lighter and will be at its maximum brightness again when the two light beams are out of phase by one wave. Consider now that the air flows through the test section and that the pressure varies at different points in the flow field. Because the lower beam passes through the test section the different rays making it up are retarded by different amounts in the various zones of the flow having different densities. Because there will be phase differences between these rays and the rays of the upper beam, an interference pattern will be formed on the screen.

Because the lower light beam is retarded by different amounts and experiences phase differences with the upper beam, a fringe interferogram will result. Figure 12-27 is an interferogram of the spiral vortex studied by Waldron [30] and taken with a Kinder interferometer. The dark bands are the loci of complete interference. From such an interferogram one may deduce the contours of constant density. It can be shown (reference 4, chap. III) that

$$\rho_2 - \rho_1 = \frac{\lambda_{\text{vacuo}}}{LK_{G\text{-}D}} \frac{l}{d} \tag{12-42}$$

where ρ_1 = density at the initial reference condition
ρ_2 = density in the initial test section
λ_{vacuo} = wavelength of light in vacuo
L = length of the test section
$K_{G\text{-}D}$ = Gladstone-Dale constant
l = distance shifted by a dark fringe in passing from 1 to 2
d = distance between dark fringes at the reference condition

Of the three optical devices so far described the interferometer is probably the most costly and the most delicate. Again it should be remembered that it complements the schlieren system and the shadowgraph but does not replace them.

12-12. Hot-wire Anemometer. One of the most versatile instruments used in gas-dynamic measurements is the hot-wire anemometer. Basically the instrument consists of an electrically heated wire introduced into a flow field. The amount of heat loss from the heated wire to the gas in general increases as the flow velocity increases. Let the resistance of a wire be denoted by R_0 at the reference condition. Then the resistance of the wire R at any other temperature is related to the temperature difference ΔT by the equation

$$R = R_0(1 + \alpha \, \Delta T) \tag{12-43}$$

where α is the temperature coefficient of electrical resistance. If the current used in heating the wire is denoted by i, the heat loss H will be

$$H = i^2 R \tag{12-44}$$

It was shown by King [40] that the rate of heat loss from the heated wire to the fluid stream is approximately

$$i^2 R = (C_1 + C_2 \sqrt{V})(T_w - T_g) \tag{12-45}$$

where C_1, C_2 = constants for a particular wire
V = velocity
T_w = temperature of wire
T_g = temperature of gas

Two types of hot-wire anemometers, the constant-current and the constant-temperature, may be devised. In the constant-current anemometer, shown in Fig. 12-28, the current through the hot wire is maintained constant. Fluctuations in wire temperature are observed as the wire resistance fluctuates as a result of changes in flow conditions. Commonly, the current is maintained constant with power from a transformer incorporated into a circuit somewhat more complicated than the one shown in Fig. 12-28. The constant-current type of anemometer is particularly well suited to applications where the flow fluctuations are very small.

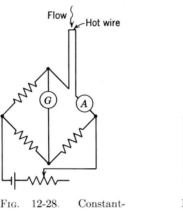

FIG. 12-28. Constant-current anemometer.

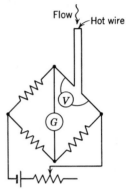

FIG. 12-29. Constant-temperature anemometer.

The simplified schematic arrangement of a constant-temperature (or constant-resistance) hot-wire anemometer is shown in Fig. 12-29. Figure 12-30 compares the two types of anemometers qualitatively. The electrical circuit actually employed is more involved and can be arranged as shown in Fig. 12-31. The current is supplied to the bridge from a direct-coupled amplifier. The unbalance of the bridge due to fluctuations experienced by the hot wire is applied to the input of the amplifier. The wire is kept at constant resistance and temperature by an electronic servo system. The amplifier produces an output current which is fed to the bridge, thereby balancing it. The velocity fluctuations are known by observing the fluctuations in the balancing current. The constant-temperature anemometer is particularly well suited in studying phenomena requiring high-frequency response.

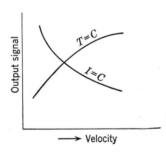

FIG. 12-30. Comparison of performance of anemometers.

If when observing a velocity phenomenon on the oscilloscope screen a periodicity is noticeable, it may be desirable to study further the frequency and the magnitude of the fluctuations. A statistical study of turbulence may even be advisable if the signal indicates randomness and lack of periodicity.

Two limitations of the hot-wire anemometer require careful consideration. One is thermal inertia or time lag of the sensing element; the other
is the nonlinear conversion of velocities to electrical signals. The hot-wire
sensing element is usually of tungsten or platinum about 0.0002 in. in

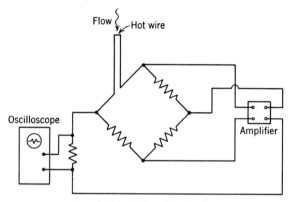

FIG. 12-31.   Hot-wire circuit.

diameter and ¼ in. in length. Figure 12-32 shows one type of hot-wire
probe. The wire is heated electrically to a temperature above that of the
fluid surrounding it. In designing the probe for a particular application it
is necessary to recognize numerous factors such as air-drag load on wire,
heat capacity, velocity and velocity direction, density, temperature, heat
conductivity, viscosity, and temperature and oxidation effects. It seems
reasonable that all requirements cannot be satisfied simultaneously and
that a compromise is necessary.

A hot-wire anemometer can be used to advantage to study flow past
flame holders, stall and surge in compressors, turbulence intensity, and

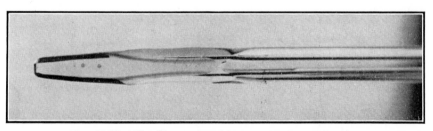

FIG. 12-32.   Hot-film sensing element.   (*Hubbard-Ling Co.*)

other phenomena. For numerous considerations in the design and use of
hot-wire anemometers the reader is referred to references 41 through 45,
which give much additional information. Figure 12-33 shows the instrument panel of a representative hot-wire anemometer.

FIG. 12-33. Instrument panel of a Hubbard-Ling constant-temperature anemometer.

12-13. Flame Temperature. A basic principle of thermometry is that the temperature-sensing element of the temperature-measuring device be in thermal equilibrium with the system under study. This is a severe restriction in the case of flame-temperature measurement because the reaction zone is obviously not in a state of equilibrium. Of course it is possible to insert the temperature-sensing element into the burned or the unburned gases outside the reaction zone. In this case it is necessary that radiation effects not be introduced, which is difficult of assurance. Again caution must be exercised in the choice of the temperature-sensing element introduced into the flame as this should not act as a catalyzer. For the last two reasons at least it is often convenient to use optical means to determine flame temperature without introducing any sensing element into the flame. Optical devices make use of the radiation emission or absorption characteristics of the flame. Although radiation methods are well suited for high temperatures because they do not pose metallurgical-failure problems, they are not advisable for low-temperature work.

It is possible to measure flame temperatures with inserted thermocouples in regions where all of the combustion is completed, as it is necessary that no reaction take place on or at the thermocouple. Experience shows that when a thermocouple is used, the flame-indicated temperature will generally be less than the actual temperature. This is because of heat losses from the thermocouple, and errors may reach or exceed 400°F. The error may be minimized by using three closely placed thermocouples each having a different size, as has already been described.

In choosing thermocouple-wire combinations one should consider whether or not the combination chosen will act as a catalyst in the flame, should the junction be used in a region where the combustion may not be complete. Consideration should also be given to the effect of the gases on the thermocouple material chosen. Iron-constantan thermocouples may be used up to about 1800°F, chromel-alumel couples up to about 2500°F, and platinum (10 per cent platinum rhodium) couples up to about 3100°F.

The flame temperature may be determined by the compensated hot-wire method proposed by Griffiths and Auberry.[46] For this method, a wire is heated electrically in a vacuum using a variable-resistance circuit and the temperature of the wire at various current settings is determined with an optical pyrometer. The data are then plotted as shown qualitatively in Fig. 12-34. The wire is now removed from the vacuum and immersed into the flame in a region where the reactions are complete. The wire is heated electrically over the same current range used already and its temperature is determined again by the optical pyrometer. For a certain current range, the curve now obtained will be situated above the one already plotted. At some heating current the two curves will cross one

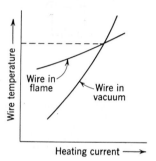

Fig. 12-34. Compensated hot-wire method.

another and then the temperature of the wire in the flame will be less than that in the vacuum. The point at which the two curves intersect indicates that the wire temperature and the flame temperature are the same. At this point the net heat transfer by conduction between the wire and the flame is zero. The heat loss from the wire by radiation and conduction is the same as when the wire is in the vacuum. At points to the left of the intersection point, less current is necessary in the flame than in the vacuum for any particular temperature.

Sodium D-line Reversal. Frequently it is not advisable to introduce thermocouples or other devices into the flame, because the temperature of the flame may be considerably higher than the melting temperature of the wire. It is also possible that the gas velocity may be high and pulsation so severe that no immersed temperature-measuring device would last for an extended period of time. Flames, moreover, are often of a transient nature. For example, to control overheating a fuel supply and consequent temperature are often reduced suddenly. For such a condition a thermometer with fast response characteristics is needed. In all of these cases it becomes desirable to employ temperature-measuring techniques which provide rapid response characteristics and which do not rely on immersed components. Optical methods are frequently used and probably the most important technique is that of sodium D-line reversal. There are many modifications of this process and several related procedures. However here we shall limit our discussion to the most simple form of sodium D-line reversal.

The apparatus used in sodium D-line reversal is an optical spectroscope, an optical pyrometer, and a tungsten ribbon lamp provided with a Variac to vary the current through it. These are arranged as shown in Fig. 12-35.

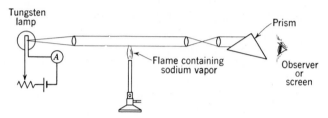

Fig. 12-35. Apparatus for sodium D-line reversal.

The tungsten ribbon lamp A is an auxiliary light source used to furnish a means of comparison. The brightness of the lamp which furnishes radiation at wavelength λ may be varied by the Variac and its temperature can be determined initially by means of an optical pyrometer. The data thus obtained are plotted as temperature vs. heating current. The flame is colored by introducing into it a suitable sodium salt such as NaCl. The salt colors the flame and furnishes radiation having a wavelength λ.

Let us represent the absorptivity of the flame at wavelength λ by $a_{f\lambda}$ and its monochromatic emissive power by $E_{f\lambda}$, and the monochromatic emissive power of the lamp at wavelength λ by $E_{L\lambda}$. The spectroscope (prism) will receive energy from two sources, the lamp and the flame. The energy emitted by the lamp is $E_{L\lambda}$ but part of this, namely $E_{L\lambda}a_{f\lambda}$, is absorbed by the flame as the rays pass through. Because the spectroscope sees the flame, it receives an amount of energy $E_{L\lambda}$ from it. Thus the energy received by the spectroscope is

$$E_{f\lambda} + E_{L\lambda} - a_{f\lambda}E_{L\lambda} = E_{f\lambda} + E_{L\lambda}(1 - a_{f\lambda}) \qquad (12\text{-}46)$$

where $0 < a < 1$.

Now if $E_{f\lambda} > a_{f\lambda}E_{L\lambda}$, we will see on the screen a bright line (the sodium D line) on the continuous spectrum. If, on the other hand,

$$E_{f\lambda} < a_{f\lambda}E_{L\lambda}$$

then a dark or reversed line will appear in place of the bright line. Finally, if

$$E_{f\lambda} = a_{f\lambda}E_{L\lambda}$$

we shall see no line because the flame is emitting as much energy at wavelength λ as it is absorbing. By the Stefan-Boltzmann law we have

$$E_{f\lambda} = \sigma T_f{}^4 \quad \text{and} \quad E_{L\lambda} = \sigma T_L{}^4$$

Thus, $$T_f{}^4 = a_{f\lambda} T_L{}^4 \tag{12-47}$$

We may then define a black-body temperature of the flame when

$$T_f{}^4 = T_L{}^4$$

and at this condition the black-body flame temperature and the lamp-filament temperature are the same. In practice we arrive at the flame temperature by changing the Variac setting until we get to the reversal point. From our original plot of filament temperature vs. current we can then determine the flame temperature. References 47 through 50 consider various aspects of this type of thermometry.

12-14. Flame Velocity. Various aspects of flame velocity were discussed in a previous chapter. Unfortunately, considerable confusion exists in defining the velocity which should be considered characteristic of a particular combustible mixture. In general, the velocity of the flame front relative to a fixed observer is called the *spatial velocity* or the *flame velocity*, and the velocity of a flame relative to the unburned gases is called the *transformation velocity* or the *burning velocity*. Another term commonly used is the *gas* or *mixture velocity*, which is defined as the velocity of the fresh mixture relative to a fixed observer. These two different definitions are shown in Fig. 12-36. It is seen that the transformation velocity is by definition the normal component of the velocity of the flame front or the reaction zone.

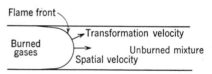

FIG. 12-36.   Flame velocity.

The flame front separates the burned products from the unburned mixture, and we assume after Tsien that a flame front may be treated like a shock front and that its thickness is infinitesimal. Because mass conservation must be obeyed we can write the continuity equation on each side of the flame as follows:

$$V_f \rho_u = V_s \rho_b \tag{12-48}$$

in which ρ_b and ρ_u are the densities of the burned products and unburned mixture respectively. Thus the flame velocity is

$$V_f = V_s \frac{\rho_b}{\rho_u} \tag{12-49}$$

The ratio ρ_u/ρ_b is the volumetric expansion ratio E, which because of the temperature increase from combustion will be greater than unity. Thus the flame velocity will be greater than the spatial velocity, and

$$V_f = \frac{V_s}{E} \qquad (12\text{-}50)$$

Experimentally, the flame velocity may be determined by either of two general methods, which are (1) closed-vessel determinations, and (2) open-tube determinations. There are several techniques under each classification and, more often than not, little agreement exists among the results found by the different techniques. To some extent this disagreement is because of misinterpretation of the definition of flame velocity. It is important to specify always the mixture studied, its strength, the pressure, and the temperature. We shall now discuss briefly some of the more important types of flame-velocity experiments.

Bunsen-burner Technique. The flame of a bunsen burner may be used in several ways to determine the burning velocity. In principle all of these techniques are based on the work of Gouy.[51] In a bunsen flame it is easy to observe the inner cone, namely, the flame front which surrounds the unburned mixture, and an outer flame. The latter constitutes the region in which unburned or partially burned fuel mixes and burns with secondary air. Gouy's method assumes that the normal combustion velocity is constant.

Consider a flame model as shown in Fig. 12-37. In order that the flame will not blow off it is necessary that the flame velocity V_f be either less or equal to the gas velocity V_g. Thus $V_f \leq V_g$. The amount of gas entering through the burner area A_b is $A_b V_g$ and this must be equal to the amount converted by the flame having a lateral area A_f. Thus,

$$A_b V_g = A_f V_f \qquad (12\text{-}51)$$

Also $\qquad A_b = \pi r_b^2 \qquad$ and $\qquad A_f = \dfrac{\pi r_b^2}{\sin \alpha}$

if we assume that the flame is a cone. Thus solving for the flame velocity we obtain

$$V_f = V_g \sin \alpha \qquad (12\text{-}52)$$

One should note that Eq. (12-51) is exact and general whereas Eq. (12-52) makes the assumption that the flame may be represented by a cone. This cone will be slender and pointed if the gas velocity is high, whereas it becomes blunter at the tip as the velocity is decreased. The assumption that the flame may be represented by a cone is more correctly valid when the flame is slender and pointed. The reader will note that the bunsen-burner method presupposes that the flow across the burner is uniform, which of course is hardly true because of the wall friction. Thus the velocity along the center line is a maximum, with the velocity decreasing some-what as the burner-tube wall is approached. This then introduces a question as to where the velocity V_g in Eq. (12-52) actually is taken. Probably the most common method is to consider the velocity which exists

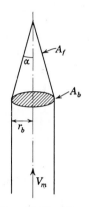

FIG. 12-37. Flame model.

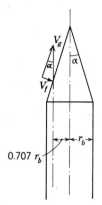

FIG. 12-38. Slope at 0.707 r_b.

at $0.707r_b$ from the burner-tube center line. The vector diagram con-structed on this premise is shown in Fig. 12-38.

The average gas velocity could also have been determined by metering the gas and then finding the velocity by the use of the equation of con-tinuity. Thus,

$$V_{g_{av}} = \frac{\text{mass rate of flow}}{A_b \rho_{g_{av}}}$$

Comparative data obtained by Dutton [52] with methane-air flames on the rim of a 0.70-cm-ID tube showed velocities at various locations, as tabu-lated.

Position	Velocity, cm/sec
Cone height..............	7.26
Slope of straight line......	22.9
Slope at $0.707r_b$.........	22.9
Frustrum...............	19.1

Constant-volume Bomb. The flame velocity may be determined by ob-serving the outward flame propagation of a mixture ignited at the center of a large spherical shell.[53] This method is advantageous because the ini-tial mixture characteristics (such as temperature, pressure, and mixture strength) are easily controlled and a relatively small amount of reactants is needed for any one test. However, this method has certain disadvan-tages. The temperature of the unburned mixture increases as the flame front travels from the centrally located ignition electrodes to the wall of the shell, and as a result the burning rate is increased. Furthermore, this method requires complex instrumentation.

Flow Tube. A simple means of determining flame velocity of gaseous air-fuel mixtures is by the flame tube. In Fig. 12-39 is sketched such a

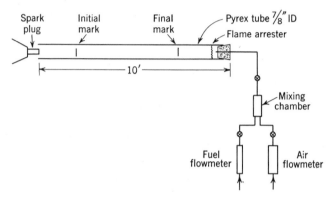

FIG. 12-39.   Flame tube.

tube made of glass. The tube is charged with air and fuel in the desired mixture strength. The ignition switch is closed and the resulting flame travels away from the spark gap where it is initiated. The flame travel is timed over the measured distance between two marks and from this the velocity can be computed. Figure 12-40 is a photograph of flame propagation of a lean mixture in such a tube taken at $\frac{1}{100}$ sec. Flame-tube

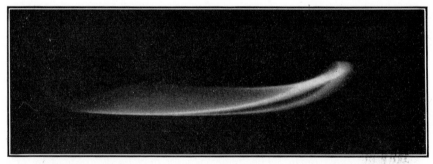

FIG. 12-40. Flame front in flame tube containing lean propane-air mixture. Flame travel is from left to right. (*Taken at 0.1 sec, Gas Dynamics Laboratory, Northwestern University.*)

measurements can be refined by using photoelectric cells or ionization gaps at start and end marks to actuate automatically the clocking mechanism.

The experimental studies show the various factors which influence the velocity in a flame tube. Thus, for example, tube characteristics such as diameter, surface, and position affect the flame velocity. As a rule, with propane-air mixtures the flame velocity is highest in a vertical tube for flame travel upward and significantly less downward. In horizontal tubes the flame velocity falls somewhere between these values for upward and downward flow.[54] It is often noted that buoyancy affects the flame. Thus, for example, in horizontal tubes of large internal diameter the flame becomes tilted, turbulence is apparent, and suddenly an abnormally high flame-front velocity results. In vertical tubes buoyancy of the hot gases causes turbulence in upward propagation, and it seems to cause stratification in downward-flame propagation.

Normally the flame front is such that the maximum velocity occurs at the center of the tube. This indicates that the flow lines change direction because they must intersect the flame front at right angles. This phenomenon is sketched in Fig. 12-41.

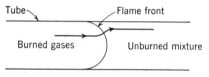

FIG. 12-41.   Flow lines.

It is desirable that the flame front reach a constant velocity relative to an outside observer soon after ignition. This type of uniform motion would represent combustion in a quiescent mixture but does not always exist. Sometimes, generally in large tubes, flame vibrations occur and these result in turbulence as well as fast and nonlaminar combustion, even resulting in detonation. As a rule it is best to initiate the flame at the open end of the tube rather than at its closed end, because the process of flame propagation is more uniform and thus the calculation of flame velocity is more reliable.

Bubble Method. Flame velocities can be determined with comparative ease photographically by measuring the expansion of a bubble in which the combustion takes place. Figure 12-42 is the sketch of a soap-bubble apparatus used by Simon and Wong.[55] In this apparatus a soap bubble or some other bubble is inflated with a fresh mixture. The bubble is formed about centrally located ignition electrodes. When the switch is closed the mixture ignites and the bubble expands. Moving pictures are used to record the expansion of the bubble and from these the velocity is computed. If d_i is the diameter of the bubble initially and d_f is the final flame diameter, the volumetric expansion ratio is $E = d_f^3/d_i^3$. The series of photographs by R. P. Choudhoury in Fig. 12-43 illustrate the growth.

Because of the buoyancy effects the bubble is not a true sphere, but the flame front is nearly spherical. Unless specific provisions are made to pressurize or evacuate the apparatus housing, this method is most suitable for pressures close to atmospheric. It is necessary that the time lapse between the filling of the bubble and the ignition of the mixture be relatively short because diffusion may occur across the bubble wall, thus altering the composition of the mixture inside. Certain corrosive mixtures such as hydrogen-chlorine and hydrogen-ozone cannot be studied in a soap bubble. Also, if the mixture is not originally saturated with water vapor, it will absorb moisture from the bubble. The initial temperatures which can be used are limited by the freezing and boiling temperatures of water. Some of these

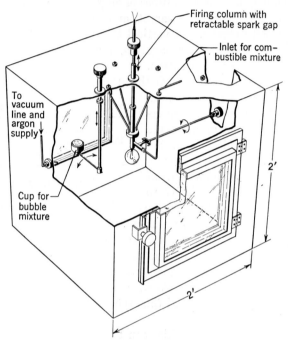

FIG. 12-42. Apparatus layout for flame-velocity determinations by use of the bubble method. (*After D. M. Simon and E. L. Wong, An Evaluation of the Soap-bubble Method for Burning Velocity Measurements Using Ethylene-Oxygen-Nitrogen and Methane-Oxygen-Nitrogen Mixtures, NACA TN 3106, February, 1954.*)

disadvantages can be eliminated by using different bubble materials as has been done by Price and Potter.[56]

Particle-track Method. In investigating the structure of flames it is of interest to know the velocity and direction of the gas flow. This may be undertaken by the particle-track method developed by Lewis and von Elbe.[57] The experimental setup is diagrammed in Fig. 12-44. Fuel and air after being metered individually are mixed in a mixing chamber. The mixture is then divided into two parts, the greater portion entering directly into the burning zone, while a small portion enters a chamber where fine magnesium oxide dust is mixed with the mixture. The magnesium oxide dust-and-fuel mixture then enters the burner and the direction of the flow through the combustion zone is observed by illuminating these particles.

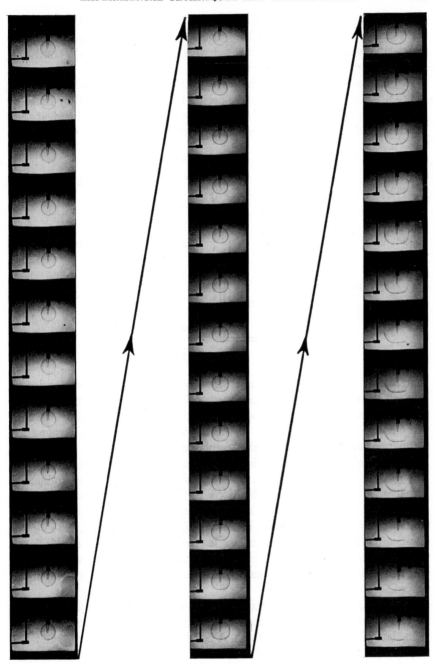

FIG. 12-43.   Motion-picture photographs of slow-burning flame using the bubble method. (*Gas Dynamics Laboratory, Northwestern University.*)

The pattern can be photographed by locating a camera at right angles to a light beam. Lewis and von Elbe [58] introduced the magnesium oxide dust by means of a pipe cleaner saturated with it. A somewhat different procedure was employed by Fristrom et al.[59]

Experimental observations indicate that the particle tracks are interrupted. The particles need not be sorted in particular, but they must be small enough so that they will follow the gas. On the other hand, if they are too small photography becomes difficult. It is desirable to know the

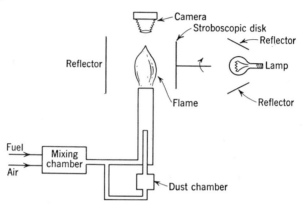

FIG. 12-44.   Particle-track apparatus.

structure of the flame because most methods used in the determination of burning velocity involve the curvature of the flame as well as the direction of the burned and unburned gases. Experimental evidence indicates that the particle tracks are parallel to the burner tube inside the burner tube but curve out before reaching the visible flame front.

Flame Probe. Most applications of flames make use of turbulent flames. The gas turbine and jet engine, the internal-combustion engine, industrial furnaces, and most other applications utilizing turbulent flames require careful design, and a thorough knowledge of turbulent flames is highly desirable. A turbulent flame can be differentiated from a laminar one by the absence of sharp boundaries and by lack of random motion of the flame front from turbulent fluctuations. The continuous variation of the shape of turbulent flames can be studied adequately by the use of electronic probes.

In a combustion zone, neutral molecules are split into positive ions and negative ions. Because the mass of the positive ions is considerably greater than that of the negative electrons, it can be postulated that the diffusion rates of the two are appreciably different. It can also be postulated that the electrons are substantially unaffected by turbulence, although the motion of the ions is materially influenced by the random motion of the gases.

It follows that since the ion density is variable with both time and location, the potential within a flame will vary with time and location as well. If a pair of electrodes is introduced into a combustion zone the electric changes or so-called *flame noises* can be amplified and studied in considerable detail. A well-designed probe and circuit show excellent response when used with turbulent flames, but no significant signal is observed with laminar flames.

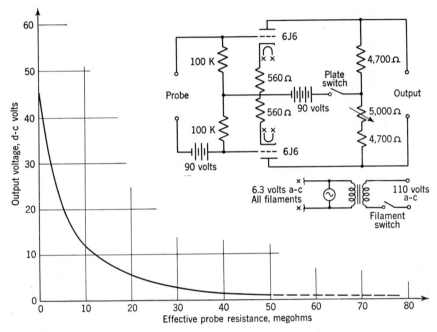

FIG. 12-45. Diagrammatic circuit of an electronic flame probe. (*After D. P. Duclos and W. M. Grounds, Flame Ionization Detector, Rev. Sci. Instr., vol.* 27, *pp.* 111–112, *February,* 1956.)

From this it is possible to obtain a statistical distribution of the changes in the flame. Several instruments (references 60 to 63) have been designed for this purpose and are being effectively applied.

The circuit of a simplified instrument [63] is shown in Fig. 12-45. The input of the circuit is connected to the probe, which may be designed to suit particular applications. The output is connected into an oscilloscope and/or vacuum-tube voltmeter depending on the particular characteristics of the flame to be measured. If the voltmeter is used, its reading will indicate the average ion density. In turn, the oscilloscope will show the variation in the ion density. Figure 12-46 shows the various components used with the design described. From the measurements, velocity fluctuations as well as the outline of the flame can be determined. Besides its utility in basic studies of flame characteristics, this instrument can be used in applied combustion. For example, it can serve as a safety device when flame blowout occurs because of the reduction in ion density of hot gases as contrasted to those in active combustion. As another type of safety device

Fig. 12-46. Instrumentation used in connection with electronic flame probe. (*Gas Dynamics Laboratory, Northwestern University.*)

in a gas turbine, it could be placed at the entrance to the turbine and reduce the fuel supply if the flame should progress into the turbine and endanger it.

For further selected study the reader is referred to references 1 to 3.

PROBLEMS

12-1. Dry air at 80°F is flowing through a duct of 2 ft diameter. The barometric pressure is 29.92 in. Hg. A pitot tube inserted in the duct indicates a velocity pressure of 0.28 in. water. Assuming that the value for this one point can be considered a representative value, (*a*) compute the air velocity and (*b*) find the flow through the duct in cubic feet per minute and in pounds per minute.

12-2. Solve Prob. 12-1 on the assumption that oxygen is flowing through the duct and that the same readings are observed.

12-3. Standard air of density 0.075 lb/ft^3 is flowing through a duct and a 10-point traverse is made of the duct, which is 6 ft in diameter. The following readings, in inches of water, are observed: 0.080, 0.095, 0.086, 0.084, 0.087, 0.083, 0.090, 0.088, 0.086, and 0.084. (*a*) Compute the flow through the duct in cubic feet per minute and in pounds per minute. (*b*) Compute the flow through the third annulus, for which the readings are 0.086 and 0.088.

12-4. A square-edged orifice of 15 in. diameter is mounted in a round duct which is 25 in. in diameter and which carries a gas of density 0.065 lb/ft³. The pressure across the orifice is 8 in. of water, measured at radius-tap positions. Compute the gas flow in cubic feet per second and in pounds per minute.

12-5. Air flowing in a duct is under a static pressure of 20 in. of water, and the barometer is at 29.45 in. Hg. A square-edged orifice with flange taps shows a differential pressure of 9.4 in. of water. The diameter of the orifice is 8 in., and that of the duct is 16 in. (*a*) Compute the density of the air, considering it to be dry and at a temperature of 60°F. (*b*) Find the air flow in cubic feet per minute and in pounds per minute.

12-6. Start with $\dfrac{2k}{k-1}\left[\left(\dfrac{p_1}{p_2}\right)^{(k-1)/k}-1\right]$ and show that for pressure ratios of p_1/p_2 less than 0.15 p_1 the expression can be reduced to

$$2\,\frac{p_1 - p_2}{p_2} = 2\,\frac{\Delta p}{p_2}$$

HINT: Take $\left(\dfrac{p_1}{p_2}\right)^{(k-1)/k} = \left[1 + \dfrac{p_1 - p_2}{p_2}\right]^{(k-1)/k} = \left(1 + \dfrac{\Delta p}{p_2}\right)^{(k-1)/k}$ and expand by the binomial theorem.

12-7. Can it be said that a schlieren system is better than a shadowgraph, and that in turn an interferometer is superior to a schlieren system? Discuss.

12-8. Compare the relative merits of constant-current and constant-temperature types of hot-wire anemometers.

12-9. What, if any, are the characteristics which differentiate a VDI orifice from an ASME orifice?

12-10. Describe the procedure to be followed in focusing a Toepler-schlieren system.

12-11. What are the relative merits of air-cooled and water-cooled mercury vapor lamps in schlieren systems?

12-12. Differentiate between Mach-Zehnder and diffraction-grating interferometers.

REFERENCES

1. Strong, J., H. V. Neher, A. E. Whitford, C. H. Cartwright, and R. Hayward: "Procedures in Experimental Physics," Prentice-Hall, Inc., Englewood Cliffs, N.J., 1938.

2. Ansley, A. J.: "An Introduction to Laboratory Technique," St. Martin's Press, Inc., New York, 1938.

3. Weber, R. L.: "Heat and Temperature Measurement," Prentice-Hall, Inc., Englewood Cliffs, N.J., 1950.

4. Shapiro, Ascher H.: "The Dynamics and Thermodynamics of Compressible Fluid Flow," vols. I and II, The Ronald Press Company, New York, 1954.

5. Kaye, J.: A Survey of Friction Coefficients, Recovery Factors, and Heat Transfer Coefficients for Supersonic Flow, *J. Aeronaut. Sci.*, vol. 21, no. 2, p. 117, 1954.

6. McAdams, W. H.: "Heat Transmission," McGraw-Hill Book Company, Inc., New York, 1954.

7. Gilbert, Mitchell: The Investigation of Low Pressure Flames, California Institute of Technology, Jet Propulsion Laboratory, Rept. 4-54, 1954.

8. Emmons, H. W.: Development of Temperature Probe—Multi-shielded Type, Elliott Company Report, 1944.

9. Franz, A.: Pressure and Temperature Measurements in Supercharger Investigations, *NACA TM* 953, 1940.

10. Hottel, H. C., and A. Kalitinski: Temperature Measurements in High Velocity Air Streams, *J. Appl. Mechanics*, vol. 12, p. A-25, 1945.

11. Fiock, E. F., and A. I. Dahl: Temperature Measurements in High Velocity Streams of Hot Gas, in *Proc. Iowa Thermodynamics Symposium, State Univ. Iowa*, April, 1953, pp. 190ff.

12. Stickney, T. M.: Recovery and Time Response Characteristics of Six Thermocouple Probes in Subsonic and Supersonic Flow, *NACA TN* 3455, July, 1955.

13. Clark, J. A., and W. M. Rohsenow: A New Method for Determining the Static Temperature of High Velocity Gas Streams, *Trans. ASME*, February, 1952, p. 219.

14. Scadron, M. D.: Analysis of a Pneumatic Probe for Measuring Exhaust Gas Temperatures with Some Preliminary Experimental Results, *NACA RM* E 52 A11, May, 1952.

15. Pinkel, I. I.: Determination of Ram-jet Combustion-chamber Temperatures by Means of Total-pressure Surveys, *NACA TN* 2526, December, 1951.

16. Vonnegut, B.: Vortex Thermometer for Measuring True Air Temperatures and True Air Speeds in Flight, *Rev. Sci. Instr.*, vol. 21, p. 136, 1950.

17. Hedge, J. C.: The Vortex Tube as a True Free Air Thermometer, Paper 243-55, American Rocket Society, November, 1955.

18. Hackemann, P.: "Ein Verfahren zur Messung Schnellveranderlicher Oberflachentemperaturen und seine Anwendung in Schusswaffenlaufen," dissertation, Aachen Technische Hochschule, 1941.

19. Boelter, L. M. K., and R. W. Lockhart: Thermocouple Conduction Error Observed in Measuring Surface Temperatures, *NACA TN* 2427, July, 1951.

20. Kiel, G.: Total Head Meter with Small Sensitivity to Yaw (translated), *NACA TM* 775, August, 1935.

21. Schulze, W. M., G. C. Ashby, Jr., and J. R. Erwin: Several Combination Probes for Surveying Static and Total Pressure and Flow Direction, *NACA TN* 2830, November, 1952.

22. Rayle, R. E.: "An Investigation of the Influence of Orifice Geometry on Static Pressure Measurements," M.S. thesis, Department of Mechanical Engineering, Massachusetts Institute of Technology, 1949.

23. Pankhurst, R. C., and D. W. Holder: "Wind-tunnel Technique," Sir Isaac Pitman and Sons, Ltd., London, 1952.

24. Boyd, B., R. G. Dorsch, and G. H. Brodie: True Air Speed Measurement by Ionization-tracer Technique, *NACA RM* E52, C31, July, 1952.

25. "Fluid Meters, Their Theory and Application," 4th ed., American Society of Mechanical Engineers, New York, 1937.

26. "Flow Measurement Power Test Codes," pt. 5, chap. 4, American Society of Mechanical Engineers, New York, 1949.

27. Standards for Discharge Measurement, *NACA TM* 952, 1940.

28. Smith, E., R. H. Reed, and H. D. Hodges: The Measurement of Low Air Speeds by the Use of Titanium Tetrachloride, *Texas Eng. Expt. Sta. Research Rept.* 25, May, 1951.

29. Application Data and Accessory Equipment for Use with A-H6 and B-H6 Mercury Lamps, GET—1248-C Lighting Division, General Electric Company, Lynn, Mass.

30. Waldron, H. F.: An Experimental Study of a Spiral Vortex Formed by Shock-wave Diffraction, *Univ. Toronto, Inst. Aerophysics Tech. Note* 2, September, 1954.

31. Barnes, N. F., and S. L. Bellinger: Analyzing Air Flow, *J. Opt. Soc. Am.*, vol. 35, p. 497, August, 1945.

32. Gawthrop, D. B., W. C. F. Shepherd, and G. St. J. Perrott: The Photography of

Waves and Vortices Produced by the Discharge of an Explosive, *J. Franklin Inst.*, vol. 211, p. 67, 1931.

33. Ladenburg, R. W., B. Lewis, R. N. Pease, and H. S. Taylor (eds.): "Physical Measurements in Gas Dynamics and Combustion," vol. IX of "High Speed Aerodynamics and Jet Propulsion," Princeton University Press, Princeton, N.J., 1954.

34. Dean, R. C., et al.: Aerodynamic Measurements, Gas Turbine Laboratory, Massachusetts Institute of Technology, 1953.

35. Mortensen, T. A.: An Improved Schlieren Apparatus Employing Multiple Slit-gratings, *Rev. Sci. Instr.*, vol. 21, no. 1, p. 3, January, 1950.

36. Lawrence, L. F., S. F. Schmidt, and F. W. Looschen: A Self-synchronizing Stroboscopic Schlieren System for the Study of Unsteady Air Flows, *NACA TN* 2509, October, 1951.

37. Holder, D. W., and R. J. North: The Toepler-schlieren Apparatus, Aeronautical Research Council R. and M. 2780, 1950.

38. Lee, J. D.: Design and Performance of a Small Mach-Zehnder Interferometer, *Univ. Toronto, Inst. Aerophysics Rept.* 20, October, 1952.

39. Hall, J. G.: The Design and Performance of a 9-inch Plate Mach-Zehnder Interferometer, *Univ. Toronto, Inst. Aerophysics Rept.* 27, March, 1954.

40. King, L. V.: On the Convection of Heat from Small Cylinders in a Stream of Fluid: Determination of the Convection Constants of Small Platinum Wires with Application to Hot-wire Anemometry, *Phil. Trans. Roy. Soc. London*, ser. A, vol. 214, p. 373, 1914.

41. Kovasznay, L. S. G.: Development of Turbulence Measuring Equipment, *NACA TN* 2839, January, 1953.

42. Corrsin, S.: Extended Applications of the Hot Wire Anemometer, *NACA TN* 1864, April, 1949.

43. Dryden, H. L., and A. M. Kuethe: The Measurement of Fluctuations of Air Speed by the Hot Wire Anemometer, *NACA TR* 320, 1929.

44. Wise, B., and D. L. Schultz: The Hot-wire Anemometer for Turbulence Measurements, Aeronautical Research Council, Apr. 15, 1954.

45. Laurence, J. C., and L. G. Landes: Applications of the Constant Temperature Hot-wire Anemometer to the Study of Transient Air-flow Phenomena, *Proc. Instr. Soc. Am.*, Paper 52-12-5, 1952.

46. Griffiths, E., and J. H. Auberry: *Proc. Roy. Soc. (London)*, vol. 123, p. 401, 1929.

47. Kuhns, P. W.: Determination of Flame Temperature from 2000°K to 3000°K, by Microwave Absorption, *NACA TN* 3254, August, 1954.

48. Gaydon, A. G.: "Spectroscopy and Combustion Theory," 2d ed., Chapman & Hall, Ltd., London, 1948.

49. Heidmann, M. F., and R. J. Priem: A Modified Sodium Line Reversal Technique for the Measurement of Combustion Temperatures in Rocket Engines, American Rocket Society paper, December, 1952.

50. El Wakil, M. M., P. S. Meyers, and O. A. Uyehara: An Instantaneous and Continuous Sodium Line Reversal Pyrometer, *Trans. ASME*, February, 1952, p. 255.

51. Gouy, G.: *Ann. chim. et phys.*, vol. 5, no. 18, p. 27, 1879.

52. Dutton, R. A.: "Velocities in Methane-Air Mixtures," M.S. thesis, Department of Mechanical Engineering, Northwestern University, August, 1953.

53. Fiock, E. F., C. F. Marvin, Jr., F. R. Caldwell, and C. H. Roeder: Flame Speeds and Energy Considerations for Explosions in a Spherical Bomb, *NACA TR* 682, 1940.

54. Levine, P.: Flame Propagation in Cylindrical Tubes, *Mech. Eng.*, vol. 74, no. 6, p. 483, 1952.

320 GAS DYNAMICS

55. Simon, D. M., and E. L. Wong: An Evaluation of the Soap-bubble Method for Burning Velocity Measurements Using Ethylene-Oxygen-Nitrogen and Methane-Oxygen-Nitrogen Mixtures, *NACA TN* 3106, February, 1954.
56. Price, T. W., and J. H. Potter: Flame Velocities in Carbon Monoxide-Oxygen Mixture, *Trans. ASME*, vol. 75, pp. 91–96, January, 1953.
57. Lewis, B., and G. von Elbe: *J. Chem. Phys.*, vol. 11, p. 75, 1943.
58. Lewis, B., and G. von Elbe: "Combustion, Flames and Explosions of Gases," Academic Press, Inc., New York, 1951.
59. Fristrom, R. M., R. Prescott, R. K. Neumann, and W. H. Avery: Temperature Profiles in Propane-Air Flame Fronts, *4th Symposium on Combustion*, p. 267, The Williams & Wilkins Company, Baltimore, 1953.
60. Karlovitz, B.: Application of Electronic Probes to Measurements in Turbulent Flames, paper presented at ASME Combustion Meeting, Cambridge, Mass., June, 1955.
61. Summerfield, M., S. H. Reiter, V. Kebely, and R. W. Mascolo: The Structure and Propagation Mechanism of Turbulent Flames in High Speed Flow, *Jet Propulsion*, vol. 25, no. 8, p. 377, 1955.
62. Marsden, R. S., Jr.: The Electrical Noise of Turbulent Flames, Phillips Petroleum Company, Research Division, Report 107-12-52R, rev.
63. Duclos, D. P., and W. M. Grounds: Flame Ionization Detector, *Rev. Sci. Instr.*, vol. 27, pp. 111–112, February, 1956.

CHAPTER 13

AEROTHERMOCHEMISTRY

13-1. Introduction. In this chapter we shall discuss phenomena involving the chemical changes which occur in gas-dynamic systems. Because in such problems, aerodynamics, thermodynamics, and chemistry are involved, this chapter has been entitled Aerothermochemistry as von Kármán proposed some time ago. It should, however, be mentioned that the treatment of the subject as presented here is not planned as a profound analysis of this most complex subject. The discussion here might at best introduce the uninitiated reader to the subject matter and prepare him for further study in some of the excellent papers and books which are scattered throughout the technical literature.

13-2. Fundamental Equations of Aerothermochemistry. Aerothermochemical problems may be solved to a great extent by methods similar to those applicable to aerothermodynamic problems. However, the viewpoint must be broadened because the chemical aspects make the problems more complex.

In solving an aerothermochemical problem use can be made of the continuity equation, the momentum equation, and the energy equation. Since these equations describe the history of the system, the name *equations of change* has been suggested by Hirschfelder, Curtiss, and Bird.[1] Appropriate equations of state must also be known. These may be the same as those used in a gas-dynamic problem. However, in a flow process involving chemical phenomena it is not sufficient to consider the continuity of mass in simple form, but account must also be taken of the formation of each species and continuity equations must be written for each component. Thus the number of fundamental equations necessary to solve a problem is increased. In addition to the basic equations it is necessary to know other parameters which give an indication of the transport phenomena. The situation here is also complicated because aerothermochemical phenomena take place at very high temperatures, and the thermophysical properties of systems at high temperatures are relatively unknown. Finally, the rate at which various species are produced during the course of the reactions and the thermal energy which is released must be known. An accurate and complete knowledge of transport coefficients is not available, but fortunately much research work is being done in this field and the available data are increasing at a rapid rate. In this connection the reader is referred to at least one compilation, namely, that by Hilsenrath et al.[2]

Terminology. In writing the equations of aerothermochemistry, there occur certain terms which are not commonly encountered elsewhere. Also some of the nomenclature is not standardized and hence it appears necessary to discuss in brief certain concepts here. For greater detail the reader is referred to reference 1 and to the works of Chapman and Cowling,[3] Penner,[4] Rossini,[5] and Lewis, Pease, and Taylor.[6] We now define the various terms to be used in this brief discussion:

D_{ij} = multicomponent diffusion coefficients, where D_{ii} are identically equal to zero

$\mathbf{d}_j$ = vectors representing gradients

α_i = thermal diffusion constant of species i

M_i = molecular weight of component i

K_i = rate of production of species i due to chemical reaction; it is the reaction rate under static conditions of pressure, temperature, and composition, and in flow processes the actual value of K_i may be expected to be quite different; in flames, where there are large temperature gradients, K_i may again be different

$$\sum_i M_i K_i = 0$$

n_i = number of moles of component i in unit volume

n = total number of moles

ρ = macroscopic mass density of gas mixture; it is defined as

$$\rho = \sum_i n_i M_i$$

$\mathbf{v}_i$ = average velocity of molecules of component i, with respect to a fixed observer

$\mathbf{V}$ = average macroscopic stream velocity of the gas; it is defined as

$$\mathbf{V} = \frac{1}{\rho} \sum_i n_i M_i \mathbf{v}_i$$

$_t\mathbf{V}_i$ = thermal diffusion velocity as defined by Chapman;[3,7] the thermal diffusion velocity is defined as

$$_t\mathbf{V}_i = -\frac{1}{n_1 M_1} \alpha_i \nabla \ln T$$

$_p\mathbf{V}_i$ = ordinary diffusion velocity and may be due to (1) pressure gradients, (2) conduction gradients, (3) external forces; it is defined as

$$_p\mathbf{V}_i = \frac{n^2}{n_i\rho} \sum_{j\neq i} M_j D_{ij}\mathbf{d}_j$$

$\mathbf{V}_i$ = diffusion velocity; it is an indication of mass transport and is related to the diffusion coefficients; it may be defined as a vectorial difference, namely,

$$\mathbf{V}_i = \mathbf{v}_i - \mathbf{V}$$

however, diffusion may take place as a consequence of several phenomena and thus the diffusional phenomena may be separated as follows:

$$\mathbf{V}_i = {}_p\mathbf{V}_i + {}_t\mathbf{V}_i$$

$n_i\mathbf{v}_i$ = average flux of component i, in moles per unit area and time
$n_iM_i\mathbf{V}_i$ = molar flux of component i, with respect to the average mass velocity; it follows that

$$\sum_i n_iM_i\mathbf{V}_i = 0$$

Fundamental Equations. It was noted earlier that in order to describe a gas-dynamic system, we must satisfy the equations of continuity, momentum, and energy and in addition know an appropriate equation of state together with the pertinent thermodynamic properties. Basically, the same approach may be used in aerothermochemistry, but it is necessary to specify additional information. Furthermore, we must differentiate between equations which are of global nature and those which consider the chemical species or components of the chemical reaction.

It should be stated at the outset that it is easier to write the fundamental equations of aerothermochemistry than to solve them. For example, the reader will recall the difficulty of solving the Navier-Stokes equations, for which no general solution exists. The solution of the equations involving chemical phenomena is even more complex.

The description of a hypothetical physical model amenable to mathematical treatment must vary with the situation at hand. However, certain simplifying assumptions can be helpful and these will be suggested here. Although the engineer is interested in the combustion of diverse media, in most instances combustion may be assumed to take place in the gaseous phase. Thus we can profitably concern ourselves at this introductory stage by considering the aerothermochemistry of single-phase mixtures, in particular those involving semiperfect gases, and assume that the thermodynamic properties vary with temperature and composition only. As the frontiers of science advance interest will move to the combustion of multiphase mixtures and of solids, along with the phenomena associated with changes in phase.

Continuity Equation. In aerothermochemistry we consider two types of continuity equations. One continuity equation pertains to the mass flow of the fluid in a gross sense; the other refers to the chemical species taking part in the reaction. The first, namely, the global equation, has already been derived and for this we refer the reader to Sec. 10-2. There it was shown that the continuity equation, Eq. (10-3) is

$$\rho \operatorname{div} \mathbf{V} + \mathbf{V} \cdot \operatorname{grad} \rho + \frac{\partial \rho}{\partial t} = 0 \qquad (10\text{-}3)$$

which for steady flow reduces to

$$\operatorname{div} \rho \mathbf{V} = 0 \qquad (10\text{-}4)$$

Applying the continuity equation to species i, we write

$$\frac{\partial n_i}{\partial t} + \nabla \cdot n_i \mathbf{v}_i = K_i \qquad (13\text{-}1)$$

Substituting for $\mathbf{v}_i$, multiplying by M_i, and using summation notation we obtain

$$\sum_i M_i \frac{\partial n_i}{\partial t} + \sum_i \nabla \cdot n_i M_i \mathbf{V} + \sum_i \nabla \cdot n_i M_i \mathbf{V}_i = \sum_i M_i K_i \qquad (13\text{-}2)$$

Using operational notation, we can write Eq. (13-2) as follows:

$$\rho \frac{D(n_i/\rho)}{Dt} = K_i - \nabla \cdot n_i \mathbf{V}_i$$

Equation (13-2) describes the continuity of all species and a system is defined if a continuity equation for each component i is written. It can be seen that Eq. (13-2) will yield the global equation of continuity, namely, (10-3), if the various terms of Eq. (13-2) are identified. Thus, for steady flow by the conservation-of-mass principle,

$$\sum_i M_i K_i = 0$$

Also $\qquad \rho = \Sigma n_i M_i \qquad$ and $\qquad \sum_i n_i M_i \mathbf{V}_i = 0$

Therefore, Eq. (13-2), upon substitution and simplification, reverts to Eq. (10-2),

$$\frac{\partial \rho}{\partial t} + \nabla \cdot \rho \mathbf{V} = 0$$

The Equation of Motion. The equation of motion represents the physical phenomena involving momentum transfer. Thus the local flow velocity in a flow field changes because of the presence of several forces. In particular, this equation involves pressure forces, viscous forces, and external forces. Regardless of the presence of chemical reactions, for an aerothermochemical problem the equation of motion is no different than that for an aerothermodynamic one, and this was discussed in some detail in Chap. 10. It may be noted that the equation of motion may be derived most conveniently using tensor notation, but this powerful mathematical technique will not be employed here. (References 1, 4, and 5 do, however, treat this method.) The equation of motion when written in vector notation appears as

$$\rho \frac{DV}{Dt} = -\text{grad } p + \mathbf{F}_\mu + \rho \mathbf{F}_e \tag{13-3}$$

where $\mathbf{F}_\mu$ is a vector representing the viscous forces, and the vector $\mathbf{F}_e$ represents the external forces.

The fact that the equations of change can be derived from both a molecular and a global viewpoint shows that they are quite general. The equations of change are applicable to laminar and to turbulent flow and can be used [8] to advantage with non-Newtonian fluids.

The Energy Equation. The energy equation is applicable to aerothermochemical problems and this equation can be presented by any of a number of mathematical formulations. Here we will write the energy equation in general form following the pattern of Hirschfelder [1] et al., namely,

$$\rho \left(\frac{\partial u}{\partial t} + \mathbf{V} \cdot \nabla u \right) = -(\nabla \cdot \mathbf{q}) - (\mathbf{P} : \nabla \mathbf{V}) + \Sigma n_i \mathbf{V}_i \cdot \mathbf{X}_i \tag{13-4}$$

In the equation $\mathbf{q}$ is the heat flux defined as follows:

$$\mathbf{q} = -\lambda \nabla T + \sum_i n_i H_i \mathbf{V}_i - \frac{kT}{n} \sum_{i,k} \frac{n_k}{M_i D_{ik}} \alpha_i (\mathbf{V}_k - \mathbf{V}_i) \tag{13-5}$$

The first term on the right-hand side represents the conduction heat transfer and λ is the coefficient of thermal conductivity. The second term represents the flux energy from diffusion, and the last term accounts for the thermal diffusion. It should be noted that in the energy equation $\mathbf{P}$ is the pressure tensor and H_i is the enthalpy per mole of species i.

Other Equations. In addition to the fundamental equations of change, still other equations and parameters are necessary in solving aerothermochemical problems. Thus, equations of state must be selected which are applicable to the various species involved in the problem. As a first approximation the perfect-gas equation can be used with reasonable confidence. It can be written either for each individual species or for the average mixture. For an average mixture, the gas constant R_m can be obtained from the following equation:

$$R_m = \sum_i R_i Y_i$$

where R_i is the gas constant for each species i, and Y_i is the weight ratio.

If the number of unknowns exceeds the number of equations and if no solution is apparent, another equation may be had by writing an equation for the change in entropy. However, the reader should be cautioned in using this because more often than not the entropy equation introduces additional unknowns and thus the problem may be even more complicated. In any case, the equation for the rate of entropy change for a small element moving with the fluid can be written [5,6] as follows:

$$\rho \frac{Ds}{Dt} = - \left[\nabla \cdot \left(\frac{1}{T} \mathbf{q} - \sum_i \frac{1}{T} \mu_i n_i \mathbf{V}_i \right) \right] + \dot{s} \qquad (13\text{-}6)$$

In the entropy-change equation, the bracketed term accounts for the entropy changes due to heat flow and to diffusion. In turn the last term on the right-hand side defines the local rate of entropy production due to irreversibilities.

Finally, we can define several useful parameters or their combinations. In this connection von Kármán [49] suggests the following: the ratio of specific heats, the Mach number, the Reynolds number, the Prandtl number, the Schmidt number, the Peclet number, as well as Damköhler's first and second ratios.

As can be seen from the above incomplete and brief discussion, several equations and parameters are involved in defining an aerothermochemical problem. The difficulties which we face in finding possible solutions are both mathematical and experimental in nature. The equations are non-linear and there is no readily available general solution. Experimentally, complications arise because the data [50] are difficult to obtain at the high temperatures involved. Finally, the composition of the system changes and of course the changes in such problems take place very rapidly.

An aerothermochemical problem will be described if in addition to the equations of state we know the form of the appropriate equation of state as well as the parameters describing the thermodynamic behavior and the transport properties of the gases. Furthermore, we must have information concerning the rate of the reactions and the energies released. There is no general solution of the problem, but nevertheless it can be solved for various cases if the proper simplifications are made or proper methodology is used. The reader is referred to reference 9 for a discussion of this topic.

13-3. Flame Velocity. A rational understanding of the mechanism of flame propagation is very essential to the engineer who may be designing combustors, rocket motors, and other applications of modern combustion. A general theory of flame propagation would consider all aspects of flames such as the transport involving the diffusion of free radicals, the conduction of heat, as well as the aerodynamical equations. Unfortunately, the mathematics of general theories is quite involved and our present knowledge of chemical kinetics is insufficient. Accordingly, it becomes necessary at times to use simplified theories of flame propagation. These simplified theories can be classified under three headings: *thermal theories*, *diffusion theories*, and *comprehensive theories*.

According to the thermal theories, combustion will be sustained if the rate of heat liberation exceeds the rate of heat loss to the surroundings. On the other hand, according to theories of diffusion of active particles, combustion will be self-sustaining if the formation of active particles such as atoms and free radicals exceeds the rate at which they are destroyed. In other words, the rate of formation of chain carriers must exceed the rate of formation of chain breakers. Actually, it is very difficult to arrive at a truly satisfactory explanation of combustion phenomena by relying solely on one transport phenomenon without considering others. Thus the comprehensive theories do not emphasize solely either energy or mass transport as being dominant, but take all possible factors into consideration.

Several methods of approach are possible. These have been used in formulating diversified theories of flame propagation and they give, depending on the situation under study, more or less adequate results. In choosing a theory of flame propagation we first decide whether the fluid dynamics † is of paramount importance and the combustion process is incidental, or whether the opposite is to be assumed. If the first is applicable we write the general equations of fluid dynamics, namely, the laws of mass conservation, momentum conservation, and energy conservation as well as the thermodynamic equation of state. We may write the basic equations in one-, two-, or three-dimensional form as the situation warrants. The energy addition due to the chemical process we add on as a single term, usually called the *reaction rate*, to the energy equation. In many cases the mixture is quite lean and we may neglect the mass of the fuel. In others, we may take care of this in the continuity equation. This approach is a fluid-dynamical one and has been applied cleverly by Lees.[10]

In contrast to the above approach we may feel that the aerodynamics of the process should be minimized in importance. In this case we generally use a one-dimensional approach but write the relations of reaction kinetics and transport phenomena with greater interest. It is not advisable to prefer one method over the other for every case. The approach should be chosen by its suitability to a certain problem, by the known aspects of the

† By *fluid dynamics* here is meant the dynamics of the gases containing the combustion process without consideration of the nature of the latter.

phenomena, by the dexterity and intuition of the engineer. Probably an analysis using one-dimensional equations with the chemical effects considered as a "lumped term" is the easiest because the number of unknowns and the number of available equations is the same. Of course this is a rather restrictive analysis, but nevertheless it may be most useful in giving an introductory insight into a little-known phenomenon.

In attempting the solution of aerothermochemical equations we are faced with two serious difficulties. One is mathematical. The solution of the equations of motion of fluid flow in three dimensions is formidable but solutions have been obtained for a variety of applications. Numerical solutions as well as the use of computing machines are making and will continue to make important contributions in this field. The second type of difficulty lies in our inadequate knowledge of high-velocity combustion as a physical phenomenon. More knowledge is required for setting up the equations and solving them. Some information is available about reaction kinetics in static systems, and knowing the pressure and temperature in these systems we apply the information to flames at the same temperature and pressure as the static system. There is no substantial evidence, however, that this is acceptable as the processes in a flame take place so rapidly that equilibrium is difficult to imagine. The thermodynamicist is well aware of the imponderables that are introduced when information gathered from a static system or a system in equilibrium is applied to a system undergoing a dynamic process or an irreversible process.

Another typical place where knowledge is insufficient is called the *ignition temperature*. We do know that the ignition temperature is not a constant but varies widely under different circumstances. Thus it cannot be called a true property, but nevertheless we know that it affects the combustion.[11-13]

The physical phenomena pertinent to a flame are difficult to study because a flame zone is very thin, ranging from a fraction of a millimeter to a fraction of an inch depending on the conditions imposed. If we divide zone length by the gas velocity we obtain the residence time in the reaction zone, which it will be easy to see is an extremely small period, on the order of a millisecond or a microsecond. Measurements of any phenomenon in such a short time in an extremely small physical zone, especially when equilibrium does not exist, are exceedingly difficult to make.

13-4. Thermal Theories of Flame Propagation. The proponents of the thermal theories of flame propagation are Zeldovich, Frank-Kamenetsky, and Semenov. As far as the thermal theories of flame propagation are concerned, we shall limit ourselves to reviewing briefly the study of Semenov,[14] which includes references to other work from the Russian school.

Basically, Semenov makes three assumptions. The first is that the reactions take place in accordance with the Arrhenius equation. The second

assumption is that the ignition temperature is less than the final temperature. The third assumption is that the problem may be treated as one-
dimensional because the curvature of the flame front is assumed to be
small. Starting with these assumptions, Semenov writes an energy balance in differential form.

Consider that the parallelepiped of Fig. 13-1 represents the reaction
zone. There will be present three types of thermal effects: from conduction, from convection, and from the liberation of heat of the combustion

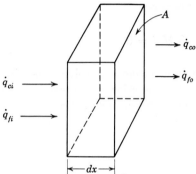

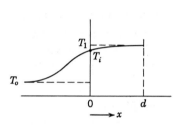

FIG. 13-1. Simplified model for thermal
theory of flame propagation.

FIG. 13-2. Temperature distribution in x direction.

process. The temperature distribution in the x direction may be approximated by a curve such as in Fig. 13-2. If we consider the left face in Fig.
13-1 as the reference, the heat conducted into the parallelepiped will be

$$\dot{q}_{ci} = -kA \frac{dT}{dx} \tag{13-7}$$

and the heat conducted out of the right face will be

$$\dot{q}_{co} = -\left[kA \frac{dT}{dx} + \frac{d}{dx}\left(kA \frac{dT}{dx} \right) \right]$$

The heat influx due to mass transport will be at the left face and is

$$\dot{q}_{fi} = V\rho A H$$

The heat efflux due to mass transport across the right face will be

$$\dot{q}_{fo} = V\rho A H + \frac{d}{dx}(V\rho A H) \tag{13-8}$$

where V = velocity of gases
ρ = density of gases
H = enthalpy of gases

The heat liberated in the parallelepiped during the combustion process will depend on the heat of reaction and the rate of reaction. If we express the heat of reaction as an enthalpy H in heat units per unit mole and the rate of reaction n' in moles per unit volume per unit time, then the heat produced per unit volume per unit time is Hn'. The energy balance will then give

$$-\frac{d}{dx}\left(kA\,\frac{dT}{dx}\right) + \frac{d}{dx}\,(V\rho AH) + \frac{d}{dx}\,(Hn'A\,dx) = 0$$

If we let $dH = c_p\,dT$ we get, upon simplification,

$$k\frac{d^2T}{dx^2} - V\rho c_p\frac{dT}{dx} + Hn' = 0 \tag{13-9}$$

This is the basic equation which we must now attempt to solve. In doing this we must consider two matters, namely, the order of the reaction and whether or not the reaction rate is constant. According to Arrhenius the order of the reaction n is defined by the equation

$$n' = Kc^n e^{-ER/T} \tag{13-10}$$

where K = constant
    c = concentration
    E = activation energy
    R = gas constant
    T = temperature

The equation may be solved in several ways depending on the assumptions made. Several methods have been used by different authors at various times. Probably the simplest, but by no means the best, considers a constant-reaction rate. Let us consider that the gases experience the temperature variation shown in Fig. 13-2. We set up two regions, namely, the heating zone and the reaction zone. Our boundary conditions are as follows:

Region of heating, $n' = 0$

$$x \to -\infty \qquad T = T_0$$
$$x = 0 \qquad T = T_i$$

Region of reaction, n' = constant

$$x = 0 \qquad T = T_i$$
$$x = d \qquad T = T_f$$

The distance d is defined in terms of the flame velocity V_0:

$$d = \frac{n_0 V_0}{C}$$

where n_0 = number of molecules per unit volume in the initial cold mixture

V_0 = normal flame velocity

C = constant = $\dfrac{\text{no. of molecules of combustible burned}}{\text{unit volume} \times \text{unit time}}$

The product $n_0 V_0$ gives the number of molecules approaching a unit area (one-dimensional flow was assumed) of flame front in unit time. Because C is assumed to be constant, and because it is assumed that no active molecules are consumed in region I, it follows that d is the length of the volume required to burn all the molecules. Solution of the differential equation yields for the flame velocity the following equation:

$$V_0 = \sqrt{\frac{2kC}{c_p \rho_0 n_0} \frac{T_f - T_i}{T_f - T_0}} \qquad (13\text{-}11)$$

More recent solutions of the basic differential equation assume the reaction rate to be expressed by an Arrhenius-type equation. If the order of the reaction is allowed for, the flame velocity with a first-order reaction is defined by

$$V_0 = \sqrt{\frac{2kK}{\rho_0 c_p} \frac{T_0}{T_f} \frac{e^{-E/RT_f}}{(T_f - T_0)^2} \left(\frac{RT_f^2}{E}\right)^2} \qquad (13\text{-}12)$$

In turn, for a second-order reaction the flame velocity is

$$V_0 = \sqrt{\frac{4kKa_0}{\rho_0 c_p} \left(\frac{T_0}{T_f}\right)^2 \frac{e^{-E/RT_f}}{(T_f - T_0)^3} \left(\frac{RT_f^2}{E}\right)^3} \qquad (13\text{-}13)$$

13-5. Diffusion Theories of Flame Propagation. Among the diffusion theories, the one whose impact has been felt most is that proposed by Tanford and Pease.[15-17] Tanford and Pease based their theory on the observation that although a mixture of carbon monoxide and dry air is practically noncombustible, the mixture does become combustible if hydrogen is added to it. They suspected that burning velocity and radical concentration may be related to one another, and after examining several radicals found that a correlation between burning velocity and the H-atom concentration exists. They explained the pronounced effect of hydrogen by the fact that, hydrogen being very light, its rate of diffusion will be quite high. Tanford and Pease studied the relative importance of heat transfer and diffusion. They calculated respectively the number of hydrogen atoms produced thermally by dissociation and the hydrogen atoms supplied by diffusion. They found that at the same temperature the hydrogen-atom concentration due to thermal effects is appreciably less than the hydrogen-atom concentration due to diffusion. They concluded that a theory of flame propagation should be based on diffusion phenomena and derived their well-known square-root law of burning velocity.

In developing their equation they suggested the following rate equation for a second-order reaction between fuel molecules and active species:

$$\frac{d(\text{product})}{dt} = \sum_i k_i c_i c_f \qquad (13\text{-}14)$$

where k_i = rate constant of component i
c_i = concentration of the radical i
c_f = concentration of the fuel

Tanford and Pease considered a flame front in a tube and after some manipulations arrived at the square-root law of burning velocity V_0, namely,

$$V_0 = \left(\sum_i \frac{k_i c_f p_i D_i}{Q B_i} \right)^{\frac{1}{2}} \qquad (13\text{-}15)$$

where p_i = partial pressure
D_i = diffusion coefficient of component i into cold unburnt gas
Q = mole fraction of potential combustion product in gas
B_i = correction factor for loss of radicals in chemical process

The Tanford-Pease theory has been corroborated to a limited extent by experimental data, but universal agreement with the predictions of their theory has not been found. This is probably because of some of their assumptions which may oversimplify the problem.

13-6. Comprehensive Theories of Flame Propagation. As was already stated, the comprehensive theories of flame propagation take into account all factors which influence laminar flame propagation. The two important ones are those developed by Hirschfelder and his associates [1] and by von Kármán and Penner.[18]

Hirschfelder studies flame propagation by writing the equations of change on a molecular level. He considers a one-dimensional steady flow and introduces a flame holder for mathematical reasons, that is, to establish the boundary conditions. The flame holder is a unidirectional porous plug. Thus it acts as a rectifier and denies reverse diffusion. Distances are measured from the plug as shown in Fig. 13-3.

A minimum of simplifying assumptions are made. The properties of the mixture are known and chemical and thermal equilibrium is assumed to occur as $z \to \infty$. The four basic equations of change are then written. These are the equation of continuity, equation of motion, equation of energy balance, and the diffusion equations for the individual species. The equations are written from a molecular viewpoint and the transport phenomena are accounted for. The equations when applied to decomposition reactions yield calculated results in fair agreement with experimental data.

The importance of the Hirschfelder approach is that it has a minimum of simplifying assumptions, does not necessitate a rate equation, and is most rigorous. The validity of the results is limited by the availability of detailed information concerning the steps of the chain reactions. Undoubtedly the usefulness of the Hirschfelder approach will improve with time as the availability of computing machines improves, and as more information is obtained describing the intermediary steps of chemical reaction.

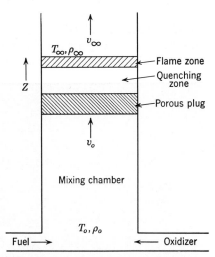

The approach followed by von Kármán and Penner [9,11,18] is more amenable to engineering analysis. They write three basic equations, namely, conservation of mass and of energy and the diffusion equation. They consider one-dimensional steady flow and constant-pressure deflagration. Rather than attempt to solve the equations in a general manner, the authors, by use of intuition and brilliant insight, are able to make simplifying assumptions. In comparing the results for the decomposition of ozone, Hirschfelder's method yields a veloc-

FIG. 13-3. One-dimensional flame model. (*J. O. Hirschfelder, C. F. Curtiss, and R. B. Bird, "The Molecular Theory of Gases and Liquids," John Wiley & Sons, Inc., New York, 1954.*)

ity of 51 cm/sec, von Kármán and Penner obtain 46 cm/sec, and the experimental value determined by Lewis and von Elbe is 55 cm/sec.

13-7. Empirical Equations of Flame Propagation. In previous sections we discussed theoretical equations for the determination of laminar velocities. These equations although of great significance are not always helpful because the data on reaction kinetics and transport properties are still quite scarce. Thus, it is quite useful to develop empirical equations in the laboratory especially because there exist correlations between laminar flame velocity and combustion efficiency in ram-jet burners. The laminar flame velocity has further been found to be useful in anticipating the performance of jet-engine afterburners.

The experimental procedure which may be used was discussed in Chap. 12. Using many refinements, Dugger has undertaken the determination of numerous configurations. His work is described in reference 19.

It is evident that the empirical equations are determined for particular fuel-oxidizer combinations under specific conditions. Thus a variety of equations become necessary and the reader is referred to the literature for detailed information. However, an example will be given here to better picture empirical equations. Thus, for propane, Dugger has proposed the following equation:

$$S_u = 10 + 3.42 \times 10^{-4} T_0^2 \qquad (13\text{-}16)$$

where S_u = laminar flame velocity, cm/sec, and T_0 = initial temperature, °K.

13-8. Flame Stabilization. Consider a flame attached to the rim of a bunsen burner. Experience shows that as the velocity of the mixture is increased a limiting velocity is reached at which the flame is blown off the

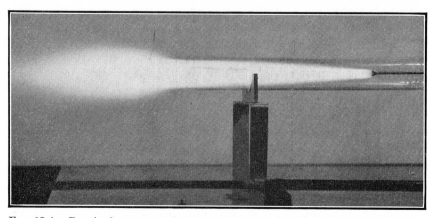

FIG. 13-4. Premixed propane-air flame stabilized on a conical flame holder. (*Gas Dynamics Laboratory, Northwestern University.*)

burner. This occurs when the gas velocity is greater than the flame velocity. Conversely, if the gas velocity is less than the flame velocity the flame flashes back into the burner tube and flashback occurs. In most technological applications it is desirable to obtain high velocities for large thrust, and therefore it becomes necessary to create conditions which will delay blowoff. Among the important variables which may be considered in studying blowoff are the air-fuel ratio, the type of fuel used, the pressure, the temperature, and the burner configuration. However, even drastic manipulations of these factors are not sufficient in obtaining high-mixture velocities such as those necessary in jet engines. One finds, however, that if a bluff body commonly called a *flame holder* is inserted into the mixture the flame may be stabilized or anchored onto this flame holder. By the use of a flame holder the blowoff velocity can easily be raised by a factor of 10 or more. The actual velocities which may be obtained with different flame holders will vary with design, but nevertheless the underlying explanation is substantially the same.

It is known by experience that a flame in a burner will be blown off if the gas velocity exceeds the flame velocity. Thus unless some provision is made, the velocities at which flames can be stabilized are quite low. This velocity depends on the mixture temperature, the ambient pressure, and the fuel-oxidizer combination. For example, a hydrocarbon-air flame will be blown off at a much lower velocity than a hydrogen-oxygen flame. Because in technology high velocities are desired, some means have to be provided to anchor the flame in the confines of a jet-engine afterburner,

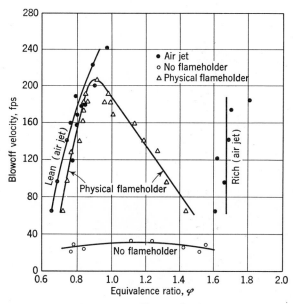

FIG. 13-5.   Blowout curves.

a ram-jet, or even a furnace. This is commonly done by using flame holders. In Fig. 13-4 is shown a premixed propane-air flame which is anchored by means of a conical-shaped flame holder in a Vycor tube. A comparison of the performance of this flame holder with the case when the flame holder is removed is shown in Fig. 13-5, which has been taken from data of Schaffer and Cambel.[29,30] Thus it is noticed that the presence of a flame holder will greatly increase the velocity at which a flame can be maintained. Different conditions can easily raise the blowout velocity above the figure of 210 fps shown in Fig. 13-5.

Williams, Hottel, and Scurlock [20,21] studied flame stabilization and propagation in high-velocity gas streams. They studied the stabilizing effects of variously shaped objects, such as rods and gutters, placed perpendicular to the gas flow. They observed that there exists a region of high shear stresses between the mixture stream moving rapidly and the fluid decelerated in the boundary layer formed on the bluff body. These shear stresses cause the shedding of eddies downstream of the flame holder and there occurs a reversed flow. The phenomena about a bluff-body flame holder may be seen in Fig. 13-6. The various zones when a flame is stabilized on a

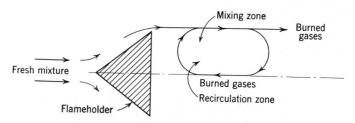

FIG. 13-6.   Bluff-body flame-stabilization mechanism.

horizontal rod that is $\frac{1}{2}$ in. in diameter and placed perpendicular to the stream are shown in a descriptive photograph by Zukoski and Marble [22, 23] in Fig. 13-7. According to Marble and Zukoski, the length of the recirculation zone was found to vary as the square root of the characteristic flameholder dimension.

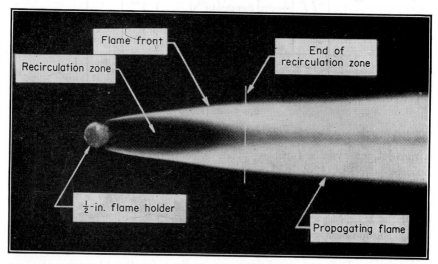

FIG. 13-7.   Side view of flame stabilized on cylindrical flame holder. (*E. E. Zukoski and F. E. Marble, The Role of Wake Transition in the Process of Flame Stabilization on Bluff Bodies, Combustion Researches and Reviews, 1955, pp. 167ff.*)

Zukoski and Marble defined the characteristic time or the ignition-delay time τ as follows:

$$\tau = \frac{L}{V_{\text{BO}}} \qquad (13\text{-}17)$$

where V_{BO} is the blowoff velocity determined experimentally and L is the recirculation-zone length. The blowoff condition is then defined by

$$\frac{V_{BO}}{L} = 1 \qquad (13\text{-}18)$$

It has been suggested by Zukoski and Marble [23] that at low Reynolds numbers where the flow immediately downstream of the flame holder is

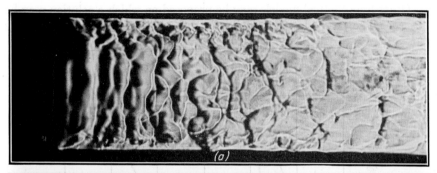

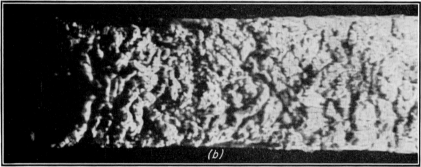

FIG. 13-8. (a) Lean propane-air flame stabilized on vertical-rod flame holder at low Reynolds number (Re ≈ 3,000). (b) Rich propane-air flame stabilized on vertical-rod flame holder at high Reynolds number (Re ≈ 40,000). (*Gas Dynamics Laboratory, Northwestern University.*)

laminar, the mass transport into the wake occurs by molecular diffusion, whereas when the flow is turbulent, there is turbulent exchange. These two conditions, photographed by K. L. Gunther and H. H. Rudolph, are shown in Fig. 13-8a and b.

In the absence of a rigorous mathematical explanation, much of the work on flame stabilization is based on correlative evidence. For example, Spalding [24] showed that when molecular transport can be neglected, the criterion of flame extinction is given by

$$V_{\mathrm{BO}} = f(D\rho S_u^2) \qquad (13\text{-}19)$$

where S_u is the laminar-flame velocity. Spalding and Tall [25] showed that the Peclet number serves as a criterion for correlation. Thus

$$\frac{V_{\mathrm{BO}}D}{\alpha} = f'\left(\frac{S_u D}{\alpha}\right)^2 \qquad (13\text{-}20)$$

where α is the thermal diffusivity.

Other hypothetical models may be proposed on which a solution may be based. The peak blowoff velocity for different fuels will not necessarily

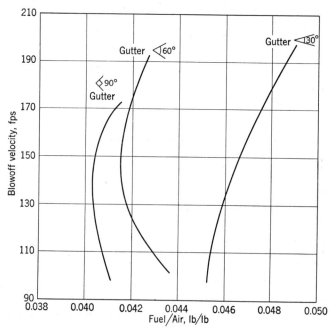

FIG. 13-9. Relation of fuel-air ratio to velocity of blowoff for different apex angles.

occur at the same equivalence ratio because the maximum blowoff velocity is related to the flame temperature. Thus Fig. 13-9 by McManus and Cambel [26] shows portions of the lean blowoff limits when premixed gasoline-vitiated air flames are stabilized on V-gutters having apex angles of 30°, 60°, and 90° respectively.

Experience indicates that the approach section to the bluff body has an effect on flame stabilization. In order to provide means of comparing data obtained in different places, the Office National d'Etudes et de Recherches Aeronautiques [27] together with the Advisory Group for Aeronautical Research and Development has developed disk-type flame holders, the dimensions of which are shown in Fig. 13-10. Experiments with different configurations of this probe indicate that the strut dimension e and the rod length L influence the performance, whereas the rod diameter D seems to be unimportant in the range studied.

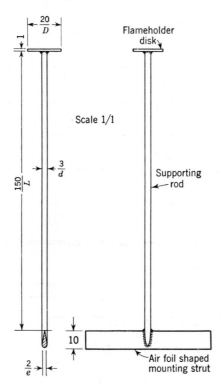

FIG. 13-10.   AGARD-ONERA flame holder.

In this same report it is shown that the performance of disk-type flame holders may be correlated if the ratio V/D is plotted rather than the blowoff velocity.

The effect of turbulence intensity of the approach mixture has been studied by Sedlacek,[28] and is shown in Fig. 13-11.

Although bluff-body flame holders are used extensively in jet-engine afterburners and ram-jet engines, they have one major drawback, namely, the considerable drag they present with a resulting loss in thrust. Two flame-holder configurations of a different nature have been developed recently. One of these, the so-called *opposing-jet flame holder* by Cambel et al., is described in references 29, 30, 51, and 52. This mode of flame stabilization employs gaseous jets injected into the mixture stream on

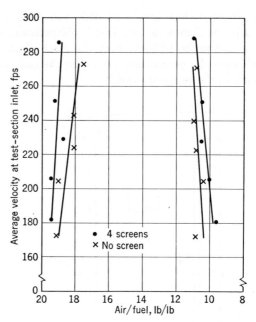

FIG. 13-11.   Effect of upstream turbulence intensity on flame stabilization.

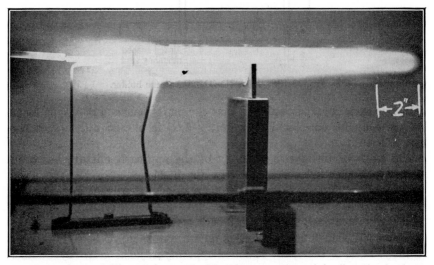

FIG. 13-12.   Photograph of flame stabilized by an opposing air jet when velocity of mixture is 140 fps.   (*Gas Dynamics Laboratory, Northwestern University.*)

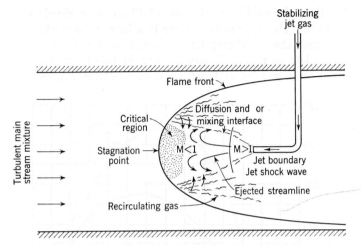

FIG. 13-13. Model for the stabilization mechanism.

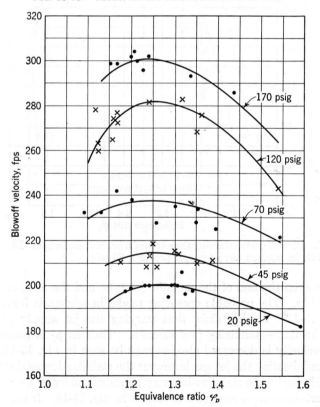

FIG. 13-14. Blowoff curves at various jet-supply pressures for an opposing air jet having a tube of 0.033 in. ID.

which the flame is stabilized. Figure 13-12 shows a simple application of this method. The approach mixture in a large tube travels from right to left, whereas the stabilizing jet is ejected from the thin central tube to flow from left to right. It can be seen in this figure that the flame is stabilized on a gas jet and not on a physical body because the dis-

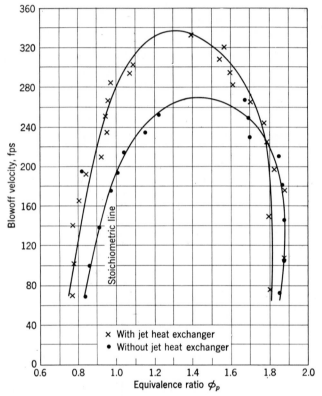

FIG. 13-15. Blowoff curves showing the effect of a jet heat exchanger. Discharge tube, 0.059 in. ID; jet medium air; jet supply pressure, 70 psig.

tance between the end of the metallic jet tube and the apex of the flame is some 2 in. The probable operating model in schematic form is shown in Fig. 13-13. Studies show that varying the jet supply pressure p_j affects the flame-stabilizing performance. Thus as p_j is decreased, the blowoff velocity is decreased also, as may be seen in Fig. 13-14. On the other hand, heating the jet gas improves the stabilization as shown in Fig. 13-15. Similarly, the stabilization may be improved by using combustible jets of certain mixture strengths as shown in Fig. 13-16. If the stabilizing jet is introduced into the stream at an angle, as shown in Fig. 13-17, the

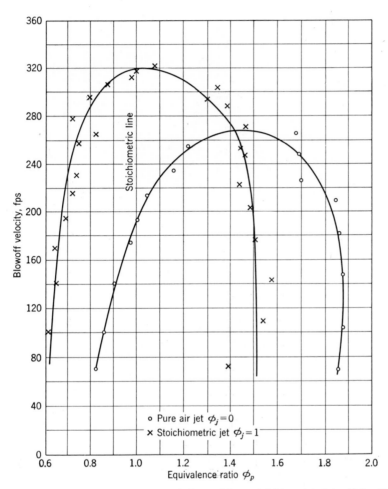

Fig. 13-16. Blowoff curves for a pure-air jet and for a stoichiometric jet. Tube, 0.059 in. ID; jet supply pressure, 70 psig.

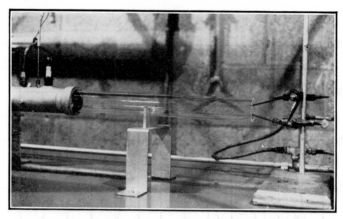

Fig. 13-17. Photograph of test section with double converging jets installed. (*Gas Dynamics Laboratory, Northwestern University.*)

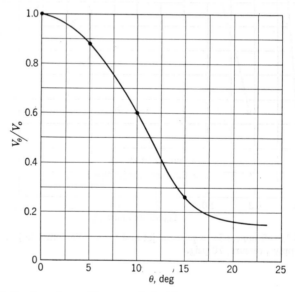

Fig. 13-18. Ratio of maximum blowout velocity V_θ at any incidence angle θ to maximum blowout velocity V_0 at an incidence angle of $0°$ vs. θ.

performance of the flame holder is markedly lowered, as shown in Fig.
13-18.

Stabilizing flames on gaseous jets has the advantage that it serves as a
removable flame holder. Thus the pilot of jet aircraft could conceivably
turn on the stabilizing jet when cutting in the afterburner by bleeding air

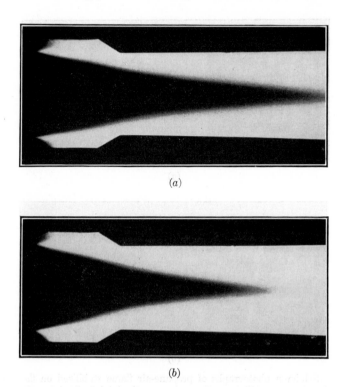

(a)

(b)

FIG. 13-19. Direct photograph of propane-air flame stabilized on flame holder 3 for
approach velocity of 110 fps, flow from left to right. Equivalence ratio (a) 0.8, (b) 1.3.
(*Gas Dynamics Laboratory, Northwestern University.*)

from the compressor. However, this jet stream could be turned off and
the flame-holder drag be nullified while cruising without the afterburner.
Other advantages, theoretical and practical, of this mode of flame stabilization are conceivable, but will not be discussed here.

Flames in high-velocity streams may be stabilized on recesses in the combustion-chamber walls as shown in Figs. 13-19 and 13-20, and this has been
studied by Huellmantel, Ziemer, and Cambel.[31] A recess or wall flame
holder stabilizes a flame in a manner similar to a bluff body. Thus, there
occurs near the leading edge of the recessed contour a separation of the
boundary layer. The recess itself acts as a pocket for recirculating gases.

The hot gases in the recess ignite the fresh mixture in the flow stream and initiate a flame front which travels across the chamber. The importance of the volume of recirculation is evident from Fig. 13-21 and it may be inferred that increasing the depth of the recess has the same effect as increasing the size of a bluff-body flame holder. Although a reasonable recirculation vol-

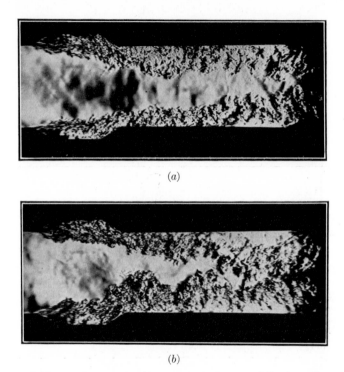

(a)

(b)

Fig. 13-20. Schlieren photographs of propane-air flame stabilized on flame holder 3 for approach velocity of 110 fps. Equivalence ratio (a) 0.8, (b) 1.3. (*Gas Dynamics Laboratory, Northwestern University.*)

ume is necessary for adequate flame stabilization, the shape of the recess does not seem to influence appreciably the stabilization performance.

13-9. Combustion Instability. One formidable problem which confronts the design engineer is the so-called *phenomenon of combustion instability.* By this is meant the rapid changes in combustion-chamber pressure. Pulsating or oscillatory combustion occurs in many applications, such as rocket motors, ram-jets, afterburners, and even in residential heating systems. Not all oscillatory combustion is undesirable; as a matter of fact some engines such as pulse-jets are expressly designed to operate in an oscillatory manner. Thus, pulsating combustion systems have been proposed for gas turbines and other applications as noted in references 32, 33, and 34. We shall not discuss here the applications of pulsating phenomena, but rather mention some of the difficulties encountered in studying this type of combustion.

The phenomena associated with combustion instability are extremely difficult to analyze because of the numerous factors involved, since chemical processes such as reaction kinetics and ignition, physical problems such

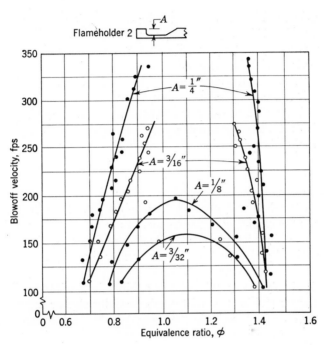

FIG. 13-21. Effect of recess depth of flame holder 2 on blowout velocity for propane-air mixtures.

as geometry, injection, evaporation and heat transfer, fluid-dynamic processes such as turbulence and unsteady flow, and gas-dynamic phenomena of deflagration and detonation are all involved. Hence, it is not difficult to realize that the analytical as well as the experimental approaches to solving the problem are extremely complex. As yet there are no general explanations of the problem, but many interesting analyses have been made. In this chapter an attempt will be made merely to introduce the reader into this field. For greater detail, beyond the scope of this book, we refer the reader to works by Crocco, Cheng, and Grey,[35,36] Tischler and Male,[37] and Ross and Datner.[38]

There is disagreement concerning combustion instability, and this can be attributed to a variety of reasons which include semantics, mathematics, and experimentation. It is customary to classify the instability according to the frequencies which are involved, and it seems convenient to assign three ranges: low-frequency instability for frequencies less than 100 cps, an intermediate range for oscillations on the order of 600 cps, and a high-frequency range for oscillations higher than 1,000 cps. Low-frequency instability has been called *chugging*, and there seems to be reasonable agreement that this is affected by phenomena in the combustion chamber as well as in the feed lines. Sabersky [39] has studied the effect of compressibility in propellant lines on low-frequency instability. He has shown that the frequency may not necessarily change greatly by changing the line length. It is advisable therefore to take cognizance of the time lag in attempting to rectify the instability by varying the engine design.

In chugging, pressure oscillations are brought about because the rate of burning and the rate of exhaust are not balanced. This in turn affects the injection rate, thereby bringing about coupled pressure oscillations between the propellant injection and the chamber pressure. In order for a liquid fuel to burn, it must be evaporated and enough heat must be received by it. This takes a finite amount of time and thus there is a time lag between combustion and injection. There is then introduced a phase difference between the supply and the combustion. Low-frequency instability lowers the efficiency of the engine. In solid propellant rockets, low-frequency instability has been called *chuffing*, and there are indications that the self-heating by chemical reaction is greater than the heat loss by conduction.

It is quite likely that combustion instability in the intermediate and in the high ranges can be treated by substantially similar arguments. Instabilities having frequencies in the range from several hundred to several thousand cycles per second are not affected by changes in the propellant feed system and the combustion is said to be intrinsically unstable. In these cases the instability is associated with the propagation of sound waves in the combustion chamber and the frequencies which are encountered are of the same order as the natural frequencies of the combustion chamber. Other names which have been used are *screaming* and *screech*. It has been stated that the efficiency of a rocket motor will increase during high-frequency instability. Although this seems reasonable intuitively, substantiating it in the laboratory is quite difficult because of the rapidity with which the events take place. Berman and Cheney [40] have studied combustion instability in an experimental motor using oxygen and alcohol.

In attempting to study combustion instability one may use different methods of approach. For example, Summerfield [41] has developed an analysis assuming that the time lag is independent of the chamber pressure. Crocco and his associates in studying high-frequency instability have considered the time lag to be a variable and have studied various configurations such as a concentrated combustion front and uniformly distributed combustion. Combustion instability has been treated by Tsien,[42] who used concepts of feedback control.

Oscillatory combustion has been studied not only in rocket motors, but also in afterburners, ram jets, and domestic heating equipment. Thus,

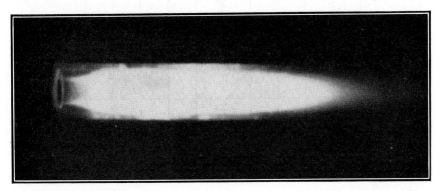

FIG. 13-22. Smooth burning. (*Gas Dynamics Laboratory, Northwestern University.*)

Rogers and Marble [43] studied high-frequency oscillations in ram jets and afterburners. They found that vortices are formed and shed from the tips of V-gutter flame holders at regular intervals numerically equal to the period of the combustion oscillations. The periodic appearance of vortices in the recirculation zone corresponds to a periodic heat release. Kaskan

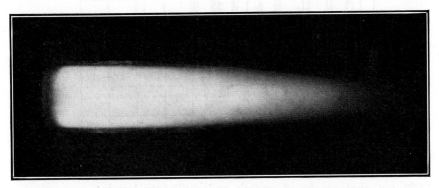

FIG. 13-23. Oscillatory burning. (*Gas Dynamics Laboratory, Northwestern University.*)

and Noreen [44] observed similar vortex shedding and suggested that a periodic heat release arises because of the distortion of the flame in the vicinity of the flame holder. This distortion brings about an oscillatory release of heat, thus maintaining the fluctuating pressure component. Considerable work about ram jets has been undertaken by the National Advisory Committee for Aeronautics. Typical unclassified studies are those by Sterbentz and Evvard,[45] by Blackshear, Rayle, and Tower,[46] and by Mirels.[47]

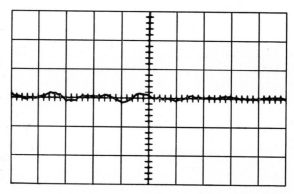

FIG. 13-24. Smooth burning. (*Gas Dynamics Laboratory, Northwestern University.*)

In a preliminary investigation Ross[48] studied instability phenomena when a premixed propane-air flame is stabilized at a sudden expansion. Instability was observed for certain combinations of tube length, expansion ratio, mixture strength, and entrance velocity. Figures 13-22 and

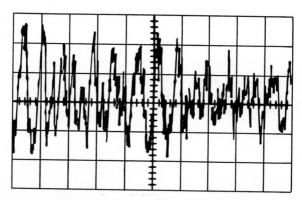

FIG. 13-25. Oscillatory burning. (*Gas Dynamics Laboratory, Northwestern University.*)

13-23 are photographs of smooth and oscillatory burning, respectively. Figures 13-24 and 13-25 show oscilloscope traces for smooth and rough burning conditions, respectively.

REFERENCES

1. Hirschfelder, J. O., C. F. Curtiss, and R. B. Bird: "The Molecular Theory of Gases and Liquids," John Wiley & Sons, Inc., New York, 1954.
2. Hilsenrath, J., et al.: Tables of Thermal Properties of Gases, *Natl. Bur. Standards Circ.* 564, Government Printing Office, 1955.
3. Chapman, S., and T. G. Cowling: "The Mathematical Theory of Non-uniform Gases," 2d ed., Cambridge University Press, New York, 1953.
4. Penner, S. S.: Introduction to the Study of Chemical Reactions in Flow Systems, *AGARDograph* 7, Butterworths Scientific Publications, London, 1955.
5. Rossini, F. D. (ed.): "Thermodynamics of Physics and Matter," vol. I, "High Speed Aerodynamics and Jet Propulsion," Princeton University Press, Princeton, N.J., 1955.
6. Lewis, B., R. N. Pease, and H. S. Taylor (eds.): "Combustion Processes," vol. II, "High Speed Aerodynamics and Jet Propulsion," Princeton University Press, Princeton, N.J., 1956.
7. Chapman, S.: Thermal Diffusion, Lecture Series No. 19, The Institute of Fluid Dynamics and Applied Mathematics, University of Maryland, 1952.
8. Bird, R. B.: Correlation of Friction Factors in Non-Newtonian Flow, *AIChE J.*, Apr. 7, 1956.
9. Penner, S. S., and T. H. Crowe: Correlation of Laminar Flame Velocities for Hydrocarbon-Oxygen-Inert Gas Mixtures, *Proc. Gas Dynamics Symposium on Aerothermochemistry*, pp. 113ff., Northwestern University–American Rocket Society, 1956.
10. Lees, L.: Fluid Mechanical Aspects of Flame Stabilization, *Jet Propulsion*, vol. 24, no. 4, p. 234, July–August, 1954.
11. von Kármán, Theodore, and G. Millán: Thermal Theory of a Laminar Flame Front near a Cold Wall, *4th Symposium on Combustion*, p. 173, The Williams & Wilkins Company, Baltimore, 1953.
12. Thomas, N.: Structure and Propagation of Combustion Waves, Heat Transfer and Fluid Mechanics Institute, University of California, Berkeley, Calif., 1954.
13. Mullins, B. P.: Spontaneous Ignition of Liquid Fuels, *AGARDograph* 4, Butterworths Scientific Publications, London, 1955.
14. Semenov, N. N.: Thermal Theory of Combustion and Explosion. III. Theory of Normal Flame Propagation, *Progr. Phys. Sci.* (*U.S.S.R.*), vol. 24, no. 4, 1940; (trans.) *NACA Mem.* 1026, 1942.
15. Tanford, C., and R. N. Pease: Equilibrium Atom and Free Radical Concentrations in Carbon Monoxide Flames and Correlation with Burning Velocities, *J. Chem. Phys.*, vol. 15, no. 7, p. 431, July, 1947.
16. Tanford, C.: Theory of Burning Velocity. I. Temperature and Free Radical Concentrations Near the Flame Front, Relative Importance of Heat Conduction and Diffusion, *J. Chem. Phys.*, vol. 15, no. 7, p. 433, July, 1947.
17. Tanford, C., and Robert N. Pease: Theory of Burning Velocity. II. The Square Root Law for Burning Velocity, *J. Chem. Phys.*, vol. 15, no. 12, p. 861, December, 1947.
18. von Kármán, Th., and S. S. Penner: Fundamental Approach to Laminar Flame Propagation, p. 5 in "Selected Combustion Problems," AGARD, Butterworths Scientific Publications, London, 1954.
19. Dugger, G. L., and D. D. Graab: Flame Velocities of Propane and Ethylene-Oxygen-Nitrogen Mixtures, *NACA RM* E52J24, Jan. 2, 1953.

20. Scurlock, A. C.: Flame Stabilization and Propagation in High Velocity Gas Streams, *Mass. Inst. Technol. Meteor Rept.* 19, May, 1948.
21. Williams, G. C., H. C. Hottel, and A. C. Scurlock: Flame Stabilization and Propagation in High Velocity Gas Streams, 3d *Symposium on Combustion*, The Williams & Wilkins Company, Baltimore, 1949.
22. Zukoski, E. E., and F. E. Marble: Experiments Concerning the Mechanism of Flame Blowoff from Bluff Bodies, *Proc. Gas Dynamics Symposium*, pp. 205ff., Northwestern University, 1956.
23. Zukoski, E. E., and F. E. Marble: The Role of Wake Transition in the Process of Flame Stabilization on Bluff Bodies, *Combustion Researches and Reviews*, 1955, pp. 167ff.
24. Spalding, D. B.: Theoretical Aspects of Flame Stabilization, *Aircraft Eng.*, vol. 25, pp. 264ff., September, 1953.
25. Spalding, D. B., and B. J. Tall: Flame Stabilization in High Velocity Gas Streams and the Effect of Heat Losses at Low Pressures, *Aeronaut. Quart.*, vol. 5, September, 1954.
26. McManus, H. N., Jr., and A. B. Cambel: Flameholding Characteristics of Open-vee Gutters, *Proc. Iowa Thermodynamics Symposium*, State University of Iowa, 1953.
27. Confrontation des resultats experimentaux sur la stabilisation des flammes par obstacles, ONERA, Paris, France, March, 1956.
28. Sedlacek, M. F.: "Effect of Turbulence Level on Flameholder Performance," M.S. thesis in mechanical engineering, State University of Iowa, February, 1954.
29. Schaffer, A., and A. B. Cambel: The Effect of an Opposing Jet on Flame Stability, *Jet Propulsion*, June, 1955, p. 284.
30. Schaffer, A., and A. B. Cambel: Continued Investigations of the Opposing Jet Flameholder, *Jet Propulsion*, July, 1956, p. 576.
31. Huellmantel, L. W., R. W. Ziemer, and A. B. Cambel: Stabilization of Pre-mixed Propane-Air Flames in Recessed Ducts, *Jet Propulsion*, vol. 27, no. 1, p. 31, 1957.
32. Schultz-Grunow, F.: Gas Dynamics of the Pulse Jet Tube, pts. I and II, *NACA TM* 1131, 1947.
33. Kahane, A., A. A. Marino, C. W. Messinger, and H. J. Shafer: A Theoretical and Experimental Investigation of the Feasibility of the Intermittent Ram Jet Engine, Project Squid Technical Report PR-45-R, Princeton University, Aug. 1, 1951.
34. Reynst, F. H.: Pulsating, Pressure Generating Combustion Systems for Gas Turbines, *ASME Paper* 55-A-56, ASME Diamond Jubilee Annual Meeting, November, 1955.
35. Crocco, Luigi, and Sin-I Cheng: Theory of Combustion Instability in Liquid Propellant Rocket Motors, *AGARDograph* 8, Butterworths Scientific Publications, London, 1956.
36. Crocco, L., and J. Grey: Combustion Instability, *Proc. Gas Dynamics Symposium on Aerothermochemistry*, p. 55, Northwestern University, 1956.
37. Tischler, A. O., and T. Male: Oscillatory Combustion in Rocket Propulsion Engines, *Proc. Gas Dynamics Symposium on Aerothermochemistry*, p. 71, Northwestern University, 1956.
38. Ross, C. C., and P. D. Datner: Combustion Instability in Liquid Propellant Rocket Motors—A Survey, p. 352 in "Selected Combustion Problems," I, AGARD, Butterworths Scientific Publications, London, 1954.
39. Sabersky, R. H.: Effect of Wave Propagation in Feed Lines on Low-frequency Rocket Instability, *Jet Propulsion*, vol. 24, no. 3, p. 172, May–June, 1954.
40. Berman, K., and S. H. Cheney, Jr.: Rocket Motor Instability Studies, *Jet Propulsion*, vol. 25, no. 10, p. 513, October, 1955.

41. Summerfield, M.: A Theory of Unstable Combustion in Liquid Propellant Rocket Systems, *J. Am. Rocket Soc.*, vol. 21, p. 108, 1951.
42. Tsien, H. S.: Servo-stabilization of Combustion in Rocket Motors, *J. Am. Rocket Soc.*, September–October, 1952, p. 256.
43. Rogers, D. E., and F. E. Marble: A Mechanism for High Frequency Oscillation in Ramjet Combustors and Afterburners, Heat Transfer and Fluid Mechanics Institute, University of California, Berkeley, Calif., June, 1955.
44. Kaskan, W. E., and A. E. Noreen: High Frequency Oscillations of a Flame Held by a Bluff Body, *Trans. ASME*, August, 1955, p. 835.
45. Sterbentz, William H., and John C. Evvard: Criterions for Prediction and Control of Ram-jet Flow Pulsations, *NACA TN* 3506, August, 1955.
46. Blackshear, Perry L., Warren D. Rayle, and Leonard K. Tower: Study of Screeching Combustion in a 6-inch Simulated Afterburner, *NACA TN* 3567, October, 1955.
47. Mirels, Harold: Acoustic Analysis of Ram-jet Buzz, *NACA TN* 3574, November, 1955.
48. Ross, Peter M.: "An Investigation of Oscillatory Combustion in Sudden Expansions," M.S. thesis, Department of Mechanical Engineering, Northwestern University.
49. von Kármán, Theodore: Fundamental Equations in Aerothermochemistry, in M. W. Thring, J. Ducarme, J. Fabri, and P. H. Price (eds.), "Selected Combustion Problems," II, AGARD, Butterworths Scientific Publications, London, 1956.
50. Transport Properties in Gases, in Ali Bulent Cambel and John B. Fenn (eds.), *2d Gas Dynamics Symposium*, American Rocket Society–Northwestern University, Northwestern University Press, Evanston, Ill., 1958.
51. Cambel, Ali Bulent: A Review of Flame Stabilization by Gaseous Jets, 12th Meeting, AGARD Combustion Panel, Washington, D.C., Nov. 18–26, 1957.
52. Duclos, D. P., A. Schaffer, and A. B. Cambel: Flame Stabilizing Effects of Inclined Air Jets, *Ind. Eng. Chem.*, vol. 49, p. 2063, December, 1957.

APPENDIX

z, ft	t, °F	T, °R	a/a_{SL}	a, fps	a, mph	p/p_{SL}	p, psf	p, mb	$\sigma = \rho/\rho_{SL}$	ρ, slugs/ft³	$\sigma^{1/2}$	$\mu \times 10^7$, slugs/ft-sec	$\nu \times 10^4$, ft²/sec	q/M^2, lb/ft²
0	59.00	518.70	1.0000	1,117	761.6	1.0000	2,116.2	1,013.2	1.0000	0.002378	1.0000	3.719	1.564	1,481.3
1,000	55.43	515.13	0.9966	1,113	759.0	0.9644	2,040.9	977.1	0.9711	0.002310	0.9854	3.699	1.602	1,428.6
2,000	51.87	511.57	0.9931	1,109	756.3	0.9298	1,967.7	942.1	0.9428	0.002242	0.9710	3.679	1.641	1,377.4
3,000	48.31	508.01	0.9896	1,105	753.7	0.8963	1,896.7	908.1	0.9151	0.002177	0.9566	3.659	1.681	1,327.7
4,000	44.74	504.44	0.9862	1,102	751.0	0.8637	1,827.7	875.1	0.8881	0.002112	0.9424	3.639	1.723	1,279.4
5,000	41.18	500.88	0.9827	1,098	748.4	0.8321	1,760.8	843.0	0.8617	0.002049	0.9283	3.618	1.766	1,232.6
6,000	37.62	497.32	0.9792	1,094	745.7	0.8014	1,696.0	812.0	0.8359	0.001988	0.9143	3.598	1.810	1,187.2
7,000	34.05	493.75	0.9756	1,090	743.0	0.7717	1,633.0	781.8	0.8107	0.001928	0.9004	3.577	1.855	1,143.1
8,000	30.49	490.19	0.9721	1,086	740.4	0.7428	1,571.9	752.6	0.7860	0.001869	0.8866	3.557	1.903	1,100.3
9,000	26.92	486.62	0.9686	1,082	737.7	0.7148	1,512.8	724.3	0.7620	0.001812	0.8729	3.536	1.951	1,059.0
10,000	23.36	483.06	0.9650	1,078	734.9	0.6877	1,455.4	696.8	0.7385	0.001756	0.8594	3.515	2.002	1,018.8
11,000	19.80	479.50	0.9614	1,074	732.2	0.6614	1,399.8	670.2	0.7156	0.001702	0.8459	3.495	2.054	979.9
12,000	16.23	475.93	0.9579	1,070	729.5	0.6360	1,345.9	644.4	0.6932	0.001649	0.8326	3.474	2.107	942.1
13,000	12.67	472.37	0.9543	1,066	726.8	0.6113	1,293.7	619.4	0.6714	0.001597	0.8194	3.453	2.163	905.6
14,000	9.10	468.82	0.9507	1,062	724.0	0.5875	1,243.2	595.2	0.6500	0.001546	0.8063	3.432	2.220	870.2
15,000	5.54	465.24	0.9470	1,058	721.2	0.5644	1,194.3	571.8	0.6292	0.001497	0.7933	3.411	2.280	836.0
16,000	1.98	461.68	0.9434	1,054	718.5	0.5420	1,147.0	549.1	0.6090	0.001448	0.7804	3.390	2.341	802.9
17,000	-1.59	458.11	0.9397	1,050	715.7	0.5203	1,101.1	527.2	0.5892	0.001401	0.7676	3.369	2.404	770.8
18,000	-5.15	454.55	0.9361	1,046	712.9	0.4994	1,056.9	506.0	0.5699	0.001355	0.7549	3.347	2.470	739.8
19,000	-8.72	450.98	0.9324	1,041	710.1	0.4792	1,014.0	485.5	0.5511	0.001311	0.7424	3.326	2.538	709.8
20,000	-12.28	447.42	0.9287	1,037	707.3	0.4596	972.6	465.6	0.5328	0.001267	0.7299	3.305	2.608	680.8
21,000	-15.84	443.86	0.9250	1,033	704.5	0.4406	932.5	446.4	0.5150	0.001225	0.7176	3.283	2.681	652.8
22,000	-19.41	440.29	0.9213	1,029	701.6	0.4223	893.8	427.9	0.4976	0.001183	0.7054	3.262	2.757	625.7
23,000	-22.97	436.73	0.9175	1,025	698.8	0.4047	856.4	410.0	0.4807	0.001143	0.6933	3.240	2.834	599.5
24,000	-26.54	433.16	0.9138	1,021	695.9	0.3876	820.3	392.7	0.4642	0.001104	0.6813	3.218	2.915	574.2
25,000	-30.10	429.60	0.9100	1,017	693.1	0.3711	785.3	376.0	0.4481	0.001066	0.6694	3.196	2.999	549.7
26,000	-33.66	426.04	0.9062	1,012	690.2	0.3552	751.7	359.9	0.4325	0.001029	0.6576	3.174	3.087	526.2
27,000	-37.23	422.47	0.9024	1,008	687.3	0.3399	719.2	344.3	0.4173	0.000993	0.6460	3.153	3.177	503.4
28,000	-40.79	418.91	0.8986	1,004	684.4	0.3251	687.6	329.3	0.4025	0.000957	0.6345	3.130	3.270	481.5
29,000	-44.36	415.34	0.8948	999	681.5	0.3108	657.6	314.9	0.3882	0.000923	0.6230	3.108	3.367	460.3
30,000	-47.92	411.78	0.8909	995	678.5	0.2970	628.5	300.9	0.3741	0.000890	0.6116	3.086	3.469	440.0
31,000	-51.48	408.22	0.8871	991	675.6	0.2837	600.4	287.5	0.3606	0.000858	0.6005	3.064	3.573	420.3
32,000	-55.05	404.65	0.8832	987	672.6	0.2709	573.3	274.3	0.3473	0.000826	0.5894	3.041	3.682	401.3
33,000	-58.61	401.09	0.8793	982	669.7	0.2586	547.3	262.0	0.3345	0.000796	0.5784	3.019	3.795	383.1
34,000	-62.18	397.52	0.8754	978	666.7	0.2467	522.2	250.0	0.3220	0.000766	0.5675	2.997	3.913	365.5
35,000	-65.74	393.96	0.8714	973	663.7	0.2353	498.0	238.4	0.3099	0.000737	0.5567	2.974	4.036	348.6

z	t (°F)	T (°R)	a (ft/sec)	a/a_{SL}	a (mph)	p/p_{SL}	p (lb/ft²)	ρ/ρ_{SL}	p (mb)	ρ (slug/ft³)	$\sqrt{\rho/\rho_{SL}}$	$\mu \times 10^7$	$\nu \times 10^4$	q (M=1)
35,332	-67.6	392.10	971	0.8693	662.1	0.2314	489.8	0.3058	234.5	0.000727	0.5530	2.961	4.073	342.9
36,000	-67.6	392.10	971	0.8693	662.1	0.2244	474.8	0.2981	227.3	0.000709	0.5460	2.951	4.176	332.4
37,000	-67.6	392.10	971	0.8693	662.1	0.2138	452.5	0.2845	216.7	0.0006766	0.5334	2.961	4.376	316.8
38,000	-67.6	392.10	971	0.8693	662.1	0.2038	431.2	0.2711	206.5	0.0006448	0.5207	2.961	4.592	301.8
39,000	-67.6	392.10	971	0.8693	662.1	0.1942	411.0	0.2584	196.8	0.0006145	0.5083	2.961	4.819	287.7
40,000	-67.6	392.10	971	0.8693	662.1	0.1851	391.8	0.2463	187.6	0.0005857	0.4963	2.961	5.055	274.3
41,000	-67.6	392.10	971	0.8693	662.1	0.1764	373.4	0.2347	178.8	0.0005582	0.4845	2.961	5.305	261.4
42,000	-67.6	392.10	971	0.8693	662.1	0.1681	355.8	0.2237	170.4	0.0005320	0.4730	2.961	5.566	249.1
43,000	-67.6	392.10	971	0.8693	662.1	0.1603	339.1	0.2132	162.4	0.0005071	0.4617	2.961	5.839	237.4
44,000	-67.6	392.10	971	0.8693	662.1	0.1527	323.2	0.2032	154.8	0.0004833	0.4508	2.961	6.127	226.2
45,000	-67.6	392.10	971	0.8693	662.1	0.1456	308.0	0.1936	147.5	0.0004605	0.4400	2.961	6.430	215.6
46,000	-67.6	392.10	971	0.8693	662.1	0.1387	293.6	0.1846	140.6	0.0004390	0.4296	2.961	6.745	205.5
47,000	-67.6	392.10	971	0.8693	662.1	0.1322	279.8	0.1759	134.0	0.0004184	0.4194	2.961	7.077	195.9
48,000	-67.6	392.10	971	0.8693	662.1	0.1260	266.6	0.1676	127.7	0.0003987	0.4094	2.961	7.427	186.6
49,000	-67.6	392.10	971	0.8693	662.1	0.1201	254.1	0.1598	121.7	0.0003800	0.3997	2.961	7.792	177.9
50,000	-67.6	392.10	971	0.8693	662.1	0.1145	242.2	0.1523	116.0	0.0003622	0.3902	2.961	8.175	169.5
60,000	-67.6	392.10	971	0.8693	662.1	0.0713	150.9	0.0942	72.2	0.0002240	0.3069	2.961	13.219	105.6
70,000	-67.6	392.10	971	0.8693	662.1	0.0442	93.5	0.0584	44.8	0.0001389	0.2417	2.961	21.317	65.5
80,000	-67.6	392.10	971	0.8693	662.1	0.0274	58.0	0.0362	27.8	0.0000861	0.1903	2.961	34.390	40.6
90,000	-67.6	392.10	971	0.8693	662.1	0.0170	36.0	0.0225	17.2	0.0000535	0.1500	2.961	55.346	25.2
100,000	-67.6	392.10	971	0.8693	662.1	0.0106	22.4	0.0140	10.7	0.0000331	0.1183	2.961	89.456	15.7
104,987	-67.6	392.10	971	0.8693	662.1	0.00831	17.59	0.0110	8.42	0.0000261	0.1048	2.961	113.4	12.31
110,000	-47.4	412.30	996	0.8917	679.0	0.00658	13.92	0.00827	6.66	0.0000197	0.09093	3.090	157.2	9.744
120,000	-7.2	452.50	1,043	0.9346	711.1	0.00426	9.026	0.00488	4.32	0.0000116	0.06988	3.339	287.6	6.318
130,000	33.0	492.70	1,089	0.9749	742.5	0.00287	6.071	0.00302	2.91	0.00000717	0.05493	3.579	498.9	4.250
140,000	73.3	533.00	1,132	1.0143	771.8	0.00199	4.213	0.00193	2.02	0.00000460	0.04399	3.809	827.9	2.949
150,000	113.5	573.20	1,174	1.0510	800.5	0.00142	3.003	0.00128	1.45	0.00000305	0.03582	4.032	1,322	2.102
160,000	153.7	613.40	1,215	1.0877	828.4	0.00103	2.190	0.00087	1.05	0.00000208	0.02957	4.247	2,043	1.533
164,042	170.0	629.70	1,231	1.1021	839.3	0.000916	1.938	0.00075	0.928	0.00000179	0.02746	4.332	2,417	1.357
170,000	170.0	629.70	1,231	1.1021	839.3	0.000767	1.624	0.00063	0.777	0.00000150	0.02513	4.332	2,886	1.137
180,000	170.0	629.70	1,231	1.1021	839.3	0.000570	1.206	0.00047	0.577	0.00000111	0.02165	4.332	3,885	0.8442
190,000	170.0	629.70	1,231	1.1021	839.3	0.000423	0.8956	0.00035	0.429	0.00000083	0.01866	4.332	5,232	0.6269
196,850	170.0	629.70	1,231	1.1021	839.3	0.000345	0.7305	0.00028	0.350	0.00000068	0.01685	4.332	6,412	0.5114
200,000	159.4	619.10	1,220	1.0931	831.8	0.000314	0.6645	0.00026	0.318	0.00000062	0.01621	4.277	6,844	0.4652
210,000	125.9	585.60	1,187	1.0627	809.3	0.000230	0.4869	0.00020	0.233	0.00000048	0.01427	4.099	8,467	0.3408
220,000	92.4	552.10	1,152	1.0322	785.5	0.000166	0.3504	0.00015	0.168	0.00000037	0.01247	3.916	10,600	0.2453
230,000	58.9	518.60	1,117	1.0000	761.6	0.000117	0.2470	0.00012	0.118	0.00000028	0.01080	3.727	13,400	0.1729
240,000	25.3	485.00	1,080	0.9669	736.4	0.000080	0.1699	0.00009	0.081	0.00000020	0.00926	3.533	17,330	0.1189
250,000	-8.2	451.50	1,042	0.9329	710.5	0.000054	0.1139	0.00006	0.054	0.00000015	0.00786	3.333	22,700	0.0797
255,905	-28.0	431.70	1,019	0.9123	694.8	0.000042	0.0886	0.00005	0.042	0.00000011	0.00709	3.212	26,880	0.0621
260,000	-28.0	431.70	1,019	0.9123	694.8	0.000035	0.0742	0.00004	0.035	0.00000010	0.00649	3.212	32,090	0.0520

z = height
p = pressure
μ = coefficient of viscosity

T, t = temperature
ρ = density
ν = coefficient of kinematic viscosity

a = velocity of sound
σ = density relative to sea level
SL = sea level (z = 0)

† From *NACA TN 1428*.

TABLE A-2. CONSTANTS FOR GASES AND VAPORS †

Gas or vapor	Chemical symbol	Molecular weight M_w	R, ft-lb$_f$/ (lb)(°R)	R, ft-lb$_f$/ (slug) × (°R)	Specific heat at 70°F and low pressure, Btu/(lb)(°R)		$k = \dfrac{c_p}{c_v}$
					c_p	c_v	
Air.............	...	28.97	53.34	1,716	0.240	0.171	1.40
Argon...........	A	39.94	38.70	1,245	0.124	0.075	1.66
Carbon dioxide....	CO_2	44.00	35.12	1,130	0.206	0.158	1.30
Carbon monoxide..	CO	28.00	55.14	1,774	0.243	0.174	1.40
Ethane..........	C_2H_6	30.05	51.38	1,653	0.413	0.339	1.22
Helium..........	He	4.00	386.00	12,419	1.25	0.75	1.66
Hydrogen........	H_2	2.016	765.86	24,641	3.42	2.44	1.40
Methane........	CH_4	16.03	96.31	3,099	0.528	0.403	1.31
Nitrogen........	N_2	28.02	54.99	1,769	0.248	0.176	1.40
Octane..........	C_8H_{18}	114.14	13.55	436	0.349	0.210	1.66
Oxygen..........	O_2	32.00	48.25	1,552	0.219	0.156	1.40
Propane.........	C_3H_8	44.06	35.04	1,127	0.473	0.411	1.15
Steam...........	H_2O	18.01	85.6	2,754	0.45	0.35	1.28
Sulfur dioxide.....	SO_2	64.07	24.10	775	0.154	0.123	1.25

† Universal gas constant: 1,545.3 ft-lb$_f$/(lb mole)(°R) = 1.986 Btu/(lb mole)(°R) = 1.986 cal/(g mole)(°C).

TABLE A-3. THERMODYNAMIC PROPERTIES OF AIR AT LOW PRESSURES †

°R	°F	h, Btu per lb	u, Btu per lb	s_p	p_r	°R	°F	h, Btu per lb	u, Btu per lb	s_p	p_r
400	−59.7	−14.364	−41.780	−0.03348	0.6140	430	−29.7	−7.182	−36.650	−0.01615	0.7902
401		14.125	41.609	0.03288	0.6193	431		6.943	36.479	0.01559	0.7966
402		13.885	41.438	0.03228	0.6247	432		6.703	36.308	0.01504	0.8031
403		13.646	41.267	0.03169	0.6301	433		6.464	36.137	0.01449	0.8095
404		13.406	41.096	0.03110	0.6356	434		6.224	35.966	0.01394	0.8161
405		−13.167	−40.925	−0.03051	0.6411	435		−5.985	−35.795	−0.01339	0.8227
406		12.928	40.754	0.02992	0.6467	436		5.746	35.624	0.01284	0.8294
407		12.688	40.583	0.02933	0.6522	437		5.506	35.453	0.01229	0.8361
408		12.449	40.412	0.02874	0.6578	438		5.267	35.282	0.01174	0.8428
409		12.209	40.241	0.02815	0.6635	439		5.027	35.111	0.01119	0.8495
410	−49.7	−11.970	−40.070	−0.02756	0.6692	440	−19.7	−4.788	−34.940	−0.01064	0.8563
411		11.731	39.899	0.02699	0.6749	441		4.549	34.769	0.01011	0.8631
412		11.491	39.728	0.02642	0.6806	442		4.309	34.598	0.00958	0.8699
413		11.252	39.557	0.02585	0.6864	443		4.070	34.427	0.00904	0.8768
414		11.012	39.386	0.02527	0.6922	444		3.830	34.256	0.00850	0.8837
415		−10.773	−39.215	−0.02469	0.6981	445		−3.591	−34.085	−0.00796	0.8907
416		10.534	39.044	0.02411	0.7039	446		3.352	33.914	0.00742	0.8977
417		10.294	38.873	0.02353	0.7099	447		3.112	33.743	0.00688	0.9048
418		10.055	38.702	0.02295	0.7158	448		2.873	33.572	0.00634	0.9119
419		9.815	38.531	0.02237	0.7218	449		2.633	33.401	0.00580	0.9190
420	−39.7	−9.576	−38.360	−0.02179	0.7279	450	−9.7	−2.394	−33.230	−0.00526	0.9262
421		9.337	38.189	0.02122	0.7340	451		2.155	33.059	0.00473	0.9334
422		9.097	38.018	0.02065	0.7401	452		1.915	32.888	0.00420	0.9406
423		8.858	37.847	0.02008	0.7463	453		1.676	32.717	0.00367	9.9479
424		8.618	37.676	0.01951	0.7525	454		1.436	32.546	0.00314	0.9552
425		−8.379	−37.505	−0.01895	0.7587	455		−1.197	−32.375	−0.00261	0.9625
426		8.140	37.334	0.01839	0.7649	456		0.958	32.204	0.00208	0.9700
427		7.900	37.163	0.01783	0.7712	457		0.718	32.033	0.00156	0.9775
428		7.661	36.992	0.01727	0.7775	458		0.479	31.862	0.00104	0.9849
429		7.421	36.821	0.01671	0.7838	459		0.240	31.691	0.00052	0.9924
Difference or c_p, c_v		$c_p = 0.240$	$c_v = 0.171$	60–56				$c_p = 0.240$	$c_v = 0.171$	56–52	

† From B. H. Jennings and W. L. Rogers, "Gas Turbine Analysis and Practice," McGraw-Hill Book Company, Inc., New York, 1953.

TABLE A-3. THERMODYNAMIC PROPERTIES OF AIR AT LOW PRESSURES (*Continued*)

°R	°F	h, Btu per lb	u, Btu per lb	s_p	p_r	°R	°F	h, Btu per lb	u, Btu per lb	s_p	p_r
460	0.3	0.000	−31.520	0.00000	1.000	495		8.396	−25.534	0.01753	1.292
461		0.240	31.349	0.00050	1.007	496		8.635	25.363	0.01802	1.301
462		0.480	31.178	0.00100	1.015	497		8.875	25.192	0.01852	1.310
463		0.719	31.007	0.00151	1.023	498		9.115	25.020	0.01901	1.319
464		0.959	30.836	0.00201	1.031	499		9.355	24.849	0.01952	1.328
465		1.199	−30.666	0.00252	1.038	500	40.3	9.595	−24.678	0.02003	1.338
466		1.439	30.495	0.00303	1.046	501		9.835	24.507	0.02049	1.347
467		1.679	30.324	0.00353	1.054	502		10.075	24.336	0.02095	1.357
468		1.918	30.153	0.00404	1.062	503		10.315	24.164	0.02142	1.367
469		2.158	29.982	0.00455	1.070	504		10.555	23.993	0.02188	1.376
470	10.3	2.398	−29.811	0.00506	1.078	505		10.795	−23.822	0.02235	1.385
471		2.638	29.640	0.00558	1.086	506		11.034	23.651	0.02281	1.395
472		2.878	29.469	0.00609	1.094	507		11.274	23.480	0.02328	1.404
473		3.118	29.298	0.00660	1.102	508		11.514	23.308	0.02375	1.414
474		3.358	29.127	0.00712	1.110	509		11.754	23.137	0.02422	1.424
475		3.598	−28.957	0.00763	1.118	510	50.3	11.994	−22.966	0.02469	1.434
476		3.837	28.786	0.00815	1.127	511		12.234	22.795	0.02516	1.444
477		4.077	28.615	0.00867	1.135	512		12.474	22.624	0.02563	1.453
478		4.317	28.444	0.00919	1.143	513		12.714	22.452	0.02610	1.463
479		4.557	28.273	0.00970	1.151	514		12.954	22.281	0.02657	1.473
480	20.3	4.797	−28.102	0.01021	1.160	515		13.194	−22.110	0.02705	1.483
481		5.037	27.931	0.01069	1.168	516		13.433	21.939	0.02752	1.494
482		5.277	27.760	0.01117	1.177	517		13.673	21.768	0.02800	1.504
483		5.517	27.588	0.01166	1.185	518		13.913	21.596	0.02847	1.514
484		5.757	27.417	0.01214	1.194	519		14.153	21.425	0.02896	1.524
485		5.997	−27.246	0.01263	1.203	520	60.3	14.393	−21.254	0.02944	1.535
486		6.236	27.075	0.01311	1.212	521		14.633	21.082	0.02989	1.545
487		6.476	26.904	0.01360	1.220	522		14.873	20.911	0.03033	1.555
488		6.716	26.732	0.01409	1.229	523		15.113	20.739	0.03078	1.566
489		6.956	26.561	0.01457	1.238	524		15.353	20.567	0.03123	1.576
490	30.3	7.196	−26.390	0.01506	1.247	525		15.593	−20.396	0.03167	1.587
491		7.436	26.219	0.01555	1.256	526		15.833	20.224	0.03212	1.597
492		7.676	26.048	0.01605	1.265	527		16.075	20.052	0.03257	1.608
493		7.916	25.876	0.01654	1.274	528		16.317	19.880	0.03303	1.619
494		8.156	25.705	0.01703	1.283	529		16.559	19.709	0.03348	1.629
Difference or c_p, c_v		$c_p =$ 0.240	$c_v =$ 0.171	50–49				$c_p =$ 0.240	$c_v =$ 0.171	49–45	

TABLE A-3. THERMODYNAMIC PROPERTIES OF AIR AT LOW PRESSURES (*Continued*)

°R	°F	h, Btu per lb	u, Btu per lb	s_p	p_r	°R	°F	h, Btu per lb	u, Btu per lb	s_p	p_r
530	70.3	16.800	−19.537	0.03393	1.640	570	110.3	26.396	−12.660	0.05141	2.116
531		17.040	19.365	0.03438	1.651	571		26.637	12.488	0.05183	2.129
532		17.280	19.194	0.03484	1.662	572		26.877	12.316	0.05225	2.142
533		17.519	19.022	0.03529	1.673	573		27.117	12.144	0.05267	2.155
534		17.759	18.850	0.03575	1.684	574		27.357	11.972	0.05310	2.169
535		17.999	−18.678	0.03621	1.695	575		27.597	−11.800	0.05352	2.182
536		18.239	18.507	0.03666	1.706	576		27.838	11.628	0.05394	2.195
537		18.479	18.335	0.03712	1.717	577		28.078	11.456	0.05436	2.209
588		18.718	18.163	0.03758	1.728	578		28.318	11.284	0.05479	2.222
539		18.958	17.992	0.03804	1.740	579		28.558	11.112	0.05522	2.236
540	80.3	19.198	−17.820	0.03850	1.751	580	120.3	28.798	−10.940	0.05565	2.249
541		19.438	17.648	0.03892	1.762	581		29.039	10.768	0.05605	2.263
542		19.678	17.476	0.03936	1.774	582		29.279	10.596	0.05645	2.276
543		19.917	17.304	0.03979	1.785	583		29.520	10.424	0.05685	2.290
544		20.157	17.132	0.04022	1.797	584		29.760	10.252	0.05726	2.304
545		20.397	−16.960	0.04065	1.808	585		30.001	−10.080	0.05766	2.318
546		20.637	16.788	0.04109	1.820	586		30.241	9.908	0.05806	2.332
547		20.877	16.616	0.04152	1.832	587		30.482	9.736	0.05847	2.346
548		21.116	16.444	0.04195	1.844	588		30.722	9.564	0.05887	2.360
549		21.356	16.272	0.04239	1.855	589		30.963	9.392	0.05928	2.374
550	90.3	21.596	−16.100	0.04282	1.867	590	130.3	31.203	− 9.220	0.05969	2.388
551		21.836	15.928	0.04326	1.879	591		31.444	9.048	0.06010	2.402
552		22.076	15.756	0.04370	1.891	592		31.684	8.876	0.06051	2.416
553		22.315	15.584	0.04414	1.903	593		31.925	8.704	0.06092	2.431
554		22.555	15.412	0.04457	1.915	594		32.165	8.532	0.06132	2.445
555		22.795	−15.240	0.04501	1.927	595		32.406	− 8.360	0.06173	2.460
556		23.035	15.068	0.04545	1.939	596		32.646	8.188	0.06214	2.474
557		23.275	14.896	0.04589	1.952	597		32.887	8.016	0.06255	2.489
558		23.514	14.724	0.04634	1.964	598		33.127	7.844	0.06296	2.503
559		23.754	14.552	0.04678	1.976	599		33.368	7.672	0.06338	2.518
560	100.3	23.994	−14.380	0.04723	1.989	600	140.3	33.608	− 7.500	0.06379	2.533
561		24.235	14.208	0.04764	2.001	601		33.849	7.328	0.06418	2.547
562		24.475	14.036	0.04806	2.014	602		34.090	7.156	0.06457	2.562
563		24.715	13.864	0.04848	2.026	603		34.330	6.984	0.06496	2.578
564		24.955	13.692	0.04889	2.039	604		34.571	6.812	0.06534	2.593
565		25.195	−13.520	0.04930	2.052	605		34.811	− 6.640	0.06573	2.608
566		25.436	13.348	0.04971	2.064	606		35.052	6.468	0.06612	2.623
567		25.676	13.176	0.05014	2.077	607		35.293	6.296	0.06652	2.638
568		25.916	13.004	0.05056	2.090	608		35.533	6.124	0.06691	2.653
569		26.156	12.832	0.05098	2.103	609		35.774	5.952	0.06730	2.669
Difference or c_p, c_v		$c_p =$ 0.240	$c_v =$ 0.172	45–42				$c_p =$ 0.240	$c_v =$ 0.172	42–39	

TABLE A-3. THERMODYNAMIC PROPERTIES OF AIR AT LOW PRESSURES *(Continued)*

°R	°F	h, Btu per lb	u, Btu per lb	s_p	p_r	°R	°F	h, Btu per lb	u, Btu per lb	s_p	p_r
610	150.3	36.014	−5.780	0.06769	2.684	650	190.3	45.646	+1.100	0.08298	3.356
611		36.255	5.608	0.06809	2.699	651		45.887	1.273	0.08335	3.374
612		36.496	5.436	0.06848	2.716	652		46.128	1.446	0.08372	3.393
613		36.736	5.264	0.06887	2.731	653		46.369	1.619	0.08410	3.410
614		36.977	5.092	0.06927	2.748	654		46.610	1.792	0.08447	3.429
615		37.217	−4.920	0.06966	2.763	655		46.851	+1.965	0.08484	3.447
616		37.458	4.748	0.07006	2.778	656		47.092	2.138	0.08522	3.466
617		37.699	4.576	0.07046	2.794	657		47.333	2.311	0.08559	3.485
618		37.939	4.404	0.07086	2.811	658		47.574	2.484	0.08597	3.504
619		38.180	4.232	0.07126	2.826	659		47.815	2.657	0.08634	3.522
620	160.3	38.420	−4.060	0.07166	2.842	660	200.3	48.056	+2.830	0.08672	3.540
621		38.661	3.888	0.07204	2.859	661		48.298	3.003	0.08708	3.559
622		38.902	3.716	0.07241	2.875	662		48.539	3.176	0.08743	3.578
623		39.142	3.544	0.07279	2.890	663		48.781	3.349	0.08779	3.597
624		39.383	3.372	0.07317	2.907	664		49.022	3.522	0.08815	3.616
625		39.623	−3.200	0.07355	2.923	665		49.263	+3.695	0.08851	3.637
626		39.864	3.028	0.07392	2.940	666		49.505	3.868	0.08886	3.655
627		40.105	2.856	0.07430	2.956	667		49.746	4.041	0.08922	3.674
628		40.345	2.684	0.07468	2.974	668		49.988	4.214	0.08958	3.695
629		40.586	2.512	0.07506	2.990	669		50.229	4.387	0.08994	3.714
630	170.3	40.826	−2.340	0.07544	3.007	670	210.3	50.470	+4.560	0.09030	3.734
631		41.067	2.168	0.07583	3.023	671		50.712	4.733	0.09066	3.753
632		41.308	1.996	0.07621	3.039	672		50.953	4.906	0.09102	3.773
633		41.549	1.824	0.07659	3.057	673		51.194	5.079	0.09138	3.792
634		41.790	1.652	0.07697	3.074	674		51.436	+5.252	0.09174	3.812
635		42.031	−1.480	0.07736	3.091	675		51.677	+5.425	0.09210	3.832
636		42.272	1.308	0.07774	3.108	676		51.919	5.598	0.09246	3.853
637		42.513	1.136	0.07812	3.125	677		52.160	5.771	0.09283	3.872
638		42.754	0.964	0.07851	3.143	678		52.402	5.944	0.09319	3.892
639		42.995	0.792	0.07890	3.160	679		52.643	6.117	0.09356	3.912
640	180.3	43.236	−0.620	0.07929	3.177	680	220.3	52.884	+6.290	0.09393	3.932
641		43.477	0.448	0.07966	3.195	681		53.126	6.463	0.09428	3.954
642		43.718	0.276	0.08002	3.213	682		53.368	6.636	0.09462	3.974
643		43.959	0.104	0.08039	3.220	683		53.609	6.809	0.09497	3.994
644		44.200	+0.068	0.08076	3.248	684		53.851	6.982	0.09532	4.014
645		44.441	+0.240	0.08113	3.266	685		54.092	+7.155	0.09566	4.036
646		44.682	0.412	0.08150	3.283	686		54.334	7.328	0.09601	4.056
647		44.923	0.584	0.08186	3.301	687		54.576	7.501	0.09636	4.078
648		45.164	0.756	0.08224	3.319	688		54.817	7.674	0.09671	4.098
649		45.405	0.928	0.08261	3.338	689		55.059	7.847	0.09706	4.119
Difference or c_p, c_v		$c_p = $ 0.241	$c_v = $ 0.172	40–37				$c_p = $ 0.241	$c_v = $ 0.172, 0.173	37–35	

TABLE A-3. THERMODYNAMIC PROPERTIES OF AIR AT LOW PRESSURES (*Continued*)

°R	°F	h, Btu per lb	u, Btu per lb	s_p	p_r	°R	°F	h, Btu per lb	u, Btu per lb	s_p	p_r
690	230.3	55.300	+ 8.020	0.09741	4.142	730	270.3	64.980	+14.960	0.11107	5.057
691		55.542	8.193	0.09776	4.162	731		65.223	15.134	0.11140	5.081
692		55.784	8.366	0.09811	4.184	732		65.466	15.308	0.11173	5.106
693		56.026	8.539	0.09846	4.205	733		65.709	15.482	0.11207	5.130
694		56.268	8.712	0.09881	4.227	734		65.952	15.656	0.11240	5.156
695		56.510	+ 8.885	0.09916	4.248	735		66.195	+15.830	0.11273	5.180
696		56.752	9.058	0.09952	4.270	736		66.438	16.004	0.11306	5.205
697		56.994	9.231	0.09987	4.291	737		66.681	16.178	0.11339	5.230
698		57.236	9.404	0.10022	4.313	738		66.924	16.352	0.11373	5.256
699		57.478	9.577	0.10058	4.336	739		67.167	16.526	0.11406	5.281
700	240.3	57.720	+ 9.750	0.10093	4.357	740	280.3	67.410	+16.700	0.11440	5.306
701		57.962	9.923	0.10127	4.379	741		67.653	16.874	0.11472	5.332
702		58.204	10.096	0.10162	4.401	742		67.895	17.048	0.11505	5.357
703		58.446	10.269	0.10195	4.423	743		68.138	17.222	0.11537	5.382
704		58.688	10.442	0.10229	4.446	744		68.380	17.396	0.11569	5.407
705		58.930	+10.615	0.10264	4.467	745		68.623	+17.570	0.11602	5.434
706		59.172	10.788	0.10298	4.490	746		68.865	17.744	0.11634	5.459
707		59.414	10.961	0.10332	4.513	747		69.108	17.918	0.11666	5.486
708		59.656	11.134	0.10366	4.535	748		69.350	18.092	0.11698	5.511
709		59.898	11.307	0.10400	4.558	749		69.593	18.266	0.11731	5.538
710	250.3	60.140	+11.480	0.10434	4.581	750	290.3	69.835	+18.440	0.11763	5.563
711		60.382	11.654	0.10468	4.603	751		70.078	18.614	0.11795	5.590
712		60.624	11.828	0.10502	4.626	752		70.320	18.788	0.11828	5.616
713		60.866	12.002	0.10536	4.649	753		70.563	18.962	0.11860	5.643
714		61.108	12.176	0.10570	4.672	754		70.805	19.136	0.11892	5.669
715		61.350	+12.350	0.10604	4.696	755		71.048	+19.310	0.11925	5.696
716		61.592	12.524	0.10639	4.719	756		71.290	19.484	0.11957	5.723
717		61.834	12.698	0.10673	4.742	757		71.533	19.658	0.11989	5.749
718		62.076	12.872	0.10707	4.766	758		71.775	19.832	0.12021	5.777
719		62.318	13.046	0.10741	4.790	759		72.018	20.006	0.12054	5.804
720	260.3	62.560	+13.220	0.10775	4.812	760	300.3	72.260	+20.180	0.12087	5.830
721		62.802	13.394	0.10808	4.836	761		72.503	20.354	0.12119	5.858
722		63.044	13.568	0.10841	4.860	762		72.745	20.528	0.12150	5.885
723		63.286	13.742	0.10875	4.883	763		72.988	20.702	0.12192	5.912
724		63.528	13.916	0.10908	4.907	764		73.230	20.876	0.12213	5.940
725		63.770	+14.090	0.10941	4.931	765		73.433	+21.050	0.12245	5.968
726		64.012	14.264	0.10972	4.955	766		73.715	21.224	0.12277	5.995
727		64.254	14.438	0.11007	4.979	767		73.938	21.398	0.12308	6.023
728		64.496	14.612	0.11040	5.003	768		74.200	21.572	0.12340	6.050
729		64.738	14.786	0.11074	5.027	769		74.443	21.746	0.12371	6.078
Difference or c_p, c_v		$c_p =$ 0.242	$c_v =$ 0.173, 0.174	35–34				$c_p =$ 0.243	$c_v =$ 0.174	33–31	

TABLE A-3. THERMODYNAMIC PROPERTIES OF AIR AT LOW PRESSURES (*Continued*)

°R	°F	h, Btu per lb	u, Btu per lb	s_p	p_r	°R	°F	h, Btu per lb	u, Btu per lb	s_p	p_r
770	310.3	74.685	+21.920	0.12403	6.108	810	350.3	84.420	+28.910	0.13637	7.311
771		74.928	22.094	0.12435	6.136	811		84.664	29.085	0.13667	7.343
772		75.170	22.268	0.12466	6.163	812		84.908	29.260	0.13697	7.375
773		75.413	22.442	0.12498	6.193	813		85.152	29.435	0.13727	7.408
774		75.655	22.616	0.12529	6.220	814		85.396	29.610	0.13757	7.440
775		75.898	+22.790	.012561	6.248	815		85.640	+29.785	0.13787	7.473
776		76.140	22.964	0.12593	6.277	816		85.884	29.960	0.13818	7.506
777		76.383	23.138	0.12624	6.306	817		86.128	30.135	0.13848	7.538
778		76.625	23.312	0.12656	6.336	818		86.372	30.310	0.13878	7.571
779		76.868	23.486	0.12687	6.363	819		86.616	30.485	0.13908	7.604
780	320.3	77.110	+23.660	0.12719	6.393	820	360.3	86.860	+30.660	0.13938	7.637
781		77.353	23.835	0.12750	6.422	821		87.104	30.836	0.13967	7.670
782		77.596	24.010	0.12781	6.451	822		87.348	31.012	0.13997	7.703
783		77.839	24.185	0.12811	6.480	823		87.592	31.188	0.14026	7.737
784		78.082	24.360	0.12842	6.510	824		87.836	31.364	0.14056	7.770
785		78.325	+24.535	0.12873	6.539	825		88.080	+31.540	0.14085	7.804
786		78.568	24.710	0.12904	6.568	826		88.324	31.716	0.14114	7.837
787		78.811	24.885	0.12935	6.599	827		88.568	31.892	0.14144	7.871
788		79.054	25.060	0.12965	6.628	828		88.812	32.068	0.14173	7.906
789		79.297	25.235	0.12996	6.658	829		89.056	32.244	0.14203	7.940
790	330.3	79.540	+25.410	0.13027	6.689	830	370.3	89.300	+32.420	0.14232	7.974
791		79.784	25.585	0.13058	6.719	831		89.544	32.596	0.14261	8.008
792		80.028	25.760	0.13089	6.748	832		89.788	32.772	0.14291	8.042
793		80.272	25.935	0.13119	6.779	833		90.032	32.948	0.14320	8.076
794		80.516	26.110	0.13150	6.809	834		90.276	33.124	0.14350	8.112
795		80.760	+26.285	0.13181	6.839	835		90.520	+33.300	0.14379	8.146
796		81.004	26.460	0.13212	6.871	836		90.764	33.476	0.14408	8.180
797		81.248	26.635	0.13243	6.901	837		91.008	33.652	0.14438	8.216
798		81.492	26.810	0.13273	6.932	838		91.252	33.828	0.14467	8.251
799		81.736	26.985	0.13304	6.962	839		91.496	34.004	0.14497	8.285
800	340.3	81.980	+27.160	0.13336	6.994	840	380.3	91.740	+34.180	0.14527	8.321
801		82.224	27.335	0.13366	7.025	841		91.985	34.356	0.14556	8.356
802		82.468	27.510	0.13396	7.056	842		92.230	34.532	0.14585	8.392
803		82.712	27.685	0.13426	7.087	843		92.475	34.708	0.14613	8.427
804		82.956	27.860	0.13456	7.119	844		92.720	34.884	0.14642	8.463
805		83.200	+28.035	0.13487	7.151	845		92.965	+35.060	0.14671	8.499
806		83.444	28.210	0.13517	7.182	846		93.210	35.236	0.14700	8.535
807		83.688	28.385	0.13547	7.214	847		93.455	35.412	0.14729	8.570
808		83.932	28.560	0.13577	7.246	848		93.700	35.588	0.14757	8.607
809		84.176	28.735	0.13607	7.277	849		93.945	35.764	0.14786	8.644
Difference or c_p, c_v		c_p = 0.243, 0.244	c_v = 0.175	32–30				c_p = 0.244, 0.245	c_v = 0.176	30–29	

TABLE A-3. THERMODYNAMIC PROPERTIES OF AIR AT LOW PRESSURES (*Continued*)

°R	°F	h, Btu per lb	u, Btu per lb	s_p	p_r	°R	°F	h, Btu per lb	u, Btu per lb	s_p	p_r
850	390.3	94.190	+35.940	0.14815	8.682	885		102.770	+42.125	0.15804	10.032
851		94.435	36.116	0.14844	8.719	886		103.016	42.302	0.15832	10.073
852		94.680	36.292	0.14873	8.756	887		103.262	42.479	0.15859	10.113
853		94.925	36.468	0.14901	8.793	888		103.508	42.656	0.15887	10.154
854		95.170	36.644	0.14930	8.829	889		103.754	42.833	0.15914	10.196
855		95.415	+36.829	0.14959	8.866	890	430.3	104.000	+43.010	0.15942	10.236
856		95.660	36.996	0.14988	8.904	891		104.246	43.187	0.15970	10.278
857		95.905	37.172	0.15017	8.941	892		104.492	43.364	0.15997	10.319
858		96.150	37.348	0.15045	8.979	893		104.738	43.541	0.16025	10.360
859		96.395	37.524	0.15074	9.016	894		104.984	43.718	0.16052	10.402
860	400.3	96.640	+37.700	0.15103	9.053	895		105.230	+43.895	0.16080	10.444
861		96.885	37.877	0.15131	9.090	896		105.478	44.072	0.16108	10.486
862		97.130	38.054	0.15159	9.128	897		105.722	44.249	0.16135	10.528
863		97.375	38.231	0.15187	9.166	898		105.968	44.426	0.16163	10.571
864		97.620	38.408	0.15215	9.204	899		106.214	44.603	0.16190	10.612
865		97.865	+38.585	0.15244	9.242	900	440.3	106.460	+44.780	0.16219	10.654
866		98.110	38.762	0.15272	9.280	901		106.706	44.958	0.16246	10.699
867		98.355	38.939	0.15300	9.319	902		106.952	45.136	0.16273	10.740
868		98.600	39.116	0.15328	9.357	903		107.198	45.314	0.16300	10.783
869		98.845	39.293	0.15356	9.395	904		107.444	45.492	0.16327	10.825
870	410.3	99.090	+39.470	0.15384	9.435	905		107.690	+45.670	0.16354	10.868
871		99.335	39.647	0.15412	9.474	906		107.936	45.848	0.16381	10.911
872		99.580	39.824	0.15440	9.513	907		108.182	46.026	0.16408	10.954
873		99.825	40.001	0.15468	9.551	908		108.428	46.204	0.16435	10.999
874		100.070	40.178	0.15496	9.590	909		108.674	46.382	0.16462	11.042
875		100.315	+40.355	0.15525	9.630	910	450.3	108.920	+46.560	0.16489	11.086
876		100.560	40.532	0.15553	9.669	911		109.166	46.738	0.16516	11.129
877		100.805	40.709	0.15581	9.709	912		109.412	46.916	0.16543	11.174
878		101.050	40.886	0.15609	9.749	913		109.658	47.094	0.16570	11.218
879		101.295	41.063	0.15637	9.788	914		109.904	47.272	0.16597	11.261
880	420.3	101.540	+41.240	0.15666	9.829	915		110.150	+47.450	0.16624	11.305
881		101.786	41.417	0.15694	9.869	916		110.396	47.628	0.16651	11.351
882		102.032	41.594	0.15721	9.908	917		110.642	47.806	0.16678	11.395
883		102.278	41.771	0.15749	9.949	918		110.888	47.984	0.16705	11.440
884		102.524	41.948	0.15776	9.989	919		111.134	48.162	0.16732	11.485
Difference or c_p, c_v		$c_p =$ 0.245, 0.246	$c_v =$ 0.176, 0.177	29–27				$c_p =$ 0.246	$c_v =$ 0.177, 0.178	28–27	

TABLE A-3. THERMODYNAMIC PROPERTIES OF AIR AT LOW PRESSURES (*Continued*)

°R	°F	h, Btu per lb	u, Btu per lb	s_p	p_r	°R	°F	h, Btu per lb	u, Btu per lb	s_p	p_r
920	460.3	111.380	+48.340	0.16760	11.530	960	500.3	121.275	+55.480	0.17812	13.442
921		111.627	48.519	0.16787	11.574	961		121.523	55.659	0.17838	13.492
922		111.874	48.698	0.16813	11.619	962		121.770	55.838	0.17863	13.543
923		112.121	48.877	0.16840	11.665	963		122.018	56.017	0.17889	13.594
924		112.368	49.056	0.16866	11.711	964		122.265	56.196	0.17914	13.645
925		112.615	+49.235	0.16893	11.756	965		122.513	+56.375	0.17940	13.696
926		112.862	49.414	0.16919	11.802	966		122.760	56.554	0.17965	13.747
927		113.109	49.593	0.16946	11.847	967		123.008	56.733	0.17991	13.799
928		113.356	49.772	0.16972	11.894	968		123.255	56.912	0.18016	13.850
929		113.603	49.951	0.16999	11.940	969		123.502	57.091	0.18042	13.902
930	470.3	113.850	+50.130	0.17025	11.987	970	510.3	123.750	+57.270	0.18067	13.954
931		114.097	50.309	0.17052	12.032	971		123.998	57.450	0.18093	14.006
932		114.344	50.488	0.17078	12.079	972		124.246	57.630	0.18118	14.059
933		114.591	50.667	0.17105	12.126	973		124.494	57.810	0.18144	14.111
934		114.838	50.846	0.17131	12.173	974		124.742	57.990	0.18169	14.163
935		115.085	+51.025	0.17158	12.220	975		124.990	+58.170	0.18195	14.216
936		115.332	51.204	0.17184	12.267	976		125.238	58.350	0.18220	14.269
937		115.579	51.383	0.17211	12.315	977		125.486	58.530	0.18246	14.315
938		115.826	51.562	0.17237	12.362	978		125.734	58.710	0.18271	14.367
939		116.073	51.741	0.17264	12.409	979		125.982	58.890	0.18297	14.421
940	480.3	116.320	+51.910	0.17291	12.457	980	520.3	126.230	+59.070	0.18323	14.474
941		116.568	52.089	0.17317	12.505	981		126.479	59.250	0.18348	14.528
942		116.816	52.268	0.17343	12.553	982		126.727	59.430	0.18373	14.581
943		117.064	52.447	0.17369	12.601	983		126.976	59.610	0.18398	14.635
944		117.312	52.626	0.17395	12.649	984		127.224	59.790	0.18423	14.689
945		117.560	+52.805	0.17421	12.697	985		127.473	+59.970	0.18449	14.744
946		117.808	52.984	0.17447	12.746	986		127.721	60.150	0.18474	14.798
947		118.056	53.163	0.17473	12.795	987		127.970	60.330	0.18499	14.852
948		118.304	53.342	0.17499	12.843	988		128.218	60.510	0.18524	14.907
949		118.552	53.521	0.17525	12.892	989		128.467	60.690	0.18549	14.962
950	490.3	118.800	+53.700	0.17551	12.941	990	530.3	128.715	+60.870	0.18574	15.016
951		119.048	53.879	0.17577	12.990	991		128.964	61.050	0.18599	15.072
952		119.295	54.058	0.17603	13.039	992		129.212	61.230	0.18624	15.126
953		119.543	54.237	0.17629	13.089	993		129.461	61.410	0.18649	15.182
954		119.790	54.416	0.17655	13.138	994		129.709	61.590	0.18674	15.237
955		120.038	+54.595	0.17681	13.189	995		129.958	+61.770	0.18700	15.293
956		120.285	54.774	0.17707	13.238	996		130.206	61.950	0.18725	15.349
957		120.533	54.953	0.17733	13.289	997		130.455	62.130	0.18750	15.405
958		120.780	55.132	0.17759	13.338	998		130.703	62.310	0.18775	15.460
959		121.028	55.311	0.17785	13.389	999		130.952	62.490	0.18800	15.517
Difference or c_p, c_v	$c_p =$ 0.247, 0.248	$c_v =$ 0.179	27–26				$c_p =$ 0.248, 0.249	$c_v =$ 0.179, 0.180	26–25		

TABLE A-3. THERMODYNAMIC PROPERTIES OF AIR AT LOW PRESSURES (*Continued*)

°R	°F	h, Btu per lb	u, Btu per lb	s_p	p_r	°R	°F	h, Btu per lb	u, Btu per lb	s_p	p_r
1000	540.3	131.200	+62.670	0.18825	15.582	1040	580.3	141.180	+69.910	0.19804	17.972
1001		131.449	62.851	0.18850	15.639	1041		141.430	70.092	0.19828	18.036
1002		131.698	63.032	0.18874	15.696	1042		141.680	70.274	0.19852	18.100
1003		131.947	63.213	0.18899	15.753	1043		141.930	70.456	0.19875	18.163
1004		132.196	63.394	0.18924	15.810	1044		142.180	70.638	0.19899	18.226
1005		132.445	+63.575	0.18949	15.867	1045		142.430	+70.820	0.19923	18.290
1006		132.694	63.756	0.18973	15.924	1046		142.680	71.002	0.19947	18.353
1007		132.943	63.937	0.18998	15.982	1047		142.930	71.184	0.19971	18.418
1008		133.192	64.118	0.19023	16.039	1048		143.180	71.366	0.19994	18.482
1009		133.441	64.299	0.19047	16.097	1049		143.430	71.548	0.20018	18.547
1010	550.3	133.690	+64.480	0.19072	16.156	1050	590.3	143.680	+71.730	0.20042	18.612
1011		133.939	64.661	0.19097	16.213	1051		143.930	71.912	0.20066	18.676
1012		134.189	64.842	0.19121	16.271	1052		144.180	72.094	0.20090	18.741
1013		134.439	65.023	0.19146	16.330	1053		144.430	72.276	0.20113	18.805
1014		134.688	65.204	0.19171	16.389	1054		144.680	72.458	0.20137	18.871
1015		134.938	+65.385	0.19196	16.447	1055		144.930	+72.640	0.20161	18.937
1016		135.187	65.566	0.19220	16.506	1056		145.180	72.822	0.20185	19.003
1017		135.436	65.747	0.19245	16.566	1057		145.430	73.004	0.20209	19.069
1018		135.686	65.928	0.19270	16.624	1058		145.680	73.186	0.20232	19.135
1019		135.935	66.109	0.19294	16.684	1059		145.930	73.368	0.20256	19.201
1020	560.3	136.185	+66.290	0.19319	16.743	1060	600.3	146.180	+73.550	0.20280	19.267
1021		136.434	66.471	0.19343	16.804	1061		146.431	73.732	0.20303	19.334
1022		136.684	66.652	0.19367	16.864	1062		146.682	73.914	0.20327	19.401
1023		136.934	66.833	0.19392	16.923	1063		146.933	74.096	0.20350	19.467
1024		137.183	67.014	0.19416	16.983	1064		147.184	74.278	0.20374	19.534
1025		137.433	+67.195	0.19440	17.044	1065		147.435	+74.460	0.20397	19.601
1026		137.682	67.376	0.19464	17.105	1066		147.686	74.642	0.20420	19.670
1027		137.931	67.577	0.19488	17.165	1067		147.937	74.824	0.20444	19.737
1028		138.181	67.738	0.19513	17.226	1068		148.188	75.006	0.20467	19.804
1029		138.430	67.919	0.19537	17.287	1069		148.439	75.188	0.20491	19.873
1030	570.3	138.680	+68.100	0.19561	17.348	1070	610.3	148.690	+75.370	0.20514	19.940
1031		138.930	68.281	0.19582	17.410	1071		148.941	75.552	0.20537	20.008
1032		139.179	68.462	0.19609	17.472	1072		149.192	75.734	0.20561	20.077
1033		139.429	68.643	0.19634	17.533	1073		149.443	75.916	0.20584	20.145
1034		139.678	68.824	0.19658	17.595	1074		149.694	76.098	0.20608	20.213
1035		139.928	+69.005	0.19682	17.656	1075		149.945	+76.280	0.20631	20.283
1036		140.177	69.186	0.19706	17.718	1076		150.196	76.462	0.20654	20.353
1037		140.427	69.367	0.19730	17.781	1077		150.447	76.644	0.20678	20.421
1038		140.676	69.548	0.19755	17.843	1078		150.698	76.826	0.20701	20.491
1039		140.926	69.729	0.19779	17.905	1079		150.949	77.008	0.20725	20.561
Difference or c_p, c_v		$c_p =$ 0.249, 0.250	$c_v =$ 0.181	25–24				$c_p =$ 0.250, 0.251	$c_v =$ 0.182	24	

TABLE A-3. THERMODYNAMIC PROPERTIES OF AIR AT LOW PRESSURES (*Continued*)

°R	°F	h, Btu per lb	u, Btu per lb	s_p	p_r	°R	°F	h, Btu per lb	u, Btu per lb	s_p	p_r
1080	620.3	151.200	+77.190	0.20749	20.630	1115		160.010	+83.610	0.21552	23.193
1081		151.451	77.373	0.20772	20.699	1116		160.262	83.794	0.21574	23.269
1082		151.702	77.556	0.20795	20.770	1117		160.514	83.978	0.21597	23.346
1083		151.953	77.739	0.20818	20.841	1118		160.766	84.162	0.21620	23.423
1084		152.204	77.922	0.20841	20.912	1119		161.018	84.346	0.21642	23.501
1085		152.455	+78.105	0.20865	20.983	1120	660.3	161.270	+84.530	0.21665	23.578
1086		152.706	78.288	0.20888	21.054	1121		161.523	84.714	0.21687	23.655
1087		152.957	78.471	0.20911	21.125	1122		161.776	84.898	0.21710	23.734
1088		153.208	78.654	0.20934	21.196	1123		162.029	85.082	0.21732	23.811
1089		153.459	78.837	0.20957	21.267	1124		162.282	85.266	0.21754	23.890
1090	630.3	153.710	+79.020	0.20980	21.339	1125		162.535	+85.450	0.21777	23.968
1091		153.962	79.203	0.21003	21.412	1126		162.788	85.634	0.21799	24.047
1092		154.214	79.386	0.21026	21.484	1127		163.041	85.818	0.21821	24.125
1093		154.466	79.569	0.21049	21.556	1128		163.294	86.002	0.21843	24.204
1094		154.718	79.752	0.21072	21.628	1129		163.547	86.186	0.21866	24.283
1095		154.970	+79.935	0.21096	21.702	1130	670.3	163.800	+86.370	0.21888	24.362
1096		155.222	80.118	0.21119	21.774	1131		164.053	86.554	0.21910	24.442
1097		155.474	80.301	0.21142	21.848	1132		164.306	86.738	0.21933	24.522
1098		155.726	80.484	0.21165	21.921	1133		164.559	86.922	0.21955	24.602
1099		155.978	80.667	0.21188	21.995	1134		164.812	87.106	0.21977	24.682
1100	640.3	156.230	+80.850	0.21211	22.068	1135		165.065	+87.290	0.22000	24.762
1101		156.482	81.034	0.21234	22.142	1136		165.318	87.474	0.22022	24.843
1102		156.734	81.218	0.21256	22.215	1137		165.571	87.658	0.22044	24.924
1103		156.986	81.402	0.21279	22.289	1138		165.824	87.842	0.22066	25.005
1104		157.238	81.586	0.21302	22.362	1139		166.077	88.026	0.22089	25.086
1105		157.490	+81.770	0.21325	22.437	1140	680.3	166.330	+88.210	0.22112	25.167
1106		157.742	81.954	0.21347	22.512	1141		166.583	88.395	0.22133	25.248
1107		157.994	82.138	0.21370	22.586	1142		166.836	88.580	0.22156	25.331
1108		158.246	82.322	0.21393	22.661	1143		167.089	88.765	0.22178	25.412
1109		158.498	82.506	0.21415	22.736	1144		167.342	88.950	0.22200	25.494
1110	650.3	158.750	+82.690	0.21438	22.812	1145		167.595	+89.135	0.22222	25.577
1111		159.002	82.874	0.21461	22.888	1146		167.848	89.320	0.22244	25.659
1112		159.254	83.058	0.21483	22.964	1147		168.101	89.505	0.22266	25.741
1113		159.506	83.242	0.21506	23.040	1148		168.354	89.690	0.22288	25.825
1114		159.758	83.426	0.21529	23.116	1149		168.607	89.875	0.22310	25.909
Difference or c_p, c_v		$c_p =$ 0.251, 0.252	$c_v =$ 0.183, 0.184	23				$c_p =$ 0.252, 0.253	$c_v =$ 0.184, 0.185	22	

TABLE A-3. THERMODYNAMIC PROPERTIES OF AIR AT LOW PRESSURES (*Continued*)

°R	°F	h, Btu per lb	u, Btu per lb	s_p	p_r	°R	°F	h, Btu per lb	u, Btu per lb	s_p	p_r
1150	690.3	168.860	+90.060	0.22332	25.994	1190	730.3	179.020	+97.470	0.23201	29.507
1151		169.114	90.245	0.22354	26.070	1191		179.275	97.656	0.23222	29.596
1152		169.367	90.430	0.22376	26.159	1192		179.530	97.842	0.23244	29.685
1153		169.621	90.615	0.22398	26.248	1193		179.785	98.028	0.23265	29.774
1154		169.874	90.800	0.22420	26.324	1194		180.040	98.214	0.23287	29.875
1155		170.128	+90.985	0.22442	26.413	1195		180.295	+98.400	0.23308	29.964
1156		170.381	91.170	0.22464	26.501	1196		180.550	98.586	0.23329	30.052
1157		170.634	91.355	0.22486	26.577	1197		180.805	98.772	0.23351	30.154
1158		170.888	91.540	0.22508	26.666	1198		181.060	98.958	0.23372	30.243
1159		171.142	91.725	0.22530	26.755	1199		181.315	99.144	0.23394	30.344
1160	700.3	171.395	+91.910	0.22553	26.844	1200	740.3	181.570	+99.330	0.23415	30.433
1161		171.649	92.095	0.22575	26.920	1201		181.825	99.517	0.23436	30.521
1162		171.902	92.280	0.22596	27.008	1202		182.080	99.704	0.23457	30.623
1163		172.156	92.465	0.22618	27.097	1203		182.335	99.891	0.23478	30.712
1164		172.409	92.650	0.22640	27.186	1204		182.590	100.078	0.23499	30.813
1165		172.663	+92.835	0.22662	27.262	1205		182.845	+100.265	0.23521	30.902
1166		172.916	93.020	0.22683	27.350	1206		183.100	100.452	0.23542	31.003
1167		173.169	93.205	0.22705	27.439	1207		183.355	100.639	0.23563	31.092
1168		173.423	93.390	0.22727	27.528	1208		183.610	100.826	0.23584	31.193
1169		173.676	93.575	0.22748	27.617	1209		183.865	101.013	0.23605	31.295
1170	710.3	173.930	+93.760	0.22770	27.705	1210	750.3	184.120	+101.200	0.23626	31.383
1171		174.184	93.945	0.22792	27.794	1211		184.375	101.387	0.23647	31.485
1172		174.438	94.130	0.22813	27.883	1212		184.630	101.574	0.23668	31.573
1173		174.692	94.315	0.22835	27.972	1213		184.885	101.761	0.23689	31.675
1174		174.946	94.500	0.22857	28.060	1214		185.140	101.948	0.23710	31.776
1175		175.200	+94.685	0.22879	28.149	1215		185.395	+102.135	0.23732	31.865
1176		175.454	94.870	0.22900	28.238	1216		185.650	102.322	0.23753	31.966
1177		175.708	95.055	0.22922	28.326	1217		185.905	102.509	0.23774	32.068
1178		175.962	95.240	0.22944	28.415	1218		186.160	102.696	0.23795	32.169
1179		176.216	95.425	0.22965	28.504	1219		186.415	102.883	0.23816	32.271
1180	720.3	176.470	+95.610	0.22987	28.593	1220	760.3	186.670	+103.070	0.23837	32.359
1181		176.725	95.796	0.23008	28.681	1221		186.926	103.257	0.23858	32.461
1182		176.980	95.982	0.23030	28.770	1222		187.182	103.444	0.23879	32.562
1183		177.235	96.168	0.23051	28.859	1223		187.438	103.631	0.23899	32.663
1184		177.490	96.354	0.23073	28.947	1224		187.694	103.818	0.23920	32.765
1185		177.745	+96.540	0.23094	29.036	1225		187.950	+104.005	0.23941	32.854
1186		178.000	96.726	0.23115	29.138	1226		188.206	104.192	0.23962	32.955
1187		178.255	96.912	0.23137	29.226	1227		188.462	104.379	0.23982	33.056
1188		178.510	97.098	0.23158	29.315	1228		188.718	104.566	0.24003	33.158
1189		178.765	97.284	0.23180	29.404	1229		188.974	104.753	0.24024	33.259
Difference or c_p, c_v		c_p = 0.254, 0.255	c_v = 0.185, 0.186	22				c_p = 0.255, 0.256	c_v = 0.186, 0.187	21	

TABLE A-3. THERMODYNAMIC PROPERTIES OF AIR AT LOW PRESSURES (*Continued*)

°R	°F	h, Btu per lb	u, Btu per lb	s_p	p_r	°R	°F	h, Btu per lb	u, Btu per lb	s_p	p_r
1230	770.3	189.230	+104.940	0.24045	33.363	1270	810.3	199.500	+112.470	0.24866	37.613
1231		189.486	105.127	0.24066	33.465	1271		199.757	112.659	0.24886	37.727
1232		189.742	105.314	0.24087	33.566	1272		200.014	112.848	0.24907	37.828
1233		189.998	105.501	0.24107	33.667	1273		200.271	113.037	0.24927	37.942
1234		190.254	105.688	0.24128	33.769	1274		200.528	113.226	0.24947	38.056
1235		190.510	+105.875	0.24149	33.870	1275		200.785	+113.415	0.24968	38.170
1236		190.766	106.062	0.24170	33.972	1276		201.042	113.604	0.24988	38.285
1237		191.022	106.249	0.24191	34.086	1277		201.299	113.793	0.25008	38.399
1238		191.278	106.436	0.24211	34.187	1278		201.556	113.982	0.25028	38.513
1239		191.534	106.623	0.24232	34.289	1279		201.813	114.171	0.25049	38.627
1240	780.3	191.790	+106.810	0.24253	34.390	1280	820.3	202.070	+114.360	0.25069	38.728
1241		192.047	106.998	0.24274	34.491	1281		202.328	114.549	0.25089	38.842
1242		192.304	107.186	0.24294	34.593	1282		202.586	114.738	0.25109	38.956
1243		192.561	107.374	0.24315	34.707	1283		202.844	114.927	0.25129	39.070
1244		192.818	107.562	0.24335	34.808	1284		203.102	115.116	0.25149	39.185
1245		193.075	+107.750	0.24356	34.910	1285		203.360	+115.305	0.25169	39.311
1246		193.332	107.938	0.24376	35.011	1286		203.618	115.494	0.25188	39.425
1247		193.589	108.126	0.24397	35.125	1287		203.876	115.683	0.25208	39.540
1248		193.846	108.314	0.24417	35.227	1288		204.134	115.872	0.25228	39.654
1249		194.103	108.502	0.24438	35.328	1289		204.392	116.061	0.25248	39.768
1250	790.3	194.360	+108.690	0.24458	35.442	1290	830.3	204.650	+116.250	0.25268	39.882
1251		194.617	108.879	0.24479	35.544	1291		204.908	116.440	0.25288	39.996
1252		194.874	109.068	0.24499	35.645	1292		205.166	116.630	0.25308	40.123
1253		195.131	109.257	0.24520	35.759	1293		205.424	116.820	0.25328	40.237
1254		195.388	109.446	0.24540	35.860	1294		205.682	117.010	0.25348	40.351
1255		195.645	+109.635	0.24561	35.974	1295		205.940	+117.200	0.25368	40.465
1256		195.902	109.824	0.24581	36.076	1296		206.198	117.390	0.25387	40.592
1257		196.159	110.013	0.24602	36.190	1297		206.456	117.580	0.25407	40.706
1258		196.416	110.202	0.24622	36.291	1298		206.714	117.770	0.25427	40.820
1259		196.673	110.391	0.24643	36.405	1299		206.972	117.960	0.25447	40.947
1260	800.3	196.930	+110.580	0.24663	36.507	1300	840.3	207.230	+118.150	0.25468	41.061
1261		197.187	110.769	0.24683	36.621	1301		207.488	118.340	0.25488	41.175
1262		197.444	110.958	0.24704	36.722	1302		207.746	118.530	0.25507	41.302
1263		197.701	111.147	0.24724	36.836	1303		208.004	118.720	0.25527	41.416
1264		197.958	111.336	0.24744	36.951	1304		208.262	118.910	0.25547	41.530
1265		198.215	+111.525	0.24765	37.052	1305		208.520	+119.100	0.25567	41.657
1266		198.472	111.714	0.24785	37.166	1306		208.778	119.290	0.25586	41.783
1267		198.729	111.903	0.24805	37.280	1307		209.036	119.480	0.25606	41.897
1268		198.986	112.092	0.24825	37.382	1308		209.294	119.670	0.25626	42.024
1269		199.243	112.281	0.24846	37.496	1309		209.552	119.860	0.25645	42.138
Difference or c_p, c_v		$c_p =$ 0.256, 0.257	$c_v =$ 0.187, 0.189	21				$c_p =$ 0.257, 0.258	$c_v =$ 0.189, 0.190	20	

TABLE A-3. THERMODYNAMIC PROPERTIES OF AIR AT LOW PRESSURES (*Continued*)

°R	°F	h, Btu per lb	u, Btu per lb	s_p	p_r	°R	°F	h, Btu per lb	u, Btu per lb	s_p	p_r
1310	850.3	209.810	+120.050	0.25665	42.268	1345		218.890	+126.715	0.26347	46.694
1311		210.068	120.240	0.25685	42.383	1346		219.150	126.906	0.26366	46.821
1312		210.326	120.430	0.25704	42.509	1347		219.410	127.097	0.26385	46.948
1313		210.584	120.620	0.25724	42.623	1348		219.670	127.288	0.26405	47.087
1314		210.842	120.810	0.25744	42.750	1349		219.930	127.479	0.26424	47.214
1315		211.101	+121.000	0.25764	42.877	1350	890.3	220.190	+127.670	0.26443	47.353
1316		211.360	121.190	0.25783	43.000	1351		220.450	127.861	0.26462	47.480
1317		211.619	121.380	0.25803	43.121	1352		220.710	128.052	0.26481	47.620
1318		211.878	121.570	0.25823	43.245	1353		220.970	128.243	0.26501	47.746
1319		212.137	121.760	0.25842	43.369	1354		221.230	128.434	0.26520	47.886
1320	860.3	212.396	+121.950	0.25862	43.490	1355		221.490	+128.625	0.26539	48.013
1321		212.656	122.140	0.25881	43.612	1356		221.750	128.816	0.26558	48.152
1322		212.916	122.331	0.25901	43.739	1357		222.010	129.007	0.26577	48.292
1323		213.176	122.522	0.25920	43.866	1358		222.270	129.198	0.26597	48.418
1324		213.436	122.712	0.25940	43.993	1359		222.530	129.389	0.26616	48.558
1325		213.695	+122.903	0.25959	44.119	1360	900.3	222.790	+129.590	0.26636	48.697
1326		213.954	123.093	0.25978	44.246	1361		223.050	129.782	0.26655	48.824
1327		214.213	123.284	0.25998	44.373	1362		223.310	129.974	0.26674	48.964
1328		214.472	123.474	0.26017	44.500	1363		223.570	130.166	0.26693	49.103
1329		214.731	123.665	0.26037	44.627	1364		223.830	130.358	0.26712	49.243
1330	870.3	214.990	+123.855	0.26056	44.753	1365		224.090	+130.550	0.26731	49.369
1331		215.250	124.046	0.26075	44.880	1366		224.350	130.742	0.26750	49.509
1332		215.510	124.236	0.26095	45.007	1367		224.610	130.934	0.26769	49.648
1333		215.770	124.427	0.26114	45.134	1368		224.870	131.126	0.26788	49.788
1334		216.030	124.617	0.26134	45.260	1369		225.130	131.318	0.26807	49.927
1335		216.290	+124.807	0.26153	45.387	1370	910.3	225.390	+131.510	0.26826	50.067
1336		216.550	124.998	0.26172	45.514	1371		225.650	131.702	0.26845	50.206
1337		216.810	125.189	0.26192	45.641	1372		225.910	131.894	0.26864	50.346
1338		217.070	125.379	0.26211	45.780	1373		226.170	132.086	0.26883	50.485
1339		217.330	125.569	0.26231	45.907	1374		226.430	132.278	0.26902	50.624
1340	880.3	217.590	+125.760	0.26251	46.034	1375		226.690	+132.470	0.26921	50.764
1341		217.850	125.951	0.26270	46.161	1376		226.950	132.662	0.26940	50.903
1342		218.110	126.142	0.26289	46.300	1377		227.210	132.854	0.26959	51.043
1343		218.370	126.333	0.26309	46.427	1378		227.470	133.046	0.26978	51.182
1344		218.630	126.524	0.26328	46.554	1379		227.730	133.238	0.26997	51.322
Difference or c_p, c_v		c_p = 0.258, 0.260	c_v = 0.190, 0.191	19				c_p = 0.260	c_v = 0.191, 0.192	19	

TABLE A-3. THERMODYNAMIC PROPERTIES OF AIR AT LOW PRESSURES (*Continued*)

°R	°F	h, Btu per lb	u, Btu per lb	s_p	p_r	°R	°F	h, Btu per lb	u, Btu per lb	s_p	p_r
1380	920.3	227.990	+133.430	0.27016	51.464	1420	960.3	238.450	+141.140	0.27763	57.394
1381		228.251	133.622	0.27035	51.616	1421		238.712	141.334	0.27781	57.546
1382		228.512	133.814	0.27054	51.756	1422		238.974	141.528	0.27800	57.711
1383		228.773	134.006	0.27072	51.895	1423		239.236	141.722	0.27818	57.863
1384		229.034	134.198	0.27091	52.035	1424		239.498	141.916	0.27836	58.016
1385		229.295	+134.390	0.27110	52.187	1425		239.760	+142.110	0.27855	58.168
1386		229.556	134.582	0.27129	52.326	1426		240.022	142.304	0.27873	58.333
1387		229.817	134.774	0.27148	52.466	1427		240.284	142.498	0.27891	58.485
1388		230.078	134.966	0.27166	52.618	1428		240.546	142.692	0.27909	58.637
1389		230.339	135.158	0.27185	52.757	1429		240.808	142.886	0.27928	58.802
1390	930.3	230.600	+135.350	0.27204	52.909	1430	970.3	241.070	+143.080	0.27946	58.954
1391		230.861	135.542	0.27223	53.049	1431		241.332	143.274	0.27964	59.119
1392		231.122	135.734	0.27242	53.188	1432		241.594	143.468	0.27983	59.271
1393		231.383	135.926	0.27260	53.341	1433		241.856	143.662	0.28001	59.436
1394		231.644	136.118	0.27279	53.480	1434		242.118	143.856	0.28019	59.588
1395		231.905	+136.310	0.27298	53.632	1435		242.380	+144.050	0.28038	59.753
1396		232.166	136.502	0.27317	53.772	1436		242.642	144.244	0.28056	59.905
1397		232.427	136.694	0.27336	53.924	1437		242.904	144.438	0.28074	60.070
1398		232.688	136.886	0.27354	54.076	1438		243.166	144.632	0.28092	60.222
1399		232.949	137.078	0.27373	54.215	1439		243.428	144.826	0.28111	60.387
1400	940.3	233.210	+137.280	0.27392	54.368	1440	980.3	243.690	+145.020	0.28130	60.552
1401		233.472	137.473	0.27411	54.520	1441		243.953	145.214	0.28148	60.704
1402		233.734	137.666	0.27429	54.659	1442		244.216	145.408	0.28168	60.869
1403		233.996	137.859	0.27448	54.811	1443		244.479	145.602	0.28184	61.034
1404		234.258	138.052	0.27466	54.963	1444		244.742	145.796	0.28202	61.199
1405		234.520	+138.245	0.27485	55.116	1445		245.005	+145.990	0.28221	61.363
1406		234.782	138.438	0.27503	55.255	1446		245.268	146.184	0.28239	61.516
1407		235.044	138.631	0.27522	55.407	1447		245.531	146.378	0.28257	61.680
1408		235.306	138.824	0.27540	55.559	1448		245.794	146.572	0.28275	61.845
1409		235.568	139.017	0.27559	55.712	1449		246.057	146.766	0.28293	62.010
1410	950.3	235.830	+139.210	0.27577	55.864	1450	990.3	246.320	+146.960	0.28311	62.175
1411		236.092	139.403	0.27596	56.016	1451		246.583	147.154	0.28329	62.340
1412		236.354	139.596	0.27614	56.168	1452		246.846	147.348	0.28347	62.505
1413		236.616	139.789	0.27633	56.320	1453		247.109	147.542	0.28365	62.670
1414		236.878	139.982	0.27651	56.472	1454		247.372	147.736	0.28383	62.834
1415		237.140	+140.175	0.27670	56.624	1455		247.635	+147.930	0.28402	62.999
1416		237.402	140.368	0.27688	56.777	1456		247.898	148.124	0.28420	63.177
1417		237.664	140.561	0.27707	56.929	1457		248.161	148.318	0.28438	63.342
1418		237.926	140.754	0.27725	57.081	1458		248.424	148.512	0.28456	63.506
1419		238.188	140.947	0.27744	57.233	1459		248.687	148.706	0.28474	63.671
Difference or c_p, c_v		$c_p =$ 0.261, 0.262	$c_v =$ 0.192, 0.193	19				$c_p =$ 0.262, 0.263	$c_v =$ 0.194	18	

TABLE A-3. THERMODYNAMIC PROPERTIES OF AIR AT LOW PRESSURES (*Continued*)

°R	°F	h, Btu per lb	u, Btu per lb	s_p	p_r	°R	°F	h, Btu per lb	u, Btu per lb	s_p	p_r
1460	1000.3	248.950	+148.900	0.28493	63.844	1495		258.180	+155.740	0.29117	69.943
1461		249.213	149.095	0.28511	64.009	1496		258.444	155.936	0.29134	70.121
1462		249.476	149.290	0.28529	64.186	1497		258.708	156.132	0.29152	70.311
1463		249.739	149.485	0.28547	64.351	1498		258.972	156.328	0.29170	70.489
1464		250.002	149.680	0.28565	64.516	1499		259.236	156.524	0.29187	70.666
1465		250.265	+149.875	0.28583	64.693	1500	1040.3	259.500	+156.720	0.29206	70.857
1466		250.528	150.070	0.28600	64.858	1501		259.765	156.916	0.29224	71.034
1467		250.791	150.265	0.28618	65.023	1502		260.030	157.112	0.29241	71.212
1468		251.054	150.460	0.28636	65.201	1503		260.295	157.308	0.29259	71.402
1469		251.317	150.655	0.28654	65.366	1504		260.560	157.504	0.29276	71.580
1470	1010.3	251.580	+150.850	0.28672	65.543	1505		260.825	+157.700	0.29294	71.770
1471		251.844	151.045	0.28690	65.721	1506		261.090	157.896	0.29311	71.948
1472		252.108	151.240	0.28708	65.886	1507		261.355	158.092	0.29329	72.138
1473		252.372	151.435	0.28726	66.050	1508		261.620	158.288	0.29346	72.315
1474		252.636	151.630	0.28744	66.228	1509		261.885	158.484	0.29364	72.506
1475		252.900	+151.825	0.28762	66.406	1510	1050.3	262.150	+158.680	0.29381	72.683
1476		253.164	152.020	0.28779	66.570	1511		262.415	158.876	0.29399	72.874
1477		253.428	152.215	0.28797	66.748	1512		262.680	159.072	0.29416	73.064
1478		253.692	152.410	0.28815	66.926	1513		262.945	159.268	0.29434	73.241
1479		253.956	152.605	0.28833	67.103	1514		263.210	159.464	0.29451	73.432
1480	1020.3	254.220	+152.800	0.28851	67.270	1515		263.475	+159.660	0.29469	73.622
1481		254.484	152.996	0.28869	67.446	1516		263.740	159.856	0.29486	73.812
1482		254.748	153.192	0.28886	67.623	1517		264.005	160.052	0.29504	74.003
1483		255.012	153.388	0.28904	67.801	1518		264.270	160.248	0.29521	74.193
1484		255.276	153.584	0.28922	67.978	1519		264.535	160.444	0.29539	74.370
1485		255.540	+153.780	0.28940	68.143	1520	1060.3	264.800	+160.640	0.29556	74.561
1486		255.804	153.976	0.28957	68.321	1521		265.065	160.837	0.29573	74.751
1487		256.068	154.172	0.28975	68.498	1522		265.330	161.034	0.29591	74.941
1488		256.332	154.368	0.28993	68.676	1523		265.595	161.231	0.29608	75.131
1489		256.596	154.564	0.29010	68.853	1524		265.860	161.428	0.29625	75.322
1490	1030.3	256.860	+154.760	0.29028	69.031	1525		266.125	+161.625	0.29643	75.512
1491		257.124	154.956	0.29046	69.221	1526		266.390	161.822	0.29660	75.715
1492		257.388	155.125	0.29063	69.399	1527		266.655	162.019	0.29677	75.905
1493		257.652	155.348	0.29081	69.576	1528		266.920	162.216	0.29694	76.096
1494		257.916	155.544	0.29099	69.754	1529		267.185	162.413	0.29712	76.286
Difference or c_p, c_v		c_p = 0.263, 0.264	c_v = 0.195, 0.196	18				c_p = 0.264, 0.265	c_v = 0.196, 0.197	17	

TABLE A-3. THERMODYNAMIC PROPERTIES OF AIR AT LOW PRESSURES (*Continued*)

°R	°F	h, Btu per lb	u, Btu per lb	s_p	p_r	°R	°F	h, Btu per lb	u, Btu per lb	s_p	p_r
1530	1070.3	267.450	+162.610	0.29729	76.478	1570	1110.3	278.090	+170.500	0.30416	84.525
1531		267.716	162.807	0.29746	76.681	1571		278.367	170.699	0.30433	84.741
1532		267.982	163.004	0.29764	76.871	1572		278.634	170.897	0.30450	84.957
1533		268.248	163.201	0.29781	77.061	1573		278.901	171.096	0.30467	85.160
1534		268.514	163.398	0.29798	77.264	1574		279.168	171.294	0.30484	85.375
1535		268.780	+163.595	0.29816	77.455	1575		279.435	+171.493	0.30501	85.578
1536		269.046	163.792	0.29833	77.645	1576		279.702	171.691	0.30517	85.794
1537		269.312	163.989	0.29850	77.848	1577		279.969	171.890	0.30534	86.010
1538		269.578	164.186	0.29867	78.038	1578		280.236	172.088	0.30551	86.225
1539		269.844	164.383	0.29885	78.241	1579		280.503	172.287	0.30568	86.428
1540	1080.3	270.110	+164.580	0.29903	78.431	1580	1120.3	280.760	+172.485	0.30586	86.644
1541		270.376	164.777	0.29920	78.634	1581		281.027	172.684	0.30603	86.860
1542		270.642	164.974	0.29937	78.825	1582		281.294	172.882	0.30620	87.075
1543		270.908	165.171	0.29955	79.028	1583		281.561	173.081	0.30636	87.291
1544		271.174	165.368	0.29972	79.231	1584		281.828	173.279	0.30653	87.507
1545		271.440	+165.565	0.29989	79.421	1585		282.095	+173.478	0.30670	87.722
1546		271.706	165.762	0.30006	79.624	1586		282.362	173.676	0.30687	87.938
1547		271.972	165.959	0.30023	79.827	1587		282.629	173.875	0.30704	88.154
1548		272.238	166.156	0.30041	80.030	1588		282.896	174.073	0.30720	88.369
1549		272.504	166.353	0.30058	80.220	1589		283.163	174.272	0.30737	88.585
1550	1090.3	272.770	+166.550	0.30075	80.423	1590	1130.3	283.430	+174.470	0.30754	88.801
1551		273.036	166.747	0.30092	80.626	1591		283.697	174.669	0.30771	89.016
1552		273.302	166.944	0.30109	80.829	1592		283.964	174.868	0.30788	89.232
1553		273.568	167.141	0.30127	81.032	1593		284.231	175.067	0.30804	89.448
1554		273.834	167.338	0.30144	81.235	1594		284.498	175.266	0.30821	89.670
1555		274.100	+167.535	0.30161	81.438	1595		284.765	+175.465	0.30838	89.886
1556		274.366	167.732	0.30178	81.641	1596		285.032	175.664	0.30855	90.106
1557		274.632	167.929	0.30195	81.844	1597		285.299	175.863	0.30872	90.330
1558		274.898	168.126	0.30213	82.047	1598		285.566	176.062	0.30888	90.546
1559		275.164	168.323	0.30230	82.250	1599		285.833	176.261	0.30905	90.766
1560	1100.3	275.430	+168.520	0.30247	82.453	1600	1140.3	286.100	+176.460	0.30922	90.990
1561		275.697	168.718	0.30264	82.655	1601		286.368	176.659	0.30939	91.209
1562		275.964	168.916	0.30281	82.871	1602		286.636	176.858	0.30955	91.433
1563		276.231	169.114	0.30298	83.074	1603		286.904	177.057	0.30972	91.652
1564		276.498	169.312	0.30315	83.277	1604		287.172	177.256	0.30988	91.877
1565		276.765	+169.510	0.30332	83.480	1605		287.440	+177.455	0.31005	92.106
1566		277.032	169.708	0.30348	83.696	1606		287.708	177.654	0.31022	92.321
1567		277.299	169.906	0.30365	83.899	1607		287.976	177.853	0.31038	92.550
1568		277.566	170.104	0.30382	84.114	1608		288.244	178.052	0.31055	92.778
1569		277.833	170.302	0.30399	84.317	1609		288.512	178.251	0.31071	92.994
Difference or c_p, c_v		$c_p =$ 0.266	$c_v =$ 0.197, 0.198	17				$c_p =$ 0.267, 0.268	$c_v =$ 0.198, 0.199	16	

APPENDIX 375

TABLE A-3. THERMODYNAMIC PROPERTIES OF AIR AT LOW PRESSURES (Continued)

°R	°F	h, Btu per lb	u, Btu per lb	s_p	p_r	°R	°F	h, Btu per lb	u, Btu per lb	s_p	p_r
1610	1150.3	288.780	+178.450	0.31088	93.244	1650	1190.3	299.515	+186.440	0.31747	102.647
1611		289.048	178.649	0.31105	93.472	1651		299.784	186.640	0.31763	102.888
1612		289.316	178.848	0.31121	93.701	1652		300.052	186.840	0.31780	103.129
1613		289.584	179.047	0.31138	93.929	1653		300.321	187.040	0.31796	103.383
1614		289.852	179.246	0.31154	94.158	1654		300.589	187.240	0.31812	103.624
1615		290.120	+179.445	0.31171	94.386	1655		300.858	+187.441	0.31829	103.865
1616		290.388	179.644	0.31188	94.614	1656		301.126	187.643	0.31845	104.119
1617		290.656	179.843	0.31204	94.843	1657		301.395	187.845	0.31861	104.360
1618		290.924	180.042	0.31221	95.071	1658		301.663	188.047	0.31877	104.614
1619		291.192	180.241	0.31237	95.300	1659		301.932	188.249	0.31894	104.855
1620	1160.3	291.460	+180.440	0.31255	95.528	1660	1200.3	302.200	+188.450	0.31910	105.109
1621		291.728	180.640	0.31271	95.756	1661		302.469	188.651	0.31926	105.350
1622		291.996	180.840	0.31288	95.985	1662		302.738	188.852	0.31942	105.604
1623		292.264	181.040	0.31304	96.226	1663		303.007	189.053	0.31958	105.857
1624		292.532	181.240	0.31321	96.454	1664		303.276	189.254	0.31974	106.099
1625		292.800	+181.440	0.31337	96.683	1665		303.545	+189.455	0.31991	106.352
1626		293.068	181.640	0.31353	96.911	1666		303.814	189.656	0.32007	106.606
1627		293.336	181.840	0.31370	97.152	1667		304.083	189.857	0.32023	106.860
1628		293.604	182.040	0.31386	97.380	1668		304.352	190.058	0.32039	107.114
1629		293.872	182.240	0.31403	97.621	1669		304.621	190.259	0.32055	107.355
1630	1170.3	294.140	+182.440	0.31419	97.850	1670	1210.3	304.890	+190.460	0.32071	107.609
1631		294.408	182.640	0.31435	98.091	1671		305.160	190.661	0.32087	107.862
1632		294.676	182.840	0.31452	98.319	1672		305.430	190.862	0.32103	108.116
1633		294.944	183.040	0.31468	98.560	1673		305.700	191.063	0.32119	108.370
1634		295.212	183.240	0.31485	98.801	1674		305.970	191.264	0.32135	108.624
1635		295.480	+183.440	0.31501	99.030	1675		306.240	+191.465	0.32152	108.878
1636		295.748	183.640	0.31517	99.271	1676		306.510	191.666	0.32168	109.144
1637		296.016	183.840	0.31534	99.639	1677		306.780	191.867	0.32184	109.398
1638		296.284	184.040	0.31550	99.740	1678		307.050	192.068	0.32200	109.652
1639		296.552	184.240	0.31567	99.981	1679		307.320	192.269	0.32216	109.905
1640	1180.3	296.830	+184.440	0.31584	100.223	1680	1220.3	307.590	+192.470	0.32233	110.172
1641		297.099	184.640	0.31600	100.464	1681		307.860	192.671	0.32249	110.426
1642		297.367	184.840	0.31617	100.705	1682		308.130	192.872	0.32265	110.680
1643		297.636	185.040	0.31633	100.946	1683		308.400	193.073	0.32281	110.946
1644		297.904	185.240	0.31649	101.187	1684		308.670	193.274	0.32297	111.200
1645		298.173	+185.440	0.31666	101.428	1685		308.940	+193.475	0.32313	111.466
1646		298.441	185.640	0.31682	101.669	1686		309.210	193.676	0.32328	111.720
1647		298.710	185.840	0.31698	101.910	1687		309.480	193.877	0.32344	111.987
1648		298.978	186.040	0.31714	102.151	1688		309.750	194.078	0.32360	112.240
1649		299.247	186.240	0.31731	102.392	1689		310.020	194.279	0.32376	112.507
Difference or c_p, c_v		$c_p =$ 0.268, 0.269	$c_v =$ 0.199, 0.200	17				$c_p =$ 0.269, 0.270	$c_v =$ 0.200, 0.201	16	

TABLE A-3. THERMODYNAMIC PROPERTIES OF AIR AT LOW PRESSURES (*Continued*)

°R	°F	h, Btu per lb	u, Btu per lb	s_p	p_r	°R	°F	h, Btu per lb	u, Btu per lb	s_p	p_r
1690	1230.3	310.290	+194.480	0.32392	112.794	1730	1270.3	321.110	+202.560	0.33025	123.703
1691		310.560	194.682	0.32408	113.048	1731		321.381	202.763	0.33041	123.982
1692		310.830	194.884	0.32424	113.312	1732		321.652	202.966	0.33056	124.262
1693		311.100	195.086	0.32440	113.581	1733		321.923	203.169	0.33072	124.554
1694		311.370	195.288	0.32456	113.847	1734		322.194	203.372	0.33087	124.833
1695		311.640	+195.490	0.32472	114.114	1735		322.465	+203.575	0.33103	125.125
1696		311.910	195.692	0.32487	114.368	1736		322.736	203.778	0.33119	125.404
1697		312.180	195.894	0.32503	114.634	1737		323.007	203.981	0.33134	125.683
1698		312.450	196.096	0.32519	114.901	1738		323.278	204.184	0.33150	125.975
1699		312.720	196.298	0.32535	115.167	1739		323.549	204.387	0.33165	126.267
1700	1240.3	312.990	+196.500	0.32552	115.434	1740	1280.3	323.820	+204.590	0.33182	126.546
1701		313.261	196.702	0.32568	115.700	1741		324.092	204.793	0.33198	126.838
1702		313.532	196.904	0.32584	115.967	1742		324.364	204.996	0.33213	127.118
1703		313.803	197.106	0.32599	116.246	1743		324.636	205.199	0.33229	127.410
1704		314.074	197.308	0.32615	116.513	1744		324.908	205.402	0.33244	127.702
1705		314.345	+197.510	0.32631	116.780	1745		325.180	+205.605	0.33260	127.994
1706		314.616	197.712	0.32647	117.046	1746		325.452	205.808	0.33275	128.286
1707		314.887	197.914	0.32663	117.325	1747		325.724	206.011	0.33291	128.578
1708		315.158	198.116	0.32678	117.591	1748		325.996	206.214	0.33306	128.869
1709		315.429	198.318	0.32696	117.858	1749		326.268	206.417	0.33322	129.161
1710	1250.3	315.700	+198.520	0.32710	118.137	1750	1290.3	326.540	+206.620	0.33337	129.453
1711		315.971	198.722	0.32726	118.404	1751		326.812	206.823	0.33353	129.745
1712		316.241	198.924	0.32742	118.683	1752		327.084	207.026	0.33368	130.037
1713		316.512	199.126	0.32757	118.949	1753		327.356	207.229	0.33384	130.329
1714		316.782	199.328	0.32773	119.229	1754		327.628	207.432	0.33399	130.621
1715		317.053	+199.530	0.32789	119.508	1755		327.900	+207.635	0.33415	130.913
1716		317.323	199.732	0.32805	119.774	1756		328.172	207.838	0.33430	131.218
1717		317.594	199.934	0.32821	120.054	1757		328.444	208.041	0.33446	131.510
1718		317.864	200.136	0.32836	120.333	1758		328.716	208.244	0.33461	131.802
1719		318.135	200.338	0.32852	120.599	1759		328.988	208.447	0.33477	132.106
1720	1260.3	318.405	+200.540	0.32869	120.879	1760	1300.3	329.260	+208.650	0.33493	132.398
1721		318.676	200.742	0.32885	121.158	1761		329.532	208.853	0.33508	132.703
1722		318.946	200.944	0.32900	121.437	1762		329.804	209.056	0.33524	132.995
1723		319.217	201.146	0.32916	121.716	1763		330.076	209.259	0.33539	133.300
1724		319.487	201.348	0.32931	121.996	1764		330.348	209.462	0.33554	133.592
1725		319.758	+201.550	0.32947	122.274	1765		330.620	+209.665	0.33570	133.897
1726		320.028	201.752	0.32963	122.554	1766		330.892	209.868	0.33585	134.201
1727		320.299	201.954	0.32978	122.833	1767		331.164	210.071	0.33600	134.493
1728		320.569	202.156	0.32994	123.112	1768		331.436	210.274	0.33615	134.798
1729		320.840	202.358	0.33009	123.404	1769		331.708	210.477	0.33631	135.102
Difference or c_p, c_v		$c_p =$ 0.270, 0.271	$c_v =$ 0.201, 0.202	16–15				$c_p =$ 0.271, 0.272	$c_v =$ 0.203	16	

TABLE A-3. THERMODYNAMIC PROPERTIES OF AIR AT LOW PRESSURES (*Continued*)

°R	°F	h, Btu per lb	u, Btu per lb	s_p	p_r	°R	°F	h, Btu per lb	u, Btu per lb	s_p	p_r
1770	1310.3	331.980	+210.680	0.33646	135.417	1810	1350.3	342.880	+218.850	0.34256	147.986
1771		332.252	210.884	0.33661	135.722	1811		343.154	219.055	0.34271	148.316
1772		332.524	211.088	0.33677	136.027	1812		343.428	219.260	0.34286	148.633
1773		332.796	211.292	0.33692	136.332	1813		343.702	219.465	0.34301	148.963
1774		333.068	211.496	0.33707	136.636	1814		343.976	219.670	0.34316	149.293
1775		333.340	+211.700	0.33723	136.941	1815		344.250	+219.875	0.34332	149.623
1776		333.612	211.904	0.33738	137.246	1816		344.524	220.080	0.34347	149.953
1777		333.884	212.108	0.33753	137.550	1817		344.798	220.285	0.34362	150.238
1778		334.156	212.312	0.33768	137.868	1818		345.072	220.490	0.34377	150.613
1779		334.428	212.516	0.33784	138.172	1819		345.346	220.695	0.34392	150.944
1780	1320.3	334.700	+212.720	0.33800	138.477	1820	1360.3	345.620	+220.900	0.34407	151.274
1781		334.973	212.924	0.33815	138.794	1821		345.894	221.105	0.34422	151.604
1782		335.246	213.128	0.33830	139.099	1822		346.168	221.310	0.34437	151.934
1783		335.519	213.332	0.33846	139.416	1823		346.442	221.515	0.34452	152.264
1784		335.792	213.536	0.33861	139.721	1824		346.716	221.720	0.34467	152.594
1785		336.065	+213.740	0.33876	140.026	1825		346.990	+221.925	0.34482	152.937
1786		336.338	213.944	0.33891	140.343	1826		347.264	222.130	0.34496	153.267
1787		336.611	214.148	0.33906	140.661	1827		347.538	222.335	0.34511	153.597
1788		336.884	214.352	0.33922	140.965	1828		347.812	222.540	0.34526	153.940
1789		337.157	214.556	0.33937	141.283	1829		348.086	222.745	0.34541	154.270
1790	1330.3	337.430	+214.760	0.33952	141.600	1830	1370.3	348.360	+222.950	0.34556	154.612
1791		337.703	214.964	0.33967	141.905	1831		348.634	223.155	0.34571	154.942
1792		337.975	215.168	0.33982	142.222	1832		348.908	223.360	0.34586	155.285
1793		338.248	215.372	0.33998	142.539	1833		349.182	223.565	0.34601	155.628
1794		338.520	215.576	0.34013	142.857	1834		349.456	223.770	0.34616	155.958
1795		338.793	+215.780	0.34028	143.174	1835		349.730	+223.975	0.34631	156.301
1796		339.065	215.984	0.34043	143.492	1836		350.004	224.180	0.34645	156.644
1797		339.338	216.188	0.34058	143.809	1837		350.278	224.385	0.34660	156.986
1798		339.610	216.392	0.34074	144.126	1838		350.552	224.590	0.34675	157.329
1799		339.883	216.596	0.34089	144.444	1839		350.826	224.795	0.34690	157.672
1800	1340.3	340.155	+216.800	0.34105	144.761	1840	1380.3	351.100	+225.000	0.34706	158.015
1801		340.428	217.005	0.34120	145.078	1841		351.374	225.205	0.34721	158.357
1802		340.700	217.210	0.34135	145.409	1842		351.648	225.410	0.34736	158.700
1803		340.973	217.415	0.34150	145.726	1843		351.922	225.615	0.34750	159.043
1804		341.245	217.620	0.34165	146.043	1844		352.196	225.820	0.34765	159.386
1805		341.518	+217.825	0.34181	146.373	1845		352.470	+226.025	0.34780	159.728
1806		341.790	218.030	0.34196	146.691	1846		352.744	226.230	0.34795	160.071
1807		342.063	218.235	0.34211	147.008	1847		353.018	226.435	0.34810	160.414
1808		342.335	218.440	0.34226	147.338	1848		353.292	226.640	0.34824	160.769
1809		342.608	218.645	0.34241	147.668	1849		353.566	226.845	0.34839	161.112
Difference or c_p, c_v		c_p = 0.272, 0.273	c_v = 0.204, 0.205	15				c_p = 0.274	c_v = 0.205	15	

TABLE A-3. THERMODYNAMIC PROPERTIES OF AIR AT LOW PRESSURES (*Continued*)

°R	°F	h, Btu per lb	u, Btu per lb	s_p	p_r	°R	°F	h, Btu per lb	u, Btu per lb	s_p	p_r
1850	1390.3	353.840	+227.050	0.34854	161.408	1890	1430.3	364.810	+235.300	0.35441	175.917
1851		354.114	227.256	0.34869	161.823	1891		365.085	235.507	0.35456	176.285
1852		354.388	227.462	0.34884	162.166	1892		365.360	235.714	0.35470	176.666
1853		354.662	227.668	0.34898	162.521	1893		365.635	235.921	0.35485	177.034
1854		354.936	227.874	0.34913	162.877	1894		365.910	236.128	0.35499	177.415
1855		355.210	+228.080	0.34928	163.220	1895		366.185	+236.335	0.35514	177.796
1856		355.484	228.286	0.34943	163.575	1896		366.460	236.542	0.35529	178.164
1857		355.758	228.492	0.34958	163.931	1897		366.735	236.749	0.35543	178.545
1858		356.032	228.698	0.34972	164.286	1898		367.010	236.956	0.35558	178.926
1859		356.306	228.904	0.34987	164.629	1899		367.285	237.163	0.35572	179.307
1860	1400.3	356.580	+229.110	0.35002	164.985	1900	1440.3	367.560	+237.370	0.35587	179.675
1861		356.854	229.316	0.35017	165.340	1901		367.836	237.577	0.35601	180.056
1862		357.128	229.522	0.35031	165.695	1902		368.112	237.784	0.35616	180.437
1863		357.402	229.728	0.35046	166.051	1903		368.388	237.991	0.35630	180.818
1864		357.676	229.934	0.35060	166.406	1904		368.664	238.198	0.35645	181.199
1865		357.950	+230.140	0.35075	166.762	1905		368.940	+238.405	0.35659	181.580
1866		358.224	230.346	0.35090	167.130	1906		369.216	238.612	0.35673	181.961
1867		358.498	230.552	0.35104	167.486	1907		369.492	238.819	0.35688	182.342
1868		358.772	230.758	0.35119	167.841	1908		369.768	239.026	0.35702	182.723
1869		359.046	230.964	0.35133	168.209	1909		370.044	239.233	0.35717	183.116
1870	1410.3	359.320	+231.170	0.35148	168.565	1910	1450.3	370.320	+239.440	0.35731	183.510
1871		359.594	231.376	0.35163	168.920	1911		370.596	239.647	0.35745	183.891
1872		359.868	231.582	0.35177	169.288	1912		370.872	239.854	0.35760	184.284
1873		360.142	231.788	0.35192	169.657	1913		371.148	240.061	0.35774	184.678
1874		360.416	231.994	0.35206	170.012	1914		371.424	240.268	0.35789	185.059
1875		360.690	+232.200	0.35221	170.380	1915		371.700	+240.475	0.35803	185.452
1876		360.964	232.406	0.35236	170.749	1916		371.976	240.682	0.35817	185.846
1877		361.238	232.612	0.35250	171.117	1917		372.252	240.889	0.35832	186.227
1878		361.512	232.818	0.35265	171.485	1918		372.528	241.096	0.35846	186.621
1879		361.786	233.024	0.35279	171.840	1919		372.804	241.303	0.35861	187.014
1880	1420.3	362.060	+233.230	0.35295	172.209	1920	1460.3	373.080	+241.510	0.35876	187.395
1881		362.335	233.437	0.35310	172.577	1921		373.356	241.717	0.35890	187.789
1882		362.610	233.644	0.35324	172.945	1922		373.632	241.924	0.35905	188.182
1883		362.885	233.851	0.35339	173.313	1923		373.908	242.131	0.35919	188.576
1884		363.160	234.058	0.35353	173.681	1924		374.184	242.338	0.35933	188.969
1885		363.435	+234.265	0.35368	174.062	1925		374.460	+242.545	0.35948	189.363
1886		363.710	234.472	0.35383	174.430	1926		374.736	242.752	0.35962	189.757
1887		363.985	234.679	0.35397	174.786	1927		375.012	242.959	0.35976	190.150
1888		364.260	234.886	0.35412	175.154	1928		375.288	243.166	0.35990	190.544
1889		364.535	235.093	0.35426	175.538	1929		375.564	243.373	0.36005	190.950
Difference or c_p, c_v		$c_p =$ 0.274, 0.275	$c_v =$ 0.206, 0.207	15				$c_p =$ 0.275, 0.276	$c_v =$ 0.207	15	

TABLE A-3. THERMODYNAMIC PROPERTIES OF AIR AT LOW PRESSURES (*Continued*)

°R	°F	h, Btu per lb	u, Btu per lb	s_p	p_r	°R	°F	h, Btu per lb	u, Btu per lb	s_p	p_r
1930	1470.3	375.840	243.580	0.36019	191.344	1970	1510.3	386.900	251.900	0.36585	207.903
1931		376.116	243.788	0.36033	191.750	1971		387.177	252.109	0.36599	208.322
1932		376.392	243.996	0.36048	192.144	1972		387.454	252.318	0.36613	208.754
1933		376.668	244.204	0.36062	192.550	1973		387.731	252.527	0.36627	209.185
1934		376.944	244.412	0.36076	192.944	1974		388.008	252.736	0.36641	209.617
1935		377.220	244.620	0.36091	193.337	1975		388.285	252.945	0.36655	210.036
1936		377.496	244.828	0.36105	193.743	1976		388.562	253.154	0.36669	210.468
1937		377.772	245.036	0.36119	194.150	1977		388.839	253.363	0.36683	210.900
1938		378.048	245.244	0.36133	194.556	1978		389.116	253.572	0.36697	211.332
1939		378.324	245.452	0.36148	194.962	1979		389.393	253.781	0.36711	211.764
1940	1480.3	378.600	245.660	0.36162	195.369	1980	1520.3	389.670	253.990	0.36726	212.196
1941		378.876	245.868	0.36176	195.775	1981		389.947	254.199	0.36740	212.627
1942		379.152	246.076	0.36190	196.181	1982		390.224	254.408	0.36754	213.059
1943		379.428	246.284	0.36204	196.588	1983		390.501	254.617	0.36768	213.491
1944		379.704	246.492	0.36218	196.994	1984		390.778	254.826	0.36782	213.923
1945		379.980	246.700	0.36233	197.413	1985		391.055	255.035	0.36796	214.355
1946		380.256	246.908	0.36247	197.832	1986		391.332	255.244	0.36809	214.799
1947		380.532	247.116	0.36261	198.238	1987		391.609	255.453	0.36823	215.231
1948		380.808	247.324	0.36275	198.645	1988		391.886	255.662	0.36837	215.676
1949		381.084	247.532	0.36289	199.064	1989		392.163	255.871	0.36851	216.120
1950	1490.3	381.360	247.740	0.36303	199.470	1990	1530.3	392.440	256.080	0.36865	216.552
1951		381.637	247.948	0.36317	199.889	1991		392.718	256.289	0.36879	216.997
1952		381.914	248.156	0.36331	200.308	1992		392.996	256.498	0.36893	217.441
1953		382.191	248.364	0.36345	200.714	1993		393.274	256.707	0.36907	217.873
1954		382.468	248.572	0.36359	201.133	1994		393.552	256.916	0.36921	218.317
1955		382.745	248.780	0.36374	201.539	1995		393.830	257.125	0.36935	218.775
1956		383.022	248.988	0.36388	201.958	1996		394.108	257.334	0.36948	219.219
1957		383.299	249.196	0.36402	202.377	1997		394.386	257.543	0.36962	219.664
1958		383.576	249.404	0.36416	202.796	1998		394.664	257.752	0.36976	220.108
1959		383.853	249.612	0.36430	203.203	1999		394.942	257.961	0.36990	220.553
1960	1500.3	384.130	249.820	0.36445	203.622	2000	1540.3	395.220	258.170	0.37005	220.997
1961		384.407	250.028	0.36459	204.041	2001		395.498	258.379	0.37019	221.442
1962		384.684	250.236	0.36473	204.460	2002		395.776	258.588	0.37033	221.886
1963		384.961	250.444	0.36487	204.879	2003		396.054	258.797	0.37046	222.331
1964		385.238	250.652	0.36501	205.298	2004		396.332	259.006	0.37060	222.788
1965		385.515	250.860	0.36515	205.717	2005		396.610	259.215	0.37074	223.245
1966		385.792	251.068	0.36529	206.148	2006		396.888	259.424	0.37088	223.690
1967		386.069	251.276	0.36543	206.567	2007		397.166	259.633	0.37102	224.147
1968		386.346	251.484	0.36557	206.986	2008		397.444	259.842	0.37115	224.592
1969		386.623	251.692	0.36571	207.418	2009		397.722	260.051	0.37129	225.049
Difference or c_p, c_v		$c_p =$ 0.276, 0.277	$c_v =$ 0.208	14				$c_p =$ 0.277, 0.278	$c_v =$ 0.209	14	

TABLE A-3. THERMODYNAMIC PROPERTIES OF AIR AT LOW PRESSURES (*Continued*)

°R	°F	h, Btu per lb	u, Btu per lb	s_p	p_r	°R	°F	h, Btu per lb	u, Btu per lb	s_p	p_r
2010	1550.3	398.000	260.260	0.37143	225.524	2050	1590.3	409.130	268.650	0.37692	244.311
2011		398.278	260.469	0.37157	225.981	2051		409.409	268.860	0.37706	244.793
2012		398.556	260.678	0.37171	226.439	2052		409.688	269.070	0.37719	245.276
2013		398.834	260.887	0.37184	226.896	2053		409.967	269.280	0.37733	245.772
2014		399.112	261.096	0.37198	227.353	2054		410.246	269.490	0.37746	246.254
2015		399.390	261.305	0.37212	227.810	2055		410.525	269.700	0.37760	246.750
2016		399.668	261.514	0.37226	228.268	2056		410.804	269.910	0.37774	247.245
2017		399.946	261.723	0.37240	228.725	2057		411.083	270.120	0.37787	247.728
2018		400.224	261.932	0.37253	229.182	2058		411.362	270.330	0.37801	248.223
2019		400.502	262.141	0.37267	229.652	2059		411.641	270.540	0.37814	248.719
2020	1560.3	400.780	262.350	0.37282	230.109	2060	1600.3	411.920	270.750	0.37828	249.202
2021		401.058	262.560	0.37296	230.567	2061		412.199	270.961	0.37842	249.697
2022		401.336	262.770	0.37309	231.037	2062		412.478	271.172	0.37855	250.193
2023		401.614	262.980	0.37323	231.494	2063		412.757	271.383	0.37869	250.675
2024		401.892	263.190	0.37337	231.964	2064		413.036	271.594	0.37882	251.171
2025		402.170	263.400	0.37351	232.434	2065		413.315	271.805	0.37896	251.679
2026		402.448	263.610	0.37364	232.891	2066		413.594	272.016	0.37909	252.174
2027		402.726	263.820	0.37378	233.348	2067		413.873	272.227	0.37923	252.657
2028		403.004	264.030	0.37392	233.818	2068		414.152	272.438	0.37936	253.153
2029		403.282	264.240	0.37405	234.276	2069		414.431	272.649	0.37950	253.661
2030	1570.3	403.560	264.450	0.37419	234.746	2070	1610.3	414.710	272.860	0.37963	254.156
2031		403.838	264.660	0.37433	235.216	2071		414.989	273.071	0.37977	254.652
2032		404.116	264.870	0.37446	235.686	2072		415.268	273.282	0.37990	255.147
2033		404.394	265.080	0.37460	236.156	2073		415.547	273.493	0.38004	255.655
2034		404.672	265.290	0.37474	236.626	2074		415.826	273.704	0.38017	256.151
2035		404.950	265.500	0.37488	237.108	2075		416.105	273.915	0.38031	256.659
2036		405.228	265.710	0.37501	237.578	2076		416.384	274.126	0.38044	257.167
2037		405.506	265.920	0.37515	238.061	2077		416.663	274.337	0.38058	257.663
2038		405.784	266.130	0.37529	238.531	2078		416.942	274.548	0.38071	258.171
2039		406.062	266.340	0.37542	239.001	2079		417.221	274.759	0.38085	258.679
2040	1580.3	406.340	266.550	0.37556	239.484	2080	1620.3	417.500	274.970	0.38098	259.187
2041		406.619	266.760	0.37570	239.953	2081		417.780	275.181	0.38111	259.695
2042		406.898	266.970	0.37583	240.423	2082		418.060	275.392	0.38125	260.203
2043		407.177	267.180	0.37597	240.906	2083		418.340	275.603	0.38138	260.711
2044		407.456	267.390	0.37610	241.389	2084		418.620	275.814	0.38151	261.220
2045		407.735	267.600	0.37624	241.871	2085		418.900	276.025	0.38165	261.741
2046		408.014	267.810	0.37638	242.354	2086		419.180	276.236	0.38178	262.249
2047		408.293	268.020	0.37651	242.837	2087		419.460	276.447	0.38191	262.757
2048		408.572	268.230	0.37665	243.320	2088		419.740	276.658	0.38204	263.278
2049		408.851	268.440	0.37678	243.802	2089		420.020	276.869	0.38218	263.799
Difference or c_p, c_v		$c_p =$ 0.278, 0.279	$c_v =$ 0.209, 0.210	14				$c_p =$ 0.279, 0.280	$c_v =$ 0.210, 0.211	14	

TABLE A-3. THERMODYNAMIC PROPERTIES OF AIR AT LOW PRESSURES (*Continued*)

°R	°F	h, Btu per lb	u, Btu per lb	s_p	p_r	°R	°F	h, Btu per lb	u, Btu per lb	s_p	p_r
2090	1630.3	420.300	+277.080	0.38231	264.319	2130	1670.3	431.490	+285.540	0.38762	285.631
2091		420.580	277.291	0.38244	264.828	2131		431.771	285.752	0.38775	286.139
2092		420.859	277.502	0.38258	265.348	2132		432.052	285.964	0.38788	286.774
2093		421.139	277.713	0.38271	265.869	2133		432.333	286.176	0.38801	287.283
2094		421.418	277.924	0.38284	266.390	2134		432.614	286.388	0.38814	287.791
2095		421.698	+278.135	0.38298	266.911	2135		432.895	+286.600	0.38828	288.299
2096		421.977	278.346	0.38311	267.419	2136		433.176	286.812	0.38841	288.934
2097		422.257	278.557	0.38324	267.940	2137		433.457	287.024	0.38854	289.443
2098		422.536	278.768	0.38337	268.461	2138		433.738	287.236	0.38867	290.078
2099		422.816	278.979	0.38351	268.982	2139		434.019	287.448	0.38880	290.586
2100	1640.3	423.095	+279.190	0.38365	269.552	2140	1680.3	434.300	+287.660	0.38894	291.194
2101		423.375	279.401	0.38378	270.087	2141		434.581	287.872	0.38907	291.730
2102		423.654	279.612	0.38392	270.595	2142		434.862	288.084	0.38920	292.288
2103		423.934	279.823	0.38405	271.103	2143		435.143	288.296	0.38933	292.873
2104		424.213	280.034	0.38418	271.612	2144		435.424	288.508	0.38946	293.382
2105		424.493	+280.245	0.38432	272.120	2145		435.705	+288.720	0.38959	293.890
2106		424.772	280.456	0.38445	272.628	2146		435.986	288.932	0.38972	294.505
2107		425.052	280.667	0.38458	273.136	2147		436.267	289.144	0.38985	295.083
2108		425.331	280.878	0.38471	273.644	2148		436.548	289.356	0.38998	295.669
2109		425.611	281.089	0.38485	274.279	2149		436.829	289.568	0.39011	296.177
2110	1650.3	425.890	+281.300	0.38498	274.788	2150	1690.3	437.110	+289.780	0.39024	296.685
2111		426.170	281.512	0.38511	275.296	2151		437.391	289.992	0.39037	297.320
2112		426.450	281.724	0.38525	275.804	2152		437.672	290.204	0.39050	297.829
2113		426.730	281.936	0.38538	276.312	2153		437.953	290.416	0.39063	298.464
2114		427.010	282.148	0.38551	276.947	2154		438.234	290.628	0.39076	298.972
2115		427.290	+282.360	0.38565	277.455	2155		438.515	+290.840	0.39089	299.607
2116		427.570	282.572	0.38578	277.964	2156		438.796	291.052	0.39102	300.116
2117		427.850	282.784	0.38591	278.472	2157		439.077	291.264	0.39115	300.751
2118		428.130	282.996	0.38604	279.040	2158		439.358	291.476	0.39128	301.259
2119		428.410	283.208	0.38618	279.615	2159		439.639	291.688	0.39141	301.768
2120	1660.3	428.690	+283.420	0.38631	280.123	2160	1700.3	439.920	+291.900	0.39155	302.403
2121		428.970	283.632	0.38644	280.691	2161		440.201	292.112	0.39168	303.038
2122		429.250	283.844	0.38657	281.267	2162		440.482	292.324	0.39181	303.546
2123		429.530	284.056	0.38670	281.775	2163		440.763	292.536	0.39194	304.182
2124		429.810	284.268	0.38683	282.283	2164		441.044	292.748	0.39207	304.690
2125		430.090	+284.480	0.38697	282.791	2165		441.325	+292.960	0.39220	305.325
2126		430.370	284.692	0.38710	283.356	2166		441.606	293.172	0.39232	305.833
2127		430.650	284.904	0.38723	283.934	2167		441.887	293.384	0.39245	306.469
2128		430.930	285.116	0.38736	284.493	2168		442.168	293.596	0.39258	306.977
2129		431.210	285.328	0.38749	285.078	2169		442.449	293.808	0.39271	307.612
Difference or c_p, c_v		$c_p =$ 0.280	$c_v =$ 0.211, 0.212	13				$c_p =$ 0.280, 0.281	$c_v =$ 0.212	13	

TABLE A-3. THERMODYNAMIC PROPERTIES OF AIR AT LOW PRESSURES (*Continued*)

°R	°F	h, Btu per lb	u, Btu per lb	s_p	p_r	°R	°F	h, Btu per lb	u, Btu per lb	s_p	p_r
2170	1710.3	442.730	+294.020	0.39284	308.296	2210	1750.3	453.990	+302.540	0.39798	332.266
2171		443.011	294.233	0.39297	308.804	2211		454.272	302.754	0.39811	332.901
2172		443.292	294.446	0.39310	309.440	2212		454.554	302.968	0.39823	333.537
2173		443.573	294.659	0.39323	309.948	2213		454.836	303.182	0.39836	334.172
2174		443.854	294.872	0.39336	310.584	2214		455.118	303.396	0.39849	334.808
2175		444.135	+295.085	0.39349	311.219	2215		455.400	+303.610	0.39862	335.443
2176		444.416	295.298	0.39361	311.727	2216		455.682	303.824	0.39874	336.079
2177		444.697	295.511	0.39374	312.363	2217		455.964	304.038	0.39887	336.587
2178		444.978	295.724	0.39387	312.871	2218		456.246	304.252	0.39900	337.223
2179		445.259	295.937	0.39400	313.506	2219		456.528	304.466	0.39912	337.858
2180	1720.3	445.540	+296.150	0.39414	314.142	2220	1760.3	456.810	+304.680	0.39926	338.494
2181		445.821	296.363	0.39427	314.650	2221		457.092	304.894	0.39939	339.129
2182		446.102	296.576	0.39440	315.285	2222		457.374	305.108	0.39951	339.765
2183		446.383	296.789	0.39452	315.921	2223		457.656	305.322	0.39964	340.401
2184		446.664	297.002	0.39465	316.429	2224		457.938	305.536	0.39977	340.909
2185		446.945	+297.215	0.39478	317.065	2225		458.220	+305.750	0.39990	341.672
2186		447.226	297.428	0.39491	317.700	2226		458.502	305.964	0.40002	342.307
2187		447.507	297.641	0.39504	318.208	2227		458.784	306.178	0.40015	342.943
2188		447.788	297.854	0.39516	318.844	2228		459.066	306.392	0.40028	343.578
2189		448.069	298.067	0.39529	319.479	2229		459.348	306.606	0.40040	344.214
2190	1730.3	448.350	+298.280	0.39542	320.115	2230	1770.3	459.630	+306.820	0.40053	344.849
2191		448.632	298.493	0.39555	320.623	2231		459.912	307.034	0.40066	345.485
2192		448.914	298.706	0.39568	321.258	2232		460.194	307.248	0.40078	346.121
2193		449.196	298.919	0.39580	321.894	2233		460.476	307.462	0.40091	346.756
2194		449.478	299.132	0.39593	322.402	2234		460.758	307.676	0.40104	347.392
2195		449.760	+299.345	0.39606	323.037	2235		461.040	+307.890	0.40117	348.027
2196		450.042	299.558	0.39619	323.673	2236		461.322	308.104	0.40129	348.663
2197		450.324	299.771	0.39632	324.308	2237		461.604	308.318	0.40142	349.298
2198		450.606	299.984	0.39644	324.816	2238		461.886	308.532	0.40155	349.934
2199		450.888	300.197	0.39657	325.452	2239		462.168	308.746	0.40167	350.569
2200	1740.3	451.170	+300.410	0.39671	326.087	2240	1780.3	462.450	+308.960	0.40180	351.205
2201		451.452	300.623	0.39684	326.723	2241		462.733	309.174	0.40193	351.840
2202		451.734	300.836	0.39696	327.358	2242		463.016	309.388	0.40205	352.475
2203		452.016	301.049	0.39709	327.866	2243		463.299	309.602	0.40218	353.169
2204		452.298	301.262	0.39722	328.502	2244		463.582	309.816	0.40230	353.864
2205		452.580	+301.475	0.39735	329.137	2245		463.865	+310.030	0.40243	354.510
2206		452.862	301.688	0.39747	329.773	2246		464.148	310.244	0.40255	355.145
2207		453.144	301.901	0.39760	330.408	2247		464.431	310.458	0.40268	355.781
2208		453.426	302.114	0.39773	331.043	2248		464.714	310.672	0.40280	356.416
2209		453.708	302.327	0.39785	331.679	2249		464.997	310.886	0.40293	357.052
Difference or c_p, c_v		c_p = 0.281, 0.282	c_v = 0.213	12				c_p = 0.282, 0.283	c_v = 0.214	13	

TABLE A-3. THERMODYNAMIC PROPERTIES OF AIR AT LOW PRESSURES (*Continued*)

°R	°F	h, Btu per lb	u, Btu per lb	s_p	p_r	°R	°F	h, Btu per lb	u, Btu per lb	s_p	p_r
2250	1790.3	465.280	+311.100	0.40305	357.716	2290	1830.3	476.600	+319.670	0.40804	384.823
2251		465.563	311.314	0.40318	358.418	2291		476.883	319.885	0.40816	385.458
2252		465.846	311.528	0.40330	359.114	2292		477.166	320.100	0.40829	386.154
2253		466.129	311.742	0.40343	359.750	2293		477.449	320.315	0.40841	386.857
2254		466.412	311.956	0.40355	360.385	2294		477.732	320.530	0.40854	387.492
2255		466.695	+312.170	0.40368	361.021	2295		478.015	+320.745	0.40866	388.255
2256		466.978	312.384	0.40380	361.696	2296		478.298	320.960	0.40878	388.891
2257		467.261	312.598	0.40393	362.419	2297		478.581	321.175	0.40891	389.653
2258		467.544	312.812	0.40405	363.055	2298		478.864	321.390	0.40903	390.289
2259		467.827	313.026	0.40418	363.690	2299		479.147	321.605	0.40916	391.052
2260	1800.3	468.110	+313.240	0.40431	364.326	2300	1840.3	479.430	+321.820	0.40928	391.688
2261		468.393	313.454	0.40443	364.962	2301		479.714	322.035	0.40940	392.450
2262		468.676	313.668	0.40456	365.724	2302		479.998	322.250	0.40952	393.213
2263		468.959	313.882	0.40468	366.360	2303		480.282	322.465	0.40965	393.849
2264		469.242	314.096	0.40481	366.995	2304		480.566	322.680	0.40977	394.612
2265		469.525	+314.310	0.40493	367.758	2305		480.850	+322.895	0.40989	395.247
2266		469.808	314.524	0.40505	368.394	2306		481.134	323.110	0.41001	396.010
2267		470.091	314.738	0.40518	369.029	2307		481.418	323.325	0.41013	396.646
2268		470.374	314.952	0.40530	369.665	2308		481.702	323.540	0.41026	397.408
2269		470.657	315.166	0.40543	370.428	2309		481.986	323.755	0.41038	398.171
2270	1810.3	470.940	+315.380	0.40555	371.063	2310	1850.3	482.270	+323.970	0.41050	398.807
2271		471.223	315.594	0.40567	371.699	2311		482.554	324.185	0.41062	399.570
2272		471.506	315.808	0.40580	372.462	2312		482.838	324.400	0.41074	400.275
2273		471.789	316.022	0.40592	373.097	2313		483.122	324.615	0.41087	400.968
2274		472.072	316.236	0.40605	373.733	2314		483.406	324.830	0.41099	401.731
2275		472.355	+316.450	0.40617	374.496	2315		483.690	+325.045	0.41111	402.366
2276		472.638	316.664	0.40629	375.131	2316		483.974	325.260	0.41123	403.129
2277		472.921	316.878	0.40642	375.767	2317		484.258	325.475	0.41135	403.892
2278		473.204	317.092	0.40654	376.529	2318		484.542	325.690	0.41148	404.528
2279		473.487	317.306	0.40667	377.165	2319		484.826	325.905	0.41160	405.290
2280	1820.3	473.770	+317.521	0.40680	377.801	2320	1860.3	485.110	+326.120	0.41173	406.053
2281		474.053	317.736	0.40692	378.563	2321		485.394	326.336	0.41185	406.816
2282		474.336	317.951	0.40705	379.299	2322		485.678	326.552	0.41197	407.452
2283		474.619	318.166	0.40717	379.962	2323		485.962	326.768	0.41210	408.214
2284		474.902	318.381	0.40730	380.597	2324		486.246	326.984	0.41222	408.977
2285		475.185	+318.596	0.40742	381.233	2325		486.530	+327.200	0.41234	409.673
2286		475.468	318.811	0.40754	381.996	2326		486.814	327.416	0.41246	410.376
2287		475.751	319.026	0.40767	382.631	2327		487.098	327.632	0.41258	411.138
2288		476.034	319.241	0.40779	383.394	2328		487.382	327.848	0.41271	411.801
2289		476.317	319.456	0.40792	384.130	2329		487.666	328.064	0.41283	412.537
Difference or c_p, c_v		$c_p =$ 0.283	$c_v =$ 0.214, 0.215	13				$c_p =$ 0.283, 0.284	$c_v =$ 0.215, 0.216	12	

TABLE A-3. THERMODYNAMIC PROPERTIES OF AIR AT LOW PRESSURES (Continued)

°R	°F	h, Btu per lb	u, Btu per lb	s_p	p_r	°R	°F	h, Btu per lb	u, Btu per lb	s_p	p_r
2330	1870.3	487.950	+328.280	0.41295	413.332	2370	1910.3	499.320	+336.920	0.41779	443.591
2331		488.234	328.496	0.41307	414.095	2371		499.605	337.136	0.41791	444.354
2332		488.518	328.712	0.41319	414.808	2372		499.890	337.352	0.41803	445.117
2333		488.802	328.928	0.41332	415.494	2373		500.175	337.568	0.41815	445.880
2334		489.086	329.144	0.41344	416.256	2374		500.460	337.784	0.41827	446.643
2335		489.370	+329.360	0.41356	417.019	2375		500.745	+338.000	0.41839	447.406
2336		489.654	329.576	0.41368	417.782	2376		501.030	338.216	0.41851	448.199
2337		489.938	329.792	0.41380	418.545	2377		501.315	338.432	0.41863	449.058
2338		490.222	330.008	0.41393	419.308	2378		501.600	338.648	0.41875	449.821
2339		490.506	330.224	0.41405	419.943	2379		501.885	338.864	0.41887	450.584
2340	1880.3	490.790	+330.440	0.41417	420.706	2380	1920.3	502.170	+339.080	0.41899	451.347
2341		491.074	330.656	0.41429	421.469	2381		502.455	339.297	0.41911	452.110
2342		491.358	330.872	0.41441	422.232	2382		502.740	339.513	0.41923	452.950
2343		491.642	331.088	0.41453	422.995	2383		503.025	339.730	0.41935	453.763
2344		491.926	331.304	0.41465	423.708	2384		503.310	339.946	0.41947	454.526
2345		492.210	+331.520	0.41478	424.420	2385		503.595	+340.163	0.41959	455.288
2346		492.494	331.736	0.41490	425.156	2386		503.880	340.379	0.41970	456.091
2347		492.778	331.952	0.41502	425.919	2387		504.165	340.596	0.41982	456.901
2348		493.062	332.168	0.41514	426.682	2388		504.450	340.812	0.41994	457.704
2349		493.346	332.384	0.41526	427.445	2389		504.735	341.029	0.42006	458.467
2350	1890.3	493.630	+332.600	0.41538	428.208	2390	1930.3	505.020	+341.245	0.42018	459.357
2351		493.914	332.816	0.41550	428.970	2391		505.305	341.462	0.42030	460.120
2352		494.198	333.032	0.41562	429.733	2392		505.590	341.678	0.42042	460.883
2353		494.482	333.248	0.41574	430.496	2393		505.875	341.895	0.42054	461.645
2354		494.766	333.464	0.41586	431.259	2394		506.160	342.111	0.42066	462.505
2355		495.050	+333.680	0.41599	432.022	2395		506.445	+342.328	0.42078	463.298
2356		495.334	333.896	0.41611	432.785	2396		506.730	342.544	0.42089	464.061
2357		495.618	334.112	0.41623	433.547	2397		507.015	342.761	0.42101	464.951
2358		495.902	334.328	0.41635	434.310	2398		507.300	342.977	0.42113	465.741
2359		496.186	334.544	0.41647	435.073	2399		507.585	343.194	0.42125	466.477
2360	1900.3	496.470	+334.760	0.41659	435.836	2400	1940.3	507.870	+343.410	0.42138	467.367
2361		496.755	334.976	0.41671	436.599	2401		508.155	343.626	0.42150	468.129
2362		497.040	335.192	0.41683	437.362	2402		508.440	343.842	0.42162	468.892
2363		497.325	335.408	0.41695	438.124	2403		508.725	344.058	0.42173	469.782
2364		497.610	335.624	0.41707	438.887	2404		509.010	344.274	0.42185	470.545
2365		497.895	+335.840	0.41719	439.650	2405		509.295	+344.490	0.42197	471.308
2366		498.180	336.056	0.41731	440.413	2406		509.580	344.706	0.42209	472.198
2367		498.465	336.272	0.41743	441.176	2407		509.865	344.922	0.42221	472.961
2368		498.750	336.488	0.41755	441.989	2408		510.150	345.138	0.42232	473.851
2369		499.035	336.704	0.41767	442.829	2409		510.435	345.354	0.42244	474.714
Difference or c_p, c_v	c_p = 0.284, 0.285	c_v = 0.216	12					c_p = 0.285	c_v = 0.216	12	

TABLE A-3. THERMODYNAMIC PROPERTIES OF AIR AT LOW PRESSURES (*Continued*)

°R	°F	h, Btu per lb	u, Btu per lb	s_p	p_r	°R	°F	h, Btu per lb	u, Btu per lb	s_p	p_r
2410	1950.3	510.720	345.570	0.42256	475.541	2445		520.720	353.172	0.42668	504.91
2411		511.005	345.787	0.42268	476.304	2446		521.006	353.390	0.42680	505.74
2412		511.292	346.004	0.42280	477.194	2447		521.292	353.608	0.42691	506.57
2413		511.578	346.221	0.42291	477.957	2448		521.578	353.825	0.42703	507.46
2414		511.864	346.438	0.42303	478.847	2449		521.864	354.043	0.42714	508.35
2415		512.150	346.655	0.42315	479.610	2450	1990.3	522.150	354.260	0.42726	509.24
2416		512.436	346.872	0.42327	480.500	2451		522.436	354.477	0.42738	510.13
2417		512.722	347.089	0.42339	481.263	2452		522.722	354.694	0.42749	510.89
2418		513.008	347.306	0.42350	482.153	2453		523.008	354.911	0.42761	511.78
2419		513.294	347.523	0.42362	482.966	2454		523.294	355.128	0.42772	512.67
2420	1960.3	513.580	347.740	0.42375	483.806	2455		523.580	355.345	0.42784	513.56
2421		513.866	347.957	0.42387	484.569	2456		523.866	355.562	0.42796	514.45
2422		514.151	348.174	0.42398	485.459	2457		524.152	355.779	0.42807	515.34
2423		514.437	348.391	0.42410	486.222	2458		524.438	355.996	0.42819	516.23
2424		514.722	348.608	0.42422	487.112	2459		524.724	356.213	0.42830	517.12
2425		515.008	348.825	0.42434	488.002	2460	2000.3	525.010	356.430	0.42843	517.95
2426		515.293	349.042	0.42445	488.825						
2427		515.579	349.259	0.42457	489.655						
2428		515.864	349.476	0.42469	490.418	2500	2040.3	536.45	365.08	0.43305	553.99
2429		516.150	349.693	0.42480	491.308	2550	2090.3	550.76	375.96	0.43872	601.80
2430	1970.3	516.435	349.910	0.42492	492.071			$c_p =$ 0.286	$c_v =$ 0.217		
2431		516.721	350.127	0.42504	492.961	2600	2140.3	565.08	386.84	0.44431	652.92
2432		517.006	350.345	0.42515	493.851	2650	2190.3	579.45	397.86	0.44980	707.33
2433		517.292	350.563	0.42527	494.674			$c_p =$ 0.287	$c_v =$ 0.220		
2434		517.577	350.780	0.42539	495.500						
2435		517.863	350.998	0.42551	496.39	2700	2240.3	593.85	408.94	0.45520	765.32
2436		518.148	351.215	0.42562	497.20	2750	2290.3	608.28	419.99	0.46052	826.98
2437		518.434	351.433	0.42574	498.05			$c_p =$ 0.288	$c_v =$ 0.221		
2438		518.719	351.650	0.42586	498.94	2800	2340.3	622.74	431.08	0.46575	892.60
2439		519.005	351.868	0.42597	499.83	2850	2390.3	637.28	442.20	0.47090	962.15
2440	1980.3	519.290	352.085	0.42610	500.59			$c_p =$ 0.290	$c_v =$ 0.222		
2441		519.576	352.303	0.42622	501.48	2900	2440.3	651.85	453.34	0.47596	1036.03
2442		519.862	352.520	0.42633	502.37	2950	2490.3	666.45	464.52	0.48096	1114.35
2443		520.148	352.738	0.42645	503.13	3000	2540.3	681.08	475.72	0.48587	1196.99
2444		520.434	352.956	0.42656	504.02			$c_p =$ 0.292	$c_v =$ 0.224		
Difference or c_p, c_v		$c_p =$ 0.285, 0.286	$c_v =$ 0.216, 0.217	12							

TABLE A-4. FRICTIONLESS, CONSTANT-AREA FLOW WITH CHANGE IN STAGNATION TEMPERATURE †

Perfect gas, $k = 1.4$ exactly

M	T_0/T_0^*	T/T^*	p/p^*	p_0/p_0^*	ρ^*/ρ V/V^*
0	0	0	2.400,0	1.2679	0
0.01	$0.0_4 80$	$0.0_3 5,76$	2.399,7	1.2678	$0.0_3 2,40$
0.02	0.001,92	0.002,30	2.398,7	1.2675	$0.0_3 9,59$
0.03	0.004,31	0.005,16	2.397,0	1.2671	0.002,16
0.04	0.007,65	0.009,17	2.394,6	1.2665	0.003,83
0.05	0.011,92	0.014,30	2.391,6	1.2657	0.005,98
0.06	0.017,12	0.020,53	2.388,0	1.2647	0.008,60
0.07	0.023,22	0.027,84	2.383,7	1.2636	0.011,68
0.08	0.030,21	0.036,21	2.378,7	1.2623	0.015,22
0.09	0.038,07	0.045,62	2.373,1	1.2608	0.019,22
0.10	0.046,78	0.056,02	2.366,9	1.2591	0.023,67
0.11	0.056,30	0.067,39	2.360,0	1.2573	0.028,56
0.12	0.066,61	0.079,70	2.352,6	1.2554	0.033,88
0.13	0.077,68	0.092,90	2.344,5	1.2533	0.039,62
0.14	0.089,47	0.106,95	2.335,9	1.2510	0.0457,8
0.15	0.101,96	0.121,81	2.326,7	1.2486	0.0523,5
0.16	0.115,11	0.137,43	2.317,0	1.2461	0.0593,1
0.17	0.128,88	0.153,77	2.306,7	1.2434	0.0666,6
0.18	0.143,24	0.170,78	2.295,9	1.2406	0.0743,8
0.19	0.158,14	0.188,41	2.284,5	1.2377	0.0824,7
0.20	0.173,55	0.206,61	2.2727	1.2346	0.0909,1
0.21	0.1894,3	0.225,33	2.2604	1.2314	0.0996,9
0.22	0.2057,4	0.2445,2	2.2477	1.2281	0.1087,9
0.23	0.2224,4	0.2641,3	2.2345	1.2248	0.1182,0
0.24	0.2394,8	0.2841,1	2.2209	1.2213	0.1279,2

M	T_0/T_0^*	T/T^*	p/p^*	p_0/p_0^*	ρ^*/ρ V/V^*
0.50	0.6913,6	0.790,12	1.7778	1.1140	0.44445
0.51	0.7058,1	0.805,09	1.7594	1.1099	0.45761
0.52	0.7199,0	0.819,55	1.7410	1.1059	0.47075
0.53	0.7336,1	0.833,51	1.7226	1.1019	0.48387
0.54	0.7469,5	0.846,95	1.7043	1.0979	0.49696
0.55	0.7599,1	0.859,87	1.6860	1.09397	0.5100,1
0.56	0.7724,8	0.872,27	1.6678	1.09010	0.5230,2
0.57	0.7846,7	0.884,15	1.6496	1.08630	0.5359,7
0.58	0.7964,7	0.895,52	1.6316	1.08255	0.5488,7
0.59	0.8078,9	0.906,37	1.6136	1.07887	0.5617,0
0.60	0.8189,2	0.916,70	1.5957	1.0752,5	0.5744,7
0.61	0.8295,6	0.926,53	1.5780	1.0717,0	0.5871,6
0.62	0.8398,2	0.935,85	1.5603	1.068,21	0.5997,8
0.63	0.8497,0	0.944,66	1.5427	1.0648,0	0.6123,2
0.64	0.8592,0	0.952,98	1.5253	1.0614,6	0.6247,7
0.65	0.8683,3	0.960,81	1.5080	1.0582,0	0.6371,3
0.66	0.8770,9	0.968,16	1.4908	1.0550,2	0.6494,1
0.67	0.8854,8	0.975,03	1.4738	1.0519,2	0.6615,9
0.68	0.8935,0	0.981,44	1.4569	1.0489,0	0.6736,7
0.69	0.9011,7	0.987,39	1.4401	1.0459,6	0.6856,4
0.70	0.9085,0	0.992,89	1.4235	1.0431,0	0.6975,1
0.71	0.9154,8	0.997,96	1.4070	1.0403,3	0.7092,7
0.72	0.9221,2	1.002,60	1.3907	1.0376,4	0.7209,3
0.73	0.9284,3	1.0068,2	1.3745	1.0350,4	0.7324,8
0.74	0.9344,2	1.0106,2	1.3585	1.0325,3	0.7439,2

TABLE A-4. FRICTIONLESS, CONSTANT-AREA FLOW WITH CHANGE IN STAGNATION TEMPERATURE (*Continued*)

Perfect gas, $k = 1.4$ exactly

M	T_0/T_0^*	T/T^*	p/p^*	p_0/p_0^*	$\dfrac{\rho^*/\rho}{V/V^*}$
1.00	1.0000,0	1.0000,0	1.0000,0	1.0000,0	1.0000,0
1.01	0.9999,3	0.9965,9	0.9884,1	1.0000,4	1.0082,8
1.02	0.9997,3	0.9930,4	0.9769,7	1.0001,9	1.0164,4
1.03	0.9994,0	0.9893,6	0.9656,9	1.0004,3	1.0245,0
1.04	0.9989,5	0.9855,6	0.9545,6	1.0007,7	1.0324,6
1.05	0.9983,8	0.9816,1	0.9435,8	1.0012,1	1.0403,0
1.06	0.9976,9	0.9775,5	0.9327,5	1.0017,5	1.0480,4
1.07	0.9969,0	0.9733,9	0.9220,6	1.0023,8	1.0556,7
1.08	0.9960,0	0.9691,3	0.9115,2	1.0031,1	1.0632,0
1.09	0.9950,1	0.9647,7	0.9011,2	1.0039,4	1.0706,2
1.10	0.9939,2	0.9603,1	0.8908,6	1.0048,6	1.0779,5
1.11	0.9927,4	0.9557,7	0.8807,5	1.0058,8	1.0851,8
1.12	0.9914,8	0.9511,5	0.8707,8	1.0069,9	1.0923,0
1.13	0.9901,3	0.9464,6	0.8609,4	1.0082,0	1.0993,3
1.14	0.9887,1	0.9416,9	0.8512,3	1.0095,1	1.1062,6
1.15	0.9872,1	0.9368,5	0.8416,6	1.0109,2	1.1131
1.16	0.9856,4	0.9319,5	0.8322,2	1.0124,3	1.1198
1.17	0.9840,0	0.9270,0	0.8229,2	1.0140,3	1.1264
1.18	0.9823,0	0.9220,0	0.8137,4	1.0157,2	1.1330
1.19	0.9805,4	0.9169,5	0.8046,8	1.0175,2	1.1395
1.20	0.9787,2	0.91185	0.7957,6	1.0194,1	1.1459
1.21	0.9768,5	0.90671	0.7869,5	1.0214,0	1.1522
1.22	0.9749,2	0.90153	0.7782,7	1.0234,8	1.1584
1.23	0.97294	0.89632	0.7697,1	1.0256,6	1.1645
1.24	0.97092	0.89108	0.7612,7	1.0279,4	1.1705
1.55	0.89669	0.72680	0.5500,2	1.1473	1.3214
1.56	0.89418	0.72173	0.5445,8	1.1527	1.3253
1.57	0.89167	0.71669	0.5392,2	1.1582	1.3291
1.58	0.88917	0.71168	0.5339,3	1.1639	1.3329
1.59	0.88668	0.70669	0.5287,1	1.1697	1.3366
1.60	0.88419	0.70173	0.5235,6	1.1756	1.3403
1.61	0.88170	0.69680	0.5184,8	1.1816	1.3439
1.62	0.87922	0.69190	0.5134,6	1.1877	1.3475
1.63	0.87675	0.68703	0.5085,1	1.1939	1.3511
1.64	0.87429	0.68219	0.5036,3	1.2002	1.3546
1.65	0.87184	0.67738	0.4988,1	1.2066	1.3580
1.66	0.86940	0.67259	0.4940,5	1.2131	1.3614
1.67	0.86696	0.66784	0.4893,5	1.2197	1.3648
1.68	0.86453	0.66312	0.4847,1	1.2264	1.3681
1.69	0.86211	0.65843	0.4801,4	1.2332	1.3713
1.70	0.85970	0.65377	0.4756,3	1.2402	1.3745
1.71	0.85731	0.64914	0.4711,7	1.2473	1.3777
1.72	0.85493	0.64455	0.4667,7	1.2545	1.3809
1.73	0.85256	0.63999	0.4624,2	1.2618	1.3840
1.74	0.85020	0.63546	0.4581,3	1.2692	1.3871
1.75	0.84785	0.63096	0.4539,0	1.2767	1.3901
1.76	0.84551	0.62649	0.4497,2	1.2843	1.3931
1.77	0.84318	0.62205	0.4455,9	1.2920	1.3960
1.78	0.84087	0.61765	0.4415,2	1.2998	1.3989
1.79	0.83857	0.61328	0.4375,0	1.3078	1.4018

M						M					
0.75	0.9400,9	1.0140,3	1.3427	1.0301,0	0.7552,5	0.25	0.2568,4	0.3044,0	2.2069	1.2177	0.1379,3
0.76	0.9454,6	1.0170,6	1.3270	1.0277,6	0.7664,6	0.26	0.2744,6	0.3249,6	2.1925	1.2140	0.1482,1
0.77	0.9505,2	1.0197,1	1.3115	1.0255,2	0.7775,5	0.27	0.2923,1	0.3457,3	2.1777	1.2102	0.1587,6
0.78	0.9552,8	1.0219,8	1.2961	1.0233,7	0.7885,2	0.28	0.3103,5	0.3666,7	2.1626	1.2064	0.1695,5
0.79	0.9597,5	1.0239,0	1.2809	1.0213,1	0.7993,8	0.29	0.3285,5	0.3877,3	2.1472	1.2025	0.1805,8
0.80	0.9639,4	1.0254,8	1.2658	1.0193,4	0.8101,2	0.30	0.3468,6	0.4088,7	2.1314	1.1985	0.1918,3
0.81	0.9678,6	1.0267,2	1.2509	1.0174,6	0.8207,5	0.31	0.3652,5	0.4300,4	2.1154	1.1945	0.2032,9
0.82	0.9715,2	1.0276,3	1.2362	1.0156,9	0.8312,6	0.32	0.3836,9	0.4511,9	2.0991	1.1904	0.2149,4
0.83	0.9749,2	1.0282,3	1.2217	1.0139,9	0.8416,4	0.33	0.4021,4	0.4722,8	2.0825	1.1863	0.2267,8
0.84	0.9780,7	1.0285,3	1.2073	1.0124,0	0.8519,0	0.34	0.4205,7	0.4932,7	2.0657	1.1821	0.2387,9
0.85	0.9809,7	1.0285,4	1.1931	1.0109,1	0.8620,4	0.35	0.4389,4	0.5141,3	2.0487	1.1779	0.2509,6
0.86	0.9836,3	1.0282,6	1.1791	1.00951	0.8720,6	0.36	0.4572,3	0.5348,2	2.0314	1.1737	0.2632,7
0.87	0.9860,7	1.0277,1	1.1652	1.00819	0.8819,6	0.37	0.4754,1	0.5553,0	2.0140	1.1695	0.2757,2
0.88	0.9882,8	1.0269,0	1.1515	1.00698	0.8917,5	0.38	0.4934,6	0.5755,3	1.9964	1.1652	0.2882,8
0.89	0.9902,8	1.0258,3	1.1380	1.00587	0.9014,2	0.39	0.5113,4	0.5954,9	1.9787	1.1609	0.3009,5
0.90	0.9920,7	1.0245,1	1.1246	1.0048,5	0.9109,7	0.40	0.5290,3	0.6151,5	1.9608	1.1566	0.3137,2
0.91	0.9936,6	1.0229,7	1.1114	1.0039,3	0.9203,9	0.41	0.5465,1	0.6344,8	1.9428	1.1523	0.3265,8
0.92	0.9950,6	1.0212,0	1.0984,2	1.0031,0	0.9297,0	0.42	0.5637,6	0.6534,5	1.9247	1.1480	0.3395,1
0.93	0.9962,7	1.0192,1	1.0855,5	1.0023,7	0.9388,9	0.43	0.5807,5	0.6720,5	1.9065	1.1437	0.3525,1
0.94	0.9972,9	1.0170,2	1.0728,5	1.0017,4	0.9479,6	0.44	0.5974,8	0.690,25	1.8882	1.1394	0.36556
0.95	0.9981,4	1.0146,3	1.0603,0	1.0012,1	0.9569,2	0.45	0.6139,3	0.708,03	1.8699	1.1351	0.37865
0.96	0.9988,3	1.0120,5	1.0479,2	1.0007,7	0.9657,6	0.46	0.6300,7	0.725,38	1.8515	1.1308	0.39178
0.97	0.9993,5	1.0092,9	1.0357,0	1.0004,3	0.9744,9	0.47	0.6458,9	0.742,28	1.8331	1.1266	0.40493
0.98	0.9997,2	1.0063,6	1.0236,4	1.0001,9	0.9831,1	0.48	0.6613,9	0.758,71	1.8147	1.1224	0.41810
0.99	0.9999,3	1.0032,6	1.0117,4	1.0000,4	0.9916,1	0.49	0.6765,5	0.774,66	1.7962	1.1182	0.43127

387

...apiro, W. R. Hawthorne, and G. M. Edelman, The Mechanics and Thermodynamics of Steady One-dimensional Gas
...erical Solutions, Meteor Report No. 14, Bureau of Ordnance Contract NOrd 9661, Dec. 1, 1947. Where no comma is indi-
... 0 to 3.00, all digits to the left of the comma are valid for linear interpolation.
...ts are valid for linear interpolation.
...0429. The notation 5370_4 signifies 5,370,000.

36
163
.2
326
1928

1.80	0.83628	0.60894	0.4335,3	1.3159	1.4046
1.81	0.83400	0.60463	0.4296,0	1.3241	1.4074
1.82	0.83174	0.60036	0.4257,3	1.3324	1.4102
1.83	0.82949	0.59612	0.4219,1	1.3408	1.4129
1.84	0.82726	0.59191	0.4181,3	1.3494	1.4156
1.85	0.82504	0.58773	0.4144,0	1.3581	1.4183
1.86	0.82283	0.58359	0.41072	1.3669	1.4209
1.87	0.82064	0.57948	0.40708	1.3758	1.4235
1.88	0.81846	0.57540	0.40349	1.3848	1.4261
1.89	0.81629	0.57135	0.39994	1.3940	1.4286
1.90	0.81414	0.56734	0.39643	1.4033	1.4311
1.91	0.81200	0.56336	0.39297	1.4127	1.4336
1.92	0.80987	0.55941	0.38955	1.4222	1.4360
1.93	0.80776	0.55549	0.38617	1.4319	1.4384
1.94	0.80567	0.55160	0.38283	1.4417	1.4408
1.95	0.80359	0.54774	0.37954	1.4516	1.4432
1.96	0.80152	0.54391	0.37628	1.4616	1.4455
1.97	0.79946	0.54012	0.37306	1.4718	1.4478
1.98	0.79742	0.53636	0.36988	1.4821	1.4501
1.99	0.79540	0.53263	0.36674	1.4925	1.4523
2.00	0.79339	0.52893	0.36364	1.5031	1.4545
2.01	0.79139	0.52526	0.36057	1.5138	1.4567
2.02	0.78941	0.52161	0.35754	1.5246	1.4589
2.03	0.78744	0.51800	0.35454	1.5356	1.4610
2.04	0.78549	0.51442	0.35158	1.5467	1.4631
2.05	0.78355	0.51087	0.34866	1.5579	1.4652
2.06	0.78162	0.50735	0.34577	1.5693	1.4673
2.07	0.77971	0.50386	0.34291	1.5808	1.4694
2.08	0.77781	0.50040	0.34009	1.5924	1.4714
2.09	0.77593	0.49697	0.33730	1.6042	1.4734

1.25	0.96886	0.88581	0.7529,4	1.0303,2	1.1764
1.26	0.96675	0.88052	0.7447,3	1.0328,0	1.1823
1.27	0.96461	0.87521	0.7366,3	1.0353,6	1.1881
1.28	0.96243	0.86988	0.7286,5	1.0380,3	1.1938
1.29	0.96022	0.86453	0.7207,8	1.0408,0	1.1994
1.30	0.95798	0.85917	0.7130,1	1.0436,5	1.2050
1.31	0.95571	0.85380	0.7053,5	1.0466,1	1.2105
1.32	0.95341	0.84843	0.6978,0	1.0496,7	1.2159
1.33	0.95108	0.84305	0.6903,5	1.0528,3	1.2212
1.34	0.94873	0.83766	0.6830,1	1.0560,8	1,2264
1.35	0.94636	0.83227	0.6757,7	1.0594,3	1.2316
1.36	0.94397	0.82689	0.6686,3	1.0628,8	1.2367
1.37	0.94157	0.82151	0.6615,9	1.0664,2	1.2417
1.38	0.93915	0.81613	0.6546,4	1.0700,6	1.2467
1.39	0.93671	0.81076	0.6477,8	1.0738,0	1.2516
1.40	0.93425	0.80540	0.6410,2	1.0776,5	1.2564
1.41	0.93178	0.80004	0.6343,6	1.0815,9	1.2612
1.42	0.92931	0.79469	0.6277,9	1.0856,3	1.2659
1.43	0.92683	0.78936	0.6213,1	1.0897,7	1.2705
1.44	0.92434	0.78405	0.6149,1	1.0940,0	1.2751
1.45	0.92184	0.77875	0.6086,0	1.0983	1.2796
1.46	0.91933	0.77346	0.6023,7	1.1028	1.2840
1.47	0.91682	0.76819	0.5962,3	1.1073	1.2884
1.48	0.91431	0.76294	0.5901,8	1.1120	1.2927
1.49	0.91179	0.75771	0.5842,1	1.1167	1.2970
1.50	0.90928	0.75250	0.5783,1	1.1215	1.3012
1.51	0.90676	0.74731	0.5725,0	1.1264	1.3054
1.52	0.90424	0.74215	0.5667,7	1.1315	1.3095
1.53	0.90172	0.73701	0.5611,1	1.1367	1.3135
1.54	0.89920	0.73189	0.5555,3	1.1420	1.3175

TABLE A-4. FRICTIONLESS, CONSTANT-AREA FLOW WITH CHANGE IN STAGNATION TEMPERATURE (Continued)

Perfect gas, $k = 1.4$ exactly

M	T_0/T_0^*	T/T^*	p/p^*	p_0/p_0^*	$\dfrac{\rho^*/\rho}{V/V^*}$	M	T_0/T_0^*	T/T^*	p/p^*	p_0/p_0^*	$\dfrac{\rho^*/\rho}{V/V^*}$
2.10	0.77406	0.49356	0.33454	1.6161	1.4753	2.60	0.69699	0.35561	0.22936	2.4177	1.5505
2.11	0.77221	0.49018	0.33181	1.6282	1.4773	2.61	0.69574	0.35341	0.22777	2.4384	1.5516
2.12	0.77037	0.48683	0.32912	1.6404	1.4792	2.62	0.69450	0.35123	0.22620	2.4593	1.5527
2.13	0.76854	0.48351	0.32646	1.6528	1.4811	2.63	0.69327	0.34906	0.22464	2.4804	1.5538
2.14	0.76673	0.48022	0.32383	1.6653	1.4830	2.64	0.69205	0.34691	0.22310	2.5017	1.5549
2.15	0.76493	0.47696	0.32122	1.6780	1.4849	2.65	0.69084	0.34478	0.22158	2.5233	1.5560
2.16	0.76314	0.47373	0.31864	1.6908	1.4867	2.66	0.68964	0.34267	0.22007	2.5451	1.5571
2.17	0.76137	0.47052	0.31610	1.7037	1.4885	2.67	0.68845	0.34057	0.21857	2.5671	1.5582
2.18	0.75961	0.46734	0.31359	1.7168	1.4903	2.68	0.68727	0.33849	0.21709	2.5892	1.5593
2.19	0.75787	0.46419	0.31110	1.7300	1.4921	2.69	0.68610	0.33643	0.21562	2.6116	1.5603
2.20	0.75614	0.46106	0.30864	1.7434	1.4939	2.70	0.68494	0.33439	0.21417	2.6342	1.5613
2.21	0.75442	0.45796	0.30621	1.7570	1.4956	2.71	0.68378	0.33236	0.21273	2.6571	1.5623
2.22	0.75271	0.45489	0.30381	1.7707	1.4973	2.72	0.68263	0.33035	0.21131	2.6802	1.5633
2.23	0.75102	0.45184	0.30143	1.7846	1.4990	2.73	0.68150	0.32836	0.20990	2.7035	1.5644
2.24	0.74934	0.44882	0.29908	1.7986	1.5007	2.74	0.68038	0.32638	0.20850	2.7270	1.5654
2.25	0.74767	0.44582	0.29675	1.8128	1.5024	2.75	0.67926	0.32442	0.20712	2.7508	1.5663
2.26	0.74602	0.44285	0.29445	1.8271	1.5040	2.76	0.67815	0.32248	0.20575	2.7748	1.5673
2.27	0.74438	0.43990	0.29218	1.8416	1.5056	2.77	0.67704	0.32055	0.20439	2.7990	1.5683
2.28	0.74275	0.43698	0.28993	1.8562	1.5072	2.78	0.67595	0.31864	0.20305	2.8235	1.5692
2.29	0.74114	0.43409	0.28771	1.8710	1.5088	2.79	0.67487	0.31674	0.20172	2.8482	1.5702
2.30	0.73954	0.43122	0.28551	1.8860	1.5104	2.80	0.67380	0.31486	0.20040	2.8731	1.5711
2.31	0.73795	0.42837	0.28333	1.9012	1.5119	2.81	0.67273	0.31299	0.19909	2.8982	1.5721
2.32	0.73638	0.42555	0.28118	1.9165	1.5134	2.82	0.67167	0.31114	0.19780	2.9236	1.5730
2.33	0.73482	0.42276	0.27905	1.9320	1.5150	2.83	0.67062	0.30931	0.19652	2.9493	1.5739
2.34	0.73327	0.41999	0.27695	1.9476	1.5165	2.84	0.66958	0.30749	0.19525	2.9752	1.5748

Left section (x = 2.35–2.59):

x					
2.35	0.73173	0.41724	0.27487	1.9634	1.5180
2.36	0.73020	0.41451	0.27281	1.9794	1.5195
2.37	0.72868	0.41181	0.27077	1.9955	1.5209
2.38	0.72718	0.40913	0.26875	2.0118	1.5223
2.39	0.72569	0.40647	0.26675	2.0283	1.5237
2.40	0.72421	0.40383	0.26478	2.0450	1.5252
2.41	0.72274	0.40122	0.26283	2.0619	1.5266
2.42	0.72129	0.39863	0.26090	2.0789	1.5279
2.43	0.71985	0.39606	0.25899	2.0961	1.5293
2.44	0.71842	0.39352	0.25710	2.1135	1.5306
2.45	0.71700	0.39100	0.25523	2.1311	1.5320
2.46	0.71559	0.38850	0.25337	2.1489	1.5333
2.47	0.71419	0.38602	0.25153	2.1669	1.5346
2.48	0.71280	0.38356	0.24972	2.1850	1.5359
2.49	0.71142	0.38112	0.24793	2.2033	1.5372
2.50	0.71005	0.37870	0.24616	2.2218	1.5385
2.51	0.70870	0.37630	0.24440	2.2405	1.5398
2.52	0.70736	0.37392	0.24266	2.2594	1.5410
2.53	0.70603	0.37157	0.24094	2.2785	1.5422
2.54	0.70471	0.36923	0.23923	2.2978	1.5434
2.55	0.70340	0.36691	0.23754	2.3173	1.5446
2.56	0.70210	0.36461	0.23587	2.3370	1.5458
2.57	0.70081	0.36233	0.23422	2.3569	1.5470
2.58	0.69953	0.36007	0.23258	2.3770	1.5482
2.59	0.69825	0.35783	0.23096	2.3972	1.5494

Right section (x = 2.85–∞):

x					
2.85	0.66855	0.30568	0.19399	3.0013	1.5757
2.86	0.66752	0.30389	0.19274	3.0277	1.5766
2.87	0.66650	0.30211	0.19151	3.0544	1.5775
2.88	0.66549	0.30035	0.19029	3.0813	1.5784
2.89	0.66449	0.29860	0.18908	3.1084	1.5792
2.90	0.66350	0.29687	0.18788	3.1358	1.5801
2.91	0.66252	0.29515	0.18669	3.1635	1.5809
2.92	0.66154	0.29344	0.18551	3.1914	1.5818
2.93	0.66057	0.29175	0.18435	3.2196	1.5826
2.94	0.65961	0.29007	0.18320	3.2481	1.5834
2.95	0.65865	0.2841	0.18205	3.2768	1.5843
2.96	0.65770	0.28676	0.18091	3.3058	1.5851
2.97	0.65676	0.28512	0.17978	3.3351	1.5859
2.98	0.65583	0.28349	0.17867	3.3646	1.5867
2.99	0.65490	0.28188	0.17757	3.3944	1.5875
3.00	0.65398	0.28028	0.17647	3.4244	1.5882
3.50	0.61580	0.21419	0.13223	5.3280	1.6198
4.00	0.58909	0.16831	0.10256	8.2268	1.6410
4.50	0.56983	0.13540	0.08177	12.502	1.6559
5.00	0.55555	0.11111	0.06667	18.634	1.6667
6.00	0.53633	0.07849	0.04669	38.946	1.6809
7.00	0.52437	0.05826	0.03448	75.414	1.6896
8.00	0.51646	0.04491	0.02649	136.62	1.6954
9.00	0.51098	0.03565	0.02098	233.88	1.6993
10.00	0.50702	0.02897	0.01702	381.62	1.7021
∞	0.48980	0	0	∞	1.7143

TABLE A-5. FRICTIONAL, ADIABATIC, CONSTANT-AREA FLOW †

Perfect gas, k = 1.4 exactly

M	T/T^*	p/p^*	p_0/p_0^*	V/V^* ρ^*/ρ	F/F^*	$4fL_{max}/D$
0	1.2000	∞	∞	0	∞	∞
0.01	1.2000	10,9.544	5,7.874	0.01095	4,5.650	7,134.40
0.02	1.1999	5,4.770	2,8.942	0.02191	22,834	1,778.45
0.03	1.1998	3,6.511	1,9.300	0.03286	15,232	7,87.08
0.04	1.1996	27,382	14,482	0.04381	11,435	4,40.35
0.05	1.1994	21,903	11,5914	0.05476	9,1584	2,80.02
0.06	1.1991	18,251	9,6659	0.06570	7,6.428	19,3.03
0.07	1.1988	15,6.42	8,2.915	0.07664	6,5.620	14,0.66
0.08	1.1985	13,6.84	7,2.616	0.08758	5,7.529	10,6.72
0.09	1.1981	12,1.62	6,4.614	0.09851	5,1.249	8,3.496
0.10	1.1976	10,9.435	5,8.218	0.10943	4.6,236	66,922
0.11	1.1971	9,9.465	5,2.992	0.12035	4.2,146	54,688
0.12	1.1966	9,1.156	4,8.643	0.13126	3.8,747	45,408
0.13	1.1960	8,4.123	4,4.968	0.14216	3.58,80	38,207
0.14	1.1953	7,8.093	4,1.824	0.15306	3.34,32	32,511
0.15	1.1946	7,2.866	3,91.03	0.16395	3.13,17	27,932
0.16	1.1939	6,82.91	3,67.27	0.17482	2.94,74	24,198
0.17	1.1931	6,42.52	3,46.35	0.18568	2.78,55	21,115
0.18	1.1923	6.06,62	3,27.79	0.19654	2.64,22	18.5,43
0.19	1.1914	5,74.48	3,11.23	0.20739	2.51,46	16,3.75
0.20	1.1905	5.45,55	2.96,35	0.21822	2.40,04	14.5,33
0.21	1.1895	5.19,36	2.82,93	0.22904	2.29,76	12.9,56
0.22	1.1885	4.95,54	2.70,76	0.23984	2.20,46	11.5,96
0.23	1.1874	4.73,78	2.59,68	0.25063	2.12,03	10.4,16
0.24	1.1863	4.53,83	2.49,56	0.26141	2.04,34	9.3,865

M	T/T^*	p/p^*	p_0/p_0^*	V/V^* ρ^*/ρ	F/F^*	$4fL_{max}/D$
0.50	1.1429	2.138,1	1.339,9	0.53453	1.202,7	1.06,908
0.51	1.1407	2.094,2	1.321,2	0.54469	1.190,3	0.99,042
0.52	1.1384	2.051,9	1.303,4	0.55482	1.178,6	0.91,741
0.53	1.1362	2.011,2	1.286,4	0.56493	1.167,5	0.84,963
0.54	1.1339	1.971,9	1.270,2	0.57501	1.157,1	0.786,62
0.55	1.1315	1.934,1	1.254,9	0.58506	1.147,2	0.728,05
0.56	1.1292	1.897,6	1.240,3	0.59507	1.137,8	0.673,57
0.57	1.1268	1.862,3	1.226,3	0.60505	1.128,9	0.622,86
0.58	1.1244	1.828,2	1.213,0	0.61500	1.120,5	0.575,68
0.59	1.1219	1.795,2	1.200,3	0.62492	1.112,6	0.531,74
0.60	1.1194	1.763,4	1.188,2	0.63481	1.1050,4	0.490,81
0.61	1.1169	1.732,5	1.176,6	0.64467	1.0979,3	0.452,70
0.62	1.1144	1.702,6	1.165,6	0.65449	1.0912,0	0.417,20
0.63	1.1118	1.673,7	1.155,1	0.66427	1.0848,5	0.384,11
0.64	1.1091	1.645,6	1.145,1	0.67402	1.0788,3	0.353,30
0.65	1.10650	1.618,3	1.135,6	0.68374	1.0731,4	0.324,60
0.66	1.10383	1.591,9	1.126,5	0.69342	1.0677,7	0.297,85
0.67	1.10114	1.566,2	1.117,9	0.70306	1.0627,1	0.272,95
0.68	1.09842	1.541,3	1.109,7	0.71267	1.0579,2	0.249,78
0.69	1.09567	1.517,0	1.101,8	0.72225	1.0534,0	0.228,21
0.70	1.09290	1.493,4	1.0943,6	0.73179	1.0491,5	0.208,14
0.71	1.09010	1.470,5	1.0872,9	0.74129	1.0451,4	0.189,49
0.72	1.08727	1.448,2	1.0805,7	0.75076	1.0413,7	0.172,15
0.73	1.08442	1.426,5	1.0741,9	0.76019	1.0378,3	0.156,06
0.74	1.08155	1.405,4	1.0681,5	0.76958	1.0345,0	0.141,13

M							M						
0.25	1.1852	4.35,46	2.40,27	0.27217	1.97,32	8.4,834	0.75	1.07856	1.384,8	1.0624,2	0.77893	1.0313,7	0.127,28
0.26	1.1840	4.18,50	2.31,73	0.28291	1.90,88	7.6,876	0.76	1.07573	1.364,7	1.0570,0	0.78825	1.0284,4	0.114,46
0.27	1.1828	4.02,80	2.23,85	0.29364	1.84,96	6.9,832	0.77	1.07279	1.345,1	1.0518,8	0.79753	1.0257,0	0.102,62
0.28	1.1815	3.88,20	2.16,56	0.30435	1.795,0	6.3,572	0.78	1.06982	1.326,0	1.0470,5	0.80677	1.0231,4	0.091,67
0.29	1.1802	3.74,60	2.09,79	0.31504	1.744,6	5.7,989	0.79	1.06684	1.3074	1.0425,0	0.81598	1.0207,5	0.081,59
0.30	1.1788	3.61,90	2.035,1	0.32572	1.697,9	5.2,992	0.80	1.06383	1.2892	1.0382,3	0.82514	1.0185,3	0.072,29
0.31	1.1774	3.50,02	1.976,5	0.33637	1.654,6	4.8,507	0.81	1.06080	1.2715	1.0342,2	0.83426	1.0164,6	0.063,75
0.32	1.1759	3.38,88	1.921,9	0.34700	1.614,4	4.44,68	0.82	1.05775	1.2542	1.0304,7	0.84334	1.0145,5	0.055,93
0.33	1.1744	3.28,40	1.870,8	0.35762	1.576,9	4.08,21	0.83	1.05468	1.2373	1.0269,6	0.85239	1.0127,8	0.048,78
0.34	1.1729	3.18,53	1.822,9	0.36822	1.542,0	3.75,20	0.84	1.05160	1.2208	1.0237,0	0.86140	1.0111,5	0.042,26
0.35	1.1713	3.09,22	1.778,0	0.37880	1.509,4	3.45,25	0.85	1.04849	1.2047	1.0206,7	0.87037	1.0096,6	0.036,32
0.36	1.1697	3.004,2	1.735,8	0.38935	1.478,9	3.18,01	0.86	1.04537	1.1889	1.0178,7	0.87929	1.0082,9	0.030,97
0.37	1.1680	2.920,9	1.696,1	0.39988	1.450,3	2.93,20	0.87	1.04223	1.1735	1.0152,9	0.88818	1.0070,4	0.026,13
0.38	1.1663	2.842,0	1.658,7	0.41039	1.423,6	2.70,55	0.88	1.03907	1.1584	1.0129,4	0.89703	1.0059,1	0.021,80
0.39	1.1646	2.767,1	1.623,4	0.42087	1.398,5	2.49,83	0.89	1.03589	1.1436	1.0108,0	0.90583	1.0049,0	0.017,93
0.40	1.1628	2.695,8	1.590,1	0.43133	1.374,9	2.30,85	0.90	1.03270	1.1291,3	1.0088,7	0.91459	1.0039,9	0.0145,13
0.41	1.1610	2.628,0	1.558,7	0.44177	1.352,7	2.13,44	0.91	1.02950	1.1150,0	1.0071,4	0.92332	1.0031,8	0.0115,19
0.42	1.1591	2.563,4	1.528,9	0.45218	1.331,8	1.97,44	0.92	1.02627	1.1011,4	1.0056,0	0.93201	1.0024,8	0.0089,16
0.43	1.1572	2.501,7	1.500,7	0.46257	1.312,2	1.82,72	0.93	1.02304	1.0875,8	1.0042,6	0.94065	1.0018,8	0.0066,94
0.44	1.1553	2.442,8	1.473,9	0.47293	1.293,7	1.69,15	0.94	1.01978	1.0743,0	1.0031,1	0.94925	1.0013,6	0.0048,15
0.45	1.1533	2.386,5	1.448,6	0.48326	1.276,3	1.56,64	0.95	1.01652	1.0612,9	1.0021,5	0.95782	1.0009,3	0.0032,80
0.46	1.1513	2.332,6	1.424,6	0.49357	1.259,8	1.45,09	0.96	1.01324	1.0485,4	1.0013,7	0.96634	1.0005,9	0.0020,56
0.47	1.1492	2.280,9	1.401,8	0.50385	1.244,3	1.34,42	0.97	1.00995	1.0360,5	1.0007,6	0.97481	1.0003,3	0.0011,35
0.48	1.1471	2.231,4	1.380,1	0.51410	1.229,6	1.24,53	0.98	1.00664	1.0237,9	1.0003,3	0.98324	1.0001,4	0.0004,93
0.49	1.1450	2.183,8	1.359,5	0.52433	1.215,8	1.15,39	0.99	1.00333	1.0117,8	1.0000,8	0.99164	1.0000,3	0.0001,20

† From A. H. Shapiro, W. R. Hawthorne, and G. M. Edelman, The Mechanics and Thermodynamics of Steady One-dimensional Gas Flow with Tables for Numerical Solutions, Meteor Report No. 14, Bureau of Ordnance Contract NOrd 9661, Dec. 1, 1947.

NOTES: 1. For values of M from 0 to 3.00, all digits to the left of the comma are valid for linear interpolation. Where no comma is indicated in this region, all digits are valid for linear interpolation.

2. The notation 0.0_3429 signifies 0.000429. The notation 5370_4 signifies 5,370,000.

Table A-5. Frictional, Adiabatic, Constant-area Flow (Continued)

Perfect gas, $k = 1.4$ exactly

M	T/T^*	p/p^*	p_0/p_0^*	V/V^* ρ^*/ρ	F/F^*	$4fL_{max}/D$
1.00	1.00000	1.0000,0	1.0000,0	1.00000	1.0000,0	0
1.01	0.99666	0.9884,4	1.0000,8	1.00831	1.0000,3	0.0001,14
1.02	0.99331	0.9771,1	1.0003,3	1.01658	1.0001,3	0.0004,58
1.03	0.98995	0.9659,8	1.0007,3	1.02481	1.0003,0	0.0010,13
1.04	0.98658	0.9550,6	1.0013,0	1.03300	1.0005,3	0.0017,71
1.05	0.98320	0.9443,5	1.0020,3	1.04115	1.0008,2	0.0027,12
1.06	0.97982	0.9338,3	1.0029,1	1.04925	1.0011,6	0.0038,37
1.07	0.97642	0.9235,0	1.0039,4	1.05731	1.0015,5	0.0051,29
1.08	0.97302	0.9133,5	1.0051,2	1.06533	1.0020,0	0.0065,82
1.09	0.96960	0.9033,8	1.0064,5	1.07331	1.0025,0	0.0081,85
1.10	0.96618	0.8935,9	1.0079,3	1.08124	1.00305	0.0099,33
1.11	0.96276	0.8839,7	1.0095,5	1.08913	1.00365	0.0118,13
1.12	0.95933	0.8745,1	1.0113,1	1.09698	1.00429	0.0138,24
1.13	0.95589	0.8652,2	1.0132,2	1.10479	1.00497	0.0159,49
1.14	0.95244	0.8560,8	1.0152,7	1.11256	1.00569	0.0181,87
1.15	0.94899	0.8471,0	1.0174,6	1.1203	1.00646	0.0205,3
1.16	0.94554	0.8382,7	1.0197,8	1.1280	1.00726	0.0229,8
1.17	0.94208	0.8295,8	1.0222,4	1.1356	1.00810	0.0255,2
1.18	0.93862	0.8210,4	1.0248,4	1.1432	1.00897	0.0281,4
1.19	0.93515	0.8126,3	1.0275,7	1.1508	1.00988	0.0308,5
1.20	0.93168	0.8043,6	1.0304,4	1.1583	1.01082	0.0336,4
1.21	0.92820	0.7962,3	1.0334,4	1.1658	1.01178	0.0365,0
1.22	0.92473	0.7882,2	1.0365,7	1.1732	1.01278	0.0394,2
1.23	0.92125	0.7803,4	1.0398,3	1.1806	1.01381	0.0424,1
1.24	0.91777	0.7725,8	1.0432,3	1.1879	1.01486	0.0454,7

M	T/T^*	p/p^*	p_0/p_0^*	V/V^* ρ^*/ρ	F/F^*	$4fL_{max}/D$
1.55	0.81054	0.5808,4	1.2116	1.3955	1.05604	0.15427
1.56	0.80715	0.5759,1	1.2190	1.4015	1.05752	0.15790
1.57	0.80376	0.5710,4	1.2266	1.4075	1.05900	0.16152
1.58	0.80038	0.5662,3	1.2343	1.4135	1.06049	0.16514
1.59	0.79701	0.5614,8	1.2422	1.4195	1.06198	0.16876
1.60	0.79365	0.5567,9	1.2502	1.4254	1.06348	0.17236
1.61	0.79030	0.5521,6	1.2583	1.4313	1.06498	0.17595
1.62	0.78695	0.5475,9	1.2666	1.4371	1.06648	0.17953
1.63	0.78361	0.5430,8	1.2750	1.4429	1.06798	0.18311
1.64	0.78028	0.5386,2	1.2835	1.4487	1.06948	0.18667
1.65	0.77695	0.5342,1	1.2922	1.4544	1.07098	0.19022
1.66	0.77363	0.5298,6	1.3010	1.4601	1.07249	0.19376
1.67	0.77033	0.5255,6	1.3099	1.4657	1.07399	0.19729
1.68	0.76703	0.5213,1	1.3190	1.4713	1.07550	0.20081
1.69	0.76374	0.5171,1	1.3282	1.4769	1.07701	0.20431
1.70	0.76046	0.5129,7	1.3376	1.4825	1.07851	0.20780
1.71	0.75718	0.5088,7	1.3471	1.4880	1.08002	0.21128
1.72	0.75392	0.5048,2	1.3567	1.4935	1.08152	0.21474
1.73	0.75067	0.5008,2	1.3665	1.4989	1.08302	0.21819
1.74	0.74742	0.4968,6	1.3764	1.5043	1.08453	0.22162
1.75	0.74419	0.4929,5	1.3865	1.5097	1.08603	0.22504
1.76	0.74096	0.4890,9	1.3967	1.5150	1.08753	0.22844
1.77	0.73774	0.4852,7	1.4070	1.5203	1.08903	0.23183
1.78	0.73453	0.4814,9	1.4175	1.5256	1.09053	0.23520
1.79	0.73134	0.4777,6	1.4282	1.5308	1.09202	0.23855

0.24189	1.09352	1.5360	1.4390	0.47407	0.72816	1.80	0.04858	1.01594	1.1952	1.0467,6	0.7649,5	0.91429	1.25
0.24521	1.09500	1.5412	1.4499	0.47042	0.72498	1.81	0.05174	1.01705	1.2025	1.0504,1	0.7574,3	0.91080	1.26
0.24851	1.09649	1.5463	1.4610	0.46681	0.72181	1.82	0.05494	1.01818	1.2097	1.0541,9	0.7500,3	0.90732	1.27
0.25180	1.09798	1.5514	1.4723	0.46324	0.71865	1.83	0.05820	1.01933	1.2169	1.0580,9	0.7427,4	0.90383	1.28
0.25507	1.09946	1.5564	1.4837	0.45972	0.71551	1.84	0.06150	1.02050	1.2240	1.0621,3	0.7355,6	0.90035	1.29
0.25832	1.1009	1.5614	1.4952	0.45623	0.71238	1.85	0.06483	1.02169	1.2311	1.0663,0	0.7284,8	0.89686	1.30
0.26156	1.1024	1.5664	1.5069	0.45278	0.70925	1.86	0.06820	1.02291	1.2382	1.0706,0	0.7215,2	0.89338	1.31
0.26478	1.1039	1.5714	1.5188	0.44937	0.70614	1.87	0.07161	1.02415	1.2452	1.0750,2	0.7146,5	0.88989	1.32
0.26798	1.1054	1.5763	1.5308	0.44600	0.70304	1.88	0.07504	1.02540	1.2522	1.0795,7	0.7078,9	0.88641	1.33
0.27116	1.1068	1.5812	1.5429	0.44266	0.69995	1.89	0.07850	1.02666	1.2591	1.0842,4	0.7012,3	0.88292	1.34
0.27433	1.1083	1.5861	1.5552	0.43936	0.69686	1.90	0.08199	1.02794	1.2660	1.0890,4	0.6946,6	0.87944	1.35
0.27748	1.1097	1.5909	1.5677	0.43610	0.69379	1.91	0.08550	1.02924	1.2729	1.0939,7	0.6881,8	0.87596	1.36
0.28061	1.1112	1.5957	1.5804	0.43287	0.69074	1.92	0.08904	1.03056	1.2797	1.0990,2	0.6818,0	0.87249	1.37
0.28372	1.1126	1.6005	1.5932	0.42967	0.68769	1.93	0.09259	1.03189	1.2864	1.1041,9	0.6755,1	0.86901	1.38
0.28681	1.1141	1.6052	1.6062	0.42651	0.68465	1.94	0.09616	1.03323	1.2932	1.1094,8	0.6693,1	0.86554	1.39
0.28989	1.1155	1.6099	1.6193	0.42339	0.68162	1.95	0.09974	1.03458	1.2999	1.1149	0.6632,0	0.86207	1.40
0.29295	1.1170	1.6146	1.6326	0.42030	0.67861	1.96	0.10333	1.03595	1.3065	1.1205	0.6571,7	0.85860	1.41
0.29599	1.1184	1.6193	1.6461	0.41724	0.67561	1.97	0.10694	1.03733	1.3131	1.1262	0.6512,2	0.85514	1.42
0.29901	1.1198	1.6239	1.6597	0.41421	0.67262	1.98	0.11056	1.03872	1.3197	1.1320	0.6453,6	0.85168	1.43
0.30201	1.1213	1.6284	1.6735	0.41121	0.66964	1.99	0.11419	1.04012	1.3262	1.1379	0.6395,8	0.84822	1.44
0.30499	1.1227	1.6330	1.6875	0.40825	0.66667	2.00	0.11782	1.04153	1.3327	1.1440	0.6338,7	0.84477	1.45
0.30796	1.1241	1.6375	1.7017	0.40532	0.66371	2.01	0.12146	1.04295	1.3392	1.1502	0.6282,4	0.84133	1.46
0.31091	1.1255	1.6420	1.7160	0.40241	0.66076	2.02	0.12510	1.04438	1.3456	1.1565	0.6226,9	0.83788	1.47
0.31384	1.1269	1.6465	1.7305	0.39954	0.65783	2.03	0.12875	1.04581	1.3520	1.1629	0.6172,2	0.83445	1.48
0.31675	1.1283	1.6509	1.7452	0.39670	0.65491	2.04	0.13240	1.04725	1.3583	1.1695	0.6118,1	0.83101	1.49
0.31965	1.1297	1.6553	1.7600	0.39389	0.65200	2.05	0.13605	1.04870	1.3646	1.1762	0.6064,8	0.82759	1.50
0.32253	1.1311	1.6597	1.7750	0.39110	0.64910	2.06	0.13970	1.05016	1.3708	1.1830	0.6012,2	0.82416	1.51
0.32538	1.1325	1.6640	1.7902	0.38834	0.64621	2.07	0.14335	1.05162	1.3770	1.1899	0.5960,2	0.82075	1.52
0.32822	1.1339	1.6683	1.8056	0.38562	0.64333	2.08	0.14699	1.05309	1.3832	1.1970	0.5908,9	0.81734	1.53
0.33104	1.1352	1.6726	1.8212	0.38292	0.64047	2.09	0.15063	1.05456	1.3894	1.2043	0.5858,3	0.81394	1.54

TABLE A-5. FRICTIONAL, ADIABATIC, CONSTANT-AREA FLOW (*Continued*)

Perfect gas, $k = 1.4$ exactly

M	T/T^*	p/p^*	p_0/p_0^*	V/V^* ρ^*/ρ	F/F^*	$4fL_{max}/D$
2.10	0.63762	0.38024	1.8369	1.6769	1.1366	0.33385
2.11	0.63478	0.37760	1.8528	1.6811	1.1380	0.33664
2.12	0.63195	0.37498	1.8690	1.6853	1.1393	0.33940
2.13	0.62914	0.37239	1.8853	1.6895	1.1407	0.34215
2.14	0.62633	0.36982	1.9018	1.6936	1.1420	0.34488
2.15	0.62354	0.36728	1.9185	1.6977	1.1434	0.34760
2.16	0.62076	0.36476	1.9354	1.7018	1.1447	0.35030
2.17	0.61799	0.36227	1.9525	1.7059	1.1460	0.35298
2.18	0.61523	0.35980	1.9698	1.7099	1.1474	0.35564
2.19	0.61249	0.35736	1.9873	1.7139	1.1487	0.35828
2.20	0.60976	0.35494	2.0050	1.7179	1.1500	0.36091
2.21	0.60704	0.35254	2.0228	1.7219	1.1513	0.36352
2.22	0.60433	0.35017	2.0409	1.7258	1.1526	0.36611
2.23	0.60163	0.34782	2.0592	1.7297	1.1539	0.36868
2.24	0.59895	0.34550	2.0777	1.7336	1.1552	0.37124
2.25	0.59627	0.34319	2.0964	1.7374	1.1565	0.37378
2.26	0.59361	0.34091	2.1154	1.7412	1.1578	0.37630
2.27	0.59096	0.33865	2.1345	1.7450	1.1590	0.37881
2.28	0.58833	0.33641	2.1538	1.7488	1.1603	0.38130
2.29	0.58570	0.33420	2.1733	1.7526	1.1616	0.38377
2.30	0.58309	0.33200	2.1931	1.7563	1.1629	0.38623
2.31	0.58049	0.32983	2.2131	1.7600	1.1641	0.38867
2.32	0.57790	0.32767	2.2333	1.7637	1.1653	0.39109
2.33	0.57532	0.32554	2.2537	1.7673	1.1666	0.39350
2.34	0.57276	0.32342	2.2744	1.7709	1.1678	0.39589

M	T/T^*	p/p^*	p_0/p_0^*	V/V^* ρ^*/ρ	F/F^*	$4fL_{max}/D$
2.60	0.51020	0.27473	2.8960	1.8571	1.1978	0.45259
2.61	0.50795	0.27307	2.9234	1.8602	1.1989	0.45457
2.62	0.50571	0.27143	2.9511	1.8632	1.2000	0.45654
2.63	0.50349	0.26980	2.9791	1.8662	1.2011	0.45850
2.64	0.50127	0.26818	3.0074	1.8691	1.2021	0.46044
2.65	0.49906	0.26658	3.0359	1.8721	1.2031	0.46237
2.66	0.49687	0.26499	3.0647	1.8750	1.2042	0.46429
2.67	0.49469	0.26342	3.0938	1.8779	1.2052	0.46619
2.68	0.49251	0.26186	3.1234	1.8808	1.2062	0.46807
2.69	0.49035	0.26032	3.1530	1.8837	1.2073	0.46996
2.70	0.48820	0.25878	3.1830	1.8865	1.2083	0.47182
2.71	0.48606	0.25726	3.2133	1.8894	1.2093	0.47367
2.72	0.48393	0.25575	3.2440	1.8922	1.2103	0.47551
2.73	0.48182	0.25426	3.2749	1.8950	1.2113	0.47734
2.74	0.47971	0.25278	3.3061	1.8978	1.2123	0.47915
2.75	0.47761	0.25131	3.3376	1.9005	1.2133	0.48095
2.76	0.47553	0.24985	3.3695	1.9032	1.2143	0.48274
2.77	0.47346	0.24840	3.4017	1.9060	1.2153	0.48452
2.78	0.47139	0.24697	3.4342	1.9087	1.2163	0.48628
2.79	0.46933	0.24555	3.4670	1.9114	1.2173	0.48803
2.80	0.46729	0.24414	3.5001	1.9140	1.2182	0.48976
2.81	0.46526	0.24274	3.5336	1.9167	1.2192	0.49148
2.82	0.46324	0.24135	3.5674	1.9193	1.2202	0.49321
2.83	0.46122	0.23997	3.6015	1.9220	1.2211	0.49491
2.84	0.45922	0.23861	3.6359	1.9246	1.2221	0.49660

x						
2.35	0.57021	0.32133	2.2953	1.7745	1.1690	0.39826
2.36	0.56767	0.31925	2.3164	1.7781	1.1703	0.40062
2.37	0.56514	0.31720	2.3377	1.7817	1.1715	0.40296
2.38	0.56262	0.31516	2.3593	1.7852	1.1727	0.40528
2.39	0.56011	0.31314	2.3811	1.7887	1.1739	0.40760
2.40	0.55762	0.31114	2.4031	1.7922	1.1751	0.40989
2.41	0.55514	0.30916	2.4254	1.7956	1.1763	0.41216
2.42	0.55267	0.30720	2.4479	1.7991	1.1775	0.41442
2.43	0.55021	0.30525	2.4706	1.8025	1.1786	0.41667
2.44	0.54776	0.30332	2.4936	1.8059	1.1798	0.41891
2.45	0.54533	0.30141	2.5168	1.8092	1.1810	0.42113
2.46	0.54291	0.29952	2.5403	1.8126	1.1821	0.42333
2.47	0.54050	0.29765	2.5640	1.8159	1.1833	0.42551
2.48	0.53810	0.29579	2.5880	1.8192	1.1844	0.42768
2.49	0.53571	0.29395	2.6122	1.8225	1.1856	0.42983
2.50	0.53333	0.29212	2.6367	1.8257	1.1867	0.43197
2.51	0.53097	0.29031	2.6615	1.8290	1.1879	0.43410
2.52	0.52862	0.28852	2.6865	1.8322	1.1890	0.43621
2.53	0.52627	0.28674	2.7117	1.8354	1.1901	0.43831
2.54	0.52394	0.28498	2.7372	1.8386	1.1912	0.44040
2.55	0.52163	0.28323	2.7630	1.8417	1.1923	0.44247
2.56	0.51932	0.28150	2.7891	1.8448	1.1934	0.44452
2.57	0.51702	0.27978	2.8154	1.8479	1.1945	0.44655
2.58	0.51474	0.27808	2.8420	1.8510	1.1956	0.44857
2.59	0.51247	0.27640	2.8689	1.8541	1.1967	0.45059

x						
2.85	0.45723	0.23726	3.6707	1.9271	1.2230	0.49828
2.86	0.45525	0.23592	3.7058	1.9297	1.2240	0.49995
2.87	0.45328	0.23458	3.7413	1.9322	1.2249	0.50161
2.88	0.45132	0.23326	3.7771	1.9348	1.2258	0.50326
2.89	0.44937	0.23196	3.8133	1.9373	1.2268	0.50489
2.90	0.44743	0.23066	3.8498	1.9398	1.2277	0.50651
2.91	0.44550	0.22937	3.8866	1.9423	1.2286	0.50812
2.92	0.44358	0.22809	3.9238	1.9448	1.2295	0.50973
2.93	0.44167	0.22682	3.9614	1.9472	1.2304	0.51133
2.94	0.43977	0.22556	3.9993	1.9497	1.2313	0.51291
2.95	0.43788	0.22431	4.0376	1.9521	1.2322	0.51447
2.96	0.43600	0.22307	4.0763	1.9545	1.2331	0.51603
2.97	0.43413	0.22185	4.1153	1.9569	1.2340	0.51758
2.98	0.43226	0.22063	4.1547	1.9592	1.2348	0.51912
2.99	0.43041	0.21942	4.1944	1.9616	1.2357	0.52064
3.00	0.42857	0.21822	4.2346	1.9640	1.2366	0.52216
3.50	0.34783	0.16763	6.7896	2.0642	1.2743	0.58643
4.00	0.28571	0.13363	10.719	2.1381	1.3029	0.63306
4.50	0.23762	0.10833	16.562	2.1936	1.3247	0.66764
5.00	0.20000	0.08944	25.000	2.2361	1.3416	0.69381
6.00	0.14634	0.06376	53.180	2.2953	1.3655	0.72987
7.00	0.11111	0.04762	104.14	2.3333	1.3810	0.75281
8.00	0.08696	0.03686	190.11	2.3591	1.3915	0.76820
9.00	0.06977	0.02935	327.19	2.3772	1.3989	0.77898
10.00	0.05714	0.02390	535.94	2.3905	1.4044	0.78683
∞	0	0	∞	2.4495	1.4289	0.82153

TABLE A-6. ENTHALPIES OF SOME FUELS, OXIDANTS, AND DILUENTS [a]

| Chemical species | At 291°K | | ΔH from substance at 300°K to combustion products at 0°K [d] | |
	Heat of formation [b]	Heat of combustion [c]	Btu/lb mole	Btu/lb
CH_4 methane............	18,240 (g)	...	343,060 liq. (at −161°C)	21,400
C_2H_2 acetylene [e]........	−53,900 (g)	...	530,460 liq. (at −81.5°C)	20,390
C_2H_4 ethylene..........	−11,000 (g)	...	563,440 liq. (at −104°C)	20,100
C_6H_6 benzene..........	...	783,400	1,362,670	17,460
C_8H_{16} di-isobutylene.....	...	1,252,400	2,124,540	18,930
C_8H_{18} n-octane..........	...	1,305,000	2,203,400	19,290
C_9H_{20} nonane	+65,040	...	2,477,200	19,330
$C_{10}H_{18}$ decalin..........	...	1,502,500	2,559,600	18,530
CH_3OH methyl alcohol...	57,450	...	281,340	8,784
C_2H_5OH ethyl alcohol....	67,140	...	540,320	11,733
C_4H_3OCHO furfural......	...	559,500	979,560	10,200
CH_3NH_2 methylamine....	...	256,100	425,770	13,710
$C_6H_5NH_2$ aniline.........	...	812,000	1,407,900	15,130
HCN hydrogen cyanide...	−24,000	...	268,270	9,939
CH_3CN acetonitrile......	−11,800	...	522,720	12,740
$C_{12}H_{12}N_2$ 1,2-diphenyl-hydrazine.............	...	1,598,800	2,786,760	15,140
CH_3NO_2 nitromethane....	27,600	...	285,660	4,680
$C_2H_5NO_2$ nitroethane....	33,000	...	552,240	7,360
$C_6H_2(CH_3)(NO_2)_3$ trinitrotoluene........	...	820,700 (s)	1,466,460 (s)	6,458
$C_3H_5(NO_3)_3$ trinitroglycerin..............	...	432,400	760,680	3,350
H_2 hydrogen...........	...	...	102,400 liq. (at −255°C)	50,790
H_2O water..............	68,370	...	−14,600	−810
H_2O_2 hydrogen peroxide...	44,860	...	29,700	873
O_2 oxygen..............	...	...	−1,818 liq. (at −183°C)	−57
O_3 ozone...............	−34,500 (g)	...	60,250 liq. (at −112°C)	1,255
N_2 nitrogen.............	...	...	−1,440 liq. (at −196°C)	−51
NH_3 ammonia...........	16,070	...	132,640	7,790
N_2H_4 hydrazine.........	−12,050	...	238,370	7,440
$N_2H_4 \cdot H_2O$ hydrazine hydrate..............	57,930	...	220,730	4,410
HNO_3 nitric acid........	41,660	...	−14,270	−226
NH_4NO_3 ammonium nitrate...............	87,130 (s)	...	65,450 (s)	998
N_2O_4 nitrogen peroxide...	6,140	...	180	1.96
Air (gaseous) (21.0% O_2-79.0% N_2)...........	...	...	3,750 (g)	130.4
Propane...............	24,820			

[a] H. C. Hottel, G. C. Williams, and C. N. Satterfield, "Thermodynamic Charts for Combustion Processes," vol. I, John Wiley & Sons, Inc., New York, 1949.

[b] Heat of formation in calories per gram mole at 291°K and 1 atm from the elements in their standard states (carbon as solid) to compound in question, in the liquid state unless specified gaseous or solid by (g) or (s).

[c] Heat of combustion in calories per gram mole at 291°K and 1 atm from liquid fuel, unless specified otherwise, to gaseous CO_2, N_2, and liquid H_2O.

[d] Heat evolved on cooling given compound in liquid form (unless specified otherwise) from 300°K (unless specified otherwise) to 0°K, plus heat released by burning with O_2 at 0°K to give CO_2, H_2O (vapor), O_2, and N_2.

[e] Acetylene sublimes at −84°C and 1 atm pressure and has a triple point at −81.5°C and 1.2 atm pressure. To exist in the liquid state, therefore, C_2H_2 must be under a minimum pressure of 1.2 atm.

TABLE A-7. ENTHALPIES AND ENTROPIES OF VARIOUS SPECIES †

Cal/gm mole

Enthalpy

Temp., °K	H	H_2	O	OH	H_2O	CO	N_2	Air-N_2	NO	O_2	CO_2	C	Temp., °K
0	80,174	57,108	58,600	37,804	0	66,769	0	0	21,400	0	0	93,969	0
200	81,167	58,468	59,593	39,203	1,581	68,158	......	1,384	22,892	1,376	1,417	94,061	200
250	81,416	58,803	59,842	39,565	1,982	68,506	......	1,731	23,255	1,725	1,824	94,131	250
300	81,664	59,145	60,090	39,923	2,380	68,854	2,086	2,078	23,612	2,077	2,256	94,224	300
400	82,160	59,839	60,586	40,632	3,190	69,551	2,781	2,829	24,326	2,797	3,196	94,472	400
600	83,154	61,238	61,580	42,044	4,876	70,978	4,197	4,185	25,788	4,280	5,328	95,167	600
800	84,148	62,647	62,574	43,462	6,673	72,468	5,668	5,651	27,321	5,855	7,697	96,051	800
1000	85,142	64,077	63,568	44,909	8,589	74,026	7,205	7,182	28,921	7,499	10,233	97,044	1000
1200	86,135	65,538	64,561	46,388	10,627	75,639	8,795	8,765	30,570	9,186	12,885	98,099	1200
1400	87,128	67,040	65,554	47,925	12,779	77,291	10,428	10,393	32,255	10,908	15,623	99,211	1400
1600	88,121	68,584	66,547	49,507	15,040	78,974	12,095	12,052	33,967	12,655	18,424	100,369	1600
1800	89,115	70,168	67,541	51,120	17,386	80,683	13,789	13,738	35,700	14,427	21,273	101,547	1800
2000	90,109	71,790	68,535	52,758	19,805	82,409	15,504	15,444	37,440	16,224	24,159	102,749	2000
2200	91,103	73,441	69,529	54,430	22,290	84,149	17,230	17,164	39,197	18,040	27,077	103,957	2200
2400	92,095	75,121	70,521	56,137	24,827	85,900	18,970	18,898	40,964	19,877	30,017	105,200	2400
2600	93,090	76,829	71,516	57,860	27,412	87,662	20,723	20,643	42,743	21,734	32,986	106,450	2600
2800	94,084	78,557	72,510	59,603	30,038	89,432	22,487	22,397	44,532	23,611	35,970	107,710	2800
3000	95,077	80,307	73,503	61,372	32,697	91,209	24,258	24,156	46,330	25,506	38,970	109,000	3000
3200	96,070	82,073	74,496	63,151	35,387	92,991	26,034	25,923	48,132	27,422	41,991	110,290	3200

† H. C. Hottel, G. C. Williams, and C. N. Satterfield, "Thermodynamic Charts for Combustion Processes," vol. I, John Wiley & Sons, Inc., New York, 1949.

TABLE A-7. ENTHALPIES AND ENTROPIES OF VARIOUS SPECIES (*Continued*)

Entropy

Temp., °K	H	H₂	O	OH	H₂O	CO	N₂	Air-N₂	NO	O₂	CO₂	C	Temp., °K
0	0	0	0	0	0	0	0	0	0	0	0	0	0
200	25.42	28.527	36.50	41.03	41.949	44.536	......	42.935	47.49	46.224	47.756	0.7238	200
250	26.53	30.022	37.61	42.64	43.722	46.089	......	44.496	49.10	47.777	49.565	1.0365	250
300	27.44	31.269	38.52	43.94	45.179	47.357	45.828	45.747	50.41	49.050	51.140	1.374	300
400	28.87	33.267	39.95	46.00	47.509	49.366	47.833	47.747	52.45	51.121	53.844	2.081	400
600	30.88	36.101	41.96	48.86	50.916	52.253	50.701	50.606	55.41	54.125	58.141	3.474	600
800	32.31	38.122	43.39	50.90	53.490	54.396	52.815	52.713	57.61	56.386	61.543	4.740	800
1000	33.42	39.719	44.50	52.51	55.614	56.133	54.526	54.417	59.40	58.214	64.370	5.846	1000
1200	34.32	41.052	45.40	53.86	57.491	57.602	55.976	55.862	60.87	59.752	66.787	6.807	1200
1400	35.07	42.209	46.15	55.03	59.150	58.876	57.236	57.115	62.17	61.079	68.895	7.663	1400
1600	35.74	43.239	46.82	56.09	60.655	59.999	58.348	58.223	63.32	62.246	70.764	8.43	1600
1800	36.33	44.172	47.41	57.04	62.034	61.005	59.344	59.214	64.35	63.289	72.441	9.13	1800
2000	36.86	45.026	47.94	57.91	63.310	61.914	60.247	60.113	65.28	64.234	73.959	9.76	2000
2200	37.31	45.813	48.39	58.70	64.496	62.742	61.070	60.932	66.10	65.100	75.349	10.34	2200
2400	37.75	46.544	48.83	59.44	65.60	63.504	61.828	61.688	66.88	65.899	76.632	10.88	2400
2600	38.16	47.227	49.24	60.13	66.64	64.209	62.530	62.385	67.60	66.643	77.824	11.37	2600
2800	38.53	47.868	49.61	60.78	67.61	64.863	63.182	63.034	68.26	67.339	78.935	11.85	2800
3000	38.87	48.471	49.95	61.39	68.53	65.480	63.792	63.641	68.88	67.992	79.970	12.29	3000
3200	39.19	49.041	50.27	61.96	69.39	66.074	64.365	64.211	69.46	68.614	80.952	12.70	3200

TABLE A-8. SPECIFIC-HEAT EQUATIONS †

Gas or vapor	Equation [C_p, Btu/(lb mole)(°F)]	Range, °R	Max. error, %
O_2.......	$C_p = 11.515 - \dfrac{172}{\sqrt{T}} + \dfrac{1{,}530}{T}$	540–5000	1.1
	$C_p = 11.515 - \dfrac{172}{\sqrt{T}} + \dfrac{1{,}530}{T} + \dfrac{0.05}{1{,}000}(T - 4000)$	5000–9000	0.3
N_2.......	$C_p = 9.47 - \dfrac{3.47 \times 10^3}{T} + \dfrac{1.16 \times 10^6}{T^2}$	540–9000	1.7
CO.......	$C_p = 9.46 - \dfrac{3.29 \times 10^3}{T} + \dfrac{1.07 \times 10^6}{T^2}$	540–9000	1.1
H_2.......	$C_p = 5.76 + \dfrac{0.578}{1{,}000}T + \dfrac{20}{\sqrt{T}}$	540–4000	0.8
	$C_p = 5.76 + \dfrac{0.578}{1{,}000}T + \dfrac{20}{\sqrt{T}} - \dfrac{0.33}{1{,}000}(T - 4000)$	4000–9000	1.4
H_2O......	$C_p = 19.86 - \dfrac{597}{\sqrt{T}} + \dfrac{7{,}500}{T}$	540–5400	1.8
CO_2......	$C_p = 16.2 - \dfrac{6.53 \times 10^3}{T} + \dfrac{1.41 \times 10^6}{T^2}$	540–6300	0.8
CH_4......	$C_p = 4.52 + 0.00737T$	540–1500	1.2
C_2H_4.....	$C_p = 4.23 + 0.01177T$	350–1100	1.5
C_2H_6.....	$C_p = 4.01 + 0.01636T$	400–1100	1.5
C_8H_{18}.....	$C_p = 7.92 + 0.0601T$	400–1100	Est. 4
$C_{12}H_{26}$....	$C_p = 8.68 + 0.0889T$	400–1100	Est. 4

† From R. L. Sweigert and M. W. Beardsley, "Empirical Specific Heat Equations Based upon Spectroscopic Data," *Georgia School Technol. Bull.* 2, 1938.

TABLE A-9. FUNCTIONS FOR METHOD OF CHARACTERISTICS †

Perfect gas, $k = 1.4$ exactly; angles ω, α, and ϕ are in degrees

ω	α	ϕ	M	M^*	A/A^*	p/p_0	ρ/ρ_0
0.0000	90.,0000	90.,0000	1.0000	1.0000	1.0000	0.52828	0.63394
0.0001	88.,9438	88.,9437	1.0002	1.0001	1.0000	0.52818	0.63385
0.0002	88.6,680	88.6,678	1.0003	1.0002	1.0000	0.52812	0.63380
0.0005	88.1,921	88.1,916	1.0005	1.0004	1.0000	0.52797	0.63367
0.0010	87.7,222	87.7,212	1.0008	1.0007	1.0000	0.52780	0.63352
0.0020	87.13,05	87.12,85	1.0013	1.0010	1.0000	0.52751	0.63328
0.0050	86.10,67	86.10,17	1.0023	1.0019	1.0000	0.5268,6	0.6327,2
0.0100	85.0,962	85.0,862	1.0037	1.0031	1.0000	0.5260,2	0.6320,0
0.0200	83.8,241	83.8,041	1.0058	1.0049	1.0000	0.5246,9	0.6308,6
0.0300	82.9,331	82.9,031	1.0077	1.0064	1.0001	0.5235,7	0.6299,0
0.0400	82.2,243	82.1,843	1.0093	1.0077	1.0001	0.5225,8	0.6290,4
0.0500	81.6,264	81.5,764	1.0108	1.0090	1.0001	0.5216,6	0.6282,5
0.0600	81.1,041	81.0,441	1.0122	1.0101	1.0001	0.5208,0	0.62751
0.0700	80.63,73	80.56,73	1.0135	1.0112	1.0002	0.51999	0.62681
0.0800	80.21,37	80.13,37	1.0148	1.0123	1.0002	0.51922	0.62615
0.0900	79.82,43	79.73,43	1.0160	1.0133	1.0002	0.51847	0.62550
0.1000	79.4,629	79.3,629	1.0172	1.0142	1.0002	0.5177,6	0.6248,9
0.1250	78.6,553	78.5,303	1.0199	1.0165	1.0003	0.5160,6	0.6234,3
0.1500	77.9,504	77.8,004	1.0225	1.0187	1.0004	0.5144,8	0.6220,6
0.1750	77.3,216	77.1,466	1.0250	1.0207	1.0005	0.5129,8	0.6207,6
0.2000	76.7,498	76.5,498	1.0274	1.0226	1.0006	0.5115,4	0.6195,3
0.2500	75.7,395	75.4,895	1.0318	1.0263	1.0008	0.5088,5	0.6171,9
0.3000	74.8,587	74.5,587	1.0360	1.0297	1.0011	0.5063,2	0.6150,0
0.3500	74.0,723	73.7,223	1.0399	1.0329	1.0013	0.5039,3	0.6129,3
0.4000	73.3,594	72.9,594	1.0437	1.0360	1.0016	0.5016,5	0.6109,4
0.4500	72.7,049	72.2,549	1.0474	1.0390	1.0018	0.4994,6	0.6090,4
0.5000	72.0,988	71.5,988	1.0509	1.0418	1.0021	0.4973,5	0.6072,0
0.6000	71.0,009	70.4,009	1.0576	1.0473	1.0027	0.4933,2	0.6036,8
0.7000	70.0,234	69.3,234	1.0640	1.0525	1.0033	0.4895,0	0.6003,4
0.8000	69.1,381	68.3,381	1.0702	1.0574	1.0040	0.4858,5	0.5971,4
0.9000	68.3,258	67.4,258	1.0761	1.0622	1.0046	0.4823,6	0.5940,7
1.0000	67.5,741	66.5,741	1.0818	1.0668	1.0053	0.4789,8	0.5911,0
1.1000	66.87,36	65.77,36	1.0874	1.0712	1.0061	0.4757,1	0.5882,1
1.2000	66.21,60	65.01,60	1.0928	1.0755	1.0068	0.4725,4	0.5854,1
1.3000	65.59,64	64.29,64	1.0981	1.0798	1.0076	0.4694,5	0.5826,7
1.4000	65.00,92	63.60,92	1.1033	1.0838	1.0084	0.4664,4	0.5800,0
1.5000	64.45,05	62.95,05	1.1084	1.0879	1.0093	0.4635,0	0.57738
1.6000	63.91,77	62.31,77	1.1134	1.0918	1.0101	0.4606,2	0.57482
1.7000	63.40,75	61.70,75	1.1183	1.0956	1.0110	0.4578,0	0.57230
1.8000	62.91,92	61.11,92	1.1231	1.0994	1.0119	0.4550,3	0.56983
1.9000	62.44,93	60.54,93	1.1279	1.1032	1.0128	0.4523,1	0.56739

† From A. H. Shapiro, "The Dynamics and Thermodynamics of Compressible Fluid Flow," The Ronald Press Company, New York, 1953.

NOTES 1. All digits to the left of the comma are valid for linear interpolation. Where no comma is indicated all digits are valid for linear interpolation.

2. $0.0_5 5371$ signifies 0.0005371. 21540_3 signifies $2,154,000$.

TABLE A-9. FUNCTIONS FOR METHOD OF CHARACTERISTICS (*Continued*)

Perfect gas, $k = 1.4$ exactly; angles ω, α, and ϕ are in degrees

ω	α	ϕ	M	M^*	A/A^*	p/p_0	ρ/ρ_0
2.0000	61.99,69	59.99,69	1.1326	1.1068	1.0137	0.44964	0.56500
2.1000	61.56,05	59.46,05	1.1372	1.1104	1.0147	0.44701	0.56263
2.2000	61.13,86	58.93,86	1.1418	1.1140	1.0157	0.44442	0.56031
2.3000	60.72,94	58.42,94	1.1464	1.1175	1.0166	0.44186	0.55800
2.4000	60.33,42	57.93,42	1.1508	1.1209	1.0176	0.43936	0.55574
2.5	59.9,500	57.4,500	1.155,3	1.124,4	1.0187	0.436,88	0.553,50
3.0	58.1,805	55.1,805	1.176,9	1.140,8	1.0240	0.424,94	0.542,65
3.5	56.6,139	53.1,139	1.197,6	1.156,5	1.0297	0.413,65	0.5323,1
4.0	55.2,048	51.2,048	1.217,7	1.171,5	1.0358	0.402,91	0.5224,0
4.5	53.9,204	49.4,204	1.2373	1.185,9	1.0423	0.3926,3	0.5128,4
5.0	52.7,383	47.7,383	1.2565	1.1999	1.0491	0.3827,4	0.5035,8
5.5	51.6,419	46.1,419	1.2753	1.2135	1.0562	0.3732,0	0.4945,9
6.0	50.6,186	44.6,186	1.2938	1.2267	1.0637	0.3639,8	0.4858,3
6.5	49.6,583	43.1,583	1.3120	1.2396	1.0715	0.3550,6	0.4772,9
7.0	48.7,528	41.7,528	1.3300	1.2522	1.0796	0.3464,0	0.4689,5
7.5	47.89,57	40.39,57	1.3478	1.2645	1.0880	0.3379,8	0.4607,8
8.0	47.08,18	39.08,18	1.3655	1.2766	1.0967	0.3297,9	0.4527,8
8.5	46.30,65	37.80,65	1.3830	1.2885	1.1058	0.3218,2	0.4449,3
9.0	45.56,60	36.56,60	1.4004	1.3002	1.1152	0.3140,4	0.4372,3
9.5	44.85,70	35.35,70	1.4177	1.3117	1.1249	0.3064,6	0.4296,6
10.0	44.17,70	34.17,70	1.4349	1.3230	1.1349	0.2990,6	0.4222,2
10.5	43.52,33	33.02,33	1.4521	1.3341	1.1453	0.2918,4	0.4149,1
11.0	42.89,40	31.89,40	1.4692	1.3451	1.1560	0.2847,8	0.4077,2
11.5	42.28,69	30.78,69	1.4862	1.3559	1.1670	0.2778,8	0.4006,4
12.0	41.70,07	29.70,07	1.5032	1.3666	1.1783	0.2711,4	0.3936,7
12.5	41.13,38	28.63,38	1.5202	1.3772	1.1900	0.2645,4	0.3868,0
13.0	40.58,49	27.58,49	1.5371	1.3876	1.2021	0.2580,9	0.3800,4
13.5	40.05,29	26.55,29	1.5540	1.3979	1.2145	0.2517,8	0.3733,8
14.0	39.53,66	25.53,66	1.5709	1.4081	1.2273	0.2456,0	0.3668,1
14.5	39.03,50	24.53,50	1.5878	1.4182	1.2405	0.2395,5	0.3603,4
15.0	38.54,74	23.54,74	1.6047	1.4282	1.2541	0.2336,3	0.3539,6
15.5	38.07,30	22.57,30	1.6216	1.4380	1.2680	0.2278,3	0.3476,6
16.0	37.61,08	21.61,08	1.6385	1.4478	1.2823	0.2221,6	0.3414,5
16.5	37.16,05	20.66,05	1.6555	1.4575	1.2970	0.2166,1	0.3353,3
17.0	36.72,12	19.72,12	1.6725	1.4671	1.3121	0.2111,7	0.3292,9
17.5	36.29,25	18.79,25	1.6895	1.4766	1.3277	0.2058,4	0.3233,4
18.0	35.87,39	17.87,39	1.7065	1.4860	1.3437	0.2006,2	0.3174,7
18.5	35.46,48	16.96,48	1.7235	1.4953	1.3602	0.1955,1	0.3116,8
19.0	35.06,48	16.06,48	1.7406	1.5046	1.3771	0.1905,1	0.3059,6
19.5	34.67,35	15.17,35	1.7578	1.5138	1.3945	0.1856,2	0.3003,2

TABLE A-9. FUNCTIONS FOR METHOD OF CHARACTERISTICS (*Continued*)

ω = vector angle of characteristic curve in hodograph plane (see diagram), deg
α = Mach angle (see diagram), deg
ϕ = angle (see diagram), deg; ϕ_I given, $\phi_{II} = -\phi_I$
M = Mach number
M^* = ratio of local velocity to critical velocity
A/A^* = ratio of cross-sectional area to critical cross-sectional area
p/p_0 = ratio of static pressure to isentropic stagnation pressure
ρ/ρ_0 = ratio of density to isentropic stagnation density

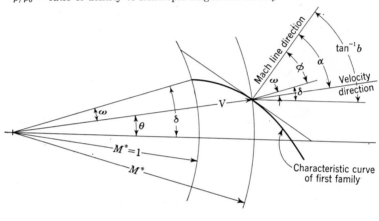

$$\pm\omega = \sqrt{\frac{k+1}{k-1}}\ \text{arctan}\ \sqrt{\frac{k-1}{k+1}(M^2 - 1)} - \text{arctan}\ \sqrt{M^2 - 1}$$

$$\alpha = \text{arcsin}\ \frac{1}{M}$$

$$M^* = \frac{\sqrt{\dfrac{k+1}{2}}\ M}{\sqrt{1 + \dfrac{k-1}{2}M^2}}$$

$$\frac{A}{A^*} = \frac{\left(1 + \dfrac{k-1}{2}M^2\right)^{(k+1)/2(k-1)}}{M\left(\dfrac{k+1}{2}\right)^{(k+1)/2(k-1)}}$$

$$\frac{p}{p_0} = \frac{1}{\left(1 + \dfrac{k-1}{2}M^2\right)^{k/(k-1)}}$$

$$\frac{\rho}{\rho_0} = \frac{1}{\left(1 + \dfrac{k-1}{2}M^2\right)^{1/(k-1)}}$$

NAME INDEX

Ackeret, J., 233, 259, 268
Aiken, W. S., Jr., 25
Altman, D., 131, 147
Anderson, T. P., 265, 269
Ansley, A. J., 317
Arrhenius, S. A., 167
Ashby, G. C., Jr., 280, 318
Auberry, J. H., 305, 319
Avery, W. H., 320

Barnes, N. F., 318
Barr, J., 187, 203
Beardsley, M. W., 25, 401
Bellinger, S. L., 318
Berlad, A. L., 204
Berman, K., 348, 352
Binder, R. C., 46, 64
Bird, R. B., 182, 321, 351
Birkhoff, G., 250, 269
Blackshear, P. L., 350, 353
Boelter, L. M. K., 278, 318
Bogart, D., 203
Bosworth, R. C. L., 182
Bothell, L. E., 281
Boyd, B. R., 281, 318
Bridgman, P. W., 245, 268
Brinkley, S. R., Jr., 182
Brodie, G. H., 281, 318
Brokaw, R. S., 204
Buckingham, E., 268
Burke, S. P., 186, 203
Busemann, A., 234

Caldwell, F. R., 319
Cambel, A. B., 131, 135, 136, 147, 254, 264, 268, 269, 335, 338, 345, 352, 353
Cartwright, C. H., 317
Chambre, P., 82
Chapman, S., 322, 351

Chen, S., 347, 352
Cheney, S. H., Jr., 348, 352
Choudhoury, R. P., 311
Clark, J. A., 276, 318
Corrsin, S., 319
Courant, R., 80, 82, 234
Cowling, T. G., 322, 351
Crocco, L., 347, 348, 352
Croft, H. O., 186, 203
Crowe, T. H., 351
Curtiss, C. F., 182, 321, 351

Dahl, A. I., 276, 318
Daniels, F., 168
Datner, P. D., 347, 352
Dean, R. C., 319
DeGroot, S. R., 43, 182
Dodge, B. F., 182
Dorsch, R. G., 281, 318
Dryden, H. L., 319
Duclos, D. P., 315, 320
Dugger, G. L., 333, 351
Duncan, W. J., 269
Dutton, R. A., 308, 319
Dyne, P. J., 204

Edelman, G. M., 82, 143, 145, 147, 387, 393
Ellenwood, F. O., 19, 25
El Wakil, M. M., 319
Emmons, H. W., 275, 317
Erwin, J. R., 280, 318
Evvard, J. C., 350, 353

Fenn, J. B., 265, 269
Fiock, E. F., 276, 318, 319
Fokker, A., 289
Frank-Kamenetsky, D. A., 328
Franz, A., 317

405

SUBJECT INDEX